# CRC Handbook of Eicosanoids: Prostaglandins and Related Lipids

## Volume II

## Drugs Acting via the Eicosanoids

Editor

**Anthony L. Willis, Ph.D.**
Principal Scientist
Atherosclerosis and Thrombosis Section
Institute of Experimental Pharmacology
Syntex Research
Palo Alto, California

CRC Press, Inc.
Boca Raton, Florida

**Library of Congress Cataloging-in-Publication Data**
(Revised for volume 2)

CRC handbook of eicosanoids.

Includes bibliographies and indexes.
Contents: v. 1. Chemical and biochemical aspects (2 v.) --v. 2. Drugs acting via the eicosanoids.
1. Arachidonic acid--Derivatives--Handbooks, manuals, etc. 2. Prostaglandins--Handbooks, manuals, etc. 3. Leukotrienes--Handbooks, manuals, etc.
I. Willis, Anthony L. II. Handbook of eicosanoids.
QP752.A7C73 1987 612′.01577 86-18779
ISBN 0-8493-3220-6 (set)



Direct all inquiries to CRC Press, Inc., 2000 Corporate Blvd., N.W., Boca Raton, Florida, 33431.



International Standard Book Number 0-8493-3220-6 (set)
International Standard Book Number 0-8493-3221-4 (v. 1, part A)
International Standard Book Number 0-8493-3222-2 (v. 1, part B)
International Standard Book Number 0-8493-3223-0 (v. 2)

Library of Congress Card Number 86-18779
Printed in the United States

# PREFACE

The biochemical and chemical aspects of eicosanoid research were detailed in Volume I of this handbook. That volume also provided tabulated data on the therapeutic potential of prostaglandin agonists. In developing such agents, the medicinal chemist seeks to imitate the natural "beneficial" or "physiological" role of eicosanoids. Indeed one could, by analogy to the endocrine area, regard this approach as replacement therapy for endogenous deficiency. Such an approach has also been begun with the administration of fatty acid precursors of the eicosanoids.

However, there are many instances when it would be more desirable to develop drugs that act to counter overexuberant production of eicosanoids or correct an imbalance in the spectrum of different eicosanoids produced. Indeed such actions explain the well-known broad spectrum of therapeutic effects for both aspirin-type drugs and the anti-inflammatory corticosteroids.

This volume of the handbook extensively reviews the drugs acting via such mechanisms. I am very grateful for the fortitude of the various contributors in undertaking the immense task of summarizing the data, which include the tables of structure/activity for different classes of compounds.

I owe special thanks to my colleague Dr. D. L. Smith for updating data in the corticosteroid area and Sir John Vane, Nobel Laureate, for writing the Foreword.

**Anthony L. Willis**

# FOREWORD

As in Volume I of this series (giving an introduction to the field and a chemical and biochemical background), Dr. A. L. Willis has assembled a wealth of information relating to the field of eicosanoids and related lipids. Volume II of this handbook deals with drugs that act via the eicosanoid system, a subject currently of great importance in medicinal chemistry, biochemistry, and pharmacology.

After the discovery in 1971 that aspirin inhibited the biosynthesis of prostaglandins,[1-3] there was an explosive increase in the eicosanoid literature (see Figure 1, Chapter 1 of Volume 1A). Later, starting with our proposal that dual inhibitors, such as BW755C, of the eicosanoid cascade would make better anti-inflammatory compounds than aspirin-like drugs,[4] inhibitors of lipoxygenase were developed, several of which are now under clinical evaluation in inflammatory disease states. Interest in such compounds was dramatically increased when Samuelsson and his colleagues[5] in 1979 announced that the well-known "slow reacting substance in anaphylaxis" or SRS-A[6] had been characterized as a mixture of leukotrienes, products of the 5-lipoxygenase pathway. Now the lipoxygenase inhibitors and leukotriene antagonists are under development not only for their potential as anti-inflammatory drugs but also for the treatment of asthma.

Since we proposed that the thrombotic process depended on a balance between vascular prostacyclin and platelet thromboxane $A_2$,[7] orally active stable prostacyclin analogues have been developed (see Volume 1B for extensive review) as have antagonists of the thromboxane/endoperoxide receptor. Earlier disadvantages of pure inhibitors of thromboxane synthetase may be overcome by dual inhibitors of thromboxane synthesis and actions such as R 68070 (this volume, Chapter 1). Indeed the whole area of eicosanoid receptor antagonists has received new impetus with development of logical receptor classifications.

Finally the discovery that corticosteroids act through induction of a peptide class named[8] the "lipocortins" has opened up new avenues in the search for selectively acting anti-inflammatory drugs.

All of these areas are reviewed in this volume of the *Handbook of Eicosanoids,* including brief discussion (in Chapter 1) of the alternate substrate approach involving dietary manipulation. Authors of the individual chapters include many of the leaders in the field and each one writes with great authority. The tables are well presented providing a cornucopia of information, with a total of more than 2,000 references cited.

I commend this volume as a standard reference work to be dipped into repeatedly by those interested in drugs acting via the eicosanoid system.

**Sir John R. Vane FRS**
**February 27, 1989**

# REFERENCES


1. **Vane, J. R.,** Inhibition of prostaglandin biosynthesis as a mechanism of action for aspirin-like drugs, *Nature (London) New Biol.,* 321, 232, 1971.
2. **Smith, J. B. and Willis, A. L.,** Aspirin selectively inhibits prostaglandin production by platelets in response to thrombin, *Nature (London) New Biol.,* 231, 235, 1971.
3. **Ferreira, S. H., Moncada, S., and Vane, J. R.,** Indomethacin and aspirin abolish prostaglandin release from the spleen, *Nature (London) New Biol.,* 231, 237, 1971.
4. **Higgs, G. A., Flower, R. J., and Vane, J. R.,** A new approach to anti-inflammatory drugs, *Biochem. Pharmacol.,* 28, 1959, 1979.

5. **Samuelsson, S.,** Leukotrienes: a novel group of compounds including SRS-A, *Prog. Lipid Res.,* 20, 23, 1982.
6. **Brocklehurst, W. E.,** The forty-year quest of ''slow reacting substance of anaphylaxis'', *Prog. Lipid Res.,* 20, 23, 1982.
7. **Moncada, S. and Vane, J. R.,** Pharmacology and endogenous roles of prostaglandin endoperoxides, thromboxane $A_2$ and prostacyclin, *Pharm. Rev.,* 30, 293, 1978.
8. **Flower, R. J.,** Eleventh Gaddum Memorial Lecture: Lipocortins and the mechanism of action of glucocorticoids, *Br. J. Pharmacol,* 94, 987, 1988.

## THE EDITOR

**Anthony L. Willis, Ph.D.,** is a Principal Scientist and Head of the Atherosclerosis and Thrombosis Section, Institute of Experimental Pharmacology, Syntex Research, Palo Alto, California.

Born in Penzance, Cornwall, England, Dr. Willis obtained degrees in pharmacology at Chelsea College, London, and at the Royal College of Surgeons of England, London. Dr. Willis is a member of several learned societies, including the British Pharmacology Society (of which he is a Sandoz Prizewinner), and a member of the Council on Atherosclerosis of the American Heart Association.

With the exception of brief sojourns at Stanford University, California, and Leeds University, England, Dr. Willis has spent his entire research career in the pharmaceutical industry: at Lilly Research (England), Hoffman-La Roche (U.S. and England), and now Syntex (U.S.)

Dr. Willis has made many fundamental and applied contributions to the area of prostaglandins and related substances now collectively termed the *eicosanoids*. He was among the first to delineate the role of prostaglandins as mediators of inflammation, including the first description of their presence in inflammatory exudate. Later, in work done alone and in collaboration, he shared in the discovery that platelets of human individuals synthesize and release prostaglandins and labile endoperoxides that induce platelet aggregation and that the mode of action of aspirin in inflammation, fever, and platelet aggregation was via inhibition of prostaglandin synthesis. His work included establishing isolation procedures for labile PG endoperoxides and description of deficient prostaglandin and endoperoxide responsiveness in hemostatic disorders.

Later, Dr. Willis pursued the now very topical idea that thrombosis and other disorders may be preventable by redirecting eicosanoid biosynthesis by addition to the diet of pure biochemical precursors of certain prostaglandins. This work led to the conclusion that there was considerable species variation in the enzymatic desaturation of unsaturated essential fatty acids and that metabolic pools of eicosanoid precursors may be of importance in basal production of prostaglandins by most tissues.

Most recently, Dr. Willis has developed several novel models of thrombotic and atherosclerotic processes that allow rapid evaluation of test compounds, including potentially antiatherosclerotic prostacyclin analogues.

Dr. Willis is author or co-author of approximately 100 scientific publications, including a previous compendium of the properties of prostaglandins, which served as the starting point for this handbook.

# ADVISORY BOARD

## CONTRIBUTORS

### Volume II


**Robert Alvarez, Ph.D.**
Senior Staff Researcher
Institute of Biological Sciences
Syntex Research
Palo Alto, California

**G. J. Blackwell, Ph.D.**
Wellcome Research Laboratories
Beckenham, Kent, England

**Richard M. Eglen, Ph.D.**
Senior Staff Researcher
Institute of Experimental Pharmacology
Syntex Research
Palo Alto, California

**Roderick J. Flower, Ph.D.**
Professor of Pharmacology
School of Pharmacy and Pharmacology
University of Bath
Bath, England

**Fusao Hirata, M.D, Ph.D.**
Associate Professor
Department of Environmental Health Sciences
School of Hygiene and Public Health
The Johns Hopkins University
Baltimore, Maryland

**A. F. Kreft, Ph.D.**
Principal Scientist
Chemical Research Section
Department of Allergy and Inflammation
Wyeth-Ayerst Research
Princeton, New Jersey

**A. J. Lewis, Ph.D.**
Assistant Vice President
Department of Pharmacology
Wyeth-Ayerst Research
Princeton, New Jersey

**John H. Musser, Ph.D.**
Associate Director
Chemical Research Section
Department of Allergy and Inflammation
Wyeth-Ayerst Research
Princeton, New Jersey

**Peter H. Nelson, Ph.D.**
Principal Scientist
Institute of Organic Chemistry
Syntex Research
Palo Alto, California

**Jürg R. Pfister, Ph.D.**
Principal Scientist
Institute of Organic Chemistry
Syntex Research
Palo Alto, California

**John H. Sanner, Ph.D.**
Consultant
Department of Biological Research
G.D. Searle and Co.
Skokie, Illinois

**Donald L. Smith, Ph.D.**
Staff Researcher
Institute of Experimental Pharmacology
Syntex Research
Palo Alto, California

**Berta Strulovici, Ph.D.**
Staff Researcher
Institute of Biological Sciences
Syntex Research
Palo Alto, California

**Keith A. M. Walker, Ph.D.**
Senior Department Head
Institute of Organic Chemistry
Syntex Research
Palo Alto, California

**Roger L. Whiting Ph.D.**
Director
Institute of Experimental Pharmacology
Syntex Research
Palo Alto, California

# VOLUME OUTLINE

## Volume I

Chemical and Biochemical Aspects

## TABLE OF CONTENTS

### Volume II

# *Introduction to the Area*

# THERAPEUTIC PROMISE OF THE EICOSANOID AREA: AN OVERVIEW

**Anthony L. Willis**

The purpose of this chapter is to serve both as an introduction to and a framework for the specialized, highly detailed contributions provided by the other authors in this volume. For an introduction to the eicosanoid area in general, the reader is referred to the introductory chapter by Willis in Volume IA of this handbook.

## THE EARLY YEARS (1930—1970)

Von Euler[1] and Bergstrom[2] recently gave personal accounts of the early years of prostaglandin research. Prostaglandins (PGs) were first discovered in the 1930s in the reproductive tract of animals and man. This explains why the name ''prostaglandin'' was coined by Von Euler. However, it was not until the 1960s that availability of pure prostaglandins and adequate assay methods allowed prostaglandin research to become properly established. By the late 1960s, much initial information was being established upon the natural occurrence of prostaglandins and their potential role in the areas of reproduction, lipid mobilization, platelet function, and inflammatory disease. Quick to seize upon the therapeutic potential of this area, the pharmaceutical industry, together with enterprising academicians, focused upon two major areas:

1. Use of natural PGs or their stable analogues as drugs to induce labor, abortion, and to inhibit gastric ulceration
2. A search for antagonists of the prostaglandins with putative effects such as anti-inflammatory compounds.

## THE ''POST-ASPIRIN ERA'' (1971—1976)

Since the early 1970s, this previous emphasis has changed drastically. This was because of the (in retrospect) very obvious finding that anti-inflammatory drugs of the aspirin type owed their historical use in a variety of ailments to inhibition of prostaglandin biosynthesis[3-8](see Figure 1).

These findings caused worldwide interest in both the scientific and lay communities. A flurry of further research was thus engendered seeking to examine the role of prostaglandins and related cyclooxygenase products in every aspect of aspirin actions and side effects.

Attempts were also initiated to develop ''selective'' nonsteroidal anti-inflammatory drugs of the aspirin type with minimized ability to inhibit PG synthesis in the stomach (causing ulceration, etc.) or in the kidney (causing sodium retention). Synthetic efforts in this direction and the corresponding biochemical and biological data are reviewed in this volume by Nelson. Ironically, this goal had already been achieved to a degree not yet surpassed, *before* the prostaglandin biosynthesis theory was accepted! Thus, acetaminophen (Tylenol®, paracetamol) inhibits brain PG synthesis more than PG biosynthesis in platelets, spleen, or inflammatory exudate.[6-10]

In addition, sodium salicylate does not effectively inhibit PG biosynthesis *in vitro*.[3-6] Administered i.p. (100 mg/kg), sodium salicylate given 50 min previously reduced the appearance of $PGE_2$ in inflammatory exudates but did not inhibit its *in vitro* biosynthesis in cell-containing samples of exudate or of rat-skin homogenates.[6,91] A similar situation was seen in the mouse brain, where administration of the same dose of salicylate (30 min previously) reduced $PGE_2$ content of freshly excised brain by 50%. Again, there was no

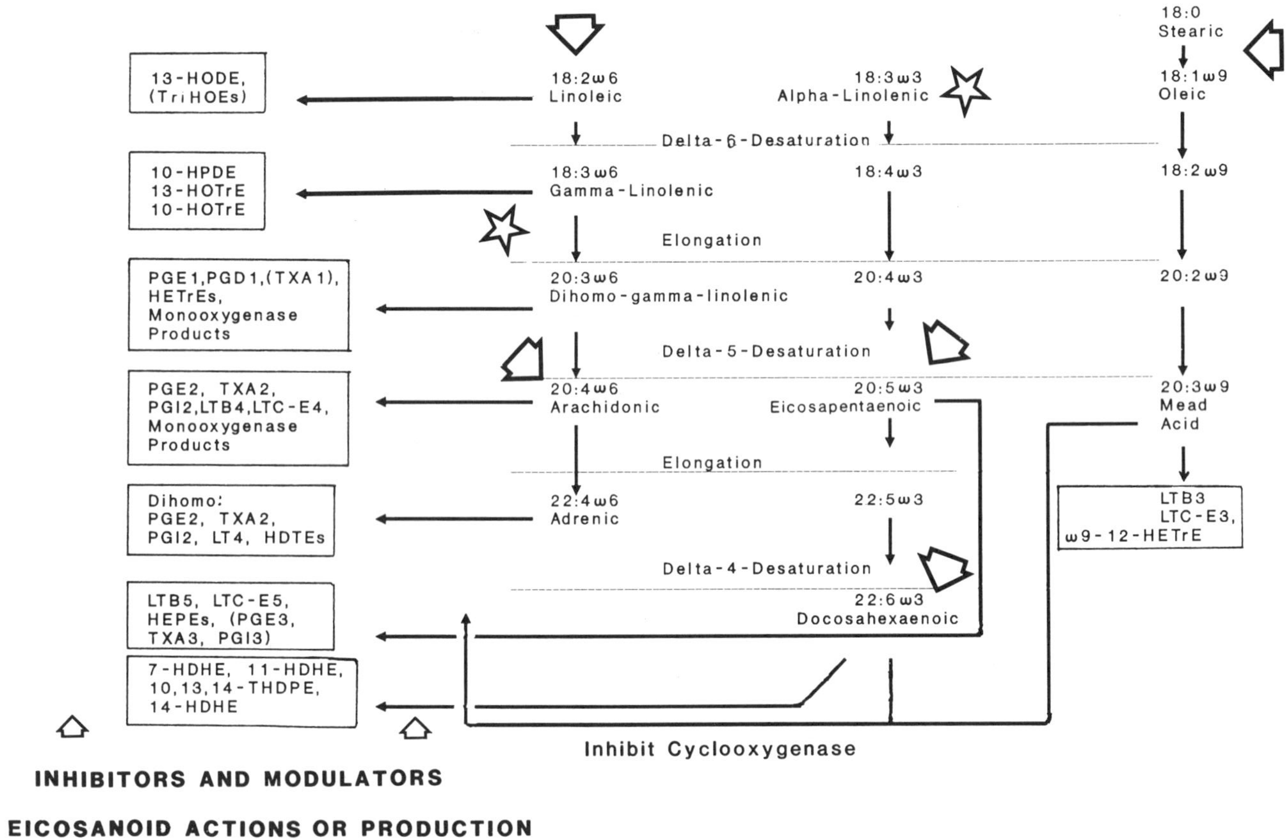


FIGURE 1. An overview of biochemical pathways involved in essential fatty acid and eicosanoid metabolism, and points of interaction and modulation by drugs or constituents of the diet.

effect of the drug on formation of PGs in brain homogenates from either endogenous or exogenous arachidonic acid, regardless of whether the drug was previously added *in vitro* (20 μg/ml) or examined *ex vivo* with brains excised from the salicylate-treated animals.[91] Finally, oral administration of salicylate reduces appearance of the major metabolites of E- and F-type PGs in the urine of man.[11]

In order to explain these findings, it was suggested[6] that salicylate may act via metabolites generated locally, with localized effects in brain (it is an anti-pyretic)[12] and inflammatory sites (it is anti-inflammatory).[12] In confirmation of this hypothesis, salicylate metabolites, including gentisic acid, do indeed inhibit PG biosynthesis *in vitro*.[10] Sodium salicylate does not, however, inhibit platelet aggregation[13] and correspondingly does not inhibit PG production in platelets whether *in vitro* or *ex vivo*;[4,14] indeed salicylate administration has been reported to prevent the inhibitory effects of aspirin on platelet cyclooxygenase.[15,16] A comparison between the *in vivo* and *in vitro* effects of salicylate on PG biosynthesis is shown in Figure 2.

Another saga commenced in the area of vascular disease, initiated by further studies on the mode of action of aspirin. It had long been known that aspirin had long-lived (several days duration) effects in inhibition of platelet aggregation and in prolongation of bleeding. However, at that time, it was known that the recognized products of cyclooxygenase (the so-called "classic" prostaglandins, $E_2$ and $F_{2\alpha}$) did not induce platelet aggregation, nor could they reverse the inhibitory effects of aspirin.[14]

It was then discovered that arachidonic acid could both prevent the inhibitory effects of aspirin[17] and induce aggregation of platelets.[18,19] These facts were explained by the finding that arachidonic acid (but not closely related fatty acids) was rapidly converted by prostaglandin-synthesizing enzyme systems into a "labile aggregation-stimulating substance".[13,20-22] The synthesis of this unstable material was blocked by aspirin and related drugs in a manner that ran parallel to their ability to inhibit platelet aggregation and to prolong bleeding.[14,23]

One of these substances was shown to be the unstable endoperoxide intermediate $PGH_2$, which was isolated and shown to be capable of inducing aggregation of platelets and the release from them of granular constituents.[14,22,24,25] Although perhaps present in lesser amounts, the related 15-hydroperoxy endoperoxide $PGG_2$ has similar effects, with an apparently greater ability to induce the platelet-release reaction.[25,26]

Later, Samuelsson's group, alone[27] and in collaboration,[28] showed that the platelet-aggregatory and vasoconstrictor actions of the endoperoxides could be amplified by conversion within the platelet to an even more unstable metabolite, with the postulated structure[27] of thromboxane $A_2$. Existence of this material was detected and measured in terms of stable end products, including the natural metabolite thromboxane $B_2$ (originally named "PHD").[27,29] Thromboxane $A_2$ has now been chemically synthesized and shown to have the requisite platelet-aggregatory and vasoconstrictor properties.[30]

## THE THROMBOXANE/PROSTACYCLIN ERA (1976—1980s)

The search then commenced for compounds that inhibited endoperoxide conversion into thromboxanes, with potential utility as antithrombotic agents. (See references 31 and 32 for early work in this area.)

Efforts toward this goal were further stimulated by the discovery that endoperoxides were converted in the blood-vessel wall into yet another unstable metabolite (prostacyclin, $PGI_2$) detected via its stable metabolite 6-keto-$PGF_{1\alpha}$). Prostacyclin possesses potent antithrombotic and vasodilator,[32,33] even potentially anti-atherosclerotic[34-36] properties. Thus (it was hypothesized), thromboxane-synthetase inhibitors would block platelet endoperoxide conversion to thromboxanes in platelets adhering to and then aggregating upon the luminal surface

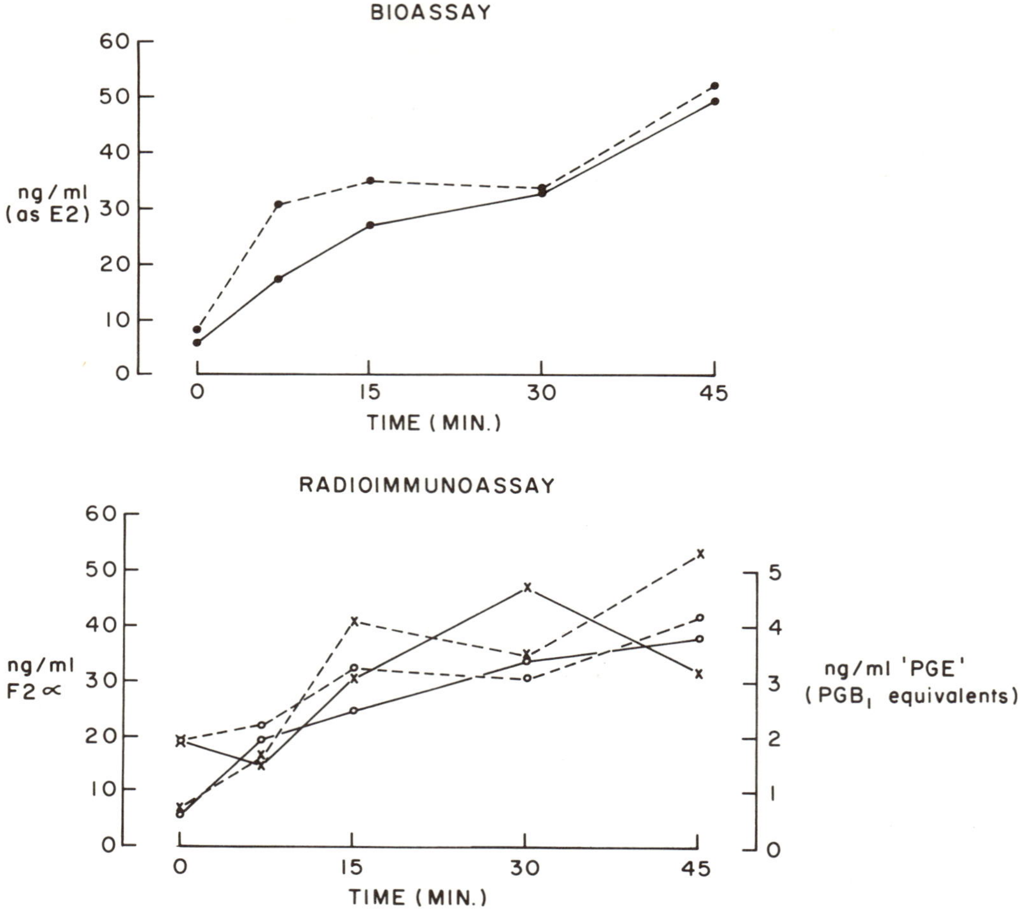


FIGURE 2. Inability of sodium salicylate (100 mg/kg, p.o.) to inhibit the spontaneous ex-vivo generation of E and F PGs during incubations of mouse brain suspensions at 37°C.

Brain tissue was freshly excised from male albino mice (19 to 25 g, Simonsen, Gilroy, CA) and immediately frozen in liquid nitrogen. It was then crushed into a fine powder under further liquid nitrogen and the powder from each brain suspended in 8 ml of Tyrode's solution. Aliquots of suspension (kept on ice for up to 30 min before use) were then incubated for 45 min at 37°C when the reaction was terminated by freezing in liquid nitrogen and the suspensions stored for up to 3 weeks on dry ice (−60°C). The prostaglandins E and F were isolated together using the extraction/column chromatography method described previously.[195,196]

Prostaglandin-$E_2$-like activity in the tyrode reconstituted extracts was estimated by bioassay on superfused rat stomach strip (upper panel) confirmed by radio-immunoassay after conversion to PGB. Also shown (lower panel) are the PGF values determined by radioimmunoassay. Both radioimmunoassay kits were obtained from Clinical Assays, Boston, Massachusetts.

of damaged blood vessels. The excess endoperoxide would then spill over into the blood-vessel wall, where it would be converted into prostacyclin as indicated by *in vivo* evidence.[37] Of course, prostacyclin may also be produced from arachidonate-derived endoperoxides produced in the blood vessel itself, in response to various stimuli that activated phospholipases of the blood-vessel wall. These stimuli may include thrombin,[38] plasma factors,[39] and mechanical trauma.[31-33] There is also some weak stimulation by platelet alpha granule proteins, including platelet-derived growth factor.[40]

Many potent, orally active inhibitors of TX-synthetase were developed (see the chapter by Walker in this volume). Indeed one compound (Dazoxiben; Pfizer) was subjected to extensive clinical evaluation.

Almost universally, however, animal and clinical studies with thromboxane-synthetase inhibitors have been disappointing from the viewpoint of developing antithrombotic therapy.[41] There has also been disappointment in another area, glomerulonephritis, where thromboxanes at first seemed implicated as mediators but where the TX-synthetase inhibitors were proved ineffective.[42]

In retrospect, such disappointments may have been due to an excessive fascination with the beauty of a simple hypothesis: it assumed that thrombotic disease is (exclusively!) due to a balance between the effects of thromboxane $A_2$ from platelets and prostacyclin from the vasculature. However, as we now know, the role of thromboxane $A_2$ has been grossly overestimated, since the PG endoperoxides are produced in amounts that easily induce aggregation of platelets, regardless of whether or not they are converted to thromboxane $A_2$.[14,16] Also, is it now obvious that vascular prostacyclin is produced in tiny amounts, except under stimulated conditions,[43] although stimuli might include the platelet/plasma activation of atherosclerotic disease;[44] certainly early claims that prostacyclin functions as a circulating hormone[45] have now been disproved.[46-49] In addition, large amounts of $PGE_2$ can be released into the circulation from tissues surrounding the vasculature, particularly during exercise.[50] Prostaglandin $E_2$ is also derived from activated platelets[4,51] and other blood cells[52] and in increased amounts in the presence of a thromboxane-synthetase inhibitor.[53-55] These considerations are very important given that $PGE_2$ can block the anti-aggregatory effects of prostacyclin.[56] Indeed, such considerations could well explain why exercise attenuates the anti-aggregatory effects of prostacyclin on platelets.[57]

Nevertheless, there still remains some promise to this area. For instance, drugs that combine inhibitory activity on both thromboxane synthetase and cyclic AMP phosphodiesterase might have useful, antithrombotic activity.[58] In this way, the small amounts of prostacyclin produced endogenously might elevate platelet cyclic AMP sufficiently to produce *in vivo* inhibition of platelet aggregation.[59]

Finally it still remains possible that some new disease areas will be delineated (in the brain or gut, for instance) in which thromboxane-synthetase inhibitors will prove effective. It is also possible that thromboxane $A_2$ has a local regulatory function in microvasculature that should be considered.[159]

Ironically, aspirin *still* seems to be the best example of a drug acting in the cardiovascular system via the eicosanoid system. Following the discovery of prostacyclin, a prolonged debate began over the optimal dose of aspirin required to exert long-lasting inhibition of platelet cyclooxygenase (thus inhibiting endoperoxide and thromboxane production), but without significantly inhibiting vessel-wall prostacyclin production.[16,31-33] Indeed, cumulative low-dose aspirin regimens have been identified in man on the basis of *ex vivo* examination of vascular specimens and/or measurements of endogenous eicosanoids.[60,61] The article by de Gaetano[16] discusses these aspects of the so-called "aspirin dilemma" at some length.

Small doses of aspirin absorbed from the gastrointestinal tract may act in the local microcirculation in a cumulative manner to inhibit platelet cyclooxygenase before being metabolized by the liver into salicylate.[62] Although accumulated salicylate may block the effects of aspirin to inhibit prostacyclin production in the blood-vessel wall,[63] it also inhibits formation of the vascular lipoxygenase product tentatively designated as "LOX",[64] which has recently been identified as 13-hydroxy-octadecadienoic acid ("13-HODE").[65] LOX possesses an action complementary to that of prostacyclin in that it inhibits platelet *adhesion* to surfaces of the blood-vessel wall.*

* In the view of this author, drugs that act like or via endogeneous 13-HODE may prove to be very useful as anti-atherosclerotic agents, since it is the adhesion-mediated release of platelet mitogens that is an important mechanism.

Among the fatty acid oxygenases of vascular endothelium, there is one that produces 15-lipoxygenated derivatives.[160,161] It is reasonable to suppose that this enzyme actually recognizes position of the double bond nearest the terminal methyl group of the fatty acid (i.e. it is ω6-lipoxygenase) and thus converts linoleic acid into 13-HODE. This assumption is based upon work in the human polymorphonuclear leukocyte,[162] in which linoleic acid is the preferred substrate for the ω6-lipoxygenase.

One area that is now receiving attention is the possibility of an increased endogenous production of prostacyclin (and perhaps also LOX?) by drugs exemplified by nafazatrom[66,67] whose mechanisms are further discussed below.

The problem of harnessing the eicosanoid area to the prevention of vascular disease has also been attacked more directly. Thus, several orally active stable prostacyclin analogues have recently been developed (see the chapter by Muchowski in Volume IB of this handbook). However, a problem reported for prostacyclin,[68] $PGE_1$,[69] and at least one synthetic analogue (Iloprost, ZK36374; Schering)[70] is possible desensitization to the anti-aggregatory effects on the platelets. Indeed, on cessation of treatment, a disturbing "rebound" phenomenon might even produce spontaneous aggregation of samples of platelet-rich plasma.[70]

Nevertheless, it is clear that if such compounds can be given in a form (by slow release?) that is well tolerated, and *without* tachyphylaxis developing, they may prove to be useful by chronic administration. If so, they may used, not only for their antithrombotic and vasodilator potential, but for attenuation of the atherosclerotic process.[34,71,72]

It is probable that over the next 5 years we shall finally see whether or not early promise of effective treatment of vascular-occlusive disease can, indeed, be developed via the eicosanoid area. For further discussion of this area, the reader is referred to recent reviews in References 16, 34, and 73.

## THE LIPOXYGENASE ERA (1980—PRESENT)

Although it had long been known that there were lipoxygenase enzymes in plants (e.g., the soybean), it was only in the mid 1970s that lipoxygenases of animal origin were discovered. First, the 12-lipoxygenase was discovered in the cytosol of blood platelets,[29,74] then leukocytes were found to possess both 5-lipoxygenases and 15-lipoxygenases.[75,76] Finally, commencing in 1979, the family of 5-lipoxygenase-derived products known as the "leukotrienes" were described.[77,78] These landmark discoveries are reviewed by Borgeat in Volume IA of this handbook.

The leukotrienes were so named to denote an origin in leukocytes and the presence of three conjugated double bonds. One family of leukotrienes (C–F) has a peptide substituent. These peptidolipids were found to be the biologically active components of "slow-reacting substance in anaphylaxis" (SRS-A). This finding provided great excitement, since Brocklehurst[79] had shown many years previously that SRS-A was a potential mediator of allergic asthma and of inflammation. In addition, the nonpeptidolipid, dihydroxy leukotriene $B_4$ was shown to act on polymorphonuclear leukocytes in a potentially inflammatory and tissue-destructive manner. It is chemokinetic, chemotactic, and induces aggregation, release of lysosomal enzymes, and oxygen free-radical generation.[80-83]

As the above story evolved, there was increasing interest in the development of drugs that inhibited lipoxygenases (see the chapter by Pfister in this volume of the handbook).

The first compound shown to inhibit lipoxygenases of both plant[84] and animal[29,74,85] origin was 5,8,11,14-eicosatetraynoic acid (ETYA). However ETYA does also inhibit cyclooxygenase and interconversion of essential fatty acids, e.g., the delta 5 desaturation of dihomo-gamma-linolenic acid to arachidonic acid.[86] ETYA is an analogue of arachidonic acid but with acetylenic rather than olefinic double bonds. This compound was originally synthesized in the laboratories of Hoffman-La Roche as the penultimate intermediate in a large-scale preparation of arachidonic acid by the Osbond[87] synthesis.* Although ETYA has been used as an experimental tool (e.g., Reference 90) it lacks good bioavailability, especially via the

* At that time there was interest in using arachidonic acid as a possible therapeutic agent because of its reported[88] cholesterol-lowering properties. Remember this was more than a decade before the recognition of arachidonic acid metabolites in platelet aggregation, confirmed *in vivo* by the finding by Seyberth et al.[89] that oral ingestion of 6 g ethyl arachidonate per day greatly enhanced *ex vivo* platelet aggregation in human volunteers.

oral route.[91] Other acetylenic fatty acid analogues have also been prepared that inhibit lipoxygenase and/or cyclooxygenase pathways (see the extensive tabulation of data by Pfister in this volume). One of the earliest of these was 5,8,11-eicosatriynoic acid, an acetylenic version of ''Mead Acid''. Interestingly, this was reported not to inhibit platelet cyclooxygenase at concentrations inhibiting the 12-lipoxygenase[92] and has since been shown to inhibit the 5-lipoxygenase pathway responsible for leukotriene production[93] and the formation of the 13-lipoxygenase product (13-HODE) previously known as LOX.[64,65]

Nordihydroguaiaretic acid is also an inhibitor of plant and animal lipoxygenases that does not inhibit cyclooxygenase.[94-96] Like the other compounds discussed above, it is limited in its *in vivo* applications.

The first lipoxygenase inhibitor specifically developed as a dual inhibitor of the cyclooxygenase and lipoxygenase was BW755C. It was derived from phenidone, a chemical commonly used in developing photographs and which had previously been found to have similar inhibitory properties on the 12-lipoxygenase.[97,98]

The first drugs introduced clinically that possessed ability to inhibit lipoxygenases were benoxaprofen (Lilly) and ibuprofen (originally from Boots in the U.K. and marketed as Motrin® by Upjohn). These drugs were introduced as anti-inflammatory agents for the treatment of arthritis. In addition to inhibiting the cyclooxygenase, they were also claimed to inhibit the 5-lipoxygenase pathways: interestingly ibuprofen* also stimulates 15-lipoxygenase.[99,100] Although benoxaprofen was withdrawn from the market due to patient deaths (apparently a drug-hypersensitivity reaction), ibuprofen has been used so widely as to reach status as an ''over-the-counter'' analgesic (Advil®).

One compound presently under investigation for the alleviation of psoriasis (lonapalene; Syntex) was discovered in a topical inflammation model in the mouse ear and has been shown probably to owe its biological activity to inhibition of lipoxygenases in the skin, including the 5-lipoxygenase.[101] These findings complement the earlier report by Vorhees et al.[102] that human psoriatic skin produces abnormally high amounts of lipoxygenase products compared to cyclooxygenase products. The reported localized EFA deficiency (and resultant accumulation of Mead acid; 20:3ω9) in psoriatic skin[103] may be expected to result in an increased ratio of lipoxygenase to cyclooxygenase products.[104] However, the lipoxygenase products elevated in psoriasis are derived from arachidonate.[102] Further work is required in order to resolve this apparent discrepancy.

The principal target sought for lipoxygenase inhibitors as a class is inhibition of the 5-lipoxygenases pathway, since the potentially deleterious effects of the leukotrienes are so well documented. Several classes of compounds[105-112] with this activity have been described, including 5,6- methano leukotriene $A_4$, retinoids, a flavanoid (biacalein), caffeic acid, bacterial products, diphenyl disulfide, and Gossypol, that is present in cotton-seed oil. Nafazatrom also inhibits the 5-lipoxygenase, an action that might be related to its ability to increase vascular production of prostacyclin,[66,67,113] since this is known to be reduced by lipid peroxides.[32,33]

Of all lipoxygenase inhibitors in early development, one of the most scientifically interesting is a prostacyclin derivative (U60257, Piriprost: Upjohn). This compound is a $PGI_1$ analogue ($PGI_1$ is not naturally occurring!) that acts orally to inhibit the *ex vivo* and *in vivo* production of leukotrienes and to alleviate allergic and inflammatory conditions in laboratory animals.[114] These actions of Piriprost seem independent from similarly reported effects of natural E-type PGs which apparently reduce leukotriene production via increased tissue cyclic AMP levels.[115]

* As discussed below, 15-lipoxygenase products of arachidonic acid and related fatty acids can inhibit the 5-lipoxygenase. Since ibuprofen stimulates 15-lipoxygenase,[100] it is possible that its inhibitory effects on 5-lipoxygenase could be mediated by 15-hydroxylated products.

For a balanced viewpoint, it is necessary to conclude this section with a cautionary note. Attempts have been made to selectively inhibit the various lipoxygenases, with a view toward minimizing side effects. Indeed, it has been widely assumed that the 5-lipoxygenase-derived leukotrienes are the most injurious of the lipoxygenase products. Thus (it might be argued) physiologically relevant 12-lipoxygenase products such as the hepoxilins (that can modulate insulin release[116]) would be spared.

To further complicate matters, it would now appear that leukotrienes may not be entirely "bad" in their biological actions. Thus, 5-lipoxygenase products might have important physiological effects including modulation of the release of "luteinizing hormone releasing hormone".[117] Perhaps more important, the activity of "natural killer (NK) cells" (specialized lymphocytes involved in tumor surveillance) may rely upon leukotriene $B_4$ as a key intracellular mediator for their actions, that are attenuated by 5-lipoxygenase inhibitors.[118]

As seems inevitable in every area of eicosanoid research, we eventually have to evoke the "double-edged sword" concept that small, correctly balanced amounts of endogenous eicosanoid biosynthesis may be physiologically proper, whereas large and/or unbalanced production of these same eicosanoids is of a pathological nature.

Clearly, more work with suitably acting inhibitors is required. This should attempt to delineate the relative advantages and disadvantages of inhibiting the various lipoxygenases with and without a corresponding inhibition of cyclooxygenase pathways. At least for *in vitro* work, suitable inhibitors have been described. Thus, AA861 (Takeda Chemical Industries, Japan) is a selective inhibitor of leukotriene production via the 5-lipoxygenase.[163] In addition, 4,7,10,13-eicosatetrynoic acid has been shown to selectively inhibit the 12-lipoxygenase (actually ω9-lipoxygenase) of platelets[164] and the 15-lipoxygenation of arachidonic acid is selectively inhibited by 14,15-dehydroarachidonic acid.[165]

There are recent reports indicating that 5-lipoxygenase[116] and 12-lipoxygenase[119-120] products of arachidonic acid may have pro-atherosclerotic effects upon, respectively, cellular cholesterol accumulation, platelet adhesion, and migration of vascular smooth-muscle cells. By contrast, a 13-lipoxygenated product of linoleic acid has potentially opposing effects.[65] Such findings augur well for the promise of such a selective approach.

## FULL CIRCLE—PRESENT TRENDS IN EICOSANOID DRUG DEVELOPMENT

Ironically, the two main eicosanoid research areas of the 1960s seem to have re-emerged as being of potential therapeutic importance.

### Prostaglandins as Drugs

First, natural prostaglandins or their synthetic analogues are now becoming used clinically in man and in veterinary medicine. $PGE_1$ is used in neonatal medicine to maintain patency of the ductus arteriosus, while $PGE_2$, $PGF_{2\alpha}$, or their synthetic analogues have been used to synchronize estrus or to induce abortion in cattle. Natural $PGE_1$ or $PGI_2$ infusions have also been used therapeutically in peripheral vascular disease and to reduce thrombotic deposits in extracorporeal shunts. Further discussion of these areas is beyond the scope of this review but is dealt with in detail by Muchowski in Volume IB of this handbook, and in References 16,32,33,73,122 cited in this chapter.

In the immediate future, the area that seems to be most promising is the use of synthetic prostaglandin analogues for the treatment of peptic ulcer disease, and possibly other disorders of the gastrointestinal tract. An overview of this area is given in reviews by Sontag,[123] Garay and Muchowski,[124] and in Volume II of the recent CRC publication *Biological Protection with Prostaglandins*, edited by M. Cohen.[125]

The synthetic analogues presently being introduced clinically for ulcer therapy include the $PGE_1$ analogues rioprostil and misoprostil and the $PGE_2$ analogues enprostil and arbaprostil. Misoprostil is presently the most advanced in commercial development and forms the subject of an extensive review by Monk and Clissold[126] and of an entire symposium proceedings.[127]

Further advances may be expected in the vascular area, both with prostacyclin mimetics[16,34] and with a recent series of compounds with mixed activity as prostacyclin mimetics and as thromboxane receptor antagonists.[128] Promise and potential pitfalls in this area are expertly reviewed by de Gaetano.[16]

An interesting new development is the potential of a cutaneously absorbed PGE analogue (Viprostil) for the reversal of male pattern baldness.[128]

**Selective-Receptor Antagonists**

The area of eicosanoid antagonists has recently received new impetus (see contributions to this volume by Sanner, Musser, and by Eglen and Whiting). Advances have been made particularly in the area of leukotriene antagonists. At Fisons Pharmaceuticals (U.K.), antagonists of SRS-A were developed almost 20 years ago, the published prototype[130] being FPL55712. However, it is only now that highly selective and orally active compounds are becoming available (see the chapter by Musser et al. in this volume). The most interesting of these compounds are orally active, including L-64,923 (that has been examined in man) and SKF104,353 (see References 131 to 133 and the contribution to this handbook by Musser et al.). It is also of great potential importance that calcium channel blockers such as nicardipine[189] may block the smooth-muscle-contracting effects of $LTC_4$ or $LTD_4$ in a manner that seems selective to the coronary vasculature.

Another important finding may lead to a resurgence in interest in the thromboxane area: a selective antagonist at thromboxane receptors (BM 13,177) inhibits the spread of ischemic damage in a ligated coronary-artery model in cats.[166] However, another thromboxane antagonist (AH238-18) is reportedly devoid of clinically demonstrable protection against angina attacks caused by myocardial ischemia.[177]

Clearly, even more meaningful progress should be obtained in the future, because of our increased knowledge of medicinal chemistry and receptor biology. Thus, production of totally chiral PG compounds is now routine and our accumulated knowledge of structure/activity relationships is rapidly increasing. This is because we are learning rapidly about the different classes of eicosanoid-receptor populations. Also, extremely rapid ligand-receptor binding assays are being developed, and computer-aided design of structures is becoming commonplace. In addition, we are learning more about the "second messengers" involved in eicosanoid action, including cyclic AMP and protein kinase C (see contributions to this volume by Alvarez and by Strulovici).

Thus we appear to be at an analogous stage to that in the 1970s when selective adrenoceptor agonists and antagonists were being successfully developed. The difference, however, is the incredible complexity of the eicosanoid field.

**Lipocortins**

Of all the drugs that act via the eicosanoids, there is one unequivocal statement that can be made concerning the anti-inflammatory steroids: they are extremely effective! Of course we now know that they work so well because they inhibit the phospholipase-mediated release of arachidonic acid that would have been converted into pro-inflammatory and otherwise injurious eicosanoids including $PGE_2$, thromboxane $A_2$, and the leukotrienes (see contributions to this volume by Smith, Hirata, and Flower et al.).

Unfortunately, the corticosteroids also have several side effects.[134] In general, these side effects are attributable to the effects of the steroids on carbohydrate biochemistry and electron-transport systems (classic glucocorticoid and mineralocorticoid effects). It is of considerable interest that (with the two possible exceptions below) side effects of the anti-inflammatory steroids cannot be attributed to diminished production of eicosanoids.[135]

The discoveries of Flower, DiRosa, Hirata, and colleagues showed that the anti-inflammatory steroids may exert their anti-phospholipase effect by inducing the synthesis of a family of peptides designated as the ''lipocortins''.[135-139] This family includes the previously described ''macrocortin''[137] and ''lipomodulin,''[138] which are probably homologues of each other. (See contribution to this volume by D. L. Smith).*

In addition, Lee et al.[167] have recently produced evidence that glucocorticoids may reduce eicosanoid production via an ability to inhibit the transcription of interleukin-1 (IL-1) genes and/or by decreasing the stability of the IL-1β mRNA; IL-1 is known to produce release of eicosanoids.

Now that the gene for lipocortin has been cloned and its peptide sequence determined,[139] much work within the pharmaceutical industry concerns attempts to prepare drugs that are synthetic analogues or fragments of the lipocortins. One might ask, ''What is the point, since we already have the anti-inflammatory steroids?'' The answer, of course, is that the side effects upon carbohydrate metabolism and electrolyte balance may be eliminated.[135,136]

There are, however, two possible criticisms of this hypothesis that remain to be answered: first, there is the question of immunosuppression produced by the anti-inflammatory steroids.[134] Would this be eliminated by lipomodulin-type agents? According to one report, there is a role of leukotriene $B_4$ in producing immune surveillance in NK cells,[118] and there is other evidence that the immunosuppressive effects of corticosteroids on T-cell proliferation and interleukin 2 may involve reduced production of leukotriene B4;[140] indeed, lipocortins have been reported to produce similar effects, at least on NK cells.[176] On the other hand, the immunosuppressive effects of $PGE_2$ are well documented,[141] which would seem to provide argument in the opposite direction.

For a second example, there is some evidence that anti-inflammatory steroids engender increased propensity for gastric ulceration.[134] Could this be attributable to reduced phospholipase activity that, in turn, reduces gastric mucosal production of cyctoprotective prostaglandins? If so, then the lipocortins may share similar drawbacks.

However, the most potentially serious problem with developing peptides as anti-inflammatory drugs is, of course, their expected short *in vivo* half life and difficulties in therapeutic delivery (they would likely be destroyed by gastrointestinal enzymes and/or not well absorbed.) However, it is also fair to say that peptide analogues are often sufficiently potent to help offset such bioavailability problems and may also be absorbed via the nasal route; such an approach has been employed with nafaralin, an analogue of ''luteinizing hormone-releasing hormone''.[142]

## WHAT OF THE MORE DISTANT FUTURE?

Clearly, the immediate future will see the clinical potential of the above approaches become finally determined. Although it seems probable that eicosanoid mimetics or modulators should be very effective in certain disease states, it remains to be seen whether their side-effect profile and/or development of refractoriness will preclude their widespread acceptance except for short-term administration.

In the opinion of this author, there are two areas that may be important in new research in the forseeable future. Both approaches involve the selective increase in the endogenous production of naturally ''protective'' eicosanoids with a concomitant reduction in production of ''injurious'' eicosanoids.

* Recent work also shows that proteins of the lipocortin are homologus with the membrane-associated cytoskeletal proteins known as calpactins, which are substrates for tyrosine kinase phosphorylation.[168,169] The calpactins act like lipomodulin to inhibit phospholipase activity, by binding to the phospholipid substrate.[169] It is not yet known whether the calpactins are inducible by corticosteroids. Homology with other peptide materials has also been seen (see contribution by D. L. Smith).

In theory, this approach is the best possible solution to harnessing eicosanoid biology to both therapeutic *and* preventive medicine. This is because natural eicosanoids are generally only produced in large amounts in response to specific stimuli that release their precursors that are normally rendered inert through being incorporated into membrane phospholipids. Thus an "on demand" prodrug form of the eicosanoid has already been developed by nature!

**Alternate Eicosanoid Substrates**

The most obvious use of this approach is to increase the dietary intake of the appropriate precursor fatty acids.[104] Most of the "deleterious" eicosanoids are produced from arachidonic acid, while "beneficial" eicosanoids ($PGE_1$, 15-HETrE) are produced from dihomo-gamma-linolenic acid (DGLA), but thromboxanes or 5-lipoxygenated leukotrienes are not because the delta-5 double bond is missing. Eicosapentanoic acid (EPA, present in fish oils) is converted to some extent to $PGI_3$ in man,[143] but owes most of its reported beneficial effects to the fact that it reduces production of arachidonate metabolites, both by displacing arachidonate from phospholipids and by competing with arachidonate for the cyclooxygenase and lipoxygenase enzymes that convert it into eicosanoids with greatly reduced biological potency.[104,144,145] In addition, EPA, being such a poor substrate for the cyclooxygenase, has a partial aspirin-like ability to reduce arachidonate conversion to cyclooxygenase-derived products including the thromboxanes.[104,144,145] Docosahexanoic acid (another fatty acid constituent of fish oil) is not converted into cyclooxygenase products at all, but does act as an inhibitor of this enzyme.[146]

Interesting interactions are possible between eicosanoid products of different fatty acids; this further complicates eventual biological outcome of administering different fatty-acid-rich dietary supplements. The best example is the fact that although DGLA is not a substrate for the 5-lipoxygenase, it can inhibit conversion of arachidonic acid to leukotrienes perhaps in part due to conversion to 15-HETrE.[147,187] Indeed, such effects may explain the reported inhibitory effects of DGLA in experimental arthritis in rats.[188] The chapters by Willis and by D. L. Smith in Volume I of this handbook give a detailed discussion of the many eicosanoids produced from different fatty acid substrates. A simplified summary is also given in Figure 1 of this chapter.

The academic community has become increasingly fascinated with both the potential medical benefits of such dietary manipulations and the complex biochemical interactions involved in eventual production of alternative eicosanoids. Indeed, the National Institutes of Health have already financed a conference and several new research grants on the effects of marine lipids rich in EPA.

However, no definitive chronic-dose-response studies with purified fatty acids have yet been done in which the appropriate precursors and products have been traced through the various lipid pools culminating in altered eicosanoid synthesis and correlated with modified biological responses. The confusion and conflicting data in studies with dietary treatment with fish oils are well exemplified in the excellent recent review by Herold and Kinsella.[148]

Until recently, only the "Health Food Industry" was marketing products in the alternative substrate area, in general without hard scientific data to support assumptions of benefit. However, segments of the conventional pharmaceutical industry (Squibb and Parke Davis) have begun U.S. marketing of fish-oil preparations. These contain about 20% EPA and 10% DHA in addition to several other fatty acids and other components. In the U.K., the original Seven Seas/Scherrer "Maxepa" fish-oil preparation has now received official clearance for prescription as a triglyceride-lowering agent and is being marketed by Glaxo. Oil of Evening Primrose (containing about 10% gamma linolenic acid, precursor for DGLA) has also been studied intensively and a clinical indication for atopic eczema has recently been granted in the U.K.

In general, however, the pharmaceutical industry has eschewed major interest in the area of alternative substrates, even though it may eventually provide considerable competition to sales of conventional cardiovascular drugs. This is undoubtedly due to the lack of patent protection. Indeed, even if pure fatty acids could be developed for therapeutic use and even though they may be regarded as completely natural, these substances would presently be treated by the FDA as drugs. Thus, proper toxicology and evidence of clinical efficacy would have to be obtained. Obviously it could be difficult to recoup the considerable expense involved, given lack of patent protection and competition from crude material presently being produced by the health food industry and by some pharmaceutical companies.

One way around this dilemma might be to make the pure fatty acid eicosanoid precursor a constituent of a hybrid molecule with a conventional drug that acts synergistically. Another possible way (that was explored at Hoffman La Roche some 10 years ago) was to consider the use of drugs that selectively blocked the $\Delta_5$ desaturase that converted DGLA to arachidonic acid. However, whether such an approach could be used without also altering lipid metabolism in harmful ways has never been adequately explored.

**Drugs That Increase Endogenous Formation of Beneficial Eicosanoids**

As already discussed above,[66,67] nafazatrom is the prototype of a drug that can apparently increase the balance between endogenous formation of a "beneficial" eicosanoid (prostacyclin) compared to a "harmful" eicosanoid (leukotrienes). In addition to its antithrombotic and antimetastatic actions *in vivo*,[66,67] Nafazatrom has recently been shown to inhibit the spread of ischemic damage in a coronary reperfusion model.[149]

Similar effects have been reported for "defibrotide" (a partially depolimerized DNA fraction, mol wt 20,000, from mammalian lung). Injected i.v., this material induces release of tissue plasminogen activator and prostacyclin from vascular endothelium and produces a prolonged-elevation of platelet-cyclic AMP.[170] The release of prostacyclin in the coronary circulation appears to be platelet dependent.[171] Interestingly, defibrotide is very active in preventing ischemic damage (and is even life saving) in a myocardial ischemia models in the cat[172-174] and rabbit.[175]

There are other classes of drug that may also increase the production of endogenous eicosanoids. For instance, it has long been known that nonthiazide diuretics increase net production of the prostaglandins by actions possibly including inhibition of the 15-dehydrogenase.[150-154] Similarly, sulfasalazine may act via inhibition of PG metabolism.[155]

It is the feeling of this author that such compounds may become prototypes for new drugs developed in the future, perhaps in obstetric medicine.[186] If so, intriguing aspects of drug/drug and drug/diet interactions will have to be taken into account.

The ability of cyclooxygenase inhibitors to block the effects of diuretic drugs in man is already documented,[151-154] but similar examples are to be expected. For example, a drug acting like nafazatrom may be rendered ineffective by large doses of aspirin-like drugs (or even the corticosteroids or lipocortins). This would be due to inhibition of vascular prostacyclin production. As a corollary, such drugs might be rendered yet *more* effective by small doses of aspirin taken intermittently. This is because aspirin can permanently inhibit the cyclooxygenase of platelets (that cannot be replaced until fresh platelets are produced), but has minimal effects on the rapidly regenerating cyclooxygenase of the blood-vessel wall.

For another example, the anti-inflammatory corticosteroids, or their lipocortin "second messengers", would tend to limit eicosanoid production to that basally produced from metabolic pools of precursor spilling over from essential fatty acid metabolism of absorbed dietary constituents or from turnover of cholesteryl esters and triglycerides. Under such circumstances, the effects of drugs that inhibit cyclooxygenase or PG metabolism might be very different from usual (even harmful, if basal PG biosynthesis has a physiological role).

Finally, it must again be emphasized that the overall amount and spectrum of various eicosanoids produced is ultimately a function of the fatty acid composition of the diet.

Therefore it would not be surprising to see differing effects of, e.g., a cyclooxygenase inhibitor in circumstances where the fatty acid composition of the diet were greatly varied. While anecdotal accounts abound,[156] the only well-documented[157] example of this above phenomenon is the reported ability of aspirin to actually *shorten* bleeding time in Eskimos on their marine lipid ("omega 3") diet. This finding is the antithesis of the well-known prolongation of bleeding produced by aspirin in individuals subsisting on the usual Western land-based diet that results in predominance of arachidonate-derived eicosanoids.

In the view of this author, the above considerations could be harnessed in the future design of drugs that are hybrids with fatty acid moeities that could then act synergistically with the drug. Another avenue that should now be re-explored is the interactions between peptide hormones and the eicosanoids. There is a recent paper[158] reporting upon a potential role of Substance P in releasing $PGE_2$ and collagenase from human synovial cells and possible implications of such mechanisms to rheumatoid arthritis. Potential utility of substance-P-receptor antagonists is thus suggested.

By contrast, the release of vasodilator eicosanoids[190] by the newly described[191] vasoconstrictor peptide endothelin might actually be beneficial.

Finally, a new feature that should be considered is the recent advances in the area of "endothelium-derived relaxing factor" (EDRF). Its activity has recently been shown to be due to nitric oxide,[179] derived from L-arginine,[192] although there is still evidence for EDRF(s) other than NO.[180] EDRF/NO have now been found to both inhibit aggregation of platelets[181,182] and the adhesion of platelets to surfaces.[183] A finding that may prove to be prescient is the marked synergism between the anti-aggregatory effects of nitric oxide (or EDRF) with those of prostacyclin.[184] These findings suggest several important possibilities that can be harnessed in the development of future cardiovascular therapy. For instance, the anti-aggregatory effects of RS93427 (an orally active prostacyclin) and two nitrodilator compounds (glyceryl trinitrate and sodium nitroprusside that are NO precursors) are mutually synergistic on platelet aggregation induced by collagen, but without a similar synergistic effect on rat blood pressure.[193] Similar, though less marked, effects have been seen with Iloprost *in vitro*.[194]

Clearly there is yet more exciting research to be done in the area of the eicosanoids. Indeed, it could be argued that it is only our previously limited knowledge that has prevented more rapid progress. We now seem poised to realize, at last, full therapeutic promise of the eicosanoids, that has long been so tantalizing.

## ADDENDUM

During 1988, some new findings were reported that further extend therapeutic potential of the eicosanoid area. Those not cited in addenda to the other chapters in this book are described below.

1. The structure of a new polypeptide vasoconstrictor derived from vascular endothelium ("endothelin") was reported[197] in April 1988, setting off an intense research effort that has already resulted in one international conference. This material is rapidly inactivated by passage through the pulmonary circulation where it also releases eicosanoids, including prostacyclin ($PGI_2$). Indeed, the release of prostacyclin and "endothelium-derived relaxing factor" (EDRF) produces a vasodilator effect that can be greater than the direct vasoconstrictor effects of endothelin.[190] Clearly endothelin has potential for a role in vascular homeostasis.[198,199]
2. There is now recent evidence implicating thromboxanes in the pathogenesis of atherosclerosis, since experimentally induced atherosclerosis in cholesterol-fed rabbits is reduced both by a thromboxane $A_2$ receptor antagonist[200] or by a thromboxane synthetase inhibitor.[201]

3. A combined thromboxane synthetase inhibitor/thromboxane receptor antagonist (R 68070) has been described[202,203] that overcomes the drawbacks inherent with conventional TX synthetase inhibitors. In this way, activation of $TXA_2$ receptors by accumulated $PGH_2$ (and $PGD_2$ and $F_{2\alpha}$ that also accumulate) is negated and a more profound inhibition seen, since the $PGD_2$ and $PGI_2$ that accumulate can now act without having to overcome residual TX-mediated effects.
4. Effects of a prostacyclin "Taprostene" (Grunenthale) were reported[204] that, upon i.v. administration, are capable of inhibiting platelet aggregation in man without the usual prostacyclin effect of reducing blood pressure. Schering have also reported upon a $PGD_2$ analog that should lack the residual TX or PGF-receptor-mediated effects of causing bronchoconstriction, elevation of blood pressure, and some partial stimulatory effects upon platelet aggregation.[205]
5. Reducing plasma cholesterol in humans may owe some of its anti-atherosclerotic potential to a reported[206] restoration of platelet sensitivity to the inhibitory effects of $PGI_2$.
6. The biological activity of the lipoxins and related substances have been well delineated in a recent proceedings supplement of *Advances in Experimental Biology and Medicine*.
7. Recent studies have shown that renal cytochrome P-450 dependent metabolites of arachidonic acid (including the epoxides 5[6]-EpETrE and 11[12]-EpETrE) are increased during the developmental stage of hypertension in spontaneously hypertensive rats, and that these increases subside when hypertension is established.[207] A role for these metabolites in the control of blood pressure is further suggested in studies of the thick ascending limb of the loop of Henle (TALH cells) in rabbits.[208]

## REFERENCES


1. **Von Euler, U. S.,** Prostaglandins, historical remarks, *Proc. Lipid Res.,* 20, xxxi, 1982.
2. **Bergström, S.,** Prostaglandins from bedside observation to a family of drugs, *Prog. Lipid Res.,* 20, 7, 1982.
3. **Vane, J. R.,** Inhibition of prostaglandin biosynthesis as a mechanism of action for aspirin-like drugs, *Nature (London) New Biol.,* 231, 232, 1971.
4. **Smith, J. B. and Willis, A. L.,** Aspirin selectively inhibits prostaglandin production by platelets in response to thrombin, *Nature (London) New Biol.,* 231, 235, 1971.
5. **Ferreira, S. H., Moncada, S., and Vane, J. R.,** Indomethacin and aspirin abolish prostaglandin release from the spleen, *Nature (London) New Biol.,* 231, 237, 1971.
6. **Willis, A. L., Davison, P., Ramwell, P. W., Brocklehurst, W. E., and Smith, J. B.,** Release and actions of prostaglandins in inflammation and fever: inhibition by anti-inflammatory and anti-pyretic drugs, in *Prostaglandins in Cellular Biology,* Ramwell, P. W. and Pharriss, B. B., Eds., Plenum Press, New York, 1972, 227.
7. **Vane, J. R.,** Inhibition of prostaglandin biosynthesis as the mechanism of action of aspirin-like drugs, *Adv. Biosci.,* 9, 395, 1973.
8. **Ferreira, S. H. and Vane, J. R.,** Mode of action of anti-inflammatory agents which are prostaglandin synthetase inhibitors, in *Anti-inflammatory Drugs,* Vane, J. R. and Ferreira, S. H., Eds., Springer-Verlag, Berlin, 1979, 348.
9. **Flower, R. J. and Vane, J. R.,** Inhibition of prostaglandin synthetase in brain explains the anti-pyretic activity of paracetamol (4-acetamidophenol), *Nature (London),* 240, 410, 1972.
10. **Flower, R. J.,** Drugs which inhibit prostaglandin biosynthesis, *Pharm. Rev.,* 26, 33, 1974.
11. **Hamberg, M.,** Inhibition of prostaglandin biosynthesis in man, *Biochem. Biophys. Res. Commun.,* 49, 720, 1972.
12. **Smith, M. J. H. and Smith, P. K., Eds.,** *The Salicylates: a Critical Bibliographic Review,* John Wiley & Sons, New York, 1966.
13. **O'Brien, J. R.,** Effect of anti-inflammatory agents on platelets, *Lancet,* i, 894, 1968.
14. **Willis, A. L. and Smith, J. B.,** Some perspectives on platelets and prostaglandins, *Prog. Lipid Res.,* 20, 387, 1982.

15. **Vargaftig, B. B.,** The inhibition of cyclooxygenase of rabbit platelets by aspirin is prevented by salicylic acid and by phenanthrolines, *Eur. J. Pharmacol.,* 50, 231, 1978.
16. **de Gaetano, G., Cerletti, C., Dejana, E., and Vermylen, J.,** Current issues in thrombosis prevention with antiplatelet drugs, *Drugs,* 31, 517, 1986.
17. **Leonardi, R. G., Alexander, B., and White, F.,** Prevention of the inhibitory effect of aspirin on platelet aggregation., *Fed Proc.,* 31, (Abstr.) 202, 1972.
18. **Vargaftig, B. B. and Zirinis, P.,** Platelet aggregation induced by arachidonic acid is accompanied by release of potential inflammatory mediators distinct from $PGE_2$ and $PF_2$, *Nature (London) New Biol.,* 244, 114, 1973.
19. **Silver, M. J., Smith, J. B., Ingerman, C., and Kocsis, J. J.,** Arachidonic acid-induced human platelet aggregation and prostaglandin formation, *Prostaglandins,* 4, 863, 1973.
20. **Willis, A. L. and Kuhn, D. C.,** A new potential mediator of arterial thrombosis whose biosynthesis is inhibited by aspirin, *Prostaglandins,* 4, 127, 1973.
21. **Willis, A. L.,** An enzymatic mechanism for the anti-thrombotic and anti-hemostatic actions of aspirin, *Science,* 183, 325, 1974.
22. **Willis, A. L., Vane, F. M., Kuhn, D. C., Scott, C. G., and Petrin, M.,** An endoperoxide aggregator (LASS) formed in platelets in response to thrombotic stimuli: purification, identification and unique biological significance, *Prostaglandins,* 8, 453, 1974.
23. **Sutor, A. H., Bowie, E. J. H., and Owen, C. A.,** Effect of aspirin, sodium salicylate and acetaminophen on bleeding, *Mayo Clin. Proc.,* 46, 178, 1971.
24. **Hamberg, M., Svensson, J., Wakabayashi, T., and Samuelsson, B.,** Isolation and structure of two prostaglandin endoperoxides that cause platelet aggregation, *Proc. Natl. Acad. Sci. U.S.A.,* 71, 345, 1974.
25. **Malsten, C., Hamberg, M., and Svensson, J.,** Physiological role of an endoperoxide in human platelets: hemostatic defect due to platelet cyclo-oxygenase deficiency, *Proc. Natl. Acad. Sci. U.S.A.,* 72, 1140, 1975.
26. **Willis, A. L.,** Platelet aggregation mechanisms and their implications in haemostasis and inflammatory disease, in *Inflammation,* Vane, J.R. and Ferreira, S. H., Eds., Springer-Verlag, Berlin, 1978, 138.
27. **Hamberg, M., Svensson, J., and Samuelsson, B.,** Thromboxanes: a new group of biologically active compounds derived from prostaglandin endoperoxides, *Proc. Natl. Acad. Sci. U.S.A.,* 72, 2994, 1975.
28. **Needleman, P., Moncada, S., Bunting, S., Vane, J. R., Hamberg, M., and Samuelsson, B.,** Identification of an enzyme in platelet microsomes which generates thromboxane $A_2$ from prostaglandin endoperoxide, *Nature (London),* 261, 558, 1976.
29. **Hamberg, M. and Samuelsson, B.,** Prostaglandin endoperoxides. Novel transformations of arachidonic acid in human platelets, *Proc. Natl. Acad. Sci. U.S.A.,* 71, 3400, 1974.
30. **Bhagwat, S. S., Hamann, P. R., Still, W. C., Bunting, S., and Fitzpatrick, F. A.,** Synthesis and structure of the platelet aggregating factor thromboxane $A_2$, *Nature (London),* 315, 511, 1985.
31. **Moncada, S., Needleman, P., Bunting, S., and Vane, J. R.,** Prostaglandin endoperoxide and thromboxane generating systems and their selective inhibition, *Prostaglandins,* 12, 323, 1976.
32. **Moncada, S. and Vane, J. R.,** Pharmacology and endogenous roles of prostaglandin endoperoxides, thromboxane $A_2$ and prostacyclin, *Pharm. Rev.,* 30, 293, 1978.
33. **Dusting, G. J., Moncada, S., and Vane, J. R.,** Prostacyclin: its biosynthesis, actions, and clinical potential, in *Prostaglandins and the Cardiovascular System, Advances in Prostaglandin, Thromboxane and Leukotriene Research,* Vol. 10, Oates, J. A., Ed., Raven Press, New York, 1982, 59.
34. **Willis, A. L., Smith, D. L., and Vigo, C.,** Suppression of principal atherosclerotic mechanisms by prostacyclins and other eicosanoids, *Prog. Lipid Res.,* 25, 645, 1986.
35. **Smith, D. L., Willis, A. L., Nguyen, N., Dave, S., Yih, R., and Nakamura, G.,** Anti-atherosclerotic properties of prostacyclins on release of mitogens from platelets and endothelial cells, in *Atherosclerosis VII: Excerpta Medica International Congress Series,* Fidge, N. H. and Nestel, P. J., Eds., Elsevier, Amsterdam, 1986, 453.
36. **Hajjar, D. P.,** Prostaglandins and cyclic nucleotides: modulation of arterial cholesterol metabolism, *Biochem. Pharmacol.,* 34, 295, 1985.
37. **Aiken, J. W., Shebuski, R. J., Miller, O. V., and Gorman, R. R.,** Endogenous prostacyclin contributes to the efficacy of a thromboxane synthetase inhibitor for preventing coronary artery thrombosis, *J. Pharmacol. Exp. Ther.,* 219, 299, 1981.
38. **Marcus, A. J., Weksler, B. B., Jaffe, E. A., and Broekman, M. J.,** Synthesis of prostacyclin from platelet-derived endoperoxides by cultured human endothelial cells, *J. Clin. Invest.,* 66, 979, 1980.
39. **Sinziger, H., Kaliman, J., Styrobl-Jager, E., Widhalm, K., and Peskar, B. A.,** Prostacyclin synthesis stimulating plasma factor in patients with primary hyperlipoproteinemia—effects of dietary and drug treatment, *Prostaglandins, Leukotrienes Med.,* 22, 170, 1986.
40. **Poggi, A., Niewiarowski, S., Stewart, G. J., Sobel, E., and Smith, J. B.,** Human platelet-secreted proteins and prostacyclin production by bovine aortic endothelial cells, *Proc. Soc. Exp. Biol. Med.,* 172, 543, 1983.

41. Numerous authors, various articles *Br. J. Clin. Pharmacol.*, 15, (Suppl.), 1983.
42. **Cook, H. T., Cattell, V., Smith, J., Salmon, J. A., and Moncada, S.,** Effect of a thromboxane synthetase inhibitor on eicosanoid synthesis and glomerular injury during acute unilateral glomerulonephritis in the rat, *Clin. Nephrol.*, 26, 195, 1986.
43. **Ingerman-Wojenski, C., Silver, M. J., Smith, J. B., Nessenbaum, M., and Sedar, A. W.,** Prostacyclin production in rabbit arteries *in situ*: inhibition by arachidonic acid-induced endothelial cell damage or by low-dose aspirin, *Prostaglandins*, 21, 655, 1981.
44. **Fitzgerald, G. A., Smith, B., Pedersen, A. K., and Brash, A. R.,** Increased prostacyclin biosynthesis in patients with severe atherosclerosis and platelet activation, *N. Engl. J. Med.*, 310, 1065, 1984.
45. **Moncada, S., Korbut, R., Bunting, S., and Vane, J. R.,** Prostacyclin is a circulating hormone, *Nature (London)*, 283, 194, 1980.
46. **Steer, M. L., MacIntyre, D. E., Levine, L., and Salzman, E. W.,** Is prostacyclin a physiologically important circulating anti-platelet agent? *Nature (London)*, 283, 194, 1980.
47. **Haslam, R. J. and McClenachan, M. D.,** Measurement of circulating prostacyclin, *Nature (London)*, 292, 364, 1981.
48. **Pace-Asciak, C. R., Carrara, M. C., and Levine, L.,** $PGI_2$ is not a circulating vasodepressor hormone, *Prog. Lipid Res.*, 20, 113, 1982.
49. **Fisher, J. M., Willis, A. L., Smith, D. L., and Donegan, D.,** Lack of circulating prostacyclin ($PGI_2$) in guinea-pig and rat, *Thromb. Hemostasis*, 46, 83, 1981.
50. **Stastweska-Barzack, J. and Herbaczynska-Cedro, K.,** Muscular work and prostaglandin release, *Br. J. Pharmacol.*, 52, 454P, 1974.
51. **Legarde, M., Guichardant, M., and Dechavanne, M.,** Human platelet $PGE_1$ and dihomogammalinolenic acid. Comparison to $PGE_2$ and arachidonic acid, *Prog. Lipid Res.*, 20, 439, 1982.
52. **Van Furth, R.,** Mononuclear phagocytes in inflammation, in *Inflammation*, Vane, J. R. and Ferriera, S. H., Eds., Springer-Verlag, Berlin, 1978, 68.
53. **Defreyn, H., Deckmyn, H., and Vermylen, A.,** A thromboxane synthetase inhibitor reorients endoperoxide metabolism in whole blood towards prostacyclin and prostaglandin $E_2$, *Thromb. Res.*, 26, 389, 1982.
54. **Orchard, M. A., Waddell, K. A., Lewis, P. J., and Blair, I. A.,** Thromboxane synthase inhibition causes redirection of prostaglandin endoperoxides to prostaglandin $D_2$ during collagen stimulated aggregation of human platelet rich plasma, *Thromb. Res.*, 39, 701, 1985.
55. **Patrignani, P., Filabozzi, P., Castella, F., Pugliese, F., and Patrono, C.,** Differential effects of dazoxiben, a selective thromboxane synthase inhibitor on platelet and renal endoperoxide metabolism, *J. Pharmacol. Exp. Ther.*, 472, 1984.
56. **Andersen, N. H., Eggerman, T. L., Harker, L. A., Wilson, C. H., and De, B.,** On the multiplicity of platelet prostaglandin receptors. I. Evaluation of competitive antagonism by aggregometry, *Prostaglandins*, 19, 711, 1980.
57. **Burghuber, O., Sinzinger, H., Silberbauer, K., Wolf, C., and Haber, P.,** Decreased prostacyclin sensitivity of human platelets after jogging and squash, *Prostaglandins Med.*, 6, 127, 1981.
58. **Smith, J. B.,** Effect of thromboxane synthetase inhibitors on platelet function: enhancement by inhibition of phosphodiesterase, *Thromb. Res.*, 28, 177, 1982.
59. **Darius, H., Lefer, A. M., Lepran, I., and Smith, J. B.,** *In vivo* interaction of prostacyclin with an inhibitor of cyclic nucleotide phosphodiesterase, HL 725, *Br. J. Pharmacol.*, 84, 735, 1985.
60. **Weksler, B. B., Tackgoldman, K., Subramanian, V. A., and Gay, W. A.,** Cumulative inhibitory effect of low-dose aspirin on vascular prostacyclin and platelet thromboxane production in patients with atherosclerosis, *Circulation*, 71, 332, 1985.
61. **Fitzgerald, G. A., Oates, J. A., Howiger, J., Maas, R. L., Roberts, L. J., II, Oates, J. A., Hawiger, J., Maas, R. L., Jackson Roberts L., II, Lawson, J. L., and Brash, A. R.,** Endogenous biosynthesis of prostacyclin and thromboxane and platelet function during chronic administration of aspirin in man, *J. Clin. Invest.*, 71, 676, 1983.
62. **Cerletti, C., Latina, R., Dejana, E., Tognoni, G., Garattini, S., and de Gaetano, G.,** Inhibition of human platelet thromboxane generation by aspirin in the absence of measurable drug levels in peripheral blood, *Biochem. Pharmacol.*, 34, 1839, 1985.
63. **Dejana, E., Cerletti, C., De Castellarnau, C., Livio, M., Galletti, F., Latini, R., and de Gaetano, G.,** Evidence that salicylate accumulating during aspirin administration may protect vascular prostacyclin from aspirin-induced inhibition, *J. Clin. Invest.*, 68, 1108, 1981.
64. **Buchanan, M. R., Butt, R. W., Magas, Z., Ryn, J. V., Hirsh, J., and Nazir, D. J.,** Endothelial cells produce a lipoxygenase derived chemo-repellent which influences platelet/endothelial cell interactions— effects of aspirin and salicylate, *Thromb. Haemostasis*, 53, 306, 1985.
64a. **Buchanan, M. R., Rischke, J. A., and Hirsh, J.,** Aspirin inhibits platelet function independent of the acetylation of cyclooxygenase, *Thromb. Res.*, 25, 363, 1982.
65. **Buchanan, M. R., Haas, T. A., Lagarde, M., and Guichardant, M.,** 13-Hydroxyoctadecadienoic acid is the vessel wall chemorepellant factor, LOX, *J. Biol. Chem.*, 260, 16056, 1985.

66. **Marnett, L. J., Siedlik, P. H., Ochs, R. D., Pagels, W. R., Das, M., Honn, K. V., Warnock, R. H., Tainer, B. E., and Eling, T. E.,** Mechanism of the stimulation of prostaglandin H synthase and prostacyclin synthase by the anti-thrombotic and anti-metastatic agent, nafazatrom, *Mol. Pharmacol.*, 26, 328, 1984.
67. **Anon.,** Nafazatrom, *Drugs Future,* 11, 520, 1986.
68. **Sinzinger, H., Silverbauer, K., Horsch, A. K., and Gall, A.,** Decreased sensitivity of human platelets to $PGI_2$ during long-term intraarterial prostacyclin infusion in patients with peripheral vascular disease—rebound phenomenon? *Prostaglandins,* 21, 49, 1981.
69. **Sinzinger, H., and Reiter, S.,** The intrainfusion platelet rebound following $PGE_1$-infusion is faster and more intensive than that with $PGI_2$, *Prostaglandins Leukotrienes Med.*, 13, 281, 1984.
70. **Yardumian, D. A., Mackie, I. J., Bull, H., and Machin, S. J.,** Platelet responses observed during and after infusion of the prostacyclin analog ZK36374, in *Advances in Prostaglandin, Thromboxane and Leukotriene Research,* Vol 13, Neri Serneri, G. G., McGiff, J. C., Paoletti, R., and Born, G. V. R., Eds., Raven Press, New York, 1985, 359.
71. **Willis, A. L., Smith, D. L., Vigo, C., and Kluge, A. F.,** Effects of prostacyclin and orally active stable mimetic agent RS93427-007 on basic mechanisms of atherogenesis, *Lancet,* 682, 1986.
72. **Willis, A. L., Smith, D. L., Vigo, C., Kluge, A., O'Yang, C., Kertesz, D., and Wu, H.,** Orally active prostacyclin-mimetic RS-93427: therapeutic potential in vascular occlusive disease associated with atherosclerosis, in *Advances in Prostaglandin, Thromboxane and Leukotriene Research,* Vol. 17, Samuelsson, B., Paoletti, R., and Ramwell, P. W., Eds., Raven Press, New York, 1987.
73. **Zipser, R. D. and Laffi, G.,** Prostaglandins, thromboxanes and leukotrienes in clinical medicine, *West. J. Med.*, 143, 485, 1985.
74. **Nugteren, D. H.,** Arachidonate lipoxygenase in blood platelets, *Biochim. Biophys. Acta,* 380, 299, 1975.
75. **Borgeat, P. and Samuelsson, B.,** Transformation of arachidonic acid by rabbit polymorphonuclear leukocytes, *J. Biol. Chem.*, 254, 2643, 1979.
76. **Borgeat, P., Hamberg, M., and Samuelsson, B.,** Transformation of arachidonic acid and homo-γ-linolenic acid by rabbit polymorphonuclear leukocytes, *J. Biol. Chem.*, 251, 7816, 1976.
77. **Samuelsson, B.,** Leukotrienes: a novel group of compounds including SRS-A, *Prog. Lipid Res.*, 20, 23, 1982.
78. **Hammarstrom, S.,** Leukotrienes, *Annu. Rev. Biochem.*, 52, 355, 1983.
79. **Brocklehurst, W. E.,** The forty-year quest of "slow reacting substance of anaphylaxis", *Prog. Lipid Res.*, 20, 23, 1982.
80. **Palmblad, J., Malmsten, C. L., Uden, A. M., Radmark, O., Engsedt, L., and Samuelsson, B.,** Leukotriene $B_4$ is a potential stereospecific stimulator of neutrophil chemotaxis and adherence, *Blood,* 58, 658, 1981.
81. **Ford-Hutchinson, A. W., Bray, M. A., Doing, M. V., Shipley, M. E., and Smith, J. H.,** Leukotriene B, a potent chemokinetic and aggregating substance released from polymorphonuclear leukocytes, *Nature (London),* 286, 264, 1980.
82. **Palmblad, J., Hafstrom, I., Malmsten, C. L., Uden, A. M., Radmark, O., Engsedt, L., and Samuelsson, B.,** Effects of leukotrienes on *in vitro* neutrophil functions, *Adv. Prostaglandin, Thromboxane Leukotriene Res.*, 9, 293, 1982.
83. **Hafstrom, I., Palmblad, J., Malmsten, C., Radmark, O., and Samuelsson, B.,** Leukotriene $B_4$ — a stereospecific stimulator for release of lysosomal enzymes from neutrophils, *FEBS Lett.*, 130, 146, 1981.
84. **Downing, D. T., Ahern, D. G., and Bachta, M.,** Enzyme inhibition by acetylenic compounds, *Biochem. Biophys. Res. Commun.*, 40, 218, 1970.
85. **Chang, J., Skowronek, M. D., Cherney, M. L., and Lewis, A. J.,** Differential effects of putative lipoxygenase inhibitors on arachidonic acid metabolism in cell-free and intact cell preparations, *Inflammation,* 8, 143, 1984.
86. **Stone, K. J.,** Unpublished data, 1976.
87. **Osbond, J. M., Philpott, P. G., and Wickens, J. C.,** Essential fatty acids. Synthesis of linoleic, γ-linolenic, arachidonic, and docosa-4,7,10,13,16-pentaenoic acid, *J. Chem. Soc.*, July, 2779, 1961.
88. **Kingsbury, K. J., Morgan, D. M., Aylott, C., and Emmerson, R.,** Effects of ethyl arachidonate, cod liver oil and corn oil on the plasma cholesterol level, *Lancet,* i, 739, 1961.
89. **Seyberth, H. W., Oelz, O., Kennedy, T., Sweetman, B. J., Danon, A., Frolich, J. C., Heimberg, M., and Oates, J. A.,** Increased arachidonate in lipids after administration to man: effects on prostaglandin biosynthesis, *Clin. Pharmacol. Ther.*, 18, 521, 1975.
90. **Shaw, J. E., Jessup, S. J., and Ramwell, P. W.,** Prostaglandin-adenylate cyclase relationships, in *Advances in Cyclic Nucleotide Research,* Vol. 1, Paoletti, R., Ed., Raven Press, New York, 1972, 479.
91. **A. L., Willis,** Unpublished observations, 1971 to 1976.
92. **Hammarstrom, S.,** Selective inhibition of platelet n-8 lipoxygenase by 5,8,11-eicosatriynoic acid, *Biochim. Biophys. Acta,* 487, 517, 1977.
93. **Kuehn, M., Holzhuetter, H. G., Schewe, T., Hiebach, C., and Rapoport, S. M.,** The mechanism of inactivation of lipoxygenase by acetylenic fatty acids, *Eur. J. Biochem.*, 139, 577, 1984.

94. **Tappel, A. L., Lundberg, W. O., and Boyer, P. D.,** Effect of temperature and anti-oxidants upon the lipoxydase-catalyzed oxidation of sodium linoleate, *Arch. Biochem. Biophys.*, 42, 239, 1953.
95. **Morris, H. R., Piper, P. J., Taylor, G. W., and Tippens, J. R.,** The role of arachidonate lipoxygenase in the release of SRS-A from guinea-pig chopped lung, *Prostaglandins,* 19, 371, 1980.
96. **Armour, C. L., Hughs, J. M., Seale, J. P., and Temple, D. M.,** Effects of lipoxygenase inhibitors on release of slow reacting substance from human lung, *Eur. J. Pharmacol.*, 72, 93, 1981.
97. **Higgs, G. A., Flower, R. J., and Vane, J. R.,** A new approach to anti-inflammatory drugs, *Biochem. Pharmacol.*, 28, 1959, 1979.
98. **Blackwell, G. J. and Flower, R. J.,** 1-Phenyl-3-pyrazolidone: an inhibitor of arachidonate oxidation in lungs and platelets, *Br. J. Pharmacol.*, 63, 360P, 1978.
99. **Harvey, J., Parish, H., Ho, P. P. K., Boot, J. R., and Dawson, W.,** The preferential inhibition of 5-lipoxygenase product formation by benoxaprofen, *J. Pharm. Pharmacol.*, 35, 44, 1983.
100. **Vanderhoek, J. Y. and Bailey, J. M.,** Activation of 15-lipoxygenase/leukotriene pathway in human polymorphonuclear leukocytes by the anti-inflammatory agent ibuprofen, *J. Biol. Chem.*, 259, 6752, 1984.
101. **Jones, G. M., Venuti, M. C., Young, J. M., Murthy, D. V., Loe, B. E., Simpson, R. A., Berks, A. H., Spires, D. A., Maloney, P. J., Kruseman, M., Rouhafza, S., Kappas, K. C., Beard, C. C., Unger, S. H., and Cheung, P. S.,** Topical nonsteroidal anti-psoriatic agents. I. 1,2,3,1-tetraoxygenated naphthalene derivatives, *J. Med. Chem.*, 29, 1501, 1985.
102. **Voorhees, J. J., Chambers, D. A., Duell, E. A., Marcelo, C. L., and Krueger, G. G.,** Molecular mechanisms in proliferative skin disease, *J. Invest. Dermatol.*, 67, 442, 1976.
103. **Ziboh, V. A., Nguyen, T. T., McCullough, J. L., and Weistein, G. D.,** Possible role of prostaglandins (PGs) in scaly dermatosis, *Prog. Lipid Res.*, 20, 857, 1981.
104. **Willis, A. L.,** Nutritional and pharmacological factors in eicosanoid biology, *Nutr. Rev.*, 39, 289, 1981.
105. **Koshihara, Y., Murota, S., and Nicolaou, K. C.,** 5,6-Methano leukotriene $A_4$: a potent specific inhibitor for 5-lipoxygenase, in *Advances in Prostaglandin, Thromboxane, and Leukotriene Research,* Vol. 11, Samuelsson, B., Paoletti, R., and Ramwell, P., Eds., Raven Press, New York, 1983, 163.
106. **Bray, M. A.,** Retinoids are potent inhibitors of the generation of rat leukocyte leukotriene $B_4$-like activity *in vitro, Eur. J. Pharmacol.*, 98, 61, 1984.
107. **Sekiya, K. and Okuda, H.,** Selective inhibition of platelet lipoxygenase by baicalin, *Biochem. Biophys. Res. Commun.*, 105, 1090, 1982.
108. **Egan, R. W., Tischler, A. N., Baptista, E. M., Ham, E. A., Soderman, D. D., and Gale, P. H.,** Specific inhibition and oxidative regulation of 5-lipoxygenase, in *Advances in Prostaglandin, Thromboxane, and Leukotriene Research,* Vol. 11, Samuelsson, B., Paoletti, R., and Ramwell, P., Eds., Raven Press, New York, 1983, 151.
109. **Koshihara, Y., Neichi, T., Murota, S., Lao, A., Fujimoto, Y., and Tatsuno, T.,** Caffeic acid is a selective inhibitor for leukotriene biosynthesis, *Biochim. Biophys. Acta,* 792, 92, 1984.
110. **Tihanyi, E., Feher, O., Gal, M., Janaky, J., Tolnay, P., and Sebestyen, L.,** Pyrazolcarboxylic acid hydrazides as anti-inflammatory agents. New selective lipoxygenase inhibitors, *Eur. J. Med. Chem.-Chim. Ther.*, 19, 433, 1984.
111. **Kitamura, S., Hashizuma, K., Iida, T., Miyashita, E., Shirata, K., and Kase, H.,** Studies on lipoxygenase inhibitors. II KF8940 (2-n-heptyl-4-hydroxyquinolone-N-oxide), a potent and selective inhibitor of 5-lipoxygenase, produced by *Pseudomonas methanica, J. Antibiot. (Tokyo),* 39, 1160, 1986.
112. **Hamasaki, Y. and Tai, H. H.,** Gossypol, a potent inhibitor of arachidonate 5- and 12-lipoxygenases, *Biochim. Biophys. Acta,* 834, 37, 1985.
113. **Honn, K. V. and Dunn, J. R.,** Nafazatrom (BAY G 6575) inhibition of tumor cell lipoxygenase activity and cellular proliferation, *FEBS Lett.*, 139, 65, 1982.
114. **Bach, M. K., Brashler, J. R., Fitzpatrick, F. A., Griffin, R. L., Iden, S. S., Johnson, H. G., McNee, M. L., McGuire, J. C., Smith, R. J., Sun, F. F., and Wasserman, M. A.,** *In vivo* and *in vitro* actions of a new selective inhibitor of leukotriene C and D synthesis, in *Advances in Prostaglandin, Thromboxane, and Leukotriene Research,* Vol. 11, Samuelsson, B., Paoletti, R., and Ramwell, P., Eds., Raven Press, New York, 1983, 39.
115. **Ham, E. A., Soderman, D. D., Zanetti, M. E., Dougherty, H. W., McCauley, E., and Keuhl, F. A., Jr.,** Inhibition by prostaglandins of leukotriene $B_4$ by release from activated neutrophils, *Proc. Natl. Acad. Sci. U.S.A.*, 80, 4349, 1983.
116. **Pace-Asciak, C. R. and Martin, J. M.,** Hepoxilin, a new family of insulin secretogogues formed by intact rat pancreatic islets, *Prostaglandins Leukotrienes Med.*, 16, 173, 1984.
117. **Naor, Z., Kiessel, L., Vanderhoek, J. Y., and Catt, K. J.,** Mechanism of action of gonadotropin releasing hormone: role of lipoxygenase products of arachidonic acid in luteinizing hormone release, *J. Steroid Biochem.*, 23, 711, 1985.
118. **Rossi, P., Lindgren, J. A., Kullman, C., and Jondal, M.,** Products of the lipoxygenase pathway in human natural killer cell cytotoxicity, *Cell. Immunol.*, 93, 1, 1985.

119. **van der Schroeff, J. G., Havekes, L., Weeheim, A. M., Emeis, J. J., and Vermeer, B. J.,** Suppression of cholesteryl ester accumulation in cultured human monocyte-derived macrophages by lipoxygenase inhibitors, *Biochem. Biophys. Res. Commun.*, 127, 366, 1985.
120. **Nakao, J., Ooyama, T., Chang, W. C., Murota, S., and Orimo, H.,** Platelets stimulate aortic smooth muscle cell migration *in vitro*-involvement of 12-L-hydroxy-5,8,10,14-eicosatetraenoic acid, *Atherosclerosis,* 43, 143, 1982.
121. **Nakao, J., Ooyama, T., Ito, H., Chang, W.-C., and Murota, S.,** Comparative effects of lipoxygenase products of arachidonic acid on rat aortic smooth muscle cell migration, *Atherosclerosis,* 44, 339, 1982.
122. **Zor, U., Naor, Z., and Kohen, F., Eds.,** Leukotrienes and prostanoids in health and disease, *Advances in Prostaglandin, Thromboxane and Leukotriene Research,* Vol. 16, Raven Press, New York, 1987.
123. **Sontag, S. J.,** Prostaglandins in peptic ulcer disease. An overview of current status and future directions, *Drugs,* 32, 445, 1986.
124. **Garay, G. L., and Muchowski, J. M.,** Agents for the treatment of peptic ulcer disease, *Annu. Rep. Med. Chem.*, 20, 93, 1985.
125. **Cohen, M., Ed.,** Biological Protection with Prostaglandins, Vol. II, CRC Press, Boca Raton, FL, 1986.
126. **Monk, J. P. and Clissold, S. P.,** Misoprostil. A preliminary review of its pharmacodynamic properties, and therapeutic efficacy in the treatment of peptic ulcer disease, *Drugs,* 33, 1, 1987.
127. **Anon.,** Prostaglandins in gastroenterology, focus on misoprostil, *Dig. Dis. Sci.*, 30 (Suppl. 11), 1985.
128. **Armstrong, R. A., Jones, R. L., MacDermot, J., and Wilson, N. H.,** Prostaglandin endoperoxide analogs which are both thromboxane receptor antagonists and prostacyclin mimetics, *Br. J. Pharmacol.*, 87, 543, 1986.
129. **Woodward, D. L., Rollins, D. E., Krueger, G., and Harris, B. J.,** A dose-ranging study of viprostol, a topically active synthetic prostaglandin, to assess the effects on cutaneous blood flow, in abstract book, 6th Int. Conf. Prostaglandins Related Compounds, 1986, 437.
130. **Augstein, S., Farmer, J. B., Lee, T. B., Sheard, P., and Tattersall, M. L.,** Selective inhibitor of slow reacting substances in anaphylaxis, *Nature (London) New Biol.*, 245, 215, 1973.
131. **Britton, J. R., Hanley, S. P., and Tattersfield, A. E.,** The effects of an oral leukotriene $D_4$ antagonist L-649,923 on the response to inhaled antigen in asthma, in abstract book, 6th Int. Conf. Prostaglandins Related Compounds, Florence, Italy, June 3 to 6, 1986, 417.
132. **Wasserman, M. A., Torphy, T. J., Hay, D. W. P., Muccitelli, R. M., Tucker, S. S., Wilson, K., Osborn, R. R., Vickery-Clark, L., Hall, F. R., Erhard, K. F., and Gleason, J. G.,** Pharmacologic profile of SKF 104353, a novel highly potent and selective peptidolipid leukotriene antagonist, in abstract book, 6th Int. Conf. Prostaglandins Related Compounds, Florence, Italy, June 3 to 6, 1986, 253.
133. **Musser, J. H., Kreft, A. F., and Lewis, A. J.,** New developments concerning leukotriene antagonists: a review, *Agents Actions,* 18, 332, 1986.
134. **Jasani, M. K.,** Anti-inflammatory steroids: mode of action in rheumatoid arthritis and homograft reaction, in *Anti-Inflammatory Drugs,* Vane, J. R. and Ferreira, S. H., Eds., Springer-Verlag, Berlin, 1979, 598.
135. **Flower, R. J.,** Background and discovery of lipocortins, *Agents Actions,* 17, 255, 1985.
136. **Flower, R. J.,** Eleventh Gaddum Memorial lecture: lipocortin and the mechanism of action of glucocorticoids, *Br. J. Pharmacol.*, 94, 987, 1988.
137. **Blackwell, G. J., Carnuccio, R., DiRosa, M., Flower, R. J., Parente, L., and Persico, P.,** Macrocortin: a polypeptide causing the anti-phospholipase effect of glucocorticoids, *Nature (London),* 287, 147, 1980.
138. **Hirata, F., Schiffman, E., Venkatasubramanian, D., Salomon, D., and Axelrod, J.,** A phospholipase $A_2$ inhibitory protein in rabbit neutrophils induced by glucocorticoids, *Proc. Natl. Acad. Sci. U.S.A.*, 77, 2533, 1980.
139. **Wallner, B. P., Mattaliano, R. J., Hession, C., Cate, R. L., Tizard, R., Sinclair, L. K., Foeller, C., Pinchang Chow, E., Browning, J. L., Ramachandran, K. L., and Pepinsky, R. B.,** Cloning and expression of human lipocortin, a phospholipase $A_2$ inhibitor with potential anti-inflammatory activity, *Nature (London),* 320, 77, 1986.
140. **Goodwin, J. S., Atluru, D., Sierakowski, S., and Lianos, E. A.,** Mechanism of action of glucocorticoids. Inhibition of T cell proliferation and interleukin 2 production by hydrocortisone is reversed by leukotriene $B_4$, *J. Clin. Invest.*, 77, 1244, 1985.
141. **Goodwin, J. S., Ed.,** *Prostaglandins and Immunity,* Martinus Nijhoff, Boston, 1985.
142. **Anik, S. T., McRae, G. I., Nurenburg, C., Worden, A., Forman, J., Wang, J., Kushinski, S., Jones, R. E., and Vickery, B. H.,** Nasal absorption of Nafarelin acetate, the decapeptide, [D-Nal(2)6]LHRH in rhesus monkeys I, *J. Pharm. Sci.*, 73, 684, 1983.
143. **Fischer, S. and Weber, P. C.,** Prostaglandin $I_3$ is formed *in vivo* in man after dietary eicosapentaenoic acid, *Nature (London),* 307, 165, 1984.
144. **Needleman, P., Whitaker, M. O., Wyche, A., Watters, K., Sprecher, H., and Raz, A.,** Manipulation of platelet aggregation by prostaglandins and their fatty acid precursors: a pharmacological basis for a therapeutic approach, *Prostaglandins,* 19, 165, 1980.
145. **Nestel, P. J., Connor, W. E., Reardon, M. F., Connor, S., Wong, S., and Boston, R.,** Suppression by diets rich in fish oil of very low density lipoprotein production in man, *J. Clin. Invest.*, 74, 82, 1984.

146. **Corey, E. J., Shih, C., and Cashman, J. R.,** Docosahexaenoic acid is a strong inhibitor of prostaglandin but not leukotriene biosynthesis, *Proc. Natl. Acad. Sci. U.S.A.,* 80, 3581, 1983.
147. **Bailey, J. M., Bryant, R. W., Low, C. E., Pupillo, M. B., and Vanderhoek, Y.,** Role of lipoxygenases in regulation of PHA and phorbol ester-induced mitogenesis, in *Leukotrienes and Other Lipoxygenase Products,* Samuelsson, B. and Paoletti, R., Eds., Raven Press, New York, 1982, 341.
148. **Herold, P. M. and Kinsella, J. E.,** Fish oil consumption and decreased risk of cardiovascular disease: a comparison of findings from animal and human feeding trials, *Am. J. Clin. Nutr.,* 43, 566, 1986.
149. **Shea, M. J., Murtagh, J. J., Jolly, S. R., Abrams, G. D., Pitt, B., and Luchesi, B. R.,** Beneficial effects of nafazatrom on ischemic reperfused myocardium, *Eur. J. Pharmacol.,* 102, 63, 1984.
150. **Paulsrud, J. R. and Miller, O. N.,** Inhibition of 15-OH prostaglandin dehydrogenase by several diuretic drugs, *Fed. Proc.,* 33, 590, 1974.
151. **Friedman, Z., Demers, L. M., Marks, K. H., Uhrman, S., and Maisels, M. J.,** Urinary excretion of prostaglandin E following administration of furosemide and indomethacin to sick low birth weight infants, *J. Pediatr.,* 93, 512, 1978.
152. **Gross, J. H., Gbeassor, F. M., and Lebel, M.,** Differential effects of diuretics on eicosanoid biosynthesis, *Prostaglandins, Leukotrienes Med.,* 24, 103, 1986.
153. **Patak, R. V., Mookerjee, B. K., Bentzel, C. J., Hysert, P. E., Babej, M., and Lee, J. B.,** Antagonism of the effects of furosemide by indomethacin in normal and hypertensive man, *Prostaglandins,* 10, 649, 1975.
154. **Tweeddale, M. G. and Ogilvie, R. I.,** Antagonism of spironolactone-induced natriuresis by aspirin in man, *N. Engl. J. Med.,* 289, 198, 1973.
155. **Moore, P. K. and Hoult, J. R. S.,** Selective action of aspirin- and sulphasalazine-like drugs against prostaglandin synthesis and breakdown, *Biochem. Pharmacol.,* 31, 969, 1982.
156. **Willis, A. L.,** Unanswered Questions in EFA and PG research, *Prog. Lipid Res.,* 20, 839, 1982.
157. **Dyerberg, J. and Bang, H. O.,** Haemostatic function and platelet polyunsaturated fatty acids in Eskimos, *Lancet,* 2, 433, 1979.
158. **Lotz, M., Carson, D. A., and Vaughan, J. H.,** Substance P activation of rheumatoid synoviocytes: neural pathway in pathogenesis of arthritis, *Science,* 235, 893, 1987.
159. **Ogletree, M. L.,** Overview of physiological and pathophysiological effects of thromboxane $A_2$, *Fed. Proc.,* 46, 133, 1987.
160. **Hopkins, N. K., Oglesby, T. D., Bundy, G. L., and Gorman, R. R.,** Biosynthesis and metabolism of 15-hydroperoxy-5,8,11,13-eicosatetraenoic acid by human umbilical vein endothelial cells, *J. Biol. Chem.,* 259, 14048, 1984.
161. **Kuhn, H., Ponicke, K., Halle, W., Weisner, R., Schewe, T., and Forster, W.,** Metabolism of [1-14C]-arachidonic acid by cultured calf aortic endothelial cells: evidence for the presence of a lipoxygenase pathway, *Prostaglandins, Leukotrienes Med.,* 17, 291, 1985.
162. **Soberman, R. J., Harper, T. W., Betteridge, D., Lewis, R. A., and Austen, K. F.,** Characterization and separation of the arachidonic acid 5-lipoxygenase and linoleic acid ω-6 lipoxygenase (arachidonic acid 15-lipoxygenase) of human polymorphonuclear leukocytes, *J. Biol. Chem.,* 260, 4508, 1985.
163. **Yoshimoto, T., Yokoyama, C., Ochi, K., Yamamoto, S., Maki, Y., Ashida, Y., Terao, S., and Shiraishi, M.,** 2,3,5-trimethyl-6-(12-hydroxy-5,10-dodecadinyl)-1,4-benzoquinone (AA861), a selective inhibitor of the 5-lipoxygenase reaction and the biosynthesis of slow-reacting substance of anaphylaxis, *Biochim. Biophys. Acta,* 713, 470, 1982.
164. **Wilhelm, T. E., Sankarappa, S. K., VanRollins, M., and Sprecher, H.,** Selective inhibitors of platelet lipoxygenase: 4,7,10,13-icosatetraynoic acid and 5,8,11,14-henicosatetraynoic acid, *Prostaglandins,* 21, 323, 1981.
165. **Corey, E. J. and Park, H.,** Irreversible inhibition of the enzymatic oxidation of arachidonic acid to 15-(hydroperoxy)-5,8,11(Z),13(E)-eicosatetraenoic acid (15-HPETE) by 14, 15-dehydroarachidonic acid, *J. Am. Chem. Soc.,* 104, 1750, 1982.
166. **Shror, K. and Thiemermann, C.,** Treatment of acute myocardial ishchaemia with a selective antagonist of thromboxane receptors (BM 13,177), *Br. J. Pharmacol.,* 87, 631, 1986.
167. **Lee, S. W., Tsou, A.-P., Chan, H., Thomas, J., Petrie, K., Eugui, E. M., and Allison, A. C.,** Glucocorticoids selectively inhibit the transcription of the interleukin 1β gene and decrease the stability of interleukin 1 β mRNA, *Proc. Soc. Natl. Acad. Sci., U.S.A.,* 85, 1204—1208, 1988.
168. **Saris, C. J., Tack, B. F., Kristensen, T., Glenney, J. R., Jr., and Hunter T.,** The cDNA sequence for the protein-tyrosine kinase substrate p36 (calpactin I heavy chain) reveals a multidomain protein with internal repeats, *Cell,* 46, 201, 1986.
169. **Davidson, F. F., Dennis, E. A., Powell, M., and Glenney, J. R., Jr.,** Inhibition of phospholipase $A_2$ by "lipocortins" and calpactins, *J. Biol. Chem.,* 262, 1698, 1987.
170. **Cizmeci, G.,** *In vivo* effects of defibrotide on platelet c-AMP and blood prostanoid levels, *Haemostasis,* 16 (Suppl. 1), 31, 1986.

171. **Lobel, P. and Schrör, K.,** Selective stimulation of coronary vascular $PGI_2$ but not of platelet thromboxane formation by defibrotide in the platelet perfused heart, *Nuanyn Schmeiderbergs Arch. Pharmacol.*, 33, 125, 1985.
172. **Niada, R., Portan, R., Pescador, R., Mantovani, M., Prino, G., and Berti, F.,** Cardioprotective effects of defibrotide in acute lethal and nonlethal myocardial ischemia in the cat, *Haemostasis,* 16 (Suppl. 1), 18, 1986.
173. **Niada, R., Porta, R., Pescador, M., Mantovani, M., and Prino, G.,** Protective activity of defibrotide against lethal acute myocardial ischemia in the cat, *Thromb. Res.*, 42, 363, 1986.
174. **Thiemermann, C., Lobel, P., and Schrör, K.,** Usefulness of defibrotide in protecting ischemic myocardium from early reperfusion damage, *Am. J. Cardiol.*, 56, 978, 1985.
175. **Berti, F., Rossoni, G., Niada, R., Omini, C., Pretolana, M., and Mandelli, C.,** Beneficial effects of defibrotide against myocardial ischemia and decline of beta-adrenoceptor function in the rabbit, *Haemostasis,* 16 (Suppl.1), 13, 1986.
176. **Hattori, T., Hirata, F., Hoffman, T., Hizuta, A., and Herberman, R. B.,** Inhibition of human natural killer cell (NK) activity and antibody dependent cellular cytotoxicity (ADCC) by lipomodulin, a phospholipase inhibitory protein, *J. Immunol.*, 131, 662, 1983.
177. **De Bono, D. P., Lumley, P., Been, M., Keery, R., and Ince, S. E.,** Effect of the specific thromboxane receptor blocking drug AH23848 in patients with angina pectoris, *Br. Heart J.*, 56, 509, 1986.
178. **Willis, A. L. and Smith, D. L.,** Biochemistry and therapeutic potential of dihomo-gamma-linolenic acid and gamma-linolenic acid in health and disease, in *New Protective Roles of Selected Nutrients,* Spiller, G. and Scala, J., Eds., Alan R. Liss, New York, in press.
179. **Palmer, R. M. J., Ferrige, A. G., and Moncada, S.,** Release of nitric oxide accounts for the biological activity of endothelium-derived relaxing factor, *Nature (London),* 327, 524, 1987.
180. **Shikano, K., Ohlstein, E. H., and Berkowitz, B. A.,** Differential selectivity of endothelium-derived relaxing factor and nitric oxide in smooth muscle, *Br. J. Pharmacol.*, 92, 483, 1987.
181. **Furlong, B., Henderson, A. H., Sweis, M. J., and Smith, J. A.,** Endothelium-derived relaxing factor inhibits *in vitro* platelet aggregation, *Br. J. Pharmacol.*, 90, 687, 1987.
182. **Radomski, M., Palmer, R. M. J., and Moncada, S.,** Comparative pharmacology of endothelium-derived relaxing factor, nitric oxide and prostacyclin in platelets, *Br. J. Pharmacol.*, 92, 181, 1983.
183. **Sneddon, J. M., Bearpark, T., and Vane, J. R.,** Endothelial derived relaxing factor (EDRF) inhibits platelet adhesion to bovine endothelial cells, *Br. J. Pharmacol.*, 93, 100P, 1988.
184. **Radomski, M. W., Palmer, R. M. J., and Moncada, S.,** The anti-aggregatory properties of vascular endothelium: interactions between prostacyclin and nitric oxide, *Br. J. Pharmacol.*, 92, 639, 1987.
185. **Hogan, J. C., Lewis, M. J., and Henderson, A. H.,** *In vivo* endothelium-derived relaxing factor inhibition of platelet aggregability, *Br. J. Pharmacol.*, 93, 103P, 1988.
186. **Nagai, K., Tanaka, T., Kenichi, T., and Mori, N.,** Regulation of placental 15-hydroxyprostaglandin dehydrogenase activity by obstetric drugs, *Prostaglandins, Leukotrienes Med.*, 29, 165, 1987.
187. **Shimizu, T., Radmark, O., and Samuelsson, B.,** Enzyme with dual lipoxygenase activities catalyzes leukotriene $A_4$ synthesis from arachidonic acid, *Proc. Natl. Acad. Sci., U.S.A.*, 81, 689, 1984.
188. **Karmali, R.,** Effect of dietary fatty acids on experimental manifestation of salmonella-associated arthritis in rats, *Prostaglandins, Leukotrienes Med.*, 29, 199, 1987.
189. **Lefer, A. M., Lepran, I., Roth, D. M., and Smith, J. B.,** Specificity of anti-leukotriene actions of nicardipine, *Pharmacol. Res. Commun.*, 16, 1141, 1984.
190. **DeNucci, G., Thomas, R., D' Orleans-Juste, P., Antunes, E., Walder, C., Warner, T. D., and Vane, J. R.,** Pressor effects of circulating endothelin are limited by its removal in the pulmonary circulation and by the release of prostacyclin and endothelium-derived relaxing factor, *Proc. Natl. Acad. Sci. U.S.A.*, 85, 9797, 1988.
191. **Yanagisawa, M., Kurihara, H., Kimura, S., Tomobe, Y., Kobayashi, M., Mitsui, Y., Yazaki, Y., Goto, K., and Masaki, T.,** A novel potent vasoconstrictor peptide produced by vascular endothelial cells, *Nature (London),* 332, 411, 1988.
192. **Palmer, R. M. J., Ashton, D. S., and Moncada, S.,** Vascular endothelial cells synthesize nitric oxide from L-arginine, *Nature (London),* 333, 664, 1988.
193. **Loveday, M., Smith, D. L., Fulks, J., Lee, C. H., Hedley, L., VanAntwerp, D., and Willis, A. L.,** *Br. J. Pharmacol.*, 95, 518P, 1988.
194. **Antunes, E., Lidbury, P. S., DeNucci, G., and Vane, J. R.,** Lack of synergism of iloprost and sodium nitroprusside on rabbit vascular smooth muscle, *Br. J. Pharmacol.*, 95, 516P, 1988.
195. **Willis, A. L. and Weiss, H. J.,** A congenital defect in platelet prostaglandin production associated with impaired hemostasis in storage pool disease, *Prostaglandins,* 4, 783, 1973.
196. **Denton, J. P., Marples, P., and Willis, A. L.,** A convenient method for isolation and bioassay of prostaglandins $E_1$, $E_2$, $F_{2a}$, and $D_2$, *Br. J. Pharmacol.*, 63, 405P, 1978.

## ADDITIONAL REFERENCES

197. **Yanagisawa, M., Kurihara, H., Kimura, S., Tomobe, Y., Kobayashi, M., Mitsui, Y., Yazaki, Y., Goto, K., and Masaki, T.,** A novel potent vasoconstrictor peptide produced by vascular endothelial cells, *Nature (London),* 332, 411—415, 1988.
198. First William Harvey Workshop on Endothelin, *J. Cardiovasc. Pharmacol. (Suppl.),* in press.
199. **Botting, R. and Vane, J. R.,** The receipt and dispatch of chemical messengers by endothelial cells, *Prostaglandins in Clinical Research: Cardiovascular System,* Schrör, K. and Sinzinger, H., Eds., Alan R. Liss, New York, 1989, 1.
200. **Osborne, J. A. and Lefer, A. M.,** Cardioprotective actions of thromboxane receptor antagonism in ischemic atherosclerotic rabbits, *Am. J. Physiol.,* 255, H318—324, 1988.
201. **Skrinska, V. A., Konieczowski, M., Gerrity, R. G., Galang, C. F., and Rebec, M. V.,** Suppression of foam cell lesions in hypercholesteremic rabbits by inhibition of thromboxane $A_2$ synthesis, *Arteriosclerosis,* 8, 359—367, 1988.
202. **De Clerck, F., Beetens, J., de Chaffoy de Courcelles, D., Vercammen, E., Freyne, E., and Janssen, P. A. J.,** R 68 070: thromboxane $A_2$ synthetase inhibition and thromboxane $A_2$/prostaglandin endoperoxide receptor blockade, combined in one molecule, *Prostaglandins in Clinical Research: Cardiovascular System,* Schrör, K. and Sinzinger, H., Eds., Alan R. Liss, New York, 1989, 567.
203. **Hoet, B., Arnout, J., and Vermylen, J.,** R 68 070, a combined thromboxane/endoperoxide receptor antagonist (TRA) and thromboxane synthase inhibitor (TSI) prolongs the bleeding time more than aspirin in man, *Prostaglandins in Clinical Research: Cardiovascular System,* Schrör, K. and Sinzinger, H., Eds., Alan R. Liss, New York, 1989, 573.
204. **Darius, H., Kopp, H., Mulfinger, A., Spielberger, M., Todt, M., Schuster, C. J., and Meyer, J.,** Pilot studies of the effects of taprostene (CG 4203) in patients with advanced peripheral arterial disease, *Prostaglandins in Clinical Research: Cardiovascular System,* Schrör, K. and Sinzinger, H., Eds., Alan R. Liss, New York, 1989, 417.
205. **Thierauch, K.-H., Stürzebecher, S., Schillinger, E., Schulz, G., Radüchel, B., Skuballa, W., Vorbrüggen, H., and Schulze, P.-E.,** ZK 110 841, a selective and potent prostaglandin $D_2$ analogue, *Prostaglandins in Clinical Research: Cardiovascular System,* Schrör, K. and Sinzinger, H., Eds., Alan R. Liss, New York, 1989, 597.
206. **Lobel, P., Steinhagen-Thiessen, E., and Schrör, K.,** Cholestyramine treatment of the Type II1 hypercholesterolemia normalizes platelet reactivity against prostacyclin, *Eur. J. Clin. Invest.,* 18, 256—260, 1988.
207. **Sacerdoti, D., Abraham, N. G., McGiff, J. C., and Schwartzman, M. L.,** Renal cytochrome P-450-dependent metabolism of arachidonic acid in spontaneously hypertensive rats, *Biochem. Pharmacol.,* 37, 521—527, 1988.
208. **Carroll, M. A., Schwartzman, M., Baba, M., Miller, M. J., and McGiff, J. C.,** Renal cytochrome P-450-related arachidonate metabolism in rabbit aortic coarctation, *Am. J. Physiol.,* 255, F151-157, 1988.

# *Inhibitors of Eicosanoid Production*

# ANTIPHOSPHOLIPASE PROTEINS: INTRODUCTION AND OVERVIEW

**Donald L. Smith**

The following is intended as an overview to the chapters in this volume by Flower et al. (Eicosanoid Release) and Hirata (Phospholipase Modulation), with emphasis on current concepts and recent findings. It is expanded and updated from a nomenclature statement published previously by Di Rosa et al. in *Prostaglandins.*[1]

Until recently, there has been confusion over the nature of the steroid-modulated antiphospholipase proteins previously named lipomodulin,[2,3] macrocortin,[4,5] and renocortin[6,7] because, despite similar biological properties, there is a disparity in their molecular weights (40 kDa, 15 kDa, and 15 kDa + 30 kDa, respectively). Until very recently, the primary structure of these proteins was not known. Results of collaborative experiments by several investigators[3,7] showed that these proteins seem functionally identical and that the observed discrepancy was produced by proteolysis.

In addition to the commonly observed forms, other species are sometimes seen. These include a very large protein of ~125 kDa[8] and another ~24 kDa.[2] The apparent molecular weight of the inhibitor in any given preparation depends upon the degree of glycosylation, the extent of proteolysis and method of estimation, and the species of origin.

It was proposed[1] that this family of compounds be known as the lipocortins. This name reflected both their activity as modulators of lipid metabolism and their adrenocortical interrelationships.

Several biological and chemical properties of the lipocortins are now known. They are glycoproteins whose rate of synthesis/secretion by several cell types is dramatically increased by glucocorticoids acting by a receptor-dependent mechanism. Lipocortins inhibit phospholipase $A_2$ and can thus inhibit release of eicosanoids induced by various stimuli *in vitro* and *in vivo* in several systems.[9-13] (See also chapter by Flower et al. in this volume.) However, as for glucocorticoids,[14] they did not inhibit eicosanoid release induced by arachidonic acid or by bradykinin (which might act by stimulating phospholipase C release),[9] and there is recent evidence that glucocorticoid treatment preferentially inhibits phospholipase $A_2$ with no effect on phospholipase C.[14,15]

Two lipocortins, called lipocortins I and II, have now been identified[16-18] as well as a recently described distinct antiphospholipase molecule (a monomeric 32 kDa protein from human placenta).[19] Sequences of cloned lipocortin I (a 35 to 37 kDa monomer) and lipocortin II (a heterotetramer of 2 copies of a 36 kDa chain 50% homologous with lipocortin I and 2 copies of a 10 kDa chain)[16,17] are shown in Figure 1. Sequencing and mapping of five proteolytic fragments of recombinant lipocortin I showed that amino acid residues 97 to 178, a region that is 70% homologous with another lipocortin, are common to all active fragments.[20] Both human and rat lipocortin I show very close structural similarity,[16,21] suggesting a high degree of evolutionary conservation. Both lipocortins I and II are highly polar, and neither lipocortin contains a leader (signal) sequence.

Phospholipase-$A_2$ activity can be blocked by depletion of $Ca^{++}$ with EDTA.[22,23] Although calcium channel blockers can inhibit prostaglandin release,[24,25] such actions might not be mediated through direct inhibition of phospholipase-$A_2$ activity.[24] A hydrophobic interaction at $Ca^{++}$ binding sites has been implicated in the inhibition of phospholipase $A_2$ by lipomodulin, since the inhibition can be reversed by high $Ca^{++}$ concentrations or by detergents.[26] (See also chapter by Hirata in this volume.) Additional evidence for a role of $Ca^{++}$ is provided by the recent findings that lipocortins I and II are homologous with the more recently described and cloned calcium-regulated phospholipid- and actin-binding proteins termed calpactins II and I, respectively.[17,27]

Several other calcium-dependent phospholipid-binding proteins that share, along with

```
                                               10
Lipocortin I        MetAlaMetValSerGluPheLeuLysGlnAlaTrpPheIleGluAsnGluGlu
Lipocortin II                                  MetSerThrValHisGluIleLeuCys
                                                               *

                       20                            30
Lipocortin I        GlnGluTyrValGlnThrValLysSerSerLysGlyGlyProGlySerAlaVal
Lipocortin II       LysLeuSerLeuGluGlyAspHisSerThrProProSerAlaTyrGlySerVal
                                             *                          *

                             40                            50
Lipocortin I        SerProTyrProThrPheAsnProSerSerAspValAlaAlaLeuHisLysAla
Lipocortin II       LysAlaTyrThrAsnPheAspAlaGluArgAspAlaLeuAsnIleGluThrAla
                           *        *              *                    *

                                   60                            70
Lipocortin I        IleMetValLysGlyValAspGluAlaThrIleIleAspIleLeuThrLysArg
Lipocortin II       IleLysThrLysGlyValAspGluValThrIleValAsnIleLeuThrAsnArg
                     *        *  *  *  *  *     *  *        *  *  *     *

                                         80                            90
Lipocortin I        AsnAsnAlaGlnArgGlnGlnIleLysAlaAlaTyrLeuGlnGluThrGlyLys
Lipocortin II       SerAsnAlaGlnArgGlnAspIleAlaPheAlaTyrGlnArgArgThrLysLys
                        *  *  *  *  *     *        *  *           *     *

                                               100
Lipocortin I        ProLeuAspGluThrLeuLysLysAlaLeuThrGlyHisLeuGluGluValVal
Lipocortin II       GluLeuAlaSerAlaLeuLysSerAlaLeuSerGlyHisLeuGluThrValIle
                        *           *  *     *  *     *  *  *  *     *

                       110                           120
Lipocortin I        LeuAlaLeuLeuLysThrProAlaGlnPheAspAlaAspGluLeuArgAlaAla
Lipocortin II       LeuGlyLeuLeuLysThrProAlaGlnTyrAspAlaSerGluLeuLysAlaSer
                     *     *  *  *  *  *  *  *     *  *     *  *     *

                             130                           140
Lipocortin I        MetLysGlyLeuGlyThrAspGluAspThrLeuIleGluIleLeuAlaSerArg
Lipocortin II       MetLysGlyLeuGlyThrAspGluAspSerLeuIleGluIleIleCysSerArg
                     *  *  *  *  *  *  *  *  *     *  *  *  *        *  *

                                   150                           160
Lipocortin I        ThrAsnLysGluIleArgAspIleAsnArgValTyrArgGluGluLeuLysArg
Lipocortin II       ThrAsnGlnGluLeuGlnGluIleAsnArgValTyrLysGluMetTyrLysThr
                     *  *     *           *  *  *  *  *     *        *

                                         170                           180
Lipocortin I        AspLeuAlaLysAspIleThrSerAspThrSerGlyAspPheArgAsnAlaLeu
Lipocortin II       AspLeuGluLysAspIleIleSerAspThrSerGlyAspPheArgLysLeuMet
                     *  *     *  *  *     *  *  *  *  *  *  *  *

                                               190
Lipocortin I        LeuSerLeuAlaLysGlyAspArgSerGluAspPheGlyVal   AsnGluAsp
Lipocortin II       ValAlaLeuAlaLysGlyArgArgAlaGluAspGlySerValIleAspTyrGlu
                           *  *  *  *     *     *  *        *

                          200                           210
Lipocortin I        LeuAlaAspSerAspAlaArgAlaLeuTyrGluAlaGlyGluArgArgLysGly
Lipocortin II       LeuIleAspGluAspAlaArgAspLeuTyrAspAlaGlyValLysArgLysGly
                     *     *     *  *  *     *  *     *  *        *  *  *

                                220                           230
Lipocortin I        ThrAspValAsnValPheAsnThrIleLeuThrThrArgSerTyrProGlnLeu
Lipocortin II       ThrAspValProLysTrpIleSerIleMetThrGluArgSerValProHisLeu
                     *  *  *                 *     *     *  *     *     *

                                      240                           250
Lipocortin I        ArgArgValPheGlnLysTyrThrLysTyrSerLysHisAspMetAsnLysVal
Lipocortin II       GlnLysValPheAspArgTyrLysSerTyrSerProTyrAspMetLeuGluSer
                           *  *        *        *  *        *  *

                                            260
Lipocortin I        LeuAspLeuGluLeuLysGlyAspIleGluLysCysLeuThrAlaIleValLys
Lipocortin II       IleArgLysGluValLysGlyAspLeuGluAsnAlaPheLeuAsnLeuValGln
                              *     *  *  *     *                    *

                    270                           280
Lipocortin I        CysAlaThrSerLysProAlaPhePheAlaGluLysLeuHisGlnAlaMetLys
Lipocortin II       CysIleGlnAsnLysProLeuTyrPheAlaAspArgLeuTyrAspSerMetLys
                     *           *  *        *  *        *           *  *

                          290                           300
Lipocortin I        GlyValGlyThrArgHisLysAlaLeuIleArgIleMetValSerArgSerGlu
Lipocortin II       GlyLysGlyThrArgAspLysValLeuIleArgIleMetValSerArgSerGlu
                     *     *  *  *     *     *  *  *  *  *  *  *  *  *  *

                                310                           320
Lipocortin I        IleAspMetAsnAspIleLysAlaPheTyrGlnLysMetTyrGlyIleSerLeu
Lipocortin II       ValAspMetLeuLysIleArgSerGluPheLysArgLysTyrGlyLysSerLeu
                        *  *        *                       *  *     *  *

                                      330                           340
Lipocortin I        CysGlnAlaIleLeuAspGluThrLysGlyAspTyrGluLysIleLeuValAla
Lipocortin II       TyrTyrTyrIleGlnGlnAspThrLysGlyAspTyrGlnLysAlaLeuLeuTyr
                              *           *  *  *  *  *     *     *

Lipocortin I        LeuCysGlyGlyAsn
Lipocortin II       LeuCysGlyGlyAspAsp
                     *  *  *  *
```

FIGURE 1. Predicted amino acid sequences of lipocortins I and II. The sequences were deduced from human cDNA clones (see References 15 and 16). Asterisks show sites of homology. Sequence numbers refer to lipocortin I. Single gap immediately after position 194 resulted in best alignment of sequences. (After Huang et al., *Cell*, 46, 191, 1986.)

lipocortins, a conserved 17 amino acid consensus sequence thought to be important for binding (Lys-Gly-X-Gly-Thr-Asp-Glu-X-X-Leu-Ile-X-Ile-Leu-Ala-X-Arg) in multiple (usually four) copies[16,18,28,29] include: endonexins, calelectrins, calcimedins, chromobindins, proteins I to III, tyrosine kinase substrates, and protein kinase C substrates.[13,17,18,27,28,30-48] These proteins were initially discovered in other fields of inquiry and have all been identified in cells or tissues without glucocorticoid treatment. It remains to be seen whether any of them are, like lipocortins,[16] induced by glucocorticoids.

Most recently, two additional 35 kDa calcium-dependent phospholipid-binding phospholipase-inhibitory proteins have been purified and characterized from rat peritoneal and bovine intestinal mucosa lavages.[49] These proteins, which have 50% sequence identity with lipocortins I and II, have been called lipocortins III and V. Like lipocortins I and II, these proteins are also highly conserved evolutionarily[16,21,49] and contain four copies of a 70-amino-acid repeating unit containing the consensus sequence of 17 amino acids.[36,39,49-51] Two other newly sequenced lipocortins, lipocortin IV (found to be identical to protein II) and lipocortin VI, also share this consensus sequence.[49]

Based on structural, physical, biochemical, and/or antigenic similarities, Pepinsky et al.[49] have suggested identities for lipocortin-related calcium-dependent phospholipid-binding proteins (see also References 13, 17, 27, 28, 30, 31, and 33 to 48). These, together with relationships suggested earlier by Saris et al.,[18] Creutz et al.,[32] and others,[12,52] can be summarized as follows:

| | Lipocortin (LC) | | | | |
|---|---|---|---|---|---|
| | **I** | **II** | **III, IV** | **V** | **VI** |
| Calpactin | II | I | — | — | — |
| Endonexin | — | — | 'Endonexin' | II | — |
| Calelectrin | — | 36 kDa (?) | 32.5 kDa | — | 67 kDa |
| Calcimedin | — | 33 kDa (?) | 35 kDa | — | 67 kDa |
| Protein kinase substrate | p35 | p36 | — | — | p68 |
| 'Protein' | — | I | II (LC IV) | — | III |
| Chromobindin | 9 | 8 | 4 | 5 | 20 |
| Others | EGF-receptor kinase substrate | pp60$^{v\text{-}src}$ kinase substrate; Lipocortin 85 | Monocyte lipocortin (32 kDa) | Anticoagulant protein | Intestinal (76 kDa); Anti-$PLA_2$ (70 kDa); Synhibin |

The relationship of p68 and protein II to the lipocortins has been verified by full-sequence structures.[46,47,53]

Recent studies have confirmed that recombinant lipocortin I, II, III, and V have the expected antiphospholipase properties *in vitro*.[16,17,21,30,31,49,54,55] In addition, lipocortin I inhibits $LTC_4$-induced thromboxane release from guinea-pig isolated perfused lungs.[9] Lipocortin from human monocytes inhibits phospholipase $A_2$ from rat pancreas in a substrate concentration-dependent manner,[71] as was seen earlier with "lipomodulin" inhibition of porcine pancreatic phospholipase $A_2$.[26] Inhibition was completely overcome at substrate (phosphatidylethanolamine) concentrations above 250 $\mu M$. Similar evidence for binding to phospholipid substrate has been seen with purified calpactins.[54]

That lipocortins can be inactivated by phosphorylation and reactivated by alkaline phosphatase treatment has been known for some time.[1,2] (See also chapter by Hirata in this volume.) Additional evidence for a role of phosphorylation in the activity of lipocortins has accumulated in recent years.[42,43,52,55-57] As noted above, lipocortins I and II have been found to be identical with the substrates (p35 and p36) for the EGF receptor kinase and the pp60$^{v\text{-}src}$ kinase, respectively.[17,18,42,43,45] Protein kinase C can catalyze the *in vivo* calcium-dependent phosphorylation of threonine residues in lipocortin I and serine residues in lipocortin II.[52] In mitogen-stimulated murine thymocytes, protein kinase C stimulates a tyrosine-specific kinase that phosphorylates lipocortin *in vivo* and *in vitro,* whereas the catalytic subunit of protein kinase A (cAMP-dependent) inhibits it.[58]

Lipocortins I and II both have a structurally-dissimilar exposed sequence of approximately 30 amino acids near the N-terminus that is sensitive to phosphorylation by tyrosine-or serine/threonine-protein kinases and to proteolysis.[20,50] This region can also regulate calcium and phospholipid binding that occurs in the common repeat sequences.[55,59] This N-terminal region is much shorter in lipocortins III, IV, and V, suggesting that they are less likely to be regulated by protein kinase.[49] The amino-terminal tail of the heavy chain of calpactin I (lipocortin II) can also be phosphorylated at tyrosine residues or form complexes with the light chain.[57] Also, human lipocortin I contains consensus sequences for both tyrosine (Tyr 21) and threonine (Thr 212) phosphorylation sites.[12,16]

Partially purified glucocorticoid-induced antiphospholipase proteins have anti-inflammatory effects, as do crude extracts.[5,60,61] For example, partially purified dexamethasone-induced antiphospholipase proteins inhibit carrageenin-induced rat hind paw edema, an effect which was reversed by arachidonic acid.[60] Effects on the immune response have also been seen.[62] Lipocortin from rabbit neutrophils inhibits human natural-killer-cell activity and antibody-dependent cellular cytotoxicity.[63] A possible role of lipocortin has also been seen, both directly and by treatment with anti-lipocortin antibody during concanavalin A stimulation: it appears to induce generation of suppressor T cells in murine thymocytes.[64] Recent studies have also shown that both lipocortin and hydrocortisone inhibit the zymosan-induced release of lyso-PAF from rat peritoneal leukocytes.[65] Purified lipocortins are also potent inhibitors of IgE production.[66]

Although direct anti-inflammatory effects of lipocortins have been seen (e.g., in septic shock[67]), one study has elucidated dexamethasone-induced low-molecular-weight (2 and 6 kDa) anti-inflammatory fragments (perhaps active fragments of the proteins initially termed vasocortins) that suppressed dextran and serotonin edema but not carrageenin inflammation or phospholipase $A_2$ activity.[68] However, in the same preparation, the 40 kDa lipocortin fraction suppressed carrageenin inflammation and phospholipase $A_2$ activity but had no effect on dextran edema.

Lipocortins may have biological effects that suggest mechanisms for glucocorticoid action in areas other than inflammation. This has only begun to be studied — for example, platelet activation has been seen to be associated with phosphorylation by protein kinase C of a 40 kDa antiphospholipase $A_2$ protein indistinguishable from lipocortin,[56] thus inhibiting activity of an antiphospholipase protein and allowing mobilization of arachidonic acid and release of prostaglandins (see also contribution to this volume by Strulovici). Also, lipocortin from rat peritoneal cells protects rats against global ischemia resulting from carotid-artery ligation.[69] Anticoagulant effects of lipocortin have also been seen.[44,45] In addition to beneficial effects, the teratogenic effects of glucocorticoids on mouse embryonic palates can also be induced with glucocorticoid-induced antiphospholipase proteins.[70]

Although the known lipocortins are structurally similar, they are different with respect to cellular distribution.[12,49] It remains for future studies to determine what range of both beneficial (anti-inflammatory and other) and adverse effects of corticosteroids can be seen with the "second messengers" of the glucocorticoids, the various lipocortins.

## ADDENDUM

Since the original writing of this chapter, recombinant lipocortins I and II (which are major substrates for the EGF receptor and pp60$^{v\text{-}src}$ tyrosine kinases, respectively[17]), were both found to be substrates for the insulin receptor tyrosine kinase *in vitro* and in intact hepatocytes from corticosteroid-treated rats.[72] Although a role for lipocortins I and II in insulin action remains to be proven, these findings are interesting in light of the report that insulin stimulates the hydrolysis of phospholipids.[73] It has been suggested that phosphorylation is required for insulin signal transduction;[74] however, an alternate suggestion has been made (based on substrated inhibition of receptor kinase activity[75]) that corticosteroid-induced lipocortins may attenuate the insulin response, thus leading to corticosteroid-induced insulin resistance.[72]

A novel lipocortin-like protein has recently been found in intact rat hepatocytes.[76] This 170 kDa protein is immunologically related to, but much more abundant than lipocortin I, and its serine phosphorylation is stimulated by insulin and epidermal growth factor.[76]

Other recent work has allowed a comparison between sites of phosphorylation of recombinant lipocortins I[77] and II.[78-80] Thus for lipocortin I, Tyr-21 is the major site of phosphorylation by several tyrosine kinases; Ser-27 and Thr-41 are the major sites of phosphorylation by protein kinase C; and Thr-216 is the major site of phosphorylation by cAMP-dependent protein kinase.[77] The sites of phosphorylation of lipocortin II seen in earlier studies were Tyr-23 (tyrosine kinases)[78] and Ser-25 (protein kinase C).[79,80]

As of this writing, it is as yet uncertain whether any of the calcium-dependent phospholipid-binding proteins thought to be identical to ''lipocortins'' III to V are, like lipocortins I and II, regulated by corticosteroids.

## REFERENCES


1. **Di Rosa, M., Flower, R. J., Hirata, F., Parente, F., and Russo-Marie, F.,** Anti-phospholipase proteins, *Prostaglandins,* 28, 441, 1984.
2. **Hirata, F.,** The regulation of lipomodulin, a phospholipase inhibitory protein, in rabbit neutrophils by phosphorylation, *J. Biol. Chem.,* 256, 7730, 1981.
3. **Hirata, F., Notsu, Y., Iwata, L., Parente, M., Di Rosa, M., and Flower, R. J.,** Identification of several species of phospholipase inhibitory proteins by radioimmunoassay for lipomodulin, *Biochem. Biophys. Res. Commun.,* 109, 223, 1982.
4. **Blackwell, G. J., Carnuccio, R., Di Rosa, M., Flower, R. J., Parente, L., and Persico, N.,** Macrocortin: a polypeptide causing the anti-phospholipase effect of glucocorticoids, *Nature (London),* 287, 147, 1980.
5. **Blackwell, G. J., Carnuccio, R., Di Rosa, M., Flower, R. J., Langhan, C. S. J., Parente, L., Persico, P., Russell-Smith, N. C., and Stone, D.,** Glucocorticoids induce the formation and release of anti-inflammatory and anti-phospholipase proteins into the peritoneal cavity of the rat, *Br. J. Pharmacol.,* 76, 185, 1982.
6. **Cloix, J. F., Colard, O., Rothhut, F., and Russo-Marie, F.,** Characterisation and partial purification of renocortins: two polypeptides formed in renal cells causing the anti-phospholipase action of glucocorticoids, *Br. J. Pharmacol.,* 79, 313, 1983.
7. **Rothhut, B., Russo-Marie, F., Wood, J., Di Rosa, M., and Flower, R. J.,** Further characterisation of the glucocorticoid-induced anti-phospholipase protein ''renocortin,'' *Biochem. Biophys. Res. Commun.,* 117, 878, 1983.
8. **Coote, P. R., Di Rosa, M., Flower, R. J., Merrett, M., Parente, L., and Wood, J. N.,** Detection and isolation of a steroid-induced anti-phospholipase protein of high molecular weight, *Br. J. Pharmacol.,* 80, 597P, 1983.
9. **Cirino, G., Flower, R. J., Browning, J. L., Sinclair, L. K., and Pepinsky, R. B.,** Recombinant human lipocortin I inhibits thromboxane release from guinea-pig isolated perfused lung, *Nature (London),* 328, 270, 1987.
10. **Cirino, G. and Flower, R. J.,** Human recombinant lipocortin I inhibits prostacyclin release from human umbilical artery *in vitro, Prostaglandins,* 34, 59, 1987.
11. **Cirino, G. and Flower, R. J.,** The inhibitory effect of lipocortin on eicosanoid synthesis is dependent upon $Ca^{++}$ ions, *Br. J. Pharmacol.,* 92, 521P, 1987.
12. **Flower, R. J.,** Eleventh Gaddum Memorial Lecture: Lipocortin and the mechanism of action of the glucocorticoids, *Br. J. Pharmacol.,* 94, 987, 1988.
13. **Rothhut, B., Comera, C., Prieur, B., Errasfa, M., Minassian, G., and Russo-Marie, F.,** Purification and characterization of a 32-kDa phospholipase $A_2$ inhibitory protein (lipocortin) from human peripheral blood mononuclear cells, *FEBS Lett.,* 219, 169, 1987.

14. **Clark, M. A., Bomalaski, J. S., Conway, T. M., Wartell, J., and Crooke, S. T.,** Differential effects of aspirin and dexamethasone on phospholipase $A_2$ and C activities and arachidonic acid release from endothelial cells in response to bradykinin and leukotriene $D_4$, *Prostaglandins,* 32, 703, 1986.
15. **De George, J. J., Ousley, A. H., McCarthy, K. K., Morell, P., and Lapetina, E. G.,** Glucocorticoids inhibit the liberation of arachidonate but not the rapid production of phospholipase C metabolites in acetylcholine-stimulated C62B glioma cells, *J. Biol. Chem.,* 262, 9979, 1987.
16. **Wallner, B. P., Mattaliano, R. J., Hession, C., Cate, R. L., Tizard, R., Sinclair, L. K., Foeller, C., Chow, E. P., Browning, J. L., Ramachandran, K. L., and Pepinsky, R. B.,** Cloning and expression of human lipocortin, a phospholipase $A_2$ inhibitor with anti-inflammatory activity, *Nature (London),* 320, 77, 1986.
17. **Huang, K.-S., Wallner, B. P., Matalliano, R. J., Tizard, R., Burne, C., Frey, A., Hession, C., McGray, P., Sinclair, L. K., Chow, E. P., Browning, J. L., Ramachandran, K. L., Tang, J., Smart, J. E., and Pepinsky, R. B.,** Two human 35 kd inhibitors of phospholipase $A_2$ are related to substrates of $pp60^{v\text{-}src}$ and to the epidermal growth factor receptor/kinase, *Cell,* 46, 191, 1986.
18. **Saris, C. J. M., Tack, B. F., Kristensen, T., Glenney, J. R., and Hunter, T.,** The cDNA sequence for the protein-tyrosine kinase substrate p36 (calpactin I heavy chain) reveals a multidomain protein with internal repeats, *Cell,* 46, 201, 1986.
19. **Hayashi, H., Owada, M. K., Sonobe, S., Kakunaga, T., Kawakatsu, H., and Yano, J.,** A 32-kDa protein associated with phospholipase $A_2$-inhibitory activity from human placenta, *FEBS Lett.,* 223, 267, 1987.
20. **Huang, K.-S., McGray, P., Mattaliano, R. J., Burne, C., Chow, F. P., Sinclair, L. K., and Pepinsky, R. B.,** Purification and characterization of proteolytic fragments of lipocortin I that inhibit phospholipase $A_2$, *J. Biol. Chem.,* 262, 7639, 1987.
21. **Pepinsky, R. B., Sinclair, L. K., Browning, J. L., Mattaliano, R. J., Smart, J. E., Chow, E. P., Falbel, T., Ribalini, A., Garwin, J. L., and Wallner, B. P.,** Purification and partial sequence analysis of a 37-kDa protein that inhibits phospholipase $A_2$ activity from rat peritoneal exudates, *J. Biol. Chem.,* 261, 4239, 1986.
22. **Van Deenan, L. L. M. and De Haas, G. H.,** The synthesis of phosphoglycerides and some biochemical applications, *Adv. Lipid Res.,* 2, 167, 1964.
23. **Van Deenan, L. L. M. and De Haas, G. H.,** Phosphoglycerides and phospholipases, *Annu. Rev. Biochem.,* 35, 157, 1966.
24. **Gerritsen, M. J., Nganele, D. M., and Rodriguez, A. M.,** Calcium ionophore (A23187) and arachidonic acid stimulated prostaglandin release from microvascular endothelial cells: effects of calcium antagonists and calmodulin inhibitors, *J. Pharmacol. Exp. Ther.,* 240, 837, 1987.
25. **Das, U. N., Chainulu, B. V., and Naik, B. R.,** Verapamil as a prostaglandin antagonist, *Indian J. Exp. Biol.,* 18, 917, 1980.
26. **Hirata, F.,** The regulation of lipomodulin, a phospholipase inhibitory protein, in rabbit neutrophils by phosphorylation, *J. Biol. Chem.,* 256, 7730, 1981.
27. **Glenney, J. R., Tack, B., and Powell, M. A.,** Calpactins: two distinct $Ca^{++}$-regulated phospholipid- and actin-binding proteins isolated from lung and placenta, *J. Cell Biol.,* 104, 503, 1987.
28. **Geisow, M. J., Fritsche, U., Hexham, J. M., Dash, B., and Johnson, T.,** A consensus amino acid sequence repeat in Torpedo and mammalian $Ca^{++}$-dependent membrane-binding proteins, *Nature (London),* 320, 636, 1986.
29. **Kretsinger, B. J. and Creutz, C. E.,** Consensus in exocytosis, *Nature (London),* 320, 573, 1986.
30. **Fauvel, J., Vicendo, P., Roques, V., Ragab-Thomas, J., Granier, C., Vilgrain, I., Chambaz, E., Rochat, H., Chap, H., and Douste-Blazy, L.,** Isolation of two 67 kDa calcium-binding proteins from pig lung differing in affinity for phospholipids and in antiphospholipase $A_2$ activity, *FEBS Lett.,* 221, 397, 1987.
31. **Fauvel, J., Salles, J.-P., Roques, V., Chap, H., Rochat, H., and Douste-Blazy, L.,** Lipocortin-like antiphospholipase $A_2$ activity of endonexin, *FEBS Lett.,* 216, 45, 1987.
32. **Creutz, C. E., Zaks, W. J., Hamman, H. C., Crane, S., Martin, W. H., Gould, K. L., Oddie, K. M., and Parsons, S. J.,** Identification of chromaffin granule-binding proteins: relationship of the chromobindins to calelectrin, synhibin, and the tyrosine kinase substrates p35 and p36, *J. Biol. Chem.,* 262, 1860, 1987.
33. **Moore, P. B.,** 67-kDa calcimedin, a new $Ca^{++}$-binding protein, *Biochem. J.,* 238, 49, 1986.
34. **Sudhof, T. C., Edbecke, M., Walker, J. H., Fritsche, U., and Boustead, C.,** Isolation of mammalian calelectrins: a new class of ubiquitous $Ca^{++}$ regulated proteins, *Biochemistry,* 23, 1103, 1984.
35. **Khanna, N. C., Hee-Chong, M., Severson, D. L., Tokuda, M., Chong, S. M., and Waisman, D. M.,** Inhibition of phospholipase $A_2$ by protein I, *Biochem. Biophys. Res. Commun.,* 139, 455, 1986.
36. **Weber, K. and Johnson, N.,** Repeating sequence homologies in the p36 target protein of retroviral protein kinases and lipocortin, the p37 inhibitor of phospholipase $A_2$, *FEBS Lett.,* 203, 95, 1986.

37. **Schlaepfer, D. D., Mehlman, T., Burgess, W. H., and Haigler, H. T.,** Structural and functional characterization of endonexin II, a calcium- and phospholipid-binding protein, *Proc. Natl. Acad. Sci. U.S.A.*, 84, 6078, 1987.
38. **Geisow, M. J.,** Common domain structure of $Ca^{2+}$ and lipid-binding proteins, *FEBS Lett.*, 203, 99, 1986.
39. **Geisow, M. J. and Walker, J. H.,** New proteins involved in cell regulation by $Ca^{2+}$ and phospholipids, *Trends Biochem. Sci.*, 11, 420, 1986.
40. **Schlaepfer, D. D. and Haigler, H. T.,** Characterization of $Ca^{2+}$-dependent phospholipid binding and phosphorylation of lipocortin I, *J. Biol. Chem.*, 262, 6931, 1987.
41. **Smith, V. L. and Dedman, J. R.,** An immunological comparison of several novel calcium binding proteins, *J. Biol. Chem.*, 261, 15815, 1986.
42. **De, B. K., Misono, K. S., Lukas, T. J., Mroczkowski, B., and Cohen, S.,** A calcium-dependent 35-kilodalton substrate for epidermal growth factor receptor/kinase isolated from normal tissue, *J. Biol. Chem.*, 261, 13784, 1986.
43. **Pepinsky, R. B. and Sinclair, L. K.,** Epidermal growth factor-dependent phosphorylation of lipocortin, *Nature (London)*, 321, 81, 1986.
44. **Funakoshi, T., Heimark, R. L., Hendrickson, L. E., McMullen, B. A., and Fujikawa, K.,** Human placental anticoagulant protein: isolation and characterization, *Biochemistry*, 26, 5572, 1987.
45. **Funakoshi, T., Heimark, R. L., Hendrickson, L. E., McMullen, B. A., and Fujikawa, K.,** Primary structure of human placental anticoagulant protein, *Biochemistry*, 26, 8087, 1987.
46. **Sudhof, T. C., Slaughter, C. A., Leznicki, I., Barjon, P., and Reynolds, G. A.,** Human 67-kDa calelectrin contains a duplication of four repeats found in 35-kDa lipocortins, *Proc. Natl. Acad. Sci. U.S.A.*, 85, 664, 1988.
47. **Weber, K., Johnsson, N., Plessman, U., Van, P. N., Soling, H.-D., Ampe, C., and Vandekerckhove, J.,** The amino acid sequence of protein II and its phosphorylation site for protein kinase C; the domain structure $Ca^{2+}$-modulated lipid binding proteins, *EMBO J.*, 6, 1599, 1987.
48. **Shadle, P. J., Gerke, V., and Weber, K.,** Three $Ca^{2+}$ binding proteins from porcine liver and intestine differ immunologically and physicochemically and are distinct $Ca^{2+}$ affinities, *J. Biol. Chem.*, 260, 16354, 1985.
49. **Pepinsky, R. B., Tizard, R., Mattaliano, R. J., Sinclair, L. K., Miller, G. T., Browning, J. L., Chow, E. P., Burne, C., Huang, K.-S., Pratt, D., Wachter, L., Hession, C., Frey, A. Z., and Wallner, B. P.,** Five distinct calcium and phospholipid binding proteins share homology with lipocortin I, *J. Biol. Chem.*, 263, 10799—10811, 1988.
50. **Brugge, J. S.,** The p35/p36 substrates of protein tyrosine kinases as inhibitors of phospholipase $A_2$, *Cell*, 46, 149, 1986.
51. **Munn, T. Z. and Mues, G. I.,** Human lipocortin similar to ras gene products, *Nature*, 322, 314, 1986.
52. **Khanna, N. C., Tokuda, M., and Waisman, D. M.,** Purification of three forms of lipocortin from bovine lung, *Cell Calcium*, 8, 217, 1987.
53. **Crompton, M. R., Owens, R. J., Totty, N. F., Moss, S. E., Waterfield, M. D., and Crumpton, M. J.,** Primary structure of the human membrane-associated $Ca^{2+}$ binding protein p68: a novel member of a protein family, *EMBO J.*, 7, 21, 1988.
54. **Davidson, F. F., Dennis, E. A., Powell, M., and Glenney, J. R.,** Inhibition of phospholipase $A_2$ by "lipocortins" and calpactins: an effect of binding to substrate phospholipids, *J. Biol. Chem.*, 262, 1698, 1987.
55. **Haigler, H. T., Schlaepfer, D. D., and Burgess, W. H.,** Characterization of lipocortin I and an immunologically unrelated 33k dalton protein as epidermal growth factor receptor/kinase substrates and phospholipase $A_2$ inhibitors, *J. Biol. Chem.*, 262, 6921, 1987.
56. **Touqui, L., Rothhut, B., Shaw, A. M., Fradin, A., Vargaftig, B. B., and Russo-Marie, F.,** Platelet activation: a role for a 40k anti-phospholipase $A_2$ protein indistinguishable from lipocortin, *Nature (London)*, 321, 177, 1986.
57. **Glenney, J. R., Boudreau, M., Galyean, R., Hunter, T., and Tack, B.,** Association of the S-100 related calpactin I light chain with the $NH_2$-terminal tail of the 36-kDa heavy chain, *J. Biol. Chem.*, 261, 10485, 1986.
58. **Hirata, F., Matsuda, K., Notsu, Y., Hattori, T., and Del Carmine, R.,** Phosphorylation at a tyrosine residue of lipomodulin in mitogen-stimulated murine thymocytes, *Proc. Natl. Acad. Sci. U.S.A.*, 81, 4717, 1984.
59. **Powell, M. A. and Glenney, J. R.,** Regulation of calpactin I phospholipid binding by calpactin I light-chain binding and phosphorylation by $p60^{v\text{-}src}$, *Biochem. J.*, 247, 321, 1987.
60. **Parente, L., Di Rosea, M., Flower, R. J., Ghiara, P., Meli, R., Persico, P., Salmon, J. A., and Wood, J. N.,** Relationship between the anti-phospholipase and anti-inflammatory effects of glucocorticoid-induced proteins, *Eur. J. Pharmacol.*, 99, 233, 1984.
61. **Di Rosa, M.,** Role in inflammation of glucocorticoid-induced phospholipase inhibitory proteins, *Prog. Biochem. Pharmacol.*, 20, 55, 1985.

62. **Uede, T., Hirata, F., Hirashima, M., and Ishizaka, K.,** Modulation of the biologic activities of IgE binding factors. I. Identification of glycosylation-inhibiting factor as a fragment of lipomodulin, *J. Immunol.*, 130, 878, 1983.
63. **Hattori, T., Hirata, F., Hoffman, T., Hizuta, A., and Herberman, R. B.,** Inhibition of natural killer (NK) activity and antibody dependent cellular cytotoxicity (ADCC) by lipomodulin, a phospholipase inhibitory protein, *J. Immunol.*, 131,662, 1983.
64. **Hirata, F. and Iwata, M.,** Role of lipomodulin, a phospholipase inhibitory protein, in immunoregulation by thymocytes, *J. Immunol.*, 130, 1930, 1983.
65. **Parente, L. and Flower, R. J.,** Hydrocortisone and ''macrocortin'' inhibit the zymosan-induced release of lyso-PAF from rat peritoneal leukocytes, *Life Sciences*, 36, 1225, 1985.
66. **Jardieu, P., Akasaki, M., and Ishizaka, K.,** Association of I-J determinants with lipomodulin/macrocortin, *Proc. Natl. Acad. Sci. U.S.A.*, 83, 160, 1986.
67. **Vadas, P., Stefanski, F., and Pruzanski, W.,** Potential therapeutic efficacy of inhibitors of human phospholipase $A_2$ in septic shock, *Agents Actions*, 19, 194, 1986.
68. **Koltai, M., Kovacs, Z., Nemecz, G., Mecs, I., and Szekeres, I.,** Glucocorticoid-induced inflammatory factors which do not inhibit phospholipase $A_2$, *Eur. J. Pharmacol.*, 134, 109, 1987.
69. **Koltai, M., Tosaki, A., Adam, G., Joo, F., Nemecz, G., and Szekeres, L.,** Prevention by macrocortin of global cerebral ischemia in Sprague-Dawley rats, *Eur. J. Pharmacol.*, 105, 347, 1984.
70. **Gupta, C., Katsumata, M., Goldman, A. S., Herold, R., and Piddington, R.,** Glucocorticoid-induced phospholipase $A_2$-inhibitory proteins mediate glucocorticoid teratogenicity *in vitro*, *Proc. Natl. Acad. Sci. U.S.A.*, 81, 1140, 1984.
71. **Aarsman, A. J., Mynbeek, G., Van den Bosch, H., Rothhut, B., Prieur, B., Comera, C., Jordan, L., and Russo-Marie, F.,** Lipocortin inhibition of extracellular phospholipase $A_2$ is substrate concentration dependent, *FEBS Lett.*, 219, 176, 1987.


## ADDITIONAL REFERENCES


72. **Karasik, A., Pepinsky, R. B., Shoelson, S. E., and Kahn, C. R.,** Lipocortins 1 and 2 as substrates for the insulin receptor kinase in rat liver, *J. Biol. Chem.*, 263, 11862—11867, 1988.
73. **Saltiel, A. R., Fox, J. A., Sherline, P., and Cuatrecasas, P.,** Insulin-stimulated hydrolysis of a novel glycolipid generates modulators of cAMP phosphodiesterase, *Science*, 233, 967—972, 1986.
74. **Ellis, L., Clauser, E., Morgan, D. O., Edery, M., Roth, R. A., and Rutter, W. J.,** Replacement of insulin receptor tyrosine residues 1162 and 1163 compromises insulin-stimulated kinase activity and uptake of 2-deoxyglucose, *Cell*, 45, 721—732, 1986.
75. **Kohanski, R. A. and Lane, M. D.,** Kinetic evidence for activating and non-activating components of autophosphorylation of the insulin receptor protein kinase, *Biochem. Biophys. Res. Commun.*, 134, 1312—1318, 1986.
76. **Karasik, A., Pepinsky, R. B., and Kahn, C.,** Insulin and epidermal growth factor stimulate phosphorylation of a 170 kDa protein in intact hepatocytes immunologically related to lipocortin 1, *J. Biol. Chem.*, 263, 18558—18562, 1988.
77. **Varticovski, L., Chahwala, S. B., Whitman, M., Cantley, L., Schindler, D., Chow, E. P., Sinclair, L. K., and Pepinsky, R. B.,** Location of sites in human lipocortin I that are phosphorylated by protein tyrosine kinases A and C, *Biochemistry*, 27, 3682—3690, 1988.
78. **Glenney, J. R. and Tack, B. F.,** Amino-terminal sequence of p36 and associated p10: identification of the site of tyrosine phosphorylation and homology with S-100, *Proc. Natl. Acad. Sci. U.S.A.*, 82, 7884—7888, 1985.
79. **Gould, K. L., Woodgett, J. R., Isacke, C. M., and Hunter, T.,** The protein-tyrosine kinase substrate p36 is also a substrate for protein kinase C *in vitro* and *in vivo*, *Mol. Cell. Biol.*, 6, 2738—2744, 1986.
80. **Khanna, N. C., Tokuda, M., and Waismann, D. M.,** Phosphorylation of lipocortins in vitro by protein kinase C, *Biochem. Biophys. Res. Commun.*, 141, 547—554, 1986.

# EFFECTS OF CORTICOSTEROIDS ON RELEASE OF EICOSANOID PRECURSORS

**R. J. Flower, G. J. Blackwell, and D. L. Smith**

It has long been known that anti-inflammatory steroids exert more profound effects than nonsteroidal anti-inflammatory drugs of the aspirin-type.[62] We now have a rational basis for this observation: anti-inflammatory corticosteroids can suppress production of all pro-inflammatory and injurious metabolites of arachidonic acid including both cyclooxygenase- and lipoxygenase-derived products. Since the mid 1970s, it has been known that this action of the corticosteroids is exerted through inhibition of arachidonic acid liberation from cell-membrane phospholipids by phospholipase $A_2$ (see References 21 to 25, 31 and Tables 1 to 4). Indeed, since phospholipase $A_2$ is also involved in production of ''platelet-activating factor'' (PAF) and its lyso derivative, corticosteroids also inhibit production of this potent inflammatory mediator.[63] Together these mediators may be involved in most, if not all, of the mechanisms of acute and chronic inflammatory disease.

By contrast, aspirin-type drugs exert their effects only through blocking production of arachidonate-derived cyclooxygenase products (PG endoperoxides and their thromboxane and prostaglandin metabolites) that produce some,[62,64-66] but not all, of the mechanisms of inflammatory disease.

Danon and Assouline[13] were the first to demonstrate that protein synthesis was necessary for corticosteroids to inhibit liberation of arachidonic acid. This finding, in turn, suggested the possibility of one or more protein or peptide ''second messengers'' of corticosteroid action. Since anti-inflammatory steroids invariably have side effects (e.g., on carbohydrate metabolism) unrelated to their primary actions, the possibility arose that these second messengers might provide prototypes for development of more potent and specific anti-inflammatory agents.[67,68]

The original discovery of ''macrocortin'' by Flower and colleagues[1,4] synthesized in lung and leukocytes in response to treatment with anti-inflammatory steroids was followed by discovery of several related materials of varying molecular weights. These included ''lipomodulin'' from rabbit neutrophils discovered by Hirata and colleagues,[3] ''renocortin'' from the kidney medulla,[8-10] and many other examples from tissues as diverse as endometrium,[12] stomach tissue,[44] and skin fibroblasts.[11] Detailed compilation of these findings is given in Tables 1 and 2.

It is now thought that all of these factors (now collectively named ''lipocortins''[69]) are subsets, cleavage products, or perhaps even aggregates of cleavage products of the largest molecular weight (about 40 kDa) member of the series. This has recently been cloned, sequenced, and named lipocortin I. Six such lipocortins (I through VI) have now been identified.[70,84] Structures of these materials and homology with other isolated substances are discussed in the contribution to this volume by D. L. Smith.

Pure lipocortin I acts identically to the original ''macrocortin'' in inhibiting eicosanoid release from isolated perfused lungs induced by various stimuli,[71] except arachidonic acid (expected because lipocortin inhibits arachidonic acid release, *not* its conversion to eicosanoids). Like the glucocorticoids themselves, lipocortin I also did not inhibit liberation of eicosanoids by bradykinin[71] that may thus stimulate an arachidonate-releasing mechanism that is not inhibited by lipocortin.* Recently lipocortin I has also been shown to

* In Swiss 3T3 mouse fibroblasts, the anti-inflammatory steroid dexamethasone did inhibit bradykinin-stimulated production of $PGE_2$, via a mechanism that seems to involve GTP-binding proteins that are coupled to both phospholipase $A_2$ and phospholipase C.[75] This situation clearly seems different from that in the isolated perfused lungs.[71]
The anti-malarial drug mepacrine does inhibit bradykinin-evoked release of eicosanoids from isolated perfused lung preparations.[76] It exerts such effects by inhibiting phospholipase(s), but possibly by a ''membrane-stabilizing'' effect that interferes with the coupling between stimulus and phospholipase activation.[66]

## Table 1
## INHIBITION OF PG BIOSYNTHESIS MEDIATED BY A CORTICOSTEROID-INDUCED FACTOR

| Glucocorticoid conc | Onset of factor production | Cell or tissue source of the factor | Proposed mechanism of action | M.W. | Ref. |
|---|---|---|---|---|---|
| Dexamethasone 2.5 μ*M* | 20 min | Isolated perfused guinea-pig lungs | Inhibition of $PLA_2$ | ? | 1 |
| Cortisol 20 μ*M* | 90 min | Resident rat peritoneal leukocytes | Inhib. of acyl hydrolases responsible for precursor fatty acid release | Nondialysable protein ? | 2 |
| Dexamethasone 1 μ*M* & others | 5—16 h | Elicited rabbit neutrophils | Inhibition of $PLA_2$ | Glycoprotein 40 kDa | 3 |
| Dexamethasone 2.5 μ*M* | 30 min | Isolated perfused guinea-pig lung | Inhibition of $PLA_2$ | Macrocortin protein 15 kDa | 4 |
| Cortisol 20 μ*M* | 30—90 min | Resident rat peritoneal leukocytes | Inhibition of $PLA_2$ | | |
| Cortisol 360 mg/kg<br>Dexamethasone 24 mg/kg | 24—48 h | Blood serum from rats treated with the steroid | Inhibition of PG synthetase | Protein-Cohn fraction IV<br>? | 5 |
| Prednisolone 5—40 mg/kg | 2—10 d | Blood plasma from rats treated with steroid | Enhanced PG breakdown, inhibition of cyclooxygenase | Reciprocal coupling factor | 6, 7 |
| Dexamethasone 0.1 μ*M* | 1—24 h | Rat renomedullary cells | Not inhibition of phospholipases | ? | 8 |
| Dexamethasone 1 μ*M* | 40 min | Rat renomedullary interstitial cells | Inhibition of $PLA_2$ | Two proteins: kDa 15 and 30 ''renocortins'' | 9 |
| Dexamethasone 100 n*M* | 24 h | Rat renomedullary interstitial cells | Inhibition of $PLA_2$ | Three proteins: 15, 30, and 45 kDa | 10 |

| | | | | | |
|---|---|---|---|---|---|
| Dexamethasone 1 μ*M* | 3 h | Human embryonic skin fibroblasts | Inhibition of $PLA_2$ | Four proteins in supernatant: <12, 15, 30, and 45 kDa<br>One protein in cell pellets: 15 kDa | 11 |
| Dexamethasone 0.01—1 μ*M* | 1—2 d | Human endometrium organ culture | Inhibition of $PLA_2$ | Lipocortin (RIA)[a] | 12 |
| Dexamethasone 1 mg/kg, s.c. | 1 h | Rat peritoneal lavage fluid | Inhibition of $PLA_2$ | Lipocortin: 40 kDa[b] | 61 |
| Dexamethasone 1 mg/kg, s.c. | 1 h | Rat peritoneal cavities | Inhibition of $PLA_2$ | Three proteins: 200 and 15 kDa protein fraction inhibited membrane-bound $PLA_2$; and 40 kDa fraction inhibited lysosomal $PLA_2$ | 81 |
| Dexamethasone 50 μ*M* | 16—18 h | Mouse thymocytes and embryonic palates | Inhibition of $PLA_2$ | Four proteins: 55, 40, 28, and 15 kDa | 82 |
| Dexamethasone 50 μ*M* | 16—18 h | Calf thymus | Inhibition of $PLA_2$ | 55 kDa | 83 |
| | | Mouse thymus and embryonic palates | Inhibition of $PLA_2$ | Four proteins: 55, 40, 28, and 15 kDa | |

[a] Progesterone also inhibited $PGF_{2\alpha}$, but not lipocortin.
[b] Vasocortins (2 and 6 kDa) from same preparation did not inhibit $PLA_2$.

**Table 2**
**ACTIONS OF CORTICOSTEROIDS REQUIRING PROTEIN AND RNA SYNTHESIS**

| Glucocorticoid conc (lowest effective) | Onset of glucocorticoid production | Cell or tissue | Stimulus for eicosanoid synthesis | Eicosanoid measured | Ref. |
|---|---|---|---|---|---|
| Cortisol 1 $\mu M$ | 60 min | Rat renal papilla | Spontaneous | $PGE_2$ | 13 |
| Dexamethasone 2.5 $\mu M$ | 20 min | Isolated perfused guinea-pig lung | Spontaneous or RCS-RF | $PGE_2$ equivalents ($PLA_2$ measured) | 1 |
| Cortisol 20 $\mu M$ | 60 min | Resident rat peritoneal leucocytes | Phagocytosis of bacteria | $PGE_2$ equivalents | 14 |
| Corticosterone 0.1 $\mu M$ | 24 h | Rat reno-medullary cells | Spontaneous | $PGE_2$ | 15 |
| Cortisol 20 $\mu M$ | 90 min | Resident rat peritoneal leucocytes | Phagocytosis of bacteria | $PGE_2$ | 2 |
| Dexamethasone 1 $\mu M$ & others | 5—16 h | Elicited rabbit neutrophils | f-MLP | $PGE_2$ & $PGF_{2\alpha}$ ($PLA_2$ measured) | 3 |
| Fluocinolone 0.1—1 n$M$<br>Dexamethasone 1—10 n$M$<br>Hydrocortisone 0.1—1 $\mu M$ | 3—4 h | Rat alveolar macrophages | Zymosan | $PGE_2$ | 16 |
| Dexamethasone 100 p$M$ | 3 h | Human embryonic skin fibroblasts | Spontaneous | $PGE_2$ | 11 |
| Dexamethasone 100 n$M$, hydrocortisone 100 n$M$ | 5—22 h | Human umbilical vein endothelial cells | Thrombin or ionophore A23187 | 6-keto-$PGF_{1\alpha}$ and $PGE_2$ | 17 |
| Dexamethasone 1—10 n$M$ | 16—18 h | Rabbit coronary microvascular endothelial cells | Spontaneous or ionophore A23187 | 6-keto-$PGF_{1\alpha}$ and $PGE_2$ | 18 |
| Dexamethasone 0.025 $\mu M$ | 0.5—1 h | Rabbit mesothelial cells | Spontaneous, bradykinin, or thrombin | 6-keto-$PGF_{1\alpha}$ | 19 |
| Dexamethasone 2.5 $\mu M$ | 90 min + | Rabbit peritoneal serosa | Spontaneous | 6-keto-$PGF_{1\alpha}$ | 20 |

## Table 3
## CORTICOSTEROID-INDUCED INHIBITION OF PG BIOSYNTHESIS *IN VITRO*

| Glucocorticoid conc (lowest effective) | Onset of glucocorticoid production | Cell or tissue | Stimulus for eicosanoid synthesis | Eicosanoid measured | Ref. |
|---|---|---|---|---|---|
| Cortisol 280 μ*M*, fludrocortisone 220 μ*M* | 10 min | Rat skin | Homogenization | $PGE_2$ & $PGF_{2\alpha}$ | 21 |
| Cortisol 2 nMol/min | Immediate | Perfused rabbit fat pads | ACTH | $PGE_2$ equivalents | 22 |
| Cortisol 1 n*M* | 8 h | $HSDM_1C_1$ (mouse fibrosarcoma cells) | Spontaneous | $PGE_2$ | 23 |
| Cortisol 1 n*M* | ~30 min | MC5-5 (methyl cholanthrene transformed mouse fibroblasts) | Serum | $PGE_2$ & $PGF_{2\alpha}$ | 24 |
| Dexamethasone 10 n*M* | 3 d in culture | Cultured human rheumatoid synovial cells | Spontaneous | $PGE_2$ & $PGF_{2\alpha}$ | 25 |
| Dexamethasone 10 n*M* | 4 d in culture | Human adherent rheumatoid synovial cells | Spontaneous | $PGE_2$ | 26 |
| Dexamethasone 1 n*M* & others | 2—4 h | MC5-5 (methyl cholanthrene transformed mouse fibroblasts) | Spontaneous | $PGE_2$ & $PGF_{2\alpha}$ | 27 |
| Dexamethasone 1-5 μ*M* & others | 10—20 min | Isolated perfused guinea-pig lung | RCS-RF | $PGE_2$ equivalents | 28 |
| Dexamethasone 1 μ*M* & others | 30 min | Isolated perfused guinea-pig lung | Spontaneous and RCS-RF | $PGE_2$ equivalents ($PLA_2$ act. also measured) | 29 |
| Dexamethasone 0.1 μ*M* & others | 24 h | Elicited guinea-pig peritoneal macrophages | Spontaneous | $PGE_2$ equivalents | 30 |
| Cortisol 20 μ*M*, | ~10 min | Perfused mesenteric rabbit blood vessels | Noradrenaline | $PGE_2$ equivalents | 31 |
| Dexamethasone 5 μ*M* | | Perfused guinea-pig lung (sensitized) | Antigen | $PGE_2$ equivalents | |
| Dexamethasone 0.1 n*M* | 24 h | Human chondrocytes | A factor in human synovial explant medium | $PGE_2$ | 32 |
| Dexamethasone 100 n*M* | ~2 d in culture | Human rheumatoid synovial explants | Spontaneous | $PGE_2$ | 33 |

**Table 3 (continued)**
**CORTICOSTEROID-INDUCED INHIBITION OF PG BIOSYNTHESIS *IN VITRO***

| Glucocorticoid conc (lowest effective) | Onset of glucocorticoid production | Cell or tissue | Stimulus for eicosanoid synthesis | Eicosanoid measured | Ref. |
|---|---|---|---|---|---|
| Dexamethasone 1 μ*M* | ~2—24 h | Resident mouse peritoneal macrophages | Spontaneous or TPA | $PGE_2$ | 34 |
| Dexamethasone 4 μg/ml<br>Fludrocortisone 20 μg/ml | 40 min | Isolated perfused guinea-pig lung | Histamine or ovalbumin | "PG & TX-like material" (contractile responses) | 35 |
| Dexamethasone 500 n*M* | 1 h | Rabbit renomedullary interstitial cells | Spontaneous | $PGE_2$ | 36 |
| Dexamethasone 1 μ*M* | 20 h | Human fibroblasts in culture | Serum | Arachidonate release | 37 |
| Hydrocortisone 10 μg/ml anti-phospholipase proteins induced by dexamethasone in carageenin-induced phagocytosis 100 μg/ml | 2 h | Rat peritoneal leukocytes | Phagocytosis of killed bacteria | $PGE_2$ and $LTB_4$ | 38 |
| Dexamethasone 10 μM | 1 h | Mouse M-MSV-transformed 3T3 cells | Serum or epidermal growth factor | Phospholipase activity | 39 |
| Dexamethasone 100 μM | 120 h | Mouse palate mesenchymal cells | Serum[a] | Phospholipase activity | 39 |
| Dexamethasone 1 n*M*<br>Hydrocortisone 20 n*M* | 6 h | Bovine pulmonary artery endothelial cells | Bradykinin or ionophore A23187 | 6-keto-$PGF_{1a}$[b] | 40 |
| Dexamethasone[c] 0.01 μg/ml | 24 h | Rat peritoneal macrophages | Serum-opsonized zymosan | 6-keto-$PGF_{1a}$[d] | 41 |
| Dexamethasone[e] 1—10 μ*M* | 12 h | Human lymphocytes and neutrophils | Spontaneous | $PGE_2$[f] | 42 |
| Dexamethasone ~1 n*M* | 1 h | Pituitary cells | Tetradecanoyl phorbol acetate (TPA) and calcium | $PGE_2$ | 43 |
| Dexamethasone-induced anti-phospholipase proteins (200, 40, and 15 kDa) 60 μg/ml | 10 min | Rat stomach tissue | Spontaneous | $PGI_2$[g] | 44 |
| Dexamethasone 1 μ*M* (maximal) | 4 h (maximal) | Human lymphocytes | Spontaneous | Arachidonate release[h] | 45 |

| | | | | | |
|---|---|---|---|---|---|
| Dexamethasone 1 μ*M* | 12 h | Bovine pulmonary artery endothelial cells | $LTD_4$[i] | Arachidonate release | 46 |
| Dexamethasone 1 n*M* | 30—60 min | Human peripheral blood monocytes | Spontaneous or Con A or lipopolysaccharide | $PGE_2$[j] | 47 |
| Dexamethasone 1 n*M*, betamethasone 10 n*M*, cortisone 10 n*M* | 20 h in culture | C62B glioma cells | Acetylcholine and LiCl | Arachidonate and glycerophosphoinositol accumulation | 48 |

[a] With EGF as stimulator, 10 μ*M* dexamethasone enhanced phospholipase activity.
[b] No effect of hydrocortisone with bradykinin as stimulus.
[c] Also, cyclosporin A 0.3 μg/ml.
[d] Basal phospholipase activity was also measured.
[e] Also, cyclosporin A 0.08 μg/ml, 20 min.
[f] $PLA_2$ activity was also measured.
[g] Assayed by inhibition of ADP-induced platelet aggregation — no effect of dexamethasone itself.
[h] But was not inhibited in lymphocytes from patients with cystic fibrosis.
[i] No effect on bradykinin-induced release.
[j] Collagenase was also suppressed.

## Table 4
## CORTICOSTEROID-INDUCED INHIBITION OF PG BIOSYNTHESIS *IN VIVO*

| Glucocorticoid conc | Time of onset | Tissue or organ | Stimulus for eicosanoid synthesis | Eicosanoid measured | Ref. |
|---|---|---|---|---|---|
| Dexamethasone 4 mg/kg | 30 min | Myocardium — beagle dogs | Myocardial depressant factor | $PGE_1$; $PGE_2$; $PGF_{2\alpha}$ | 49 |
| Cortisol 0.1—0.5 mg/kg | 20 min | Hind limb of the dog | Muscular exercise | $PGE_2$ equivalents | 50 |
| Cortisol 1 mg/kg | 20 min | Perfused spleen strips | Noradrenaline | $PGE_2$ equivalents | 51 |
| Cortisol 50 mg/kg | 2 h | Anesthetized cat — circulatory shock | Rabbit blood | $PGE_2$ equivalents | 52 |
| Dexamethasone 0.3 mg/kg | 24 h | Abdominal sponge implant in the rat | Carrageenin | $PGE_2$ equivalents | 53 |
| Prednisone 45 mg/kg | 24 h | Human rheumatoid joints | Spontaneous | 6-keto-$PGF_{1\alpha}$ | 54 |
| 5-Methyl prednisolone, 40 mg intra-articular | 3 d | Human rheumatoid joints | Spontaneous | $LTB_4$; 5-HETE | 55 |
| Dexamethasone 1 mg/kg | 1 h | Peritoneal lavage from rats | Anti-$PLA_2$ activity using phagocytosis of bacteria | $PGE_2$ | 56 |
| Dexamethasone 10 μg/ml challenge fluid | 24 h | Air pouch in the rat | Antigen (ovalb) | $PGE_2$ | 57 |
| Diflorasone, 0.05% cream | 28 h | Human psoriatic plaques | Spontaneous | 12-HETE | 58 |
| Dexamethasone, 1 mg/d s.c. | 4 d | Uterus of ovariectomized rats | Estradiol 17 beta implants | $PGF_{2\alpha}$ | 59 |
| Dexamethasone, 3 mg s.c. every 12 h | 1—4 d | Rabbit endometrium | Pregnancy | Phospholipase activity. (No inhibition of $PGE_2$, $PGF_{2\alpha}$, or 6-keto-$PGF_{1\alpha}$) | 60 |

inhibit release of eicosanoids and related mediators in several *in vitro* and even *in vivo* situations.[72-74]

Lipocortins I and II are homologous with the calcium-binding calpactins II and I, respectively,[77] and may actually act by sequestering substrate rather than inhibiting the phospholipase per se.[77] However, such findings do correspond with original definition of lipocortins, whose activity is overcome by addition of extra phospholipid substrates[69] and the recent finding that lipocortin activity is dependent upon $Ca^{++}$ ions.[73]

The above observations clearly point to the expected second-messenger role of lipocortins, especially since the gene that codes for lipocortin is induced by glucocorticoids.[70] Clearly further work needs to be done in establishing which lipocortin cleavage products are most important in different cells in relation to different stimuli.

It is also possible that anti-inflammatory corticosteroids (and thus lipocortins) may have an overlooked role in manipulating the spectrum of different eicosanoids released via selectivity for fatty acid composition of the phospholipids, or because the particular hydrolytic enzyme liberating the eicosanoid precursor is not inhibited by lipocortin (e.g., prostacyclin production in rat lung[78]).*

Finally, one should consider the possibility that material other than lipocortins could act similarly to the lipocortins. Many endogenous materials (e.g., endonexin[79]) have now been shown to inhibit phospholipase systems.** Links between synthesis of these materials and actions of corticosteroids have generally not been firmly established. There are also two recent findings that may become of great importance: firstly, Lee et al.[80] have reported evidence that glucorticoids may owe part of their anti-inflammatory actions to decreased synthesis of interleukin I-Beta that is known to induce eicosanoid production. Secondly, Koltai et al.[61] have reported that glucocorticoids induce the synthesis of low mass anti-inflammatory factors that do not inhibit phospholipase $A_2$.

* However, dexamethasone does inhibit prostaglandin release from rabbit coronary microvessel endothelium.[18]

** However, endonexins may be identical to lipocortins III, IV, and V. For more detail, see chapter in this volume by D. L. Smith.

## REFERENCES


1. **Flower, R. J. and Blackwell, G. J.,** Anti-inflammatory steroids induce biosynthesis of a phospholipase inhibitor which prevents prostaglandin generation, *Nature (London)*, 278, 456, 1979.
2. **Carnuccio, R., Di Rosa, M., and Persico, P.,** Hydrocortisone-induced inhibitor of PG biosynthesis in rat leucocytes, *Brit. J. Pharmacol.*, 68, 14, 1980.
3. **Hirata, F., Schiffman, E., Venkatasubramanian, K., Salomon, D., and Axelrod, J.,** A phospholipase $A_2$ inhibitory protein in rabbit neutrophils induced by glucocorticoids, *Proc. Natl. Acad. Sci. U.S.A.*, 77, 2533, 1980.
4. **Blackwell, G. J., Carnuccio, R., Di Rosa, M., Flower, R. J., Parente, L., and Persico, P.,** Macrocortin: a polypeptide causing the anti-phospholipase effect of glucocorticoids, *Nature (London)*, 287, 147, 1980.
5. **Saeed, S. A., McDonald-Gibson, W. J., Cuthbert, J., Copas, J. L., Schneider, C., Gardiner, P. J., Butt, N. M., and Collier, H. O. J.,** Endogenous inhibitor of prostaglandin synthetase, *Nature (London)*, 270, 32, 1977.
6. **Moore, P. K. and Hoult, J. R. S.,** Anti-inflammatory steroids reduce tissue prostaglandin synthetase activity and enhance prostaglandin breakdown, *Nature (London)*, 288, 269, 1980.
7. **Moore, P. K. and Hoult, J. R. S.,** Pathophysiological states modify levels in rat plasma of factors which inhibit synthesis and enhance breakdown of prostaglandins, *Nature (London)*, 288, 271, 1980.
8. **Russo-Marie, F. and Duval, D.,** Dexamethasone-induced inhibition of prostaglandin production does not result from a direct action on $PLA_2$ activities but is mediated through a steroid-inducible factor, *Biochim. Biophys. Acta*, 712, 177, 1982.

9. **Cloix, J. F., Colard, O., Rothhut, B., and Russo-Marie, F.,** Characterization and partial purification of 'renocortins': two polypeptides formed in renal cells causing the anti-phospholipase-like action of glucocorticoids, *Br. J. Pharmacol.*, 79, 313, 1983.
10. **Rothhut, B., Russo-Marie, F., Wood, J., Di Rosa, M., and Flower, R. J.,** Further characterization of the glucocorticoid induced antiphospholipase protein 'renocortin', *Biochem. Biophys. Res. Commun.*, 117, 878, 1983.
11. **Errasfa, M., Rothhut, B., Fradin, A., Billardon, C., Junien, J. L., Bure, J., and Russo-Marie, F.,** The presence of lipocortin in human embryonic skin fibroblasts and its regulation by anti-inflammatory steroids, *Biochim. Biophys. Acta,* 847, 247, 1985.
12. **Gurpide, E., Markiewicz, L., Schatz, F., and Hirata, F.,** Lipocortin output by human endometrium, *in vitro, J. Clin. Endocrinol. Metab.*, 63, 162, 1986.
13. **Danon, A. and Assouline, G.,** Inhibition of prostaglandin biosynthesis by corticosteroids requires RNA & protein synthesis, *Nature (London),* 273, 552, 1978.
14. **Di Rosa, M. and Persico, P.,** Mechanism of inhibition of prostaglandin biosynthesis by hydrocortisone in rat leucocytes, *Br. J. Pharmacol.*, 66, 161, 1979.
15. **Russo-Marie, F., Paing, M., and Duval, D.,** Involvement of glucocorticoid receptors in steroid induced inhibition of prostaglandin secretion, *J. Biol. Chem.*, 254, 8498, 1979.
16. **Peters-Golden, M., Bathon, J., Flores, R., Hirata, F., and Newcombe, D. S.,** Glucocorticoid inhibition of zymosan-induced arachidonic acid release by rat alveolar macrophages, *Am. Rev. Respir. Dis.*, 130, 803, 1984.
17. **De Caterina, R. and Weksler, B. B.,** Modulation of arachidonic acid metabolism in human endothelial cells by glucocorticoids, *Thromb. Haemostas.*, 55, 369, 1986.
18. **Rosenbaum, R. M., Cheli, C. D., and Gerritsen, M. E.,** Dexamethasone inhibits prostaglandin release from rabbit coronary microvessel endothelium, *Am. J. Physiol.*, 250, C970, 1986.
19. **Van de Velde, V. J., Bult, H., and Herman, A. G.,** Dexamethasone and prostacyclin biosynthesis by serosal membranes of the rabbit peritoneal cavity, *Agents Actions,* 17, 308, 1986.
20. **Van de Velde, V. J., Herman, A. G., and Bult, H.,** Effects of dexamethasone on prostacyclin biosynthesis in rabbit mesothelial cells, *Prostaglandins,* 32, 169, 1986.
21. **Greaves, M. W. and McDonald-Gibson, W.,** Inhibition of PG biosynthesis by corticosteroids, *Br. Med. J.*, ii, 83, 1972.
22. **Lewis, G. P. and Piper, P. J.,** Inhibition of release of prostaglandins as an explanation of some of the actions of anti-inflammatory corticosteroids, *Nature (London),* 254, 308, 1975.
23. **Tashijian, A. H., Jr., Voelkel, E. F., McDonough, J., and Levine, L.,** Hydrocortisone inhibits prostaglandin production by mouse fibrosarcoma cells, *Nature (London),* 258, 739, 1975.
24. **Hong, S.-L. and Levine, L.,** Inhibition of arachidonic acid release from cells as the biochemical action of anti-inflammatory corticosteroids, *Proc. Natl. Acad. Sci. U.S.A.*, 73, 1730, 1976.
25. **Kantrowitz, F., Robinson, D. R., McGuire, M. B., and Levine, L.,** Corticosteroids inhibit prostaglandin production by rheumatoid synovia, *Nature (London),* 258, 737, 1975.
26. **Dayer, J. M., Krane, S. M., Graham, R., Russell, G., and Robinson, D. R.,** Production of collagenase and prostaglandins by isolated adherent rheumatoid synovial cells, *Proc. Natl. Acad. Sci. U.S.A.*, 73, 945, 1976.
27. **Tam, S., Hong, S. C. L., and Levine, L.,** Relationships among the steroids, of anti-inflammatory properties and inhibition of prostaglandin production and arachidonic acid release by transformed mouse fibroblasts, *J. Pharmacol. Exp. Ther.*, 203, 162, 1977.
28. **Nijkamp, F. P., Flower, R. J., Moncada, S., and Vane, J. R.,** Partial purification of RCS-RF and inhibition of its activity by anti-inflammatory steroids, *Nature (London),* 263, 479, 1976.
29. **Blackwell, G. J., Flower, R. J., Nijkamp, F., and Vane, J. R.,** Phospholipase $A_2$ activity of guinea-pig isolated perfused lungs: stimulation and inhibition by anti-inflammatory steroids, *Brit. J. Pharmacol.*, 62, 78, 1978.
30. **Bray, M. A. and Gordon, D.,** Prostaglandin production by macrophages and the effect of anti-inflammatory drugs, *Brit. J. Pharmacol.*, 63, 635, 1978.
31. **Gryglewski, R. J., Panczenko, B., Korbut, R., Grodzinska, L., and Ocetkiewicz, A.,** Corticosteroids inhibit prostaglandin release from perfused mesenteric blood vessels of rabbit and from perfused lungs of sensitized guinea-pig, *Prostaglandins,* 10, 343, 1975.
32. **Meats, J. E., McGuire, M. B., and Russell, R. G. G.,** Human synovium releases a factor which stimulates chondrocyte production of PGE and a plasminogen activator, *Nature (London),* 286, 891, 1980.
33. **Brinkerhoff, C. E., McMillan, R. M., Dayer, J. M., and Harris, E. D.,** Inhibition by retinoic acid of collagenase production in rheumatoid synovial cells, *N. Engl. J. Med.*, 303, 432, 1980.
34. **Brune, K., Kalin, H., Rainsford, K. D., and Wagner, K.,** Dexamethasone inhibits the release of prostaglandins and the formation of autophagic vacuoles from stimulated macrophages, in *Advances in Prostaglandin and Thromboxane Research,* Vol. 8, Samuelsson, B., Ramwell, P. W., and Paoletti, R., Eds., Raven Press, New York, 1980, 1679.

35. **Robinson, C. and Hoult, J. R. S.,** Evidence for functionally distinct pools of phospholipase responsible for prostaglandin release from the perfused guinea-pig lung, *Eur. J. Pharmacol.*, 64, 333, 1980.
36. **Zusman, R. M. and Brown, C. A.,** Role of phospholipase in the regulation of prostaglandin biosynthesis by rabbit renomedullary interstitial cells in tissue culture: effects of angiotensin II, potassium, hyperosmolality, dexamethasone, and protein synthesis inhibition, in *Advances in Prostaglandin, Thromboxane and Leukotriene Research,* Vol. 6, Ramwell, P. W. and Samuelsson, B., Eds., Raven Press, New York, 1980, 243.
37. **Vincentini, L. M., Miller, R. J., and Villereal, M. L.,** Evidence for a role of phospholipase activity in the serum stimulation of $Na^+$ efflux in human fibroblasts, *J. Biol. Chem.*, 259, 6912, 1984.
38. **Parente, L., Di Rosa, M., Flower, R. J., Ghiara, P., Meli, R., Persico, P., Salmon, J. A., and Wood, J. N.,** Relationship between the anti-phospholipase and anti-inflammatory effects of glucocorticoid-induced proteins, *Eur. J. Pharmacol.*, 99, 233, 1984.
39. **Bulleit, R. F. and Zimmerman, E. F.,** The effects of dexamethasone on palate mesenchymal cell phospholipase activity, *Toxicol. Appl. Pharmacol.*, 75, 246, 1984.
40. **Crutchley, D. J., Ryan, U. S., and Ryan, J. W.,** Glucocorticoid modulation of prostacyclin production in cultured bovine pulmonary endothelial cells, *J. Pharmacol. Exp. Ther.*, 233, 650, 1985.
41. **Fan, T. P. and Lewis, G. P.,** Mechanism of cyclosporin A-induced inhibition of prostacyclin synthesis by macrophages, *Prostaglandins,* 30, 735, 1985.
42. **Niwa, Y., Kano, T., Taniguchi, S., Miyachi, Y., and Sakane, T.,** Effect of cyclosporin A on the membrane-associated events in human leucocytes with special reference to the similarity with dexamethasone, *Biochem. Pharmacol.*, 35, 947, 1986.
43. **Dartois, R. and Bouton, M. M.,** Role of calcium on TPA-induced secretion of ACTH and $PGE_2$ by pituitary cells: effects of dexamethasone, *Biochem. Biophys. Res. Commun.*, 138, 323, 1986.
44. **Cirino, G. and Sorrentino, L.,** Phospholipase inhibition and prostacyclin generation by gastric muscularis and mucosa layers, *Agents Actions,* 18, 535, 1986.
45. **Carlstedt-Duke, J., Bronnegard, M., and Strandvik, B.,** Pathological regulation of arachidonic acid release in cystic fibrosis: the putative basic defect, *Proc. Natl. Acad. Sci. U.S.A.*, 83, 9202, 1986.
46. **Clark, M. A., Bomalaski, J. S., Conway, T. M., Wartell, J., and Crooke, S. T.,** Differential effects of dexamethasone on phospholipase $A_2$ and C activities and arachidonic acid release from endothelial cells in response to bradykinin and leukotriene D4, *Prostaglandins,* 32, 703, 1986.
47. **Wahl, L. M. and Lampel, L. L.,** Regulation of peripheral blood monocyte collagenase by prostaglandins and anti-inflammatory drugs, *Cell Immunol.*, 105, 411, 1987.
48. **DeGeorge, J. J., Ousley, A. H., McCarthy, K. K., Morell, P., and Lapetina, E. G.,** Glucocorticoids inhibit the liberation of arachidonate but not the rapid production of phospholipase C metabolites in acetylcholine-stimulated C62B glioma cells, *J. Biol. Chem.*, 262, 9979, 1987.
49. **Bonilla, C. A. and Dupont, J.,** Fatty acid and PG composition of left ventricular myocardium from dexamethasone-treated dogs with severe low-output syndrome (LOS), *Prostaglandins,* 11, 935, 1976.
50. **Herbaczynska-Cedro, K. and Staszewska-Barczak, J.,** Suppression of the release of prostaglandin-like substances by hydrocortisone, *in vivo, Prostaglandins,* 13, 517, 1977.
51. **Grodzinska, L. and Dembinska-Kiec, A.,** Hydrocortisone and the release of prostaglandins from the spleen, *Prostaglandins,* 13, 125, 1977.
52. **Korbut, R., Ocetkiewicz, A., and Gryglewski, R. J.,** The influence of hydrocortisone and indomethacin on the release of prostaglandin-like substances during circulatory shock in cats induced by intravenous administration of rabbit blood, *Pharm. Res. Commun.*, 10, 371, 1978.
53. **Higgs, G. A., Flower, R. J., and Vane, J. R.,** A new approach to anti-inflammatory drugs, *Biochem. Pharmacol.*, 28, 1959, 1979.
54. **Brodie, M. J., Hensby, C. N., Parke, A., and Gordon, D.,** Is prostacyclin the major pro-inflammatory prostanoid in joint fluid? *Life Sci.*, 27, 603, 1980.
55. **Klickstein, L. B., Shapleigh, C., and Goetzl, E. J.,** Lipoxygenation of arachidonic acid as a source of PMN leucocyte chemotactic factors in synovial fluid and tissue in rheumatoid arthritis and spondyloarthritis, *J. Clin. Invest.*, 66, 1166, 1980.
56. **Blackwell, G. J., Carnuccio, R., Di Rosa, M., Flower, R. J., Langham, C. S. J., Parente, L., Persico, P., Russell-Smith, N. C., and Stone, D.,** Glucocorticoids induce the formation and release of anti-inflammatory and anti-phospholipase proteins into the peritoneal cavity of the rat, *Brit. J. Pharmacol.*, 76, 185, 1982.
57. **Ohuchi, K., Yoshino, S., Kanaoko, K., Tsurufuji, S., and Levine, L.,** A possible role of arachidonate metabolism in allergic air pouch inflammation of rats, *Int. Arch. Allerg. Appl. Immunol.*, 68, 326, 1982.
58. **Hammarstrom, S., Hamberg, M., Duell, E. A., Stawiski, M. A., Anderson, T. F., and Vorhees, J. J.,** Glucocorticoid in inflammatory proliferative skin disease, reduces arachidonic and hydroxyeicosatetraenoic acids, *Science,* 198, 994, 1977.
59. **Pakrasi, P., Cheng, H. C., and Dey, S. K.,** Prostaglandins in the uterus: modulation by steroid hormones, *Prostaglandins,* 26, 991, 1983.

60. **Hoffmann, L. H., Davenport, G. R., and Brash, A. R.,** Endometrial prostaglandins and phospholipase activity related to implantation in rabbits: effects of dexamethasone, *Biol. Reprod.*, 30, 544, 1984.
61. **Koltai, M., Kovács, Z., Nemecz, G., Mécs, I., and Szekeres, I.,** Glucocorticoid-induced low molecular mass anti-inflammatory factors which do not inhibit phospholipase $A_2$, *Eur. J. Pharmacol.*, 134, 109, 1987.
62. **Ferreira, S. H. and Vane, J. R., Eds.,** *Handbook of Pharmacology*, Vols. 50/I and 50/II, Inflammation and Anti-Inflammatory Drugs, Springer-Verlag, Berlin, 1978.
63. **Parente, L. and Flower, R. J.,** Hydrocortisone and 'macrocortin' inhibit the zymosan-induced release of lyso PAF from rat peritoneal leucocytes, *Life Sci.*, 36, 1225, 1985.
64. **Willis, A. L. and Smith, J. B.,** Some perspectives on platelets and prostaglandins, *Prog. Lipid Res.*, 20, 387, 1982.
65. **Higgs, G. A.,** The role of eicosanoids in inflammation, *Prog. Lipid Res.*, 25, 555, 1986.
66. **Willis, A. L.,** The eicosanoids: an introduction and an overview, in *Handbook of the Eicosanoids*, Vol. IA, Willis, A. L., Ed., CRC Press, Boca Raton, FL, 1987, 3.
67. **Flower, R. J.,** Background and discovery of lipocortins, *Agents Actions*, 17, 255, 1985.
68. **Flower, R. J.,** Eleventh Gaddum Memorial Lecture: lipocortin and the mechanism of action of the glucocorticoids, *Br. J. Pharmacol.*, 94, 987, 1988.
69. **Di Rosa, M., Flower, R. J., Hirata, F., Parente, L., and Russo-Marie, F.,** Nomenclature announcement: anti-phospholipase proteins, *Prostaglandins*, 28, 441, 1984.
70. **Wallner, B. P., Mattaliano, R. J., Hession, C., Cate, R. L., Tizard, R., Sinclair, L. K., Foeller, C., Pingchang Chow, E., Browning, J. L., Ramachandran, K. L., and Pepinsky, R. B.,** Cloning and expression of human lipocortin, a phospholipase $A_2$ inhibitor with potential anti-inflammatory activity, *Nature (London)*, 320, 77, 1986.
71. **Cirino, G., Flower, R. J., Browning, J. L., Sinclair, L. K., and Pepinsky, R. B.,** Recombinant human lipocortin 1 inhibits thromboxane release from guinea-pig isolated perfused lung, *Nature (London)*, 328, 270, 1987.
72. **Cirino, G. and Flower, R. J.,** Human recombinant lipocortin I inhibits prostacyclin release from human umbilical artery *in vitro*, *Prostaglandins*, 34, 59, 1987.
73. **Cirino, G. and Flower, R. J.,** The inhibitory effect of lipocortin on eicosanoid synthesis is dependent upon $Ca^{++}$ ions, *Br. J. Pharmacol.*, 92, 521P, 1987.
74. **Stevens, T. R. J., Drasdo, A. L., Peers, S. J., Hall, N. D., and Flower, R. J.,** Stimulus-specific inhibition of human neutrophil $H_2O_2$ production by human recombinant lipocortin 1, *Br. J. Pharmacol.*, 93, 139P, 1988.
75. **Burch, R. M. and Axelrod, J.,** Dissociation of bradykinin-induced prostaglandin formation from phosphatidylinositol turnover in Swiss 3T3 fibroblasts: evidence for G protein regulation of phospholipase $A_2$, *Proc. Natl. Acad. Sci. U.S.A.*, 84, 6374, 1987.
76. **Vargaftig, B. B. and Dao, Hai, N.,** Selective inhibition by mepacrine of the release of "rabbit aorta contracting substance" evoked by the administration of bradykinin, *J. Pharmacol.*, 24, 159, 1972.
77. **Davidson, F. F., Dennis, E. A., Powell, M., and Glenney, J. R.,** Inhibition of phospholipase $A_2$ by "lipocortins" and calpactins, *J. Biol. Chem.*, 262, 1698, 1987.
78. **Tsai, M. Y.,** Glucocorticoid and prostaglandin: lack of an inhibitory effect by dexamethasone on the synthesis of 6-ketoprostaglandin F1 alpha in rat lung, *Prostaglandins, Leukotrienes Med.*, 28, 119, 1987.
79. **Fauvel, J., Salles, J. P., Roques, V., Chap, H., Rochat, H., and Douste-Blazy, L.,** Lipocortin-like anti-phospholipase $A_2$ activity of endonexin, *FEBS Lett.*, 216, 45, 1987.
80. **Lee, S. W., Tsou, A.-P., Chang, H., Thomas, J., Petri, K., Eugui, E., and Allison, A. C.,** Glucocorticoids selectively inhibit the transcription of the interleukin IB gene and decrease the stability of IL-1B mRNA, *Proc. Natl. Acad. Sci. U.S.A.*, 85, 1204, 1988.
81. **Gupta, C. and Goldman, A. S.,** Dexamethasone-induced phospholipase $A_2$-inhibitory proteins (PLIP) influenced by the H-2 histocompatibility region, *Proc. Soc. Exp. Biol. Med.*, 178, 29, 1985.
82. **Ghiara, P., Meli, R., Parente, L., and Persico, P.,** Distinct inhibition of membrane-bound and lysosomal phospholipase $A_2$ by glucocorticoid-induced proteins, *Biochem. Pharmacol.*, 33, 1445, 1984.
83. **Gupta, C., Katsumata, M., Goldman, A. S., Herold, R., and Piddington, R.,** Glucocorticoid-induced phospholipase $A_2$-inhibitory proteins mediate glucocorticoid teratogenicity, *in vitro*, *Proc. Natl. Acad. Sci. U.S.A.*, 81, 1140, 1984.
84. **Pepinsky, R. B., Tizard, R., Mattaliano, R. J., Sinclair, L. K., Miller, G. T., Browning, J. L., Chow, E. P., Burns, C., Huang, K.-S., Pratt, D., Wachter, L., Hession, C., Frey, A. Z., and Wallner, B. P.,** Five distinct calcium and phospholipid binding proteins share homology with lipocortin I, *J. Biol. Chem.*, 263, 10799, 1988.

# DRUGS THAT INHIBIT THE ACTIVITIES OR ACTIVATION OF PHOSPHOLIPASES AND OTHER ACYLHYDROLASES

**Fusao Hirata**

## INTRODUCTION

Many cells, if not all, release arachidonic acid when they are stimulated by hormones, neurotransmitters, antibodies, and other ligands. As described in other chapters, this fatty acid is further metabolized by the two pathways; leukotrienes and hydroxyperoxides of arachidonic acid are formed by the lipoxygenase pathway, while prostaglandins and thromboxanes are synthesized via the cyclooxygenase pathway. These metabolites of arachidonic acid have a variety of biological activities in inflammation, immunoregulation, neural activities, etc. Arachidonic acid does not exist as a free fatty acid in most cells; rather, it is esterified in the 2-position of various phospholipids. The generation or release of free arachidonic acid from phospholipids by the actions of phospholipases or other acylhydrolases is then a rate-limiting step for the formation of the biologically active metabolites such as prostaglandins and leukotrienes. Therefore, drugs which inhibit release of arachidonic acid from phospholipids can reduce the production of these metabolites and consequently modulate various biological activities. In this chapter the mechanism of actions of such drugs will be discussed.

## ENZYMES THAT ARE INVOLVED IN ARACHIDONIC ACID RELEASE

### Phospholipase $A_2$

Phospholipase $A_2$ [EC 3.1.1.4] catalyzes the specific hydrolysis of fatty acid ester bond at the 2-position of 1,2-diacyl-*sn*-phosphoglycerides. The purified enzyme can hydrolyze phosphatidylcholine (PtdCho), phosphatidylethanolamine (PtdEth), and phosphatidylserine (PtdSer) as well as those of the corresponding plasmalogen.[1] This enzyme is widely distributed in tissues and organs of mammals, and those from pancreas, bee venom, and snake venoms are well characterized. In pancreas, the enzyme does not exist in the active form, but is secreted as an enzymatically inactive zymogen.[3,4] Trypsin removes seven amino acid residues from the N terminus to activate it. Even though in certain tissues such as platelets, serine proteases including trypsin cause the activation of phospholipase $A_2$,[5-7] no evidence is available indicating that similar proenzyme forms of the phospholipase are present in these tissues. Phospholipases are mostly membrane bound and are very resistant to heat, acid, and organic solvents. The purified enzymes have an average molecular weight of approximately 14,000. Phospholipase $A_2$ from certain tissues including rat spleen[8] and rabbit peritoneal exudates,[9] are a soluble form. The molecular weights of these soluble enzymes are estimated to be approximately 15,000. The striking similarity in the enzymatic and physical properties of the peritoneal-fluid phospholipase $A_2$ and the membrane-associated phospholipase $A_2$ from neutrophils suggests that the soluble form of phospholipase in the exudate is probably of leukocyte origin. The active phospholipase $A_2$ is also present in the insoluble pulmonary secretions of patients with alveolar proteinosis.[10] The molecular weight as estimated by gel filtration and SDS-polyacrylamide gel electrophoresis amounted to 75,000. The same N terminus, alanine, is detected in both pancreatic and pulmonary enzymes.[11] No sugar residues were found. The enzymatic properties of these two enzymes are also quite similar.

All phospholipases $A_2$ require $Ca^{2+}$ for their activity, although the activity varies widely from one enzyme to another. The active site of phospholipase $A_2$, where $Ca^{2+}$ is bound, appears to be hydrophobic.[12] $Ca^{2+}$ is necessary for binding of phospholipid substrates.[13] Taking advantage of these properties, the enzyme can be absorbed with phosphatidylcholine-coupled AH-sepharose 4B in the presence of $Ca^{2+}$ and can be eluted from this affinity column with EDTA-containing buffer. Optimum pH for the reaction is quite broad, ranging from pH 7.0 to pH 9.4. However, the lysosomal enzyme has an optimum pH in the acidic range around 4.

In addition to these enzymes, phosphatidic acid (PtdAcid)-specific and phosphatidylinositol (PtdIno)-specific phospholipases $A_2$ are reported.[14,15] PtdAcid-specific phospholipase $A_2$ is distinct from pancreas phospholipase $A_2$ with respect to $Ca^{2+}$ concentration requirement and optimum pH for reaction. However, purified phospholipase $A_2$ can degrade PtdIno and can be activated by PtdAcid. Further purification and characterization of these enzymes are necessary for their identification.

### Phosphatidylinositol Specific Phospholipase C and Diacylglycerol Lipase

Turnover of PtdIno increases in a variety of cells in response to external stimuli.[16,17] A key enzyme responsible is a phospholipase-C type of enzyme specific for PtdIno ([EC 3.1.4.10]). This enzyme hydrolyzes PtdIno to form 1,2-diacylglycerol and inositol monophosphate. This enzyme has a partial cyclizing activity to form inositol-1,2-cyclic phosphate.[17] These enzymes are also widely distributed in animal tissues.[16] A highly purified preparation of phospholipase C from rat-brain supernatant has a molecular weight of 36,000,[18] but the enzyme from rat-liver supernatant has a molecular weight around 70,000.[19] The findings that the PtdIno-phospholipase-C activities can be detected with several protein peaks of higher molecular weights in the brain supernatants suggest that the enzyme might be in polymeric form. PtdIno phospholipase C has been found primarily in the cytosolic fraction with some activity found in particulate and lysosomal fractions of mammalian cells. Membrane-bound enzymes described in the brain can be adequately accounted for by the contamination of soluble enzymes.[20]

PtdIno phospholipase C purified from bacterial sources hydrolyzes PtdIno specifically.[21] Generally, the enzymes from lymphocytes, intestinal mucosa, and platelets are specific for PtdIno. However, lysosomal PtdIno phospholipase C from rat brain and liver can degrade PtdCho and PtdEth as well.[22,23]

There appears to be a spectrum for $Ca^{2+}$ requirements for the activity of this enzyme from different sources or from different subcellular origins of the same source. Optimum pH for PtdIno phospholipase C is broad, ranging from 4.8 to 7.5, depending upon the source and the cellular origin of the enzyme.

Diacylglycerol, a product from PtdIno or PtdCho by the action of phospholipase C, is further hydrolyzed by diacylglycerol lipase to release arachidonic acid.[24] This enzyme is also $Ca^{2+}$ dependent. Another enzyme utilizing diacylglycerol is diacylglycerol kinase, which is involved in the PtdIno synthesis.[25] This enzyme is inhibited by $Ca^{2+}$. Therefore, $Ca^{2+}$ appears to play an important role in the PtdIno turnover.

## MECHANISM OF ACTIVATION OF PHOSPHOLIPASES

The elucidation of the chain reactions connecting stimulation of the specific receptors with activation of phospholipases is being extensively studied, but little information is available concerning mechanisms involved. Possible mechanisms are discussed briefly below:

### Limited Proteolysis

Since phospholipase $A_2$ is present as an inactive proenzyme form in the pancreas,[3,4] it is likely that serine proteases such as trypsin can activate phospholipase $A_2$. Such conversion of the inactive form to the active form is performed by the removal of a heptapeptide from the N terminus of the molecules. Moderate activation of phospholipase $A_2$ activity by the treatment with proteases has been described in various tissues, including the lysate of human red blood cells.[5,6,26] However, the question as to whether their activation is caused by a zymogen-active enzyme conversion or by removal of inhibitory peptides or proteins in response to trypsin treatment still remains to be investigated.

In addition to trypsin and other serine proteases, addition of platelet homogenates activates phospholipase activities of plasma, lysed erythrocytes, and liver plasma membranes.[27,28] This activation is ascribed to solubilization of the inactive membrane-bound enzyme. These results suggest that a more hydrophobically bound integral membrane protein is converted into a more electrostatically bound peripheral membrane protein. However, it is not clear that this is due to the conversion of proenzyme into active enzyme by proteolysis or complex formation between the inactive enzyme and the platelet factor.

In intact cells, trypsin and other proteases can activate phospholipase $A_2$ as measured by arachidonate release.[5,6] But these studies do not provide an answer to the question as to whether the proteolytic activation of membrane-bound enzyme is attributable to unraveling specific zymogen-active enzyme conversion, to proteolytic removal of inhibitory protein, to nonspecific alteration in membrane structure by the digestion of proteins, or to contamination of some activators in the protease preparations. In neutrophils, the pronase treatment results in a marked increase of arachidonic acid release.[29] This is attributable to the removal of endogenous phospholipase inhibitor protein, lipocortin (discussed in a later section).

**Phosphorylation**

Phosphorylation alters many protein functions.[30] This appears to be the case with phospholipase $A_2$. The treatment of macrophage homogenates with ATP and catalytic unit of cyclic AMP-dependent kinase causes a marked increase in phospholipase $A_2$ activity;[31] similar results are reported with brain synaptic vesicles.[32] Phosphorylation experiments with [γ32P]ATP show that proteins with mol wt 40,000, as well as 80,000, 57,000, 53,000, and 30,000, are phosphorylated. Since phospholipase $A_2$ in the brain has mol wt 14,000, phosphorylation of phospholipase $A_2$ itself is not suggested. The activity of purified pancreatic phospholipase $A_2$ is not affected by the incubation with a cyclic AMP-dependent kinase system.[33] These results suggest that some accessory proteins associated with phospholipase $A_2$ are phosphorylated or that nonspecific alteration of membrane structure by phosphorylation of membrane protein causes activation of phospholipase $A_2$. The phospholipase-inhibitory protein, lipomodulin, or lipocortin (see contributions by Flower et al. and by Smith in this volume), whose molecular weight is around 40,000, is a good substrate for various kinases; and phosphorylation inactivates the inhibitory activity of this protein on phospholipase $A_2$. Thus, the phosphorylation of this protein allows phospholipase $A_2$ to be maximally active.[33] This protein can inhibit phospholipase C as well.[33] Therefore, a quite similar mechanism of PtdIno phospholipase C can be suggested, but no data have as yet been available.

**Activators of Phospholipases**

Melittin, a peptide from bee venom, is well known to activate phospholipase $A_2$ in a variety of cells.[34,35] This peptide is quite basic and decreases the interfacial tension between air and salt solution. Toxins which have similar activities are phallolysin from poisonous mushrooms,[36] staphylococcal delta toxin,[37] direct lytic factor from snake venom,[38] and prymnesin.[39] Strong basic peptides such as poly-lysin also have an activating activity on phospholipase $A_2$. The existence of a peptide which stimulates phospholipase $A_2$ has been suggested by Nijkamp et al.[40] The almost 6000-fold purified material from sensitized guinea-pig lungs, which is a peptide of less than 10 amino acids, increases hydrolysis of PtdCho during perfusion of lungs from nonsensitized guinea pig. Such a prostaglandin-generating factor of anaphylaxis has also been purified from human lung and has been found to have a mol wt of 1450, composed of 6 Glu, 3 Asp, 2 Gly, 1 Ser, and 1 Thr. The bactericidal/permeability-increasing protein purified from rabbit neutrophils is a protein closely associated with phospholipase $A_2$ that perturbs bacterial membranes to be accessible by phospholipase $A_2$.[41]

## Calcium, Cyclic Nucleotides, and Calmodulin

### *Calcium*

Phospholipase $A_2$ and PtdIno-specific phospholipase C show an absolute requirement for $Ca^{2+}$. If $Ca^{2+}$-dependent lipases indeed function for arachidonic acid release, one can expect that events which increase availability of $Ca^{2+}$ to phospholipases in intact cells might stimulate the release of arachidonic acid. In fact, $Ca^{2+}$ fluxes are important in many receptor-mediated activations in platelets and other cells. However, the mechanism of $Ca^{2+}$ fluxes remains obscure. At least three components, the influx of $Ca^{2+}$ probably $Na^+$, $K^+$, or $Ca^{2+}$ channels; immobilization of $Ca^{2+}$ bound to membranes; and sequestration of $Ca^{2+}$ in intracellular storage granules (mainly mitochondria), are involved in these processes. The influx of $Ca^{2+}$ through various channels is also classified as voltage-sensitive and insensitive influx, respectively. The efflux of $Ca^{2+}$ as a result of increased intracellular $Ca^{2+}$ is believed to be due to the action of $Ca^{2+}$-ATPase.[42] Furthermore, immobilization of $Ca^{2+}$ bound to membranes and stored in granules appears to be energy dependent. In ATP-depleted platelets preincubated with deoxyglucose and antimycin A, the release of arachidonic acid from PtdCho and PtdIno is blocked, when it is promoted by thrombin but not when they are stimulated by $Ca^{2+}$-ionophore, A23187.[43] Since such impairment of thrombin-induced arachidonate release in energy-depleted platelets cannot be restored by the addition of $Ca^{2+}$ to the media, thrombin itself cannot carry $Ca^{2+}$ inside the cells and an ATP-dependent process is required to liberate internally stored $Ca^{2+}$. However, no data are available showing that such an energy-dependent process is necessary for other receptors such as acetylcholine receptors (nicotinic receptors) which have ion channels as their components.

### *Cyclic Nucleotides*

Cyclic AMP is known to inhibit arachidonic acid release induced by various receptor ligands. Since cyclic AMP itself or a cyclic-AMP-dependent protein kinase system do not affect phospholipase $A_2$ activity,[33] cyclic AMP appears to inhibit phospholipase activity in an indirect manner. Cyclic AMP and phosphodiesterase inhibitors such as theophylline can inhibit the receptor-mediated $Ca^{2+}$ influx in mast cells.[43] Furthermore, it is suggested that in intact cells, cyclic AMP may promote a compartmentalization of intracellular $Ca^{2+}$, thereby reducing cytoplasmic-free $Ca^{2+}$.[44] Platelet vesicles could concentrate $Ca^{2+}$, when incubated with cyclic AMP, ATP, and protein kinase.[45] This accumulated $Ca^{2+}$ can be released from the vesicle by $Ca^{2+}$ – ionophore. Thus, the inhibition of arachidonic acid release by cyclic nucleotides seems to be attributable to sequestration of $Ca^{2+}$ available for the phospholipases. However, in some tissues such as synaptic vesicles, thyroids, and lung, cyclic AMP can enhance phospholipase activities probably due to phosphorylation of inhibitory proteins for phospholipases.[32,33,46,47]

Nevertheless, the activities of phospholipases can be regulated by the availability of $Ca^{2+}$ to the enzymes' locus. Calmodulin, a calcium-binding protein, can modulate most of $Ca^{2+}$-dependent functions,[48] and this protein can enhance phospholipase $A_2$ probably due to lowering concentrations of $Ca^{2+}$ required for its activity.[49]

## Receptors and Membrane Structures

Many hormones, neurotransmitters, and other ligands for receptors stimulate prostaglandin and leukotriene formation in many cells. Arachidonic acid, a precursor for these compounds, may derive mainly from PtdCho and PtdIno by the activation of phospholipase $A_2$ and PtdIno-specific phospholipase C. Which class of phospholipids is the main source of arachidonic acid might be dependent on receptor and cell types. In purified Fcγ receptors of B lymphocytes and macrophages, phospholipase $A_2$ activity is detected.[50] However, for other receptors, no evidence is yet available showing that such phospholipases are directly associated with receptor molecules. For many receptors (e.g., those for insulin and epidermal growth factor) the kinase has been reported to be associated.[51,52] Activation of phospholipase $A_2$ by phosphorylation of inhibitory protein(s) might be carried out by this kinase, but identity of the kinase involved in *in vivo* processes has not been elucidated.

Stimulation of receptors with various ligands generally causes alteration of membrane structure, although the detailed mechanism still remains unclear.[53] One possible explanation is that phospholipid methylation stimulated by a variety of receptors results in structural and compositional alteration of membrane lipids by translocation of phospholipids. Furthermore, PtdCho synthesized by this minor pathway is rich in arachidonic acid, while the one which is formed by the CDP-choline pathway, the major synthetic pathway of PtdCho, contains less unsaturated fatty acids in the 2-position of the glycerol moiety.[54] Phospholipase $A_2$ purified from platelets can degrade almost all classes of phospholipids with comparable rates, while this enzyme in intact cells preferentially hydrolyzes PtdCho containing arachidonic acid.[55] These results suggest that membrane structures of lipid domains determine the activities of phospholipases. Recently, several domains or pools of phospholipids for phospholipases stimulated by individual receptors have been postulated.[56,57] Alternatively, lipid structures of membranes are crucial for phospholipases. PtdIno phospholipase C can hydrolyze pure PtdIno *in vitro* but cannot degrade PtdIno in membranes.[58,59] It turns out that PtdCho, a major constituent of membrane phospholipids, is a potent inhibitor of PtdIno phospholipase C. Such influence of the structural arrangement of membrane lipids on phospholipase $A_2$ activity is quite possible but the details will await the studies using reconstituted systems of a membrane-associated phospholipase $A_2$.

## THE DRUGS WHICH INHIBIT PHOSPHOLIPASES

### Drugs that Directly Inhibit Phospholipases

*Glucocorticoids and Protein Inhibitors*

Glucocorticoids have a variety of actions on various tissues and organs. Antiinflammatory activity, a major action of glucocorticoids, is due to decreasing the availability of arachidonic acid, the precursor of prostaglandins and leukotrienes.[60,61] This is due to the inhibition of phospholipases which release this fatty acid from phospholipids. For many years, this effect of glucocorticoids was attributed to their membrane-stabilizing properties.[69] More recently, however, inhibition of prostaglandin formation by glucocorticoids has been reported to be blocked by cyclohexamide and actinomycin A, inhibitors of protein synthesis.[63,64] Since glucocorticoids themselves have no effects on phospholipases, these results suggest the induction of protein(s) which inhibit phospholipases. Blackwell et al.[65,66] and Hirata et al.[33,90] isolated such factors from rat macrophages (macrocortin) and from rabbit neutrophils (lipomodulin). These two proteins had similar activities with respect to inhibition of arachidonic acid release from various tissues and antiinflammatory activity on carageenan-induced inflammation.[65,67] Immunological properties of both proteins were also similar.[68] Further analysis of biological materials which have been reported to be rich in these factors showed the presence of peptides with mol wt 40,000, 24,000, and 16,000. The latter small peptides might derive from the mol wt 40,000 peptide by proteolytic digestions. The synthesis of this protein is induced by glucocorticoid in a fashion depending upon cytosolic receptors for glucocorticoids. The periods to attain the maximal induction are 10 to 16 h in neutrophils and 2 to 3 h in macrophages. These proteins, which are now thought to be functionally identical (with differences resulting from proteolysis), are now collectively called lipocortins.[90] (See also contributions by Flower et al. and by Smith in this volume.)

The isolated proteins, lipocortins, can inhibit phospholipase $A_2$ from porcine pancreas, in a dose-dependent manner. The maximal inhibition can be attained when a stoichiometric amount of lipocortin is added to that of phospholipase $A_2$.[33] Since lipocortin changes V*max* but not K*m* of the lipase for phospholipids, a one-to-one complex is suggested to be formed. Inhibition of the phospholipase by lipocortin can be reversed by detergents and by higher concentration of $Ca^{2+}$, suggesting that lipocortin inhibits the lipase by hydrophobic interaction at $Ca^{2+}$ binding sites, active sites of phospholipases. Phosphorylation of this protein by a variety of kinases results in loss of inhibitory activity on phospholipases and loose interaction with phospholipases. This protein can inhibit phospholipase C and D as well. However, no evidence is available to show that this protein can inhibit PtdIno phospholipase C. Since this protein can inhibit arachidonate release from a variety of cells regardless of the sources of arachidonate, it is quite likely that it also inhibits PtdIno phospholipase C.

Kent and Lennarz[69] have shown the existence of a peptide in *Bacillus subtilis* that inhibits phospholipase $A_1$. This peptide has mol wt 36,000 as judged by SDS gel electrophoresis.[70] Different from lipocortin, the inhibition of phospholipase $A_1$ by this protein appears to be brought about via enzymatic processes rather than binding of this protein with phospholipase $A_1$. Extracts of Feverfew *(Chyrsanthemum partheium)* are a potent inhibitor of phospholipase $A_2$.[71] This inhibition is attributed to a heat and acid stable peptide of mol wt around 6,000. However, no detailed studies on the mechanism of inhibition have been achieved so far. Another peptide that has recently been shown to inhibit phospholipase $A_2$ activity is a 12-amino acid residue-C terminus of middle-sized tumor antigen (C-MT peptide).[95]

Interestingly, cyclosporin A (CSA), an immunosuppressive drug, has also been shown to have inhibitory effects similar to those of dexamethasone on $PGE_2$[91] and prostacyclin[92] production *in vitro*. CSA also inhibits phospholipase $A_2$ activity,[91,92] but it is not known whether it initiates lipocortin production.

*Nonsteroidal Anti-Inflammatory Drugs*

Nonsteroidal anti-inflammatory drugs such as indomethacin are well known to inhibit the cyclooxygenase pathway.[72] The concentration of indomethacin for inhibition of cyclooxygenase is approximately $10^{-7}$ *M*. At concentrations of drugs greater than that required to block the cyclooxygenase, indomethacin, sodium meclofenamate, and sodium flufenamate also inhibit purified phospholipase $A_2$ from platelets and macrophages.[73] Such inhibition is a function of $Ca^{2+}$ present in the medium; the dose for 50% inhibition with meclofenamate, an analogue of indomethacin, is 0.4 m*M* in the presence of 2.5 m*M* $Ca^{2+}$, while it is 50 n*M* in the presence of 0.5 m*M* $Ca^{2+}$. Thus, inhibition of phospholipase $A_2$ activity by nonsteroidal antiinflammatory agents is mediated through antagonism against $Ca^{2+}$. It should be noted that aspirin, another type of inhibitor of cyclooxygenase, has no inhibitory activity on phospholipase $A_2$ but can inhibit phospholipase C in a protein-synthesis-dependent manner.[93]

*Amino Acid Modifiers, P-Bromophenacyl Bromide*

Modification of phospholipase $A_2$ with p-bromophenacyl bromide, a histidine modifier, causes complete loss of enzyme activity.[74] This drug alkylates the imidazole side chain of the histidine residue at position 53 of the phospholipase $A_2$ molecule, which contains 120 amino acids in all. The treatment of intact cells with this drug also results in a marked decrease in the formation of prostaglandins.[75]

Phospholipase $A_2$ is secreted from neutrophils and kills bacteria by degradation of surface phospholipids. This action is stimulated by a protein factor. Modification of $\epsilon$-$NH_2$ groups in lysine residues of phospholipase $A_2$ by carbamylation with cyanate or by reductive methylation with formaldehyde causes reduction of enzyme activity enhanced by this bactericidal protein.[41] If such a factor plays a role in regulation of phospholipase $A_2$ or C, the modification of lysine in the phospholipases with these drugs will affect arachidonic acid release.

### Drugs That Inhibit Activation of Phospholipases

*Serine Protease Inhibitors*

As described above, certain proteases such as chymotrypsin and trypsin are involved in the activation of phospholipases by the conversion of a zymogen to an active enzyme or by the removal of phospholipase-inhibitory proteins.[29] Thereby, inhibitors of these proteases such as N-α-p-tosyl-lysine chloromethyl pentone, N-acetyl-L-tyrosine ethyl ester, α1-antitrypsin, p-tosyl-L-arginine methyl ester, aprotinine, leupeptin, and antipain can inhibit prostaglandin formation probably by blocking the phospholipase activation.[7] Interestingly, the action of phorbol esters which are well known to mobilize $Ca^{2+}$ and activate phospholipase(s) is also inhibited by these protease inhibitors.

*Inhibitors of Phosphorylation*

The identity of kinases involved in the activation of phospholipase(s) has not been clear. When membrane fractions from rabbit neutrophils are incubated with ATP, arachidonic acid release induced by fMet-Leu-Phe can be inhibited by protein kinase inhibitor Gly-Tyr-Ala-Leu-Gly. However, this peptide has no effects on *in vivo* stimulation of arachidonic acid release. This might be due to the fact that this peptide cannot penetrate into cells.[96]

ATP depletion by the treatment of cells with deoxyglucose and antimycin A also results in the inhibition of arachidonic acid release. But, the explanation for this action should be cautious, because many energy-dependent processes are present.

*Calcium Antagonists*

Phospholipases, which degrade PtdIno or PtdCho, require $Ca^{2+}$ for activity, and rough calculation of free $Ca^{2+}$ concentrations inside cells suggests approximately 1 $\mu M$ or below. Therefore, there is clearly a control mechanism on phospholipase activities by $Ca^{2+}$. Heavy metals such as $La^{2+}$, $CO^{2+}$, and $Cu^{2+}$ are antagonists of $Ca^{2+}$. Replacement of $Ca^{2+}$ by these ions leads to the inhibition of prostaglandin formation in the cells, requiring $Ca^{2+}$ in the external medium. Alternatively, phospholipase $A_2$ activity can be blocked by depletion of $Ca^{2+}$ by chelating agents such as EDTA or EGTA.[1,2]

Certain receptors trigger prostaglandin formation by initiating $Ca^{2+}$ influx into cells. Verapamil and nifedipine block $Ca^{2+}$ channels and subsequently inhibit prostaglandin formation.[76] As described in the section on "the activation mechanism of phospholipase", cyclic nucleotides can modulate sequestration or immobilization of $Ca^{2+}$ in particulate fractions. Therefore, these nucleotides also inhibit arachidonic acid release in many cells.

Some calmodulin antagonists such as trifluoperazine and phenothiazines can inhibit arachidonic acid release.[77] Calmodulin can enhance phospholipase $A_2$ but not PtdIno phospholipase C. Consequently, phospholipase $A_2$ can be inhibited by these drugs but PtdIno phospholipase C cannot.

*Drugs which Perturb Membrane Structures*

Local anesthetics such as tetracin and neuroleptics such as chlorpromazine and imipramine can inhibit arachidonic acid release. These drugs do not inhibit phospholipases directly, but they interact with $Ca^{2+}$ channels and/or alter membrane structures of lipid bilayers.[78-81] Propranolol, a β-adrenergic antagonist, also nonspecifically inhibits phospholipid turnover. Antimalarial agents such as chloroquine and mepacrine can inhibit phospholipase $A_2$ as well as triglyceride lipase. These drugs appear to form complexes with phospholipids, which accounts for the inhibition of a variety of enzymes requiring phospholipids as cofactors.[82]

**Miscellaneous Agents**

*Phospholipid Analogues*

Since phospholipases hydrolyze phospholipids, certain types of phospholipid analogues can inhibit phospholipases. Rothenthal's inhibitor is one of them.[83] Isoamide analogues of glycerolipids are also potent inhibitors of phospholipase $A_2$.[84]

ETYA (eicosatetraenoic acid) is an analogue of arachidonic acid and inhibits the lipoxygenase pathway. When intact cells are incubated with this compound, it can also inhibit phospholipase $A_2$ activity but at higher concentrations.[85]

*PtdIno-Phospholipase-C and Diacylglyceride-Lipase Inhibitors*

[1,6-di(O-carbamoyl) cyclohexanone oxamide] hexane specifically inhibits diacylglycerol lipase.[86] A 50% inhibition is obtained at 4 $\mu M$. This agent has no effect on phospholipase C at 300 $\mu M$ and slight inhibition (15%) on phospholipase $A_2$ at 100 $\mu M$.

Tumoricidal agents, oncodazole, and its analogues such as nitridazole, miconazole, mitrimidazole, and dearbazine, can inhibit phosphatidyl-inositol turnover in concanavalin-A-induced lymphocytes.[87] However, other analogues, levamisole and tribendazole, enhance the turnover of PtdIno.

## RECEPTOR-MEDIATED ARACHIDONIC ACID RELEASE AND SPECIFIC INHIBITORS

Arachidonic acid release by the activation of phospholipases is the rate-limiting step for its metabolism towards prostaglandins, leukotrienes, and other eicosanoids. The phospholipases involved in these metabolic activities have been described in this chapter. However, the mechanism of phospholipase activation mediated through receptors is still obscure. Several hypothetical mechanisms have been presented.[17,53,88] These hypotheses are mainly based on the findings of which classes of phospholipids, e.g., PtdCho or PtdIno, are the main ones that turnover. The key enzymes involved in the turnover of PtdCho and PtdIno are phospholipase $A_2$ and phospholipase C, respectively. Which enzyme has a key role in the metabolism of phospholipids appears to depend upon types of cells and receptors.[88] Phospholipase $A_2$ is a membrane-bound enzyme and can be found in certain receptor peptides such as Fcγ receptors in lymphocytes and macrophages,[50] while PtdIno phospholipase C is a soluble enzyme and no phospholipase C activity can be detected so far in the plasma membranes where most receptors are located.

## CONCLUDING REMARKS AND RECENT DEVELOPMENTS

Intracellular free $Ca^{2+}$ or fluxes of $Ca^{2+}$ through membranes usually play an important role in regulation of phospholipase activities, as described above. However, $Ca^{2+}$ also has a variety of biological activities. $Ca^{2+}$ antagonists or $Ca^{2+}$ channel blockers are useful in inhibiting arachidonic acid release. Although it is not known whether lipocortins exert their antiphospholipase activities through $Ca^{2+}$-dependent mechanisms, it is interesting that the recently cloned lipocortins are homologous with the calcium- and phospholipid-binding proteins called calpactins.[94] Also, although glucocorticoids induce the synthesis of lipocortins, these proteins are also present in cells that are not treated with glucocorticoids. Thus, lipocortins might provide clues to understanding the mechanisms of phospholipase activation.

As described in the reviews by Flower et al. and by Smith in this volume, purified and recombinant lipocortins have antiphospholipase activity and some antiinflammatory activities. Whether or not proteins specific for individual types of phospholipases are present remains to be elucidated. Several inhibitors of phospholipases are described in this chapter, but the only specific inhibitors as yet available are the lipocortins.

## REFERENCES


1. **Van Deenen, L. L. M. and De Haas, G. H.,** The synthesis of phosphoglycerides and some biochemical applications, *Adv. Lipid Res.,* 2, 167, 1964.
2. **Van Deenen, L. L. M. and De Haas, G. H.,** Phosphoglycerides and phospholipases, *Annu. Rev. Biochem.,* 35, 157, 1966.
3. **De Haas, G. H., Slotboom, A. J., Bonsen, P. P. M., Van Deenen, L. L. M., Maroux, S., Puigserver, A., and Desnuelle, P.,** Studies on phospholipase A and its zymogen from porcine pancreas. I. The complete amino acid sequence, *Biochim. Biophys. Acta,* 221, 31, 1970.
4. **Dutilh, C. E., Van Doren, P. J., Verheul, F. E. A., and De Haas, G. H.,** Isolation and properties of prophospholipase $A_2$ from ox and sheep pancreas, *Eur. J. Biochem.,* 53, 91, 1975.
5. **Pickett, W. C., Jesse, R. L., and Cohen, P.,** Trypsin-induced phospholipase activity in human platelets, *Biochem. J.,* 160, 405, 1976.
6. **Henson, P. M., Gould, D., and Becker, E. L.,** Activation of stimulus-specific serine esterases (proteases) in the initiation of platelet secretion. I. Demonstration with organophosphorus inhibitors, *J. Exp. Med.,* 144, 1657, 1976.
7. **Chang, J., Wigley, F., and Newcombe, D.,** Neutral protease activation of peritoneal macrophage prostaglandin synthesis, *Proc. Natl. Acad. Sci. U.S.A.,* 77, 4736, 1980.
8. **Sugatani, J., Kawasaki, N., and Saito, K.,** Studies on a phospholipase B from penicillium notatum, substrate specificity, *Biochim. Biophys. Acta,* 529, 29, 1978.
9. **Franson, R., Dobrov, R., Weiss, J., Elsbach, P., and Weglicki, W. B.,** Isolation and characterization of a phospholipase $A_2$ from an inflammatory exudate, *J. Lipid Res.,* 19, 18, 1978.
10. **Sahu, S. and Lynn, W. S.,** Phospholipase A in a pulmonary secretions of patients with alveolar proteinosis, *Biochim. Biophys. Acta,* 487, 354, 1977.
11. **Sahu, S. and Lynn, W. S.,** Characterization of phospholipase A from pulmonary secretions of patients with alveolar proteinosis, *Biochim. Biophys. Acta,* 489, 307, 1977.
12. **Dijkstra, B. W., Drenth, J., and Kalk, K. H.,** Active site catalytic mechanism of phospholipase $A_2$, *Nature (London),* 289, 604, 1981.
13. **Rock, C. O. and Snyder, F.,** Rapid purification of phospholipase $A_2$ from *Crotalus adamanteus* venom by affinity chromatography, *J. Biol. Chem.,* 250, 6564, 1975.
14. **Billah, M. M., Lapetina, E. G., and Cuatrecasas, P.,** Phospholipase $A_2$ activity specific for phosphatidic acid. A possible mechanism for the production of arachidonic acid in platelets, *J. Biol. Chem.,* 256, 5399, 1981.
15. **Hong, S. L. and Deykin, D.,** The activation of phosphatidylinositol-hydrolyzing phospholipase $A_2$ during prostaglandin synthesis in transformed mouse BALB/3T3 cells, *J. Biol. Chem.,* 256, 5215, 1981.
16. **Shukla, S. D.,** Minireview: phosphatidylinositol specific phospholipase C, *Life Sci.,* 30, 1323, 1982.
17. **Michell, R. H.,** Inositol phospholipids and cell surface receptor function, *Biochim. Biophys. Acta,* 415, 81, 1975.
18. **Quinn, P. J.,** The association between phosphatidylinositol phosphodiesterase activity and a specific subunit of microtubular protein in rat brain, *Biochem. J.,* 133, 273, 1973.
19. **Takenawa, T. and Nagai, Y.,** Purification of phosphatidylinositol-specific phospholipase C from rat liver, *J. Biol. Chem.,* 256, 6769, 1981.
20. **Griflin, H. D., Hawthorn, J. N., and Sykes, M.,** A calcium requirement for the phosphatidylinositol response following activation of presynaptic muscarinic receptors, *Biochem. Pharmacol.,* 28, 1143, 1979.
21. **Ikezawa, H., Yamanegi, M., Taguchi, R., Miyashita, T., and Ohyabu, T.,** Studies on phosphatidylinositol phosphodiesterase (phospholipase C type) of *Bacillus cereus.* I. Purification, properties and phosphatase-releasing activity, *Biochim. Biophys. Acta,* 450, 154, 1976.
22. **Irvine, R. F., Hemington, N., and Dowson, R. M. C.,** The hydrolysis of phosphatidylinositol by lysosomal enzymes of rat liver and brain, *Biochem. J.,* 176, 475, 1978.
23. **Irvine, R. F., Hemington, N., and Dowson, R. M. C.,** Phosphatidylinositol-degrading enzymes in liver lysosomes, *Biochem. J.,* 164, 277, 1977.
24. **Bell, R. L., Kennerly, D. A., Stanford, N., and Majerus, P. W.,** Diglyceride lipase: a pathway for arachidonate release from human platelets, *Proc. Natl. Acad. Sci. U.S.A.,* 76, 3238, 1979.
25. **Lapetina, E. G. and Hawthorne, J. N.,** The diglyceride kinase of rat cerebral cortex, *Biochem. J.,* 122, 171, 1971.
26. **Paysant, M., Bitran, M., Wald, R., and Polonovski, J.,** Phospholipase A des globules rouges chez l'homme. Action sur les phospholipides endogènes et exogènes, *Bull. Soc. Chem. Biol.,* 52, 1257, 1970.
27. **Duchesne, M. J., Etienne, J., Grüber, A., and Polonovski, J.,** Action des plaquettes sur la prophospholipase plasmatique, *Biochemie,* 54, 257, 1972.
28. **Melin, B., Maximilien, R., Friedlander, G., Etienne, J., and Alcindor, L. G.,** Activités phospholipasiques pulmonaires du foetus de rat. Variations au cours du développement, *Biochim. Biophys. Acta,* 486, 590, 1977.

29. **Hirata, F., Schiffmann, E., Venkatasuburamanian, K., Solomon, D., and Axelrod, J.**, A phospholipase $A_2$ inhibitory protein in rabbit neutrophils induced by glucocorticoids, *Proc. Natl. Acad. Sci. U.S.A.*, 77, 2533, 1980.
30. **Cohen, P.**, The role of protein phosphorylation in neural and hormonal control of cellular activity, *Nature (London)*, 296, 613, 1982.
31. **Wightman, P. D., Dahlgren, M. E., and Bonney, R. J.**, Protein kinase activation of phospholipase $A_2$ in sonicates of mouse peritoneal macrophages, *J. Biol. Chem.*, 257, 6650, 1982.
32. **Moskowitz, N., Schook, W., and Puszkin, S.**, Interaction of brain synaptic vesicles induced by endogenous $Ca^{2+}$-dependent phospholipase $A_2$, *Science*, 216, 305, 1982.
33. **Hirata, F.**, The regulation of lipomodulin, a phospholipase inhibitory protein, in rabbit neutrophils by phosphorylation, *J. Biol. Chem.*, 256, 7730, 1981.
34. **Habermann, E.**, Bee and wasp venoms. A biochemistry of their pharmacology and their peptides and enzymes are reviewed, *Science*, 177, 314, 1972.
35. **Shier, W. T.**, Activation of high levels of endogenous phospholipase $A_2$ in cultured cells, *Proc. Natl. Acad. Sci. U.S.A.*, 76, 195, 1979.
36. **Seeger, R. and Burkhardt, M.**, The hemolytic effect of phallolysin, *Naunyn-Schneidebergs Arch. Pharmakol.*, 293, 163, 1976.
37. **Bernheimer, A. W.**, Interactions between membranes and cytolytic bacterial toxins, *Biochim. Biophys. Acta*, 344, 27, 1974.
38. **Fryklund, L. and Eaker, D.**, Complete amino acid sequence of a nonneurotoxic hemolytic protein from the venom of *Haemachatus haemachates* (African renghals cobra), *Biochemistry*, 12, 661, 1973.
39. **Ulitzur, S. and Shilo, M.**, Procedure for purification and separation of prymnesium parvum toxins, *Biochim. Biophys. Acta*, 201, 350, 1970.
40. **Nijkamp, F. P., Flower, R. J., Moncada, S., and Vane, J. R.**, Partial purification of rabbit aorta contracting substance-releasing factor and inhibition of its activity by anti-inflammatory steroids, *Nature (London)*, 263, 479, 1976.
41. **Forst, S., Weiss, J., and Elsbach, P.**, The role of phospholipase $A_2$ lysines in phospholipolysis of *Escherichia coli* killed by a membrane-active neutrophil protein, *J. Biol. Chem.*, 257, 14055, 1982.
42. **Dipolo, R. and Beauge, L.**, Physiological role of ATP-driven calcium pump in squid axon, *Nature (London)*, 278, 271, 1979.

43a. **Rittenhouse-Simmons, S. and Deykin, D.**, The mobilization of arachidonic acids in platelets exposed to thrombin or ionophore A23187. Effects of adenosine triphosphate deprivation, *J. Clin. Invest.*, 60, 495, 1977.

43b. **Ishizaka, T., Hirata, F., Ishizaka, K., and Axelrod, J.**, Stimulation of phospholipid methylation $Ca^{2+}$ influx, and histamine release by bridging IgE receptors on rat mast cells, *Proc. Natl. Acad. Sci. U.S.A.*, 77, 1903, 1980.

44. **Rittenhouse-Simmons, S. and Deykin, D.**, The activation by $Ca^{2+}$ of platelet phospholipase $A_2$. Effects of dibutyryl cyclic adenosine monophosphate and 8-(N,N-diethylamino)-octyl-3,4,5-trimethoxybenzoate, *Biochim. Biophys. Acta*, 543, 409, 1978.
45. **Kaser-Glanzmann, R., Jakabova, M., George, J. N., and Luscher, E. F.**, Stimulation of calcium uptake in platelet membrane vesicles by adenosine 3′,5′-cyclic monophosphate and protein kinase, *Biochim. Biophys. Acta*, 466, 429, 1977.
46. **Van den Bosch, H. and Van den Besselaar, A. M. H. P.**, Intracellular formation and removal of lysophospholipids, in *Advances in Prostaglandins and Thromboxane Research*, Vol. 3, Galli, C., Galli, G., and Porcellati, G., Eds., Raven Press, New York, 1978, 69.
47. **Lindgren, J. A., Claesson, H. E., and Hammarström, S.**, Stimulation of arachidonic acid release and prostaglandin production in 3T3 fibroblasts by adenosine 3′,5′-monophosphate in *Advances in Prostaglandins and Thromboxane Research*, Vol. 3, Galli, C., Galli, G., and Porcellati, G., Eds., Raven Press, New York, 1978, 167.
48. **Van Eldik, L. J. and Watterson, D. M.**, Reproducible production and characterization of anti-calmodulin antisera, *Ann. N.Y. Acad. Sci.*, 356, 437, New York, 1980.
49. **Wong, P. Y. K. and Cheung, W. Y.**, Calmodulin stimulates human platelet phospholipase $A_2$, *Biochem. Biophys. Res. Commun.*, 90, 473, 1979.
50. **Nitta, T. and Suzuki, T.**, Biochemical signals transmitted by Fc gamma receptors: triggering mechanisms of the increased synthesis of adenosine -3′,5′-cyclic monophosphate mediated by Fc gamma 2a- and Fc gamma 2b-receptors of a murine macrophage-like cell line (P388D1), *J. Immunol.*, 129, 2708, 1982.
51. **Cohen, S., Chinkers, M., and Ushiro, H.**, in Cold Spring Harbor Conference on Cell Proliferation 8, 1981, 801.
52. **Kasuga, M., Karlsson, F. A., and Kahn, C. R.**, Insulin stimulates the phosphorylation of the 95,000-Dalton subunit of its own receptor, *Science*, 215, 185, 1982.
53. **Hirata, F. and Axelrod, J.**, Concanavalin A stimulates phospholipid methylation and phosphatidylserine decarboxylation in rat mast cells, *Science*, 209, 1082, 1980.

54. **Trewhella, M. A. and Collins, F. D.,** Pathways of phosphatidylcholine biosynthesis in rat liver, *Biochim. Biophys. Acta,* 296, 51, 1973.
55. **Kannagi, R., Koizumi, K., and Masuda, T.,** Limited hydrolysis of platelet membrane phospholipids, on the proposed phospholipase-susceptible domain in platelet membranes, *J. Biol. Chem.,* 256, 1177, 1981.
56. **Robinson, C. and Hoult, J. R. S.,** Evidence for functionally distinct pools of phospholipase responsible for prostaglandin release from the perfused guinea-pig lung, *Eur. J. Pharmacol.,* 64, 333, 1980.
57. **Schwartzman, M., Liberman, E., and Raz, A.** Bradykinin and angiotensin II activation of arachidonic acid deacylation and prostaglandin $E_2$ formation in rabbit kidney: hormone sensitive versus hormone-insensitive lipid pools of arachidonic acid, *J. Biol. Chem.,* 256, 2329, 1981.
58. **Allan, D. and Michell, R. H.,** Phosphatidylinositol cleavage catalysed by the soluble fraction from lymphocytes. Activity at pH 5.5 and pH 7.0, *Biochem. J.,* 142, 591, 1974.
59. **Hofmann, S. L. and Majerus, P. W.,** Modulation of phosphatidylinositol-specific phospholipase C activity by phospholipid interactions, diglycerides, and calcium ions, *J. Biol. Chem.,* 257, 4359, 1982.
60. **Hong, S. L. and Levine, L.,** Inhibition of arachidonic acid release from cells as the biochemical action of anti-inflammatory corticosteroids, *Proc. Natl. Acad. Sci. U.S.A.,* 73, 1730, 1976.
61. **Gryglewski, R. J., Panczenko, B., Korbut, R., Grodzinska, L., and Ocetkiewicz, A.,** Corticosteroids inhibit prostaglandin release from perfused mesenteric blood vessels of rabbit and from perfused lungs of sensitized guinea pig, *Prostaglandins,* 10, 343, 1975.
62. **Weissmann, G. and Thomas, L.,** Studies on lysosomes. II. The effect of cortisone on the release of acid hydrolases from a large granule fraction of rabbit liver induced by an excess of vitamin A, *J. Clin. Invest.,* 42, 661, 1963.
63. **Danon, A. and Assouline, G.,** Inhibition of prostaglandin biosynthesis by corticosteroids requires RNA and protein synthesis, *Nature (London),* 273, 552, 1978.
64. **Tsurufuji, S., Sugio, K., and Takemasa, F.,** The role of glucocorticoid receptor and gene expression in the anti-inflammatory action of dexamethasone, *Nature (London),* 280, 408, 1979.
65. **Blackwell, G. J., Carnuccio, R., DiRosa, R. M., Flower, R. J., Parente, L., and Persico, P.,** Macrocortin: a polypeptide causing the anti-phospholipase effect of glucocorticoids, *Nature (London),* 287, 147, 1980.
66. **Blackwell, G. J., Carnuccio, R., DiRosa, M., Flower, R. J., Langham, C. S. J., Parente, L., Persico, P., Russel-Smith, N. C., and Stone, D.,** Glucocorticoids induce the formation and release of anti-inflammatory and anti-phospholipase proteins into the peritoneal cavity of the rat, *Br. J. Pharmacol.,* 76, 185, 1982.
67. **Miyamoto, T., Taniguchi, K., Tanouchi, T., and Hirata, F.,** Selective inhibitor of thromboxane synthetase: pyridine and its derivatives, in *Advances in Prostaglandin and Thromboxane Research,* Vol. 6, Samuelsson, R., Paoletti, R., and Ramwell, P., Eds., Raven Press, New York, 1980, 443.
68. **Hirata, F., Notsu, Y., Iwata, M., Parente, L., DiRosa, M., and Flower, R. J.,** Identification of several species of phospholipase inhibitory protein(s) by radioimmunoassay for lipomodulin, *Biochem. Biophys. Res. Commun.,* 109, 223, 1982.
69. **Kent, C., and Lennarz, W. J.,** An osmotically fragile mutant of *Bacillus subtilis* with an active membrane-associated phospholipase $A_1$, *Proc. Natl. Acad. Sci. U.S.A.,* 69, 2793, 1972.
70. **Krag, S. S. and Lennarz, W. J.,** Purification and characterization of an inhibitor of the phospholipase $A_1$ in *Bacillus subtilis, J. Biol. Chem.,* 250, 2813, 1975.
71. **Makheja, A. N. and Bailey, J. M.,** Identification of the anti-platelet substance in Chinese black tree fungus, *N. Engl. J. Med.,* 304, 175, 1981.
72. **Flower, R. J.,** Drugs which inhibit prostaglandin biosynthesis, *Pharmacol. Rev.,* 26, 33, 1974.
73. **Franson, R. C., Eisen, D., Jesse, R., and Lanni, C.,** Inhibition of highly purified mammalian phospholipases $A_2$ by non-steroidal anti-inflammatory agents. Modulation by calcium ions, *Biochem. J.,* 186, 633, 1980.
74. **Volwerk, J. J., Pieterson, W. A., and De Haas, G. H.,** Histidine at the active site of phospholipase $A_2$, *Biochemistry,* 13, 1446, 1974.
75. **Mitchell, S., Poyser, N. L., and Wilson, N. H.,** Effect of p-bromophenacyl bromide, an inhibitor of phospholipase $A_2$, on arachidonic acid release and prostaglandin synthesis by the guinea-pig uterus *in vitro, Br. J. Pharmacol.,* 59, 107, 1977.
76. **Berridge, M. J.,** Receptors and calcium signaling, *Trends Pharmacol. Sci.,* 1, 419, 1980.
77. **Walenga, R. W., Opas, E. E., and Feinstein, M. B.,** Differential effects of calmodulin antagonists on phospholipases $A_2$ and C in thrombin-stimulated platelets, *J. Biol. Chem.,* 256, 12523, 1981.
78. **Kunze, H., Bohn, E. P. L., and Bahrke, G.,** Effects of psychotropic drugs on prostaglandin biosynthesis *in vitro, J. Pharm. Pharmacol.,* 27, 880, 1975.
79. **Markus, H. B. and Ball, E. G.,** Inhibition of lipolytic processes in rat adipose tissue by antimalaria drugs, *Biochim. Biophys. Acta,* 187, 486, 1969.
80. **Scherphof, G. L., Scarpa, A., and Van Toorenenbergen, A.,** The effect of local anesthetics on the hydrolysis of free and membrane-bound phospholipids catalyzed by various phospholipases, *Biochim. Biophys. Acta,* 270, 226, 1972.

81. **Dise, C. A., Burch, J. W., and Goodman, D. B. P.,** Direct interaction of mepacrine with erythrocyte and platelet membrane phospholipid, *J. Biol. Chem.*, 257, 4701, 1982.
82. **Mori, T., Takai, Y., Minakuchi, R., Yu, B., and Nishizuka, Y.,** Inhibitory action of chlorpromazine, dibucaine, and other phospholipid-interacting drugs on calcium-activated, phospholipid-dependent protein kinase, *J. Biol. Chem.*, 255, 8378, 1980.
83. **Frye, L. D. and Friou, G. J.,** Inhibition of mammalian cytotoxic cells by phosphatidylcholine and its analogue, *Nature (London)*, 258, 333, 1975.
84. **Chandrakumar, N. S., Boyd, V. L., and Hajdu, J.,** Synthesis of enzyme-inhibitory phospholipid analogs. III. A facile synthesis of N-acylaminoethylphosphorylcholines, *Biochim. Biophys. Acta*, 711, 357, 1982.
85. **McGiveney, A., Morita, Y., Crews, F. T., Hirata, F., Axelrod, J., and Siraganian, R. P.,** Phospholipase activation in the IgE-mediated and $Ca^{2+}$ inophore A23187-induced release of histamine from rat basophilic leukemia cells, *Arch. Biochem. Biophys.*, 212, 572, 1981.
86. **Sutherland, C. A. and Amin, D.,** Relative activities of rat and dog platelet phospholipase $A_2$ and diglyceride lipase. Selective inhibition of diglyceride lipase by RHC 80267, *J. Biol. Chem.*, 257, 14006, 1982.
87. **Miller, J. J.,** Oncodazole (R17934) an inhibitor of the turnover of phosphatidylinositol in concanavalin A induced lymphocytes, *Biochem. Pharmacol.*, 28, 2967, 1979.
88. **Takai, Y., Minakuchi, R., Kikkawa, U., Sano, K., Kaibuchi, K., Yu, B., Matsubara T., and Nishizuka, Y.,** Membrane phospholipid turnover, receptor function and protein phosphorylation, *Prog. Brain Res.*, 56, 287, 1982.
89. **Van den Bosch, H.,** Intracellular phospholipases A, *Biochim. Biophys. Acta*, 604, 191, 1980.
90. **DiRosa, M., Flower, R. J., Hirata, F., Parente, F., and Russo-Marie, F.,** Anti-phospholipase proteins, *Prostaglandins*, 28, 441, 1984.
91. **Niwa, Y., Kano, T., Taniguchi, S., Miyachi, Y., and Sakane, T.,** Effect of cyclosporin A on the membrane-associated events in human leucocytes with special reference to the similarity with dexamethasone, *Biochem. Pharmacol.*, 35, 947, 1986.
92. **Fan, T. P. D. and Lewis, G. P.,** Mechanism of cyclosporin A-induced inhibition of prostacyclin synthesis by macrophages, *Prostaglandins*, 30, 735, 1985.
93. **Bomalaski, J. S., Hirata, F., and Clark, M. A.,** Aspirin inhibits phospholipase C, *Biochem. Biophys. Res. Commun.*, 139, 115, 1986.
94. **Glenney, J. R., Tack, B., and Powell, M. A.,** Calpactins: two distinct $Ca^{2+}$-regulated phospholipid- and actin-binding proteins isolated from lung and placenta, *J. Cell Biol.*, 104, 503, 1987.
95. **Notsu, Y., Namiuchi, S., Hattori, T., Matsuda, K., and Hirata, F.,** Inhibition of phospholipases by Met-Leu-Phe-Ile-Leu-Ile-Lys-Arg-Ser-Arg-His-Phe, C terminus of middle-sized tumor antigen, *Arch. Biochem. Biophys.*, 236, 195, 1985.
96. **Hirata, F.,** Unpublished data.

# CYCLOOXYGENASE INHIBITORS

**Peter H. Nelson**

## INTRODUCTION

A search of *Chemical Abstracts,* conducted in mid 1986, produced over 2600 references to cyclooxygenase inhibition. The number of citations rose from less than ten per year up to 1972, to more than 400 in 1985. Although recent research in eicosanoid biosynthesis has been directed more towards lipoxygenase products, there remains considerable interest in the cyclooxygenase pathway. The pharmaceutical industry, which in the 1970s developed a large number of cyclooxygenase inhibitors for the treatment of chronic inflammatory diseases and pain, has in recent years sought, so far with limited success, agents which would reverse, rather than retard, the tissue destruction and loss of joint function which accompanies rheumatoid arthritis. Until more effective agents are developed, the nonsteroidal anti-inflammatory drugs, most of which are believed to act through inhibition of cyclooxygenase, will remain among the most important classes of drugs in use today.

The conversion of certain polyunsaturated 20-carbon fatty acids into prostaglandins was first demonstrated in 1964.[1-3] Since then, a network of biosynthetic pathways, dependent on the addition of two molecules of oxygen to the substrates, has been elucidated.[4] The detection, in 1969, of prostaglandins in inflammatory exudates,[5] and the observation that agents such as aspirin and indomethacin inhibited the production of prostaglandins eventually showed that this property was responsible for the observed biological effects of these compounds. These include inhibition of inflammation, pain, and pyrexia, and the inhibition of platelet aggregation.[6-8,8A] The involvement of prostaglandins in fever had been demonstrated by the production of hyperthermia following the injection of prostaglandins $E_1$ and $E_2$ into cat brains.[9] In 1974, the demonstration of a lipoxygenase enzyme in mammalian tissue[10] led to the discovery of the competing leukotriene pathway of arachidonic acid metabolism, derived from initial hydroperoxidation at C-5 and C-12.[11]

This review is concerned with compounds which inhibit the first part of the arachidonic acid cascade, shown in Scheme 1. Sequential addition of two molecules of oxygen leads to the formation of $PGG_2$, and reduction or rearrangement of the hydroperoxide produces $PGH_2$, the precursor to prostaglandins E and F, thromboxanes, and prostacyclins. These initial steps are performed by the microsomal enzyme complex termed cyclooxygenase (prostaglandin synthetase, prostaglandin-H synthase). The literature has been surveyed up to mid 1986 to produce a compilation of structures of compounds which have been reported to inhibit cyclooxygenase at physiologically relevant concentrations. Compounds which inhibit both cyclooxygenase and lipoxygenase at comparable concentrations have been excluded, and are the subject of the chapter by J. Pfister in this volume of the handbook. Several comprehensive reviews of the cyclooxygenase pathway, compounds which inhibit it, and the biological consequences thereof, have been published previously.[4,12-16]

## CYCLOOXYGENASE

### Distribution

The enzyme complex cyclooxygenase has been found in the microsomal fraction of virtually all mammalian tissues, and in tissues of many nonmammals.[17-19] The purified enzyme from several sources has been found to have a molecular weight of about 70,000 Da (see the chapter by R. J. Kulmacz in Volume IA) though both antibody-binding studies[20,21] and *in vitro* inhibition of enzyme (and/or the microsomal membranes with which the enzymes

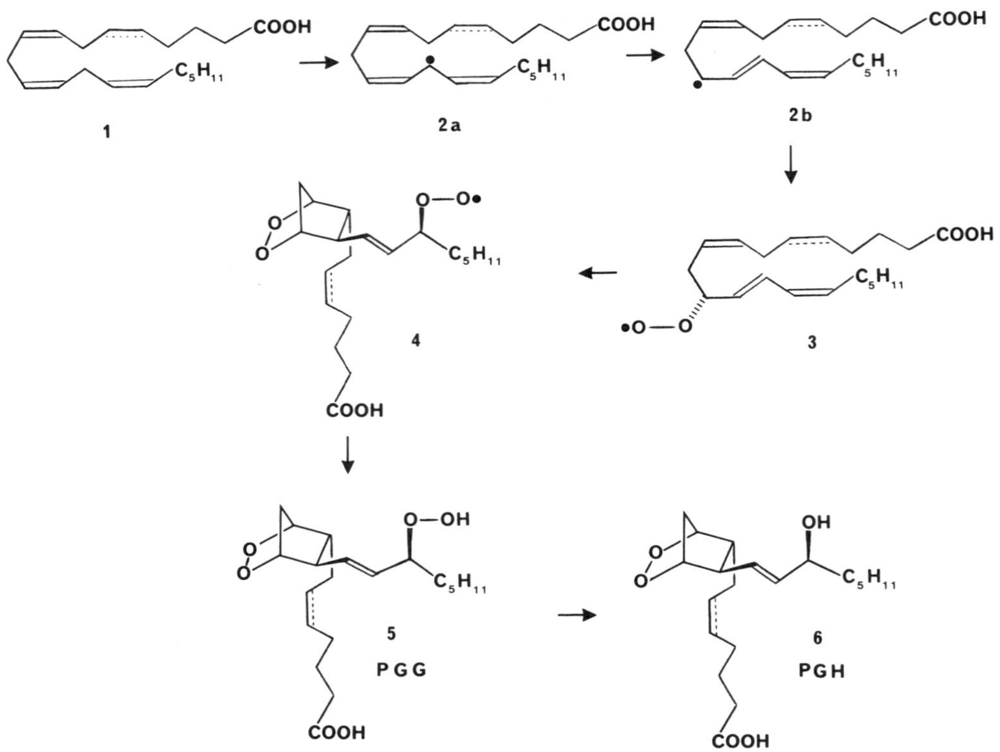


SCHEME 1

are associated) from different sources (see the section on variations in inhibitory potencies among tissues of this review) suggest that significant differences exist among enzymes from different sources. The absence of cytochrome $P_{450}$ in seminal vesicles,[22] one of the tissues in which cyclooxygenase is most abundant, suggests that $P_{450}$ is not required for prostaglandin biosynthesis.

The amount of substrate (arachidonic acid, dihomo-γ-linolenic acid, etc.) which can be transformed into prostaglandins by a given amount of tissue varies with the nature of the tissue. Whether this variation is due to differences in the amount of activity of cyclooxygenase present, or to the amount of endogenous substrate, or to tissue-to-tissue variations in the rate of self-inactivation of the enzyme, has not been determined. Seminal vesicles, kidney, and lung have the highest capacity for prostaglandin synthesis[23] and have been employed most often for studies of mechanism and inhibition.

## Function of Cyclooxygenase

Prostaglandins are not stored in tissues;[24] prostaglandins E and F, though relatively abundant in inflamed tissue, are normally only present at low concentrations. However, any stimulation of cells (mechanical, chemical, electrical) initiates the sequence of reactions shown in Figure 1, and levels of the more stable E and F prostaglandins are increased. The latter compounds, though themselves rapidly metabolized,[25] are considerably more persistent than the endoperoxides $PGG_2$ and $PGH_2$, for which half-lives under physiological conditions of 4 and 3.5 min, respectively, have been determined.[26]

The compounds are synthesized from arachidonic acid, the major unsaturated fatty acid of cell-membrane phospholipids. The acid is usually released from the phospholipids by the action of phospholipase $A_2$.[27-29] The initial step in the cyclooxygenase pathway is the ster-

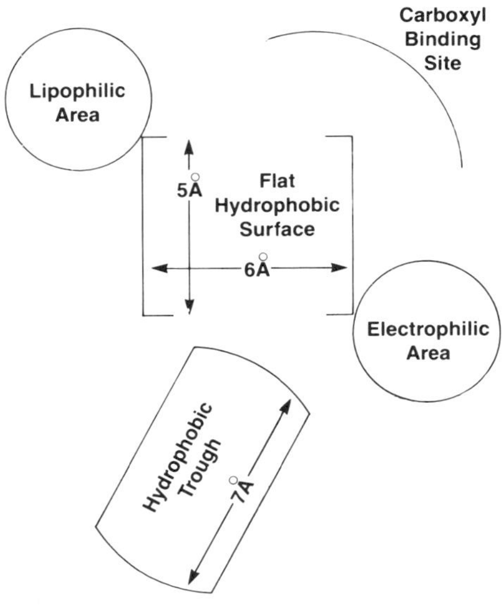


FIGURE 1

eospecific removal of the 13 (R) hydrogen[30,31] and oxygen is then added to C-11 of the allylic radical *2* to produce the hydroperoxy radical *3*, which is also the product of reaction of arachidonic acid with soybean lipoxygenase.[32] Cyclization and addition of a second oxygen molecule to C-15, then produces the endoperoxide peroxy radical *4*, which by addition of a hydrogen atom yields PGG, the endoperoxide *(5)*.[33] Biosynthetic studies using doubly labeled oxygen show that the oxygens at 9 and 11 both originate from the same oxygen molecule.[34-36] Reduction or rearrangement of *5*, mediated by the peroxidase component of cyclooxygenase produces $PGH_1$ or $PGH_2$, which are subsequently transformed into prostaglandins of the D, E, and F series (see the chapter by K. J. Kulmacz in Volume IA) or to 12-hydroxyheptadeca-5,8,10-trienoic acid (''HHT''; HHTrE) and malondialdehyde (MDA). The latter products can be formed by degradation of isolated $PGH_2$, in the absence of enzymes[37] or concurrently with the synthesis of thromboxane $A_2$, catalyzed by thromboxane synthetase.[38,39] Cyclooxygenase has a limited ability to convert arachidonic acid, possibly because it is inactivated by the uncharacterized active-oxygen species which is produced in the conversion of $PGG_2$ to $PGH_2$.[40]

Column chromatography, using DEAE-cellulose, of the detergent-solubilized microsomal fraction from bovine seminal vesicles, led to the separation of the enzyme into twofractions. Fraction 1, after a 700-fold purification by isoelectric focusing, converted eicosa-8,11,14-trienoic acid into $PGG_1$ in the presence of hematin as a cofactor, and in the presence of hemoglobin and tryptophan, $PGG_1$ was converted into $PGH_1$. The conversion of the substrate to $PGG_1$ but not the conversion of $PGG_1$ to $PGH_1$, was inhibited by indomethacin and aspirin. Fraction 2, in the presence of glutathione, catalyzed the conversion of $PGH_1$ to $PGE_1$, and this transformation was not inhibited by indomethacin or aspirin. Thus, Fraction 1 exhibited two activities, a cyclooxygenase transformation which was sensitive to cyclooxygenase inhibitors, and a peroxidase activity which was not similarly inhibited. Fraction 2, also not inhibited by cyclooxygenase inhibitors, performed the isomerase function in converting $PGH_1$ to $PGE_1$.[41,42] There are separate enzymes for production of D, E, and F-type prostaglandins from endoperoxides,[43,43A,45] with considerable variation in their activities among different tissues.[44-47]

## BIOLOGICAL PROPERTIES

### *In Vivo* Effects

The biological activity of the large group of anti-inflammatory agents known as nonsteroidal anti-inflammatory drugs (NSAID) or prostaglandin synthetase inhibitors (PSI)[48] can in large part be explained by their inhibition of the conversion of arachidonic acid into prostanoids.[49] Although several of these agents possess other biological activities which might contribute to their anti-inflammatory activity, such properties are usually demonstrable at considerably higher concentrations than are necessary for the reduction of prostaglandin biosynthesis.[50,51] Compound-to-compound variations in absorption, distribution, metabolism, and excretion, and differing inhibitory potencies against cyclooxygenase from different target tissues result in poor *in vitro-in vivo* correlation for some agents, and there are several groups of compounds (see section on compounds which inhibit cyclooxygenase) which despite being active *in vitro,* simply do not exhibit any of the *in vivo* effects which would be expected of prostaglandin synthesis inhibitors. Paradoxically, salicylic acid, a prototypical *in vivo* inhibitor of prostaglandin biosynthesis, is an extremely weak inhibitor *in vitro* (see section on salicylates and References 68 and 98). The beneficial anti-inflammatory, analgesic, and antipyretic effects, as well as the undesirable gastrointestinal toxicity exhibited at least by the large group of acidic cyclooxygenase inhibitors, can clearly be related to the reduced production of prostanoids. Inhibition of the enzyme derived from target tissues — for example, from synovial tissue, the location of some of the beneficial effects, and from gastric mucosal tissue, site of gastric ulceration, provide predictors of both activity and toxicity (see section on relationship between *in vivo* and *in vitro* potencies). The side effect of gastrointestinal ulceration may be due to the decrease in PGE and prostacyclin synthesis, resulting in vasoconstriction, decrease in blood supply to the gastric mucosa, local ischemia, necrosis, and ulceration.[14,52] The utilization of nonsteroidal anti-inflammatory agents to delay parturition, to retard the closure of the patent ductus arteriosus, and in the treatment of Bartter's syndrome[53-55] are also attributable to their inhibition of cyclooxygenase. The efficacy of these agents in the treatment of dysmenorrhea is also believed to result from the reduction in the high levels of $PGF_{2\alpha}$ which have been demonstrated in the menstrual fluid of dysmenorrheic women.[56]

There are indications that cyclooxygenase inhibitors may be of value in the treatment of certain neoplasms. Some tumors produce large amounts of prostaglandins and a number of prostaglandin synthesis inhibitors have been found to reduce both tumor size and metastatic potential.[57,58] The reduction in tumor size, and the observed success of combined therapy with antineoplastic agents and prostaglandin synthesis inhibitors in animal studies[59] may be due to a reduction in the level of cytoprotective prostaglandins, allowing the host immune response to attack the tumor.[60] The reduction in metastasis may be associated with inhibition of platelet aggregation, since metastasis has been hypothesized to occur through the adherence of tumor cells to platelets.[15] Decreased release of highly reactive arachidonic acid metabolites such as malondialdehyde, which can covalently bind to DNA, may also be relevant.[61]

The hypothesis that cyclooxygenase inhibition in tissues in which phospholipase-mediated release of arachidonic acid is occurring (inflamed or otherwise disturbed tissues) would lead to an increase in the products of the lipoxygenase pathway[62,63] has been verified experimentally, though serious clinical sequelae are rare. Indomethacin and three other anti-inflammatory agents were shown to increase slow-reacting substance of anaphylaxis (SRS-A) release from human lung.[64] In the same study, ketoprofen inhibited SRS-A release, an observation that remains unexplained. Some cyclooxygenase inhibitors cause increases in the production of the chemoattractant $LTB_4$, an effect which could promote increased leukocyte chemotaxis to a site of inflammation,[65] where they are known to be a significant locus of prostaglandin synthesis.[66]

### Mechanism of *In Vivo* Activities

The postulate that the products of cyclooxygenase-mediated metabolism of arachidonic acid are among the principal agents which cause and maintain inflammation has been reviewed exhaustively by a number of authors[49,67-69] and will not be discussed in detail in the present work. Elevated levels of prostaglandins are present in the synovial fluid of patients with rheumatoid arthritis,[70,71] in dogs,[72] and horses[73,74] during acute inflammation, and in the cerebrospinal fluid of pyrexic patients; in the latter case, administration of a prostaglandin-synthesis inhibitor causes a reduction in both prostaglandin levels and fever. Prostaglandins cause bone resorption,[75,76] potentiate the action of pro-inflammatory factors such as bradykinin,[77-80] and are pyrogenic.[80] Although they do not produce pain and inflammation at physiological concentrations, E prostaglandins are hyperalgesic at such levels, potentiating the response to nociceptive challenges.[81-83]

### Relationship between *In Vivo* and *In Vitro* Potencies

There are so many variables in the measurement of both *in vivo* and *in vitro* potencies of prostaglandin synthesis inhibitors, that the absence of linear correlations is not surprising. Measurements of *in vitro* inhibitory potencies are affected by the source of the enzyme, the substrate concentration, preincubation time, and other variables. Unless a series of compounds was examined under identical assay conditions, comparison of potencies is of doubtful validity. *In vivo* potencies are, if anything, subject to greater variability, even if attention is directed to just one anti-inflammatory, analgesic, or antipyretic assay, in which a series of compounds are examined under identical conditions. The rate and extent of absorption of the test agent (parameters which are usually only known for those agents which have progressed to clinical evaluation) are of a critical importance. Many acidic prostaglandin-synthesis inhibitors are highly bound to plasma proteins;[84] for example, meclofenamic acid to the extent of 99.8%,[85] whereas paracetamol is only 25% protein bound.[86,87] For many pharmacological agents, a high degree of protein binding would be disadvantageous, but since the microvasculature in inflamed tissue is permeable to protein, highly bound compounds could be selectively concentrated at inflammatory sites, an effect which could not only explain the high degree of efficacy of acidic compounds, but also the absence of correlations between *in vivo* and *in vitro* activities.[50,88,89] Other pharmacokinetic parameters such as lipophilicity, transport across membranes, and varying rates of metabolic inactivation and excretion combine to mitigate against precise correspondence of *in vitro* and *in vivo* potencies.

Despite the foregoing, a correlation has been demonstrated between *in vitro* inhibitory potencies in a dog-spleen assay and the *in vivo* plasma levels required for therapeutic efficacy[90] and statistically significant correlations have been found between *in vitro* inhibitory potencies and anti-inflammatory and antipyretic activity for some clinically used acidic anti-inflammatory agents.[91] Correlations have been found to be better for acidic than for nonacidic compounds; gastrointestinal and renal side-effects are more pronounced for acidic agents despite the fact that the toxicity is supposedly related to the inhibition of prostaglandin biosynthesis.[92] The accumulation of acidic, but not nonacidic compounds in parietal cells, an effect which could cause a higher degree of inhibition of prostaglandin synthesis in the gastric mucosa than in other tissues, may be responsible for the gastrointestinal side effects of this class of compounds.[93] The side effects of indomethacin in animals and in man can be reduced by coadministration of a stable $PGE_2$ analogue.[94] Aspirin and salicylic acid have similar *in vivo* potencies, but aspirin is considerably more potent an inhibitor *in vitro*[8] and benoxaprofen, though a weak inhibitor *in vitro,* causes a significant decrease in prostaglandin levels in inflammatory exudates.[95,96] This discrepancy could be related to the antichemotactic effect of benoxaprofen,[97] in view of the importance of migrating leukocytes as a source of prostaglandins.[65] Several groups of compounds exist which, although potent inhibitors of prostaglandin synthesis *in vitro,* show no anti-inflammatory effects, and do not reduce prostaglandin levels *in vivo* (see section on compounds which inhibit cyclooxygenase).

**Variations in Inhibitory Potencies among Different Tissues**

Despite the experimental variables which result in widely differing inhibitory potencies even for the same compound assayed against an enzyme from the same source, many examples of real differences in inhibitory potencies between tissues have been demonstrated, and in some cases the differences have been related to clinical effects and side effects of the compounds concerned. Thus, paracetamol was found to be ten times as potent an inhibitor of kidney and brain cyclooxygenase compared to spleen enzyme; the selectivity could account for the antipyretic and nephrotoxic properties of the compound, and the absence of anti-inflammatory effects.[68,98,99]

Aspirin is a more potent inhibitor of platelet cyclooxygenase than for the enzyme in vascular endothelial cells;[100] in addition, the effects of aspirin on platelets are cumulative and irreversible, whereas the endothelial-cell cyclooxygenase regenerates rapidly.[304,305] $IC_{50}$ values of 29 $\mu M$ and 172 $\mu M$ for platelet and synovial enzyme (compared to values of 1.33 and 1.08 $\mu M$ for indomethacin) have also been reported. The greater potency in inhibiting the platelet enzyme (especially in view of the inability of platelets to resynthesize cyclooxygenase) may explain the more prolonged and pronounced *in vivo* effects of aspirin on platelet function, compared to the anti-inflammatory responses.[101,102] In contrast, aspirin does not inhibit canine myocardial cyclooxygenase at concentrations at which spleen enzyme is inhibited.[103] Aspirin (but not acetaminophen) is similarly ineffective in human cerebral cortex homogenates.[68,304] Inhibitory potencies for indomethacin which vary by more than three orders of magnitude have been reported: rabbit spleen, $IC_{50}$ 0.14 $\mu m$; rabbit retina, 156 $\mu M$;[104] human synovial cells, 0.003 $\mu M$[105] (though it should be noted that $IC_{50}$ values for indomethacin for bovine-seminal-vesicle cyclooxygenase by 11 investigators varied from 0.07 $\mu M$ to 20 $\mu M$[13]).

It has been suggested that inhibitory potency against synovial cyclooxygenase should be more predictive of clinical efficacy in inflammatory joint disease. Only small differences were found between the inhibition of this enzyme compared to that from other sources for indomethacin and flurbiprofen,[106] but in another study, indomethacin, flurbiprofen, diclofenac, and sulindac sulphide were found to be two to ten times as potent as inhibitors of the synovial compared to the bovine-seminal-vesicle enzyme.[107]

Although clinically used cyclooxygenase inhibitors are neither immunosuppressants nor immunostimulants, their efficacy in rheumatoid arthritis, an autoimmune disease, coupled with the diverse effects of prostaglandins on the immune system,[15] may indicate that the anti-inflammatory properties are at least partly the result of prostaglandin-mediated immunomodulation. Assessment of the immunological effects of the inhibition of prostaglandin synthesis is complicated not only by the possibility of concomitant increase in lipoxygenase-pathway products but also by the fact that cyclooxygenase inhibitors have other biological properties which may affect the immune response. For example, inhibition of prostaglandin 15-dehydrogenase,[108] phosphodiesterase,[109] and of cyclic-AMP protein kinase,[110] properties displayed by some cyclooxygenase inhibitors, albeit at higher concentrations than required for the inhibition of prostaglandin biosynthesis, may also be relevant to the immunological effects of these agents (see also chapter by Smith, Stone, and Willis in Volume IA).

The proliferative response of lymphocytes to mitogens is inhibited by PGE,[111-117] but antibody production to sheep red blood cells could be either increased or decreased, depending on the time of administration.[118] Paradoxically, several of the activities of macrophages, such as phagocytosis,[119,120] lysosomal enzyme release,[121] and chemotaxis,[122] are inhibited by prostaglandins, despite the fact that macrophages produce large amounts of PGE.[15]

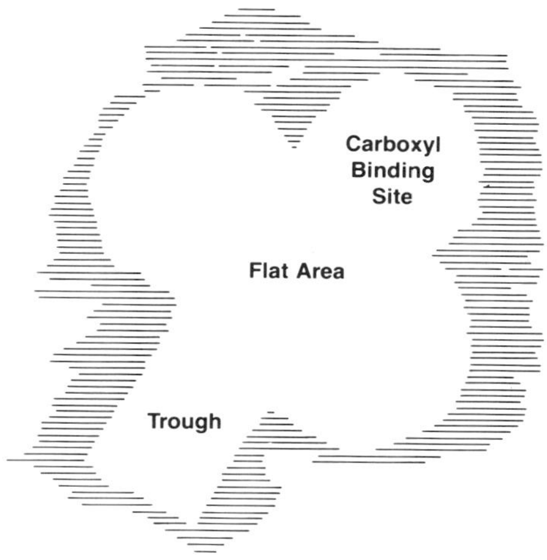


FIGURE 2

## MODELS OF THE CYCLOOXYGENASE ACTIVE SITE

A number of hypotheses have been advanced, based originally on *in vivo* structure-activity relationships, concerning the size and shape of the receptor site with which nonsteroidal anti-inflammatory agents interact in order to evoke their biological activities. The proposal of Shen in 1964,[123] upon which Figure 1 is based, was derived from the biological activities and conformations of a number of analogues of indomethacin. Ultraviolet, nuclear magnetic resonance, and X-ray crystallographic data were used to obtain information on the conformations of the compounds. The studies showed that, for compounds to be active, a second aromatic ring, usually linked to the arylacetic acid moiety by means of a carbonyl group, must be considerably out of the plane of the ring bearing the acidic function. The approximate maximum allowable sizes of these groups are indicated on Figure 1. The hydrophobic trough was postulated to accept the p-chlorophenyl group of indomethacin. A similar, though less-detailed, model was proposed in 1964 by Scherrer et al.,[124] and was designed to accommodate not only indomethacin-type compounds but also compounds of the phenylbutazone and fenamic acid series. In each case one of the aromatic rings was hypothesized to be accommodated in a liphophilic trough, separated from a binding site for an acidic moiety by a flat surface. The complete binding site is depicted schematically in Figure 2. Subsequently, indomethacin isosteres such as sulindac sulfide (Table 5, Compound 39) which, like indomethacin itself had been shown to exist preferably in a *cis* configuration,[125] reinforced the validity of these empirically derived active-site models.[126] Structure-activity relationships are discussed further in the next section.

The discovery of the effect of aspirin on prostaglandin biosynthesis and delineation of the cyclooxygenase-mediated arachidonic-acid cascade (especially isolation of the unstable endoperoxide) resulted in a number of proposals for the conformation of the substrates at the active site. Ways were also proposed by which cyclooxygenase inhibitors might mimic unstable intermediates and so effect inhibition. In 1977 Shen and Gund[127] proposed a curled, but approximately planar, orientation for arachidonic acid at the active site. The orientation brought carbons 8 and 12, which are joined in PGG, into reasonable proximity, and rationalized the stereospecificity of the transformation into endoperoxides. The model was also used to explain why, depending on the positions of the double bonds, various unsaturated fatty acids were, or were not, cyclooxygenase substrates. Indomethacin-like inhibitors were hypothesized to bind to the site such that the carboxyl group occupied the same position as

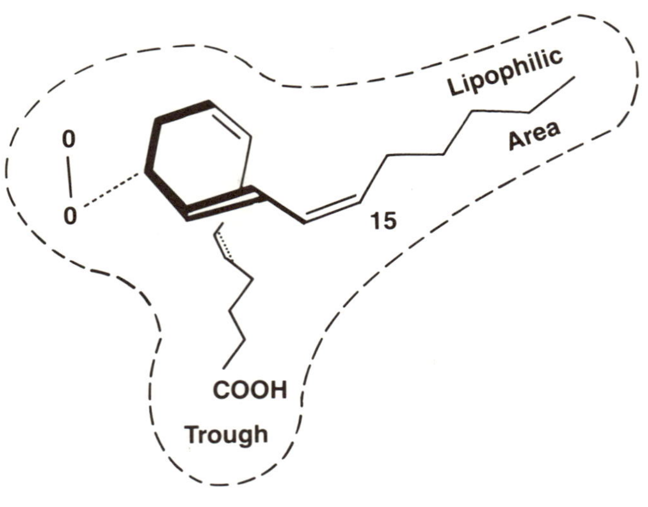


FIGURE 3

the substrate carboxyl. A later hypothesis by Appleton and Brown[128] proposed a helical conformation for the intermediate peroxy radical (Scheme 1,*3*) at the active site. Their model, which is similar to that shown in Figure 3, accommodates the carboxyl terminal of the substrate in a trough analogous to those present in Figures 1 and 2. In contrast to earlier hypotheses, however, inhibition of cyclooxygenase by arylacetic acids was proposed to occur by binding of the carboxyl group of the inhibitor to the active site in the region of the peroxy radical in Figure 3. The remainder of the inhibitor molecule was accommodated in a lipophilic region of the active site which under normal circumstances was occupied by the hydrocarbon tail of the substrate. The pronounced increase in inhibitory potency caused by introduction of a chlorine substituent into a cyclohexyl-substituted indanecarboxylic acid (Table 5, Compounds 20 and 21) was hypothesized to be due to the proximity of the introduced chlorine to C-15 of the substrate, a site which must be accessible to the enzyme in order for oxygenation to occur. The model shown in Figure 3 accommodated a variety of arylacetic- and arylpropionic-acid cyclooxygenase inhibitors in similar orientations.

Based on the crystal structure of 4-O-methylcryptochlorophaeic acid (Table 11, Compound 1), a lichen-derived compound which is a potent inhibitor of cyclooxygenase, Sankawa et al.,[129] proposed a different orientation for both arylacetic acid and fenamic acid inhibitors at the active site. Their model is based on a conformation of the substrate at the active site similar to that shown in Figure 4. This conformation, whose depiction in two dimensions is not easy, is designed to mimic the conformation of 4-O-methylcryptochlorophaeic acid such that the carboxyl terminal occupies the region of the lower left pentyl group (Table 11, Compound 1) and the area at carbon 15 coincides with the position of the carboxyl group. Inhibition is proposed to occur by prevention of oxygenation at 15, rather than by prevention of oxygenation at 11 as in the Appleton-Brown model. The region near carbons 7 to 10 of the substrate was categorized as a $\pi$-electron-acceptor region, which would accommodate the second benzene ring of the depside. The authors proposed that non-depside cyclooxygenase inhibitors could be accommodated in the receptor site in an analogous fashion, turned 180° from their proposed orientation in the Appleton-Brown model. The placing of the carboxyl terminal of the substrate in a trough below the relatively planar region is common to both models. In this orientation, the C-5 double bond is not accessible, and, in accordance with experimental observations, its presence is not required for compounds to be cyclooxygenase substrates.

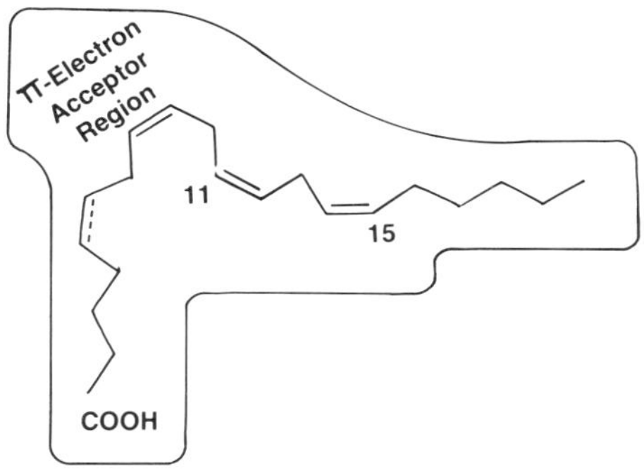


FIGURE 4

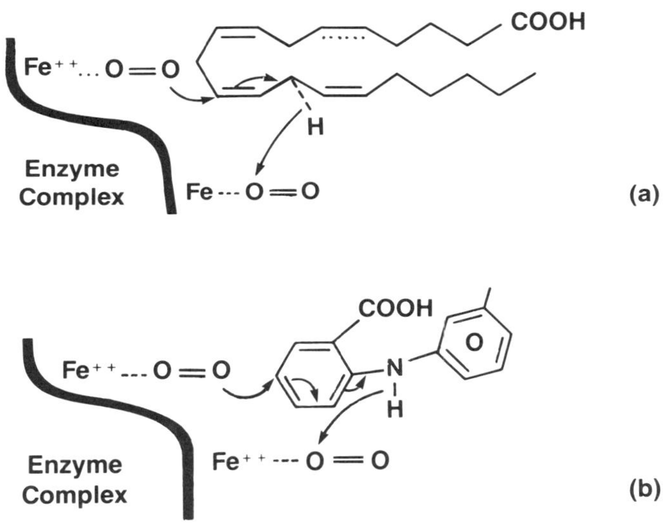


FIGURE 5

In addition to the above-described attempts to relate the structure and conformation of the substrates and their transformation products to those of cyclooxygenase inhibitors, a number of hypotheses have been proposed[130-132] for the mechanism of the oxygenation reactions, especially insofar as they involve the iron protoporphyrin IX which is a cofactor.[133,134] An early proposal by Cushman and Cheung,[135] which is shown, somewhat modified in Figure 5a proposed the stereospecific transfer of the C-13 H to haem-bound oxygen, and concomitant addition of a second bound-oxygen molecule to C-11. Subsequent cyclization of the second oxygen molecule to C-9, and oxygenation, using the first oxygen molecule, at C-15, then yielded $PGG_2$. Using this model, the inhibition of cyclooxygenase by fenamic acids, illustrated in Figure 5b, was proposed to occur by removal of the hydrogen bound to the fenamate nitrogen, and concomitant attack of the second oxygen molecule at the para position of the fenamic acid benzene ring. According to this model, the diphenylamine moiety is the minimum structure required for cyclooxygenase inhibitors in the fenamic acid series, and diphenylamine is indeed a weak inhibitor.[135] The carboxyl group and other substituents were hypothesized to optimize inhibitory potency by altering the redox potential of the diphenylamine nucleus, and by conferring appropriate physico-chemical and pharmacokinetic[136] properties on the molecule.

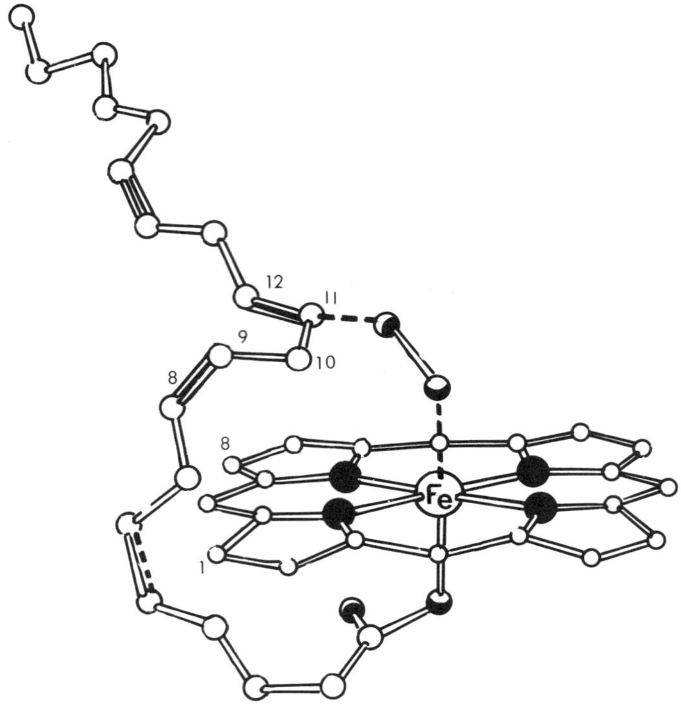


FIGURE 6

Following a number of chemical studies in which it was shown that arachidonic acid could be oxidized in the presence of $Fe^{++}$ and oxygen, and that the oxidation could be prevented by cyclooxygenase inhibitors, Peterson et al. proposed a model for the interaction between arachidonic acid and protoporphyrin IX.[130] They hypothesized that the substrate was bound via the carboxyl terminus to one side of the protoporphyrin IX (see Figure 6) and that the molecule was curled around the porphyrin ring such that carbon 11 was sufficiently close to an oxygen atom bound to the central Fe for hydrogen transfer to occur. Molecular models indicated that the proposed orientation of the three molecules was feasible; carbons 3 to 7 of the substrate were accommodated in a hydrophobic "groove" between carbons 1 and 8 of the porphyrin, an orientation which is consistent with the unimportance of the 5,6 double bond for cyclooxygenase substrates. The observed stereochemistry of hydrogen abstraction and endoperoxide formation was also rationalized by this model. Some aspects of this model (for example, the behavior of arachidonic acid in the presence of protoporphyrin IX and oxygen) are susceptible to experimental investigation.

A more detailed hypothesis for the mechanisms of the cyclooxygenase reaction, and in particular for the role of the four porphyrin-coordinated iron atoms present in each dimeric unit of the enzyme,[133,134] has recently been advanced by Corey[132] (Scheme 2). It is proposed that two of the four haem units are involved in the conversion of a suitable substrate to PGH. The "resting" enzyme, in which all iron is in the ferrous state, is activated by a hydroperoxide (for example $PGG_2$) such that one iron ($Fe_2$ in A) is oxidized to the Fe(IV) state (or Fe(III)-porphyrin radical cation). After introduction of arachidonic acid, (as in B) stereospecific removal of the 13-H, and antarafacial addition of oxygen,[30] bound to an appropriately situated Fe(II) ($Fe_1$ in A), would produce the $C_{11}$ hydroperoxy radical C. Cyclization of C leads to the endoperoxide allylic radical D. Rotation of the planar allylic radical about 12-13 bond would allow it to form a $\sigma$-bond to $Fe_1$, to produce the 15 (S)

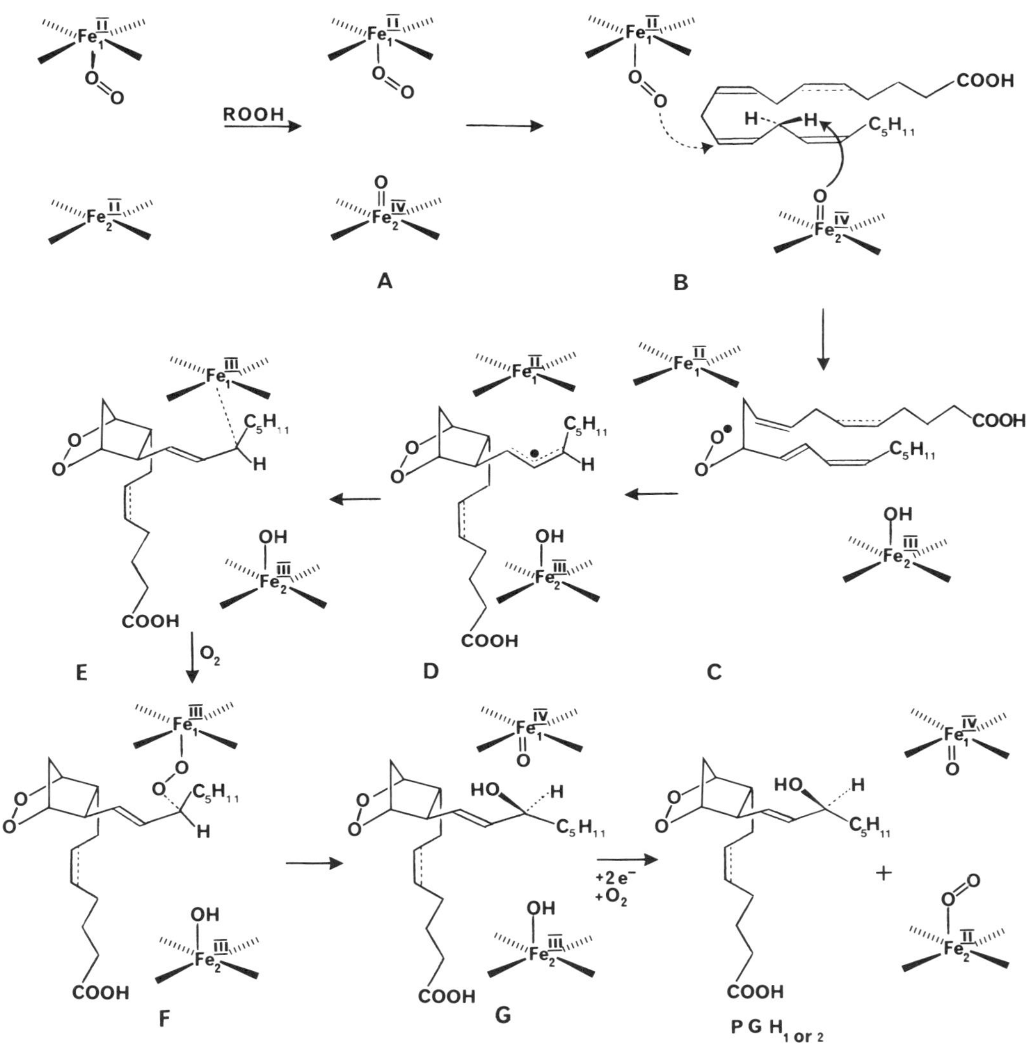


SCHEME 2

product E. Rotation of the allylic radical to give (S) absolute stereochemistry, rather than the (R) configuration in which the C-15 substituents R (the pentyl group) and H are interchanged, is presumably favored by the geometry of the active site. The second oxygen molecule would then be introduced as in F, and cleavage of the 15-peroxy group results in the formation of $PGH_2$ and oxidation of $Fe_1$ to the oxyferryl state. The transformation of F to G thus is a model for the peroxidase component of cyclooxygenase, not inhibitable by typical cyclooxygenase inhibitors (see earlier section on function of cyclooxygenase). The catalytic cycle is then completed by one-electron reductions of $Fe_1$ and $Fe_2$; coordination of oxygen to $Fe_2$ then restores the enzyme to the original activated state A, assuming that $Fe_1$ and $Fe_2$ occupy equivalent sites. If $Fe_1$ and $Fe_2$ are equivalent, then they are likely to be in different subunits of the cyclooxygenase dimer. The activated form A, derived from G, could transform a second molecule of substrate in a cycle which, after initial activation by PGG or a non-PG hydroperoxide, is catalytic and self-sustaining in the presence of oxygen. The initial activation of the enzyme presumably occurs subsequent to a disturbance of cellular integrity, an event which is known to produce a burst of prostaglandin synthesis (see earlier section). Tissue damage also produces activated-oxygen species such as superoxide which could be responsible for the initial activation of the enzyme, prior to the production of PGG. The Corey proposal may well stimulate further research into the detailed mechanism of the cyclooxygenase reaction, a subject which has received little attention since discovery of the lipoxygenase pathways, but which may be crucial to understanding the biosynthesis of prostaglandins.

## COMPOUNDS WHICH INHIBIT CYCLOOXYGENASE

### Introduction

Tables 1 to 15 contain the *Chemical Abstracts* numbers, structures, names, etc. and inhibitory potencies of ca. 170 compounds which have been reported to inhibit cyclooxygenase, and which, so far as is known, do not inhibit lipoxygenase at comparable concentrations. The compounds are classified according to their structural types, and within tables, closely similar compounds have been placed adjacent to each other if possible. The tables contain only a fraction of the total number of compounds which have been reported to be inhibitors of cyclooxygenase, but those selected are intended to include representatives of all the major chemical classes.

### Unsaturated Fatty Acids*

Unsaturated fatty acids related to the natural cyclooxygenase substrates arachidonic and dihomo-γ-linolenic acids, were among the first compounds to be examined for inhibitory potential. Not surprisingly, a number of compounds were found to be competitive, reversible inhibitors, and some of these also proved to be substrates for cyclooxygenase, and were converted into prostaglandins. Whether or not a compound is substrate for cyclooxygenase does not appear to be determined by whether it occurs naturally. Thus, clupanodonic acid (docosahexaenoic acid, 22:6ω3), a major polyunsaturated acid of fish lipids, is not converted into dihomo-prostaglandins, since it is not a substrate for cyclooxygenase. Indeed it inhibits cyclooxygenase.[224] By contrast, adrenic acid (22:4ω6), which is found in the adrenal cortex cholesteryl esters and in the triglycerides of renal lipid droplets of the kidney, *is* converted into dihomo-prostaglandins and thromboxane.[136A,136B] However, adrenic acid has also been shown to inhibit cyclooxygenase conversion of arachidonic acid into prostaglandins.[137]

A number of acetylenic acids have been found to be potent and irreversible inhibitors of cyclooxygenase, although they may also inhibit lipoxygenases. Eicosatetraynoic acid (ETYA; Ro1428; Table 1, Compound 1) inhibits the enzyme immediately and also causes a time-dependent inactivation of the enzyme for which the presence of oxygen is required, though oxygen uptake does not occur. The time-dependent, but not the immediate inhibition, is blocked by α-naphthols,[138-141] an observation which suggests that the inactivation is caused by a chain reaction involving an oxygen free-radical species which can be trapped by the phenolic compound. Compounds with acetylenic groups at positions 9 and 12 are more potent than 5-ynes, an observation consistent with the known positions of modification by cyclooxygenase. Tri- and tetra-acetylenes clearly cannot adapt the bent configurations accessible to the corresponding Z-olefins, configurations which have been invoked to explain both the production of endoperoxides and the ability of a number of anti-inflammatory agents to inhibit cyclooxygenase (see earlier section on models of the cyclooxygenase active site). Apparently the lower binding affinity of the polyacetylenic compounds at the active site is outweighed by the irreversible nature of their inhibition. It has been proposed that the irreversibility is a result of the facile isomerization of one of the acetylenic bonds to an

* See also contributions by A. L. Willis and D. L. Smith in Volume IA.

allene, a highly reactive electrophilic species which could then bond to the enzyme, possibly by addition to the allene of a sulfhydryl group.[32]

Some of the substrate analogues have demonstrated *in vivo* activities attributable to cyclooxygenase inhibition. The trienoic acid (Compound 3) showed no *in vivo* effects, but the 2-methyl analogue (Compound 4), although no more potent as an inhibitor, decreased urinary prostaglandin excretion in the rat for up to 7 d, after s.c. administration of 10 to 100mg/kg.[142] The 2-methyl substituent was introduced in an attempt to decrease β-oxidative degradation of the acid. ETYA (Compound 1) has been found to decrease prostaglandin production in isolated heart and spleen. The failure of similar compounds to cause *in vivo* effects can presumably be attributed to their susceptibility to oxidative breakdown and, in their role as arachidonic acid analogues, to their being incorporated into membrane phospholipids. ETYA does reduce yeast fever and carageenin inflammation in rats.[142A,142B]

## Endoperoxide Analogues: Table 2

A number of stable analogues of cyclic peroxides in the PGG and PGH series have been synthesized, both to determine their biological activities[143-146] and to examine their ability to inhibit cyclooxygenase. All-carbon PGH analogues (Table 2, Compounds 1 to 4) were found to be fairly weak inhibitors. The degree of inhibition was highly concentration dependent, and only Compound 1 showed significant inhibition at 0.1 m*M*. The observation that this compound had no effect on $PGF_{1\alpha}$ production, while $PGE_1$ formation was decreased dose dependently, indicates that the compound has no effect on the reductase which is responsible for formation of PGF.

Recently an oxygen-bridged analogue of $PGH_2$ (Compound 5) has been reported to have potent cyclooxygenase-inhibitory activity against microsomal preparations from platelets, seminal vesicles, and aorta.[147] The analogue also showed *in vivo* activity by oral administration against cyclooxygenase-mediated challenges. For example, the compound protected mice against arachidonic-acid-induced mortality, with an $ED_{50}$ one half that of indomethacin, and also inhibited bronchoconstriction induced by arachidonic acid, but not that induced by histamine or 9,11-azo $PGH_2$. It is likely that the promising biological profile of this compound will stimulate further research in this area.

## Prostaglandins: Table 3

Since the products of cyclooxygenase-mediated transformations of unsaturated fatty acids are endoperoxides rather than prostaglandins, there is, *a priori,* no reason to expect that prostaglandins would have high affinity for the cyclooxygenase-active site. This expectation is borne out by the finding that the more potent analogues (Table 3, Compounds 1, 2, and 3) are noncompetitive inhibitors. The mechanism by which they effect inhibition remains obscure, although since a wide variety of thiols are known to be cyclooxygenase inhibitors,[148] it may be that the inhibition caused by Compounds 1 to 3 owes more to the thiol substituents than to the prostaglandin skeletons to which they are attached. The position of the thiol group was found to have considerable influence on inhibitory potency, with 15-mercapto compounds being the most active. The conversion of $PGG_1$ to $PGH_1$ was not inhibited by these compounds.

Table 3 also contains some compounds whose structures diverge considerably from those of natural prostaglandins, and their description as prostaglandin analogues is debatable. Nevertheless, the hydrazine (compound 6) and the ether (Compound 7) are moderately potent inhibitors. The epoxide (Compound 5), a weak inhibitor, reduced the severity of $PGE_2$-induced diarrhea in the mouse, at subcutaneous doses of 10 to 40 mg/kg, an effect attributed to competitive antagonism.[149]

## Table 1
## UNSATURATED FATTY ACIDS

| Entry no. | Chemical abstracts number[a] | Structure | Chemical name (common name) | Molecular formula | Mol wt | Inhibitory potency[b] | Assay | Comments | Ref. |
|---|---|---|---|---|---|---|---|---|---|
| 1. | 1191-85-1 | 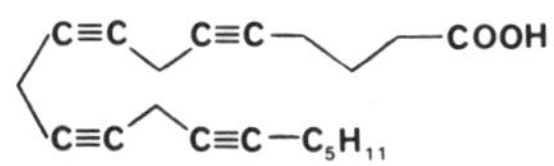 | 5,8,11,14-Eicosatetraenoic acid (ETYA; Rol428) | $C_{20}H_{22}O_2$ | 294 | $K_i$ 2.5 μ*M* | SSV | Irreversible | 140, 219, 220 |
| 2. | | 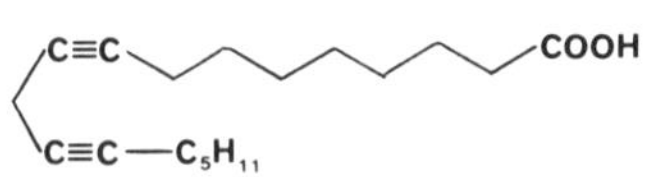 | 9,12-Octadecadiynoic acid | $C_{18}H_{28}O_2$ | 276 | $KI_i$ 0.6 μ*M* | SSV | Irreversible; inhibition increases with preincubation time | 140, 221 |
| 3. | | 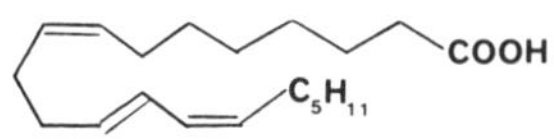 | 8(Z),12(E),14(Z)-Eicosatrienoic acid | $C_{20}H_{34}O_2$ | 306 | 150 μ*M* | BSV | Competitive | 142, 222, 223 |
| 4. | | 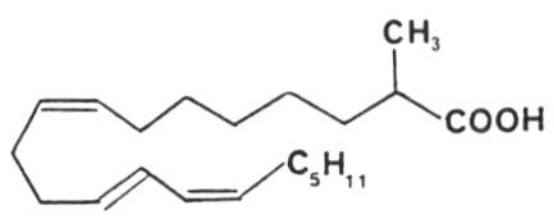 | (±) 2-Methyl-8-(Z),12(E),14(Z) eicosatrienoic acid | $C_{21}H_{36}O_2$ | 320 | 150 μ*M* | BSV | *In vivo* effects, see text | 142, 222 |
| 5. | | 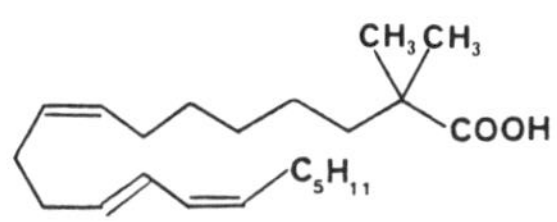 | 2,2-Dimethyl-8(Z)-12(E),14(Z)eicosatrienoic acid | $C_{22}H_{38}O_2$ | 334 | 3000 μ*M* | BSV | | 142, 222 |
| 6. | 2548-85-8 | 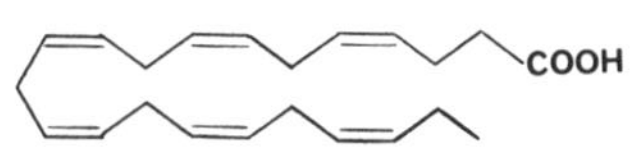 | 4(Z),7(Z),10(Z),-16(Z),19(Z)Docosahexaenoic acid (Clupanodonic acid) | $C_{22}H_{32}O_2$ | 328 | $K_i$ 0.36 μ*M* | SSV | Competitive; not a substrate, not a lipoxygenase inhibitor | 224 |

| | | | | | | | | | |
|---|---|---|---|---|---|---|---|---|---|
| 7. | 2091-25-0 | 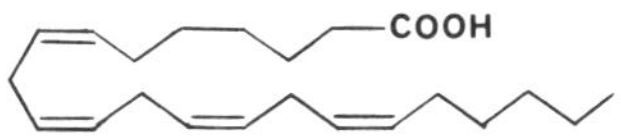 | 7(Z),10(Z),13(Z)16(Z)-Docosa-tetraenoic acid (Adrenic acid) | $C_{22}H_{36}O_2$ | 332 | ca. 1 μ*M* | Rabbit renal medulla | Competitive; converted to bishomoprostaglandins | 137, 225 |
| 8. | 112-80-1 | 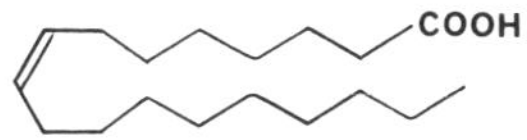 | 9-Octadecenoic acid (Oleic acid) | $C_{18}H_{36}O_2$ | 284 | $K_i$ 22 μ*M* | SSV | Competitive | 138, 226 |
| 9. | 463-40-1 | 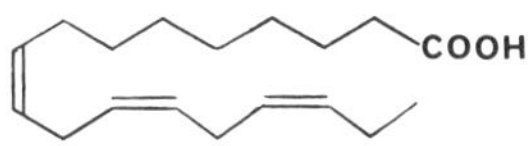 | 9(Z),12(Z),15(Z)-Octadecatrienoic acid (Linolenic acid) | $C_{18}H_{30}O_2$ | 278 | $K_i$ 15 μ*M* | SSV | | 138, 227 |
| 10. | | 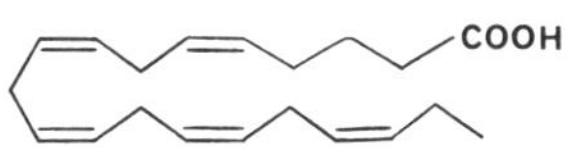 | 5(Z),8(Z),11(Z),-14(Z),17(Z)Eicosapentaenoic acid | $C_{20}H_{30}O_2$ | 302 | $K_i$ 2.5 μ*M* | SSV | Competitive | 138 |
| 11. | 67675-13-2 | 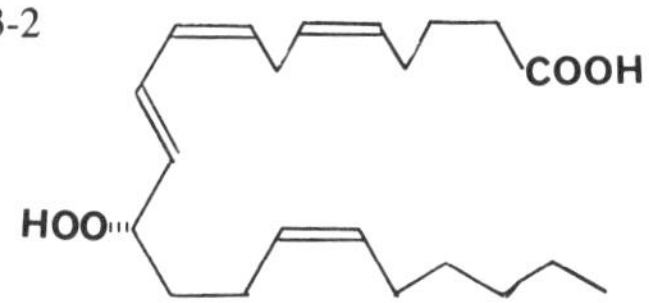 | (S)12-Hydroperoxyeicosa-5(Z),8(Z),10(E),15(Z) eicosatetraenoic acid (12-HPETE) | $C_{20}H_{34}O_4$ | 338 | ca. 1 μ*M* | Human platelets | Potency varies widely with time of preincubation | 228 |

[a] When available.
[b] $IC_{50}$ unless otherwise stated.

## Table 2
## ENDOPEROXIDE ANALOGUES

| Entry no. | Chemical abstracts number[a] | Structure | Chemical name (common name) | Molecular formula | Mol wt | Inhibitory potency | Assay | Comments | Ref. |
|---|---|---|---|---|---|---|---|---|---|
| 1. | 32021-31-1 | 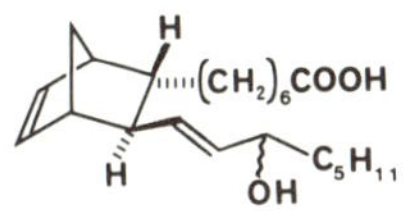 | Bicyclo[2.2.1] hept-5-ene-2-heptanoic acid, 3-(3-hydroxy-1-octenyl) | $C_{22}H_{36}O_3$ | 364 | −52% at 90 μM | SSV | Inhibits production of $PGE_1$ but not $PGF_{1\alpha}$ from eicosa-8, 11,14-trienoic acid | 229 |
| | | | | | | −100% at 50 μM | SSV | $PGE_2$ production | 230 |
| 2. | 60124-78-9 | 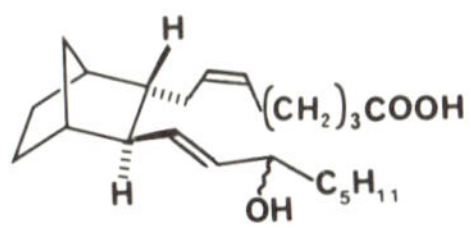 | 5-Heptenoic acid, 7-[3-(3-hydroxy-1-octenyl)bicyclo-[2.2.1]hept-2-yl] | $C_{22}H_{36}O_3$ | 364 | −100% at 50 μM | SSV | $PGE_2$ production from arachidonic acid | 230 |
| 3. | 60124-71-2 | 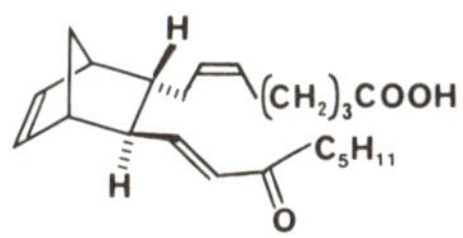 | 7-[3-(3-oxo-1-octenyl)bicyclo [2.2.1]hept-5-en-2-yl]-5-heptenoic acid [1α,2β(Z),3α (E),4α] | $C_{22}H_{32}O_3$ | 344 | −79% at 50 μM | SSV | As above | 230 |
| 4. | | 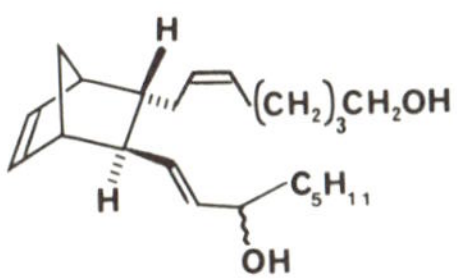 | 7-[3-(3-hydroxy-1-octenyl)bicyclo [2.2.1]hept-5-en-2-2-yl]-5-heptenol [2α,2β(Z),3α (E),4α] | $C_{22}H_{36}O_2$ | 332 | −100% at 50 μM | SSV, See text | As above | 230 |
| 5. | 103001-17-8 | 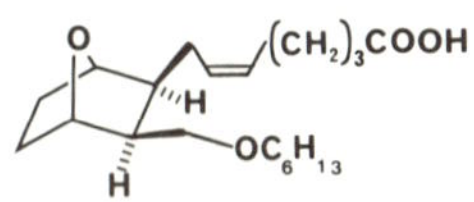 | 5-Heptenoic acid, -7-{3-[(hexyloxy)-methyl]-7-oxa-bicyclo[2.2.1]hept-5-yl}{1R-[1α,2α(Z),3α,4α]} (SQ 28852) | $C_{20}H_{34}O_4$ | 338 | 3.1 μ*M*<br>6.4 μ*M*<br>0.5 μ*M* | Human platelets<br>BSV<br>Bovine aorta | $PGE_2$ production | 147 |

[a] If available

**Salicylates: (Table 4)**

Salicylates have long been known to be active as antiphlogistics, and aspirin, synthesized in the 1880s was the first anti-inflammatory agent demonstrated to inhibit prostaglandin biosynthesis. Subsequent studies have shown that aspirin is an atypical cyclooxygenase inhibitor, in that its irreversible inhibition is caused by the transfer of the labile acetyl group to a terminal serine hydroxyl group in the enzyme.[150] This effect results in the potent and prolonged antithrombotic effect of aspirin, since platelets, unlike many other cells, are unable to synthesize cyclooxygenase, and aggregation is therefore inhibited throughout the 10 to 14 d lifetime of the platelet. The ability to effect acetylation of cyclooxygenase seems to be unique to aspirin. The O-acetyl derivatives of several other salicylic acids (e.g., Compounds 3 and 6) are equal to or less than the corresponding free phenols in inhibitory potency. It is not clear whether the rate of acetylation of cyclooxygenase is determined by the size, shape, lipophilicity, etc. of the acylating agent. Phenolic acetates can transfer an acetyl group to a myriad of other sites *in vivo,* including water, and it is reasonable to expect that a suitable balance between stability and lability must exist for an acylating agent to reach the cyclooxygenase and then be able to effect acetylation. Aspirin, which has a half-life of 20 min in human plasma, may be of such optimum stability. Although salicylic acid itself is a weak cyclooxygenase inhibitor, its *in vivo* potency is comparable to that of aspirin. However, gentisic and γ-resorcylic acid, which are metabolites of salicylic acid, are ca. 30 times as potent as cyclooxygenase inhibitors, and may be responsible for its anomolous *in vivo* potency. Simple substituted analogues of salicylic acid, as well as the methyl ether, and thiosalicylic acid, were found to be less active than the parent compounds, but cyclooxygenase-inhibitory potency was greatly increased by the introduction of an aromatic ring at the 5-position.[13]

Sulfasalazine, (Compound 8) a chemical combination of a salicylic acid and the antibacterial agent sulfapyridine, has been employed for the treatment of ulcerative colitis, and has shown promise as an antirheumatic agent.[151] Since both sulfasalazine and its salicylate metabolite, 5-aminosalicylic acid (Compound 9), are very weak cyclooxygenase inhibitors, it seems unlikely that the antirheumatic effect is due to the inhibition of arachidonic acid metabolism. Sulfasalazine is also an inhibitor of prostaglandin 15-hydroxy dehydrogenase,[152] a property which could, by maintaining the level of cytoprotective prostaglandins, contribute to its efficacy in ulcerative colitis, but which appears unlikely to be related to the control of chronic inflammation.

**Arylacetic Acids and Related Compounds: (Table 5)**

Several members of this large group of compounds have achieved considerable medical importance as agents for the treatment of chronic inflammation and pain. As a result of the intensive research which has been performed in the last 30 years, the structural requirements for biological activity among the arylacetic acids are fairly well defined. Since cyclooxygenase-inhibition data are only available for a small fraction of the compounds which have been reported, the following generalizations are based also on *in vivo* anti-inflammatory assays.

Typical compounds have an acetic acid side-chain attached to a benzenoid or heteroaromatic ring. The corresponding carboxylic acids, or homologated acetic acids (propionic, butyric, etc.) are less potent unless they are metabolically degraded to the acetic acid (e.g., Compounds 32 and 33). Groups with similar pKa to that of the acetic acid carboxyl group, such as hydroxamic acids or tetrazoles,[153] probably also serve as cyclooxygenase inhibitors. The introduction of a methyl group α- to the carboxyl has unpredictable effects on potency, though activity is not usually abolished. *In vivo* anti-inflammatory potencies of compounds bearing ethyl, propyl, etc. substituents are usually considerably lower than those of the acetic acids and α-methyl acetic acids, and it has been assumed that cyclooxygenase-inhib-

## Table 3
## PROSTAGLANDINS

| Entry no. | Chemical abstracts number[a] | Structure | Chemical name (common name) | Molecular formula | Mol wt | Inhibitory potency[b] | Assay | Comments | Ref. |
|---|---|---|---|---|---|---|---|---|---|
| 1. | 61652-66-2 | 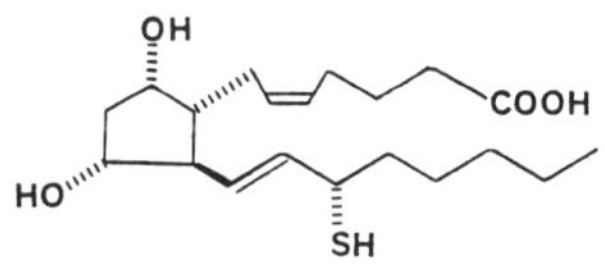 | (5Z,9α,11α,13E,15S)-9,11-Dihydroxy-15-mercapto-prosta-5,13-dienoic acid | $C_{20}H_{34}O_4S$ | 370 | 0.1 μ*M* | BSV | Noncompetitively inhibits conversion of 8,11,14-eicosa trienoic acid to $PGG_1$ | 231 |
| 2. | 61955-19-9 | 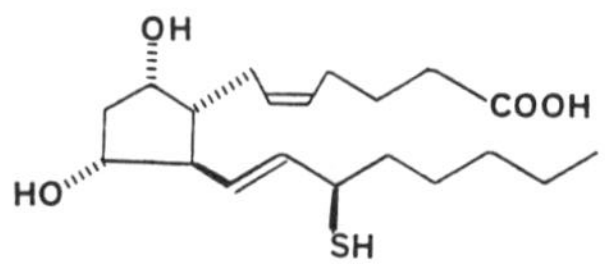 | (5Z,9α,11α,13E,15R)-9,11-Dihydroxy-15-mercapto-prosta-5,13-dienoic acid | $C_{20}H_{34}O_4S$ | 370 | 0.4 μ*M* | BSV | As above | 231 |
| 3. | 61955-17-7 | 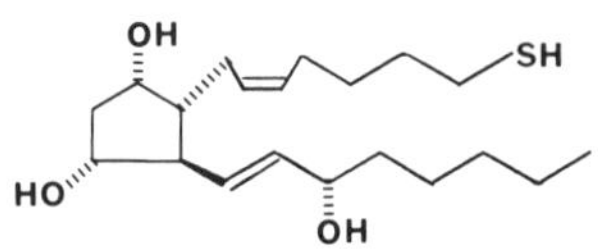 | (5Z,9α,11α,13E,15S)-1-Mercapto-9,11,15-trihydroxy-prosta-5,13-diene | $C_{20}H_{36}O_4S$ | 356 | 1.4 μ*M* | BSV | As above | 231 |
| 4. | 57154-60-6 | 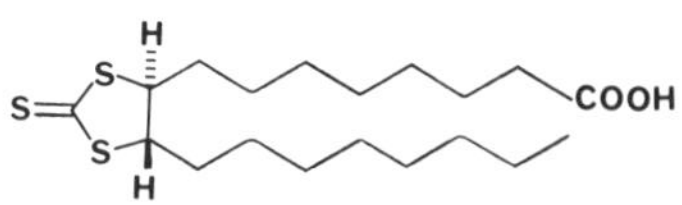 | 1,3-Dithiolane-4-octanoic acid, 5-octyl-2-thioxo, trans. | $C_{19}H_{34}O_2S_3$ | 390 | 390 μ*M* | BSV | | 149 |
| 5. | 24560-98-3 | 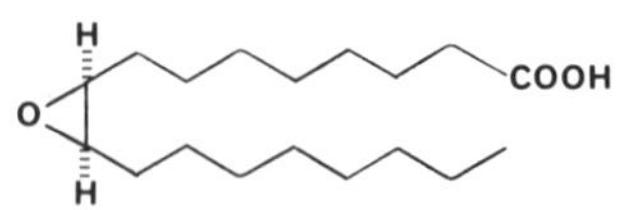 | *cis* 3-Octyloxiraneoctanoic acid | $C_{18}H_{32}O_3$ | 296 | 2000—4000 μ*M* | BSV | Inhibits $PGE_2$-induced diarrhea in mice | 149 |

| | | | | | | | | | |
|---|---|---|---|---|---|---|---|---|---|
| 6. | 85421-76-7 | 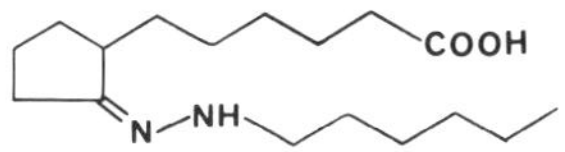 | 2-(6-Carboxyhexyl)-cyclopentanone hexylhydrazone | $C_{17}H_{32}N_2O_2$ | 296 | −29% at 0.1 μ*M*, −99% at 1 μ*M* | Human platelets | Inhibits aggregation induced by arachidonic acid but not by $PGH_2$ | 232 |
| 7. | | 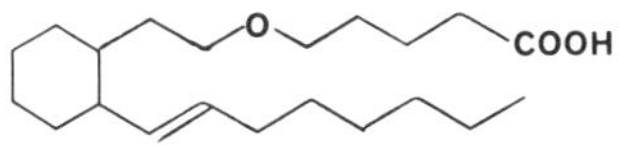 | Octanoic acid, 8-[2-(1-octenyl) cyclohexyl]-6-oxa, (Z) | $C_{21}H_{38}O_3$ | 338 | $K_i$ 32 μ*M* | BSV | Competitive | 233 |

[a] If available.
[b] $IC_{50}$ unless otherwise stated.

## Table 4
## SALICYLIC ACIDS

| Entry no. | Chemical abstracts number[a] | Structure | Chemical name (common name) | Molecular formula | Mol wt | Inhibitory potency[b] | Assay | Comments | Ref. |
|---|---|---|---|---|---|---|---|---|---|
| 1. | 69-72-7 | 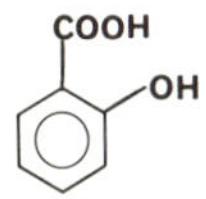 | Benzoic acid, 2-hydroxy (Salicylic acid) | $C_7H_6O_3$ | 138 | 16% inh. at 500 μ*M* | Rabbit kidney | | 234 |
| 2. | 50-78-2 | 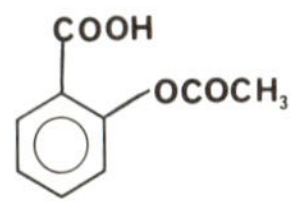 | Benzoic acid, 2-acetyloxy (Aspirin) | $C_9H_8O_4$ | 180 | 466 μ*M*<br>100 μ*M*<br>83 μ*M* | BSV<br>BSV<br>SSV | Oxygen uptake<br>$PGE_2$ production<br>Irreversible. 37 × more potent in platelets | 235<br>236<br>163 |
| 3. | 322-79-2 | 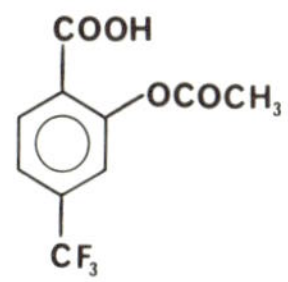 | Benzoic acid, 2-(acetyloxy)-4-trifluoromethyl (Triflusal) | $C_{10}H_7F_3O_4$ | 248 | 80 μ*M* | Human platelets | De-acetylated analogue much less potent | 237 |
| 4. | 470-79-9 | 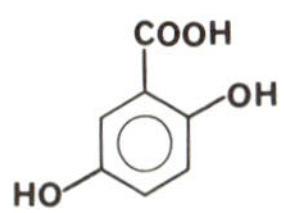 | 2,5-Dihydroxybenzoic acid (Gentisic acid) | $C_7H_6O_4$ | 154 | 92% inh. at 500 μ*M* | Rabbit kidney | Metabolite of salicylic acid | 234 |
| 5. | 303-07-1 | 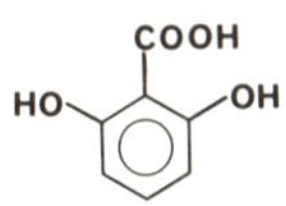 | 2,5-Dihydroxybenzoic acid (gamma-resorcylic acid) | $C_7H_6O_4$ | 154 | 89% inh. at 500 μ*M* | Rabbit kidney | | 234 |

| | | | | | | | | | |
|---|---|---|---|---|---|---|---|---|---|
| 6. | 22494-42-4 | 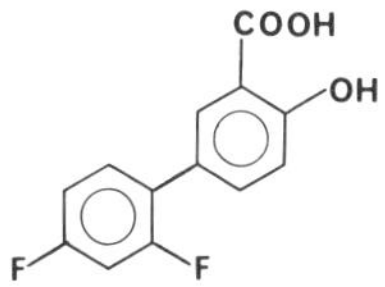 | 2′,4′-Difluoro-4-hydroxy-1,1′-diph-enyl-3-carboxylic acid (Diflunisal) | $C_{13}H_8F_2O_3$ | 250 | 3—5 μ*M*, 3—5 μ*M* | SSV Human platelets | Potency unchanged by acetylation | 13, 236 |
| 7. | 53242-70-9 | 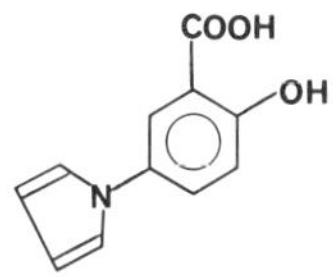 | 2-Hydroxy-5-(*N*-pyrryl)benzoic acid | $C_{11}H_9NO_3$ | 203 | 1.5 μ*M* | SSV | Less active than aspirin, *in vivo* anti-inflammatory assays | 238 |
| 8. | 599-79-1 | 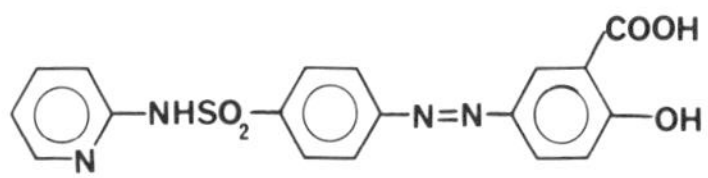 | 2-Hydroxy-5-[[4-(2-pyridinylamino) sulphonyl]-phenylazo] benzoic acid (Sulfasalazine) | $C_{18}H_{14}N_4O_5S$ | 398 | 3000 μ*M* | Human colonic mucosa | Tissue samples from quiescent ulcerative colitis patients | 239 |
| 9. | 89-57-6 | 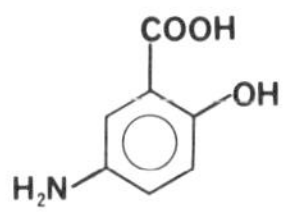 | 5-Amino-2-hydroxybenzoic acid | $C_6H_7NO_3$ | 141 | 2600 μ*M* | Human colonic mucosa | Sulfasalazine metabolite | 239 |

[a] When available.
[b] $IC_{50}$ unless otherwise stated.

## Table 5
## ARYLACETIC ACIDS AND RELATED COMPOUNDS

| Entry no. | Chemical abstracts number[a] | Structure | Chemical name (common name) | Molecular formula | Mol wt | Inhibitory potency[b] | Assay | Comments | Ref. |
|---|---|---|---|---|---|---|---|---|---|
| 1. | 22071-15-4 | 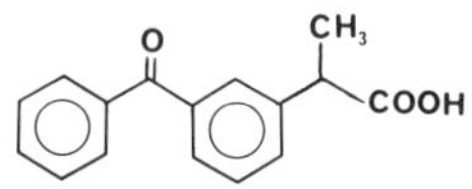 | α-Methyl-3-benzoylbenzeneacetic acid (Ketoprofen) | $C_{16}H_{14}O_3$ | 254 | 0.12 μ*M*<br>0.9 μ*M* | SSV<br>Mouse fibroblasts | | 13 |
| 2. | 33005-95-7 | 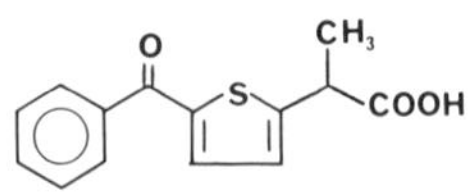 | 5-Benzoyl-α-methyl-2-thiophene-acetic acid (Tiaprofenic acid) | $C_{14}H_{12}O_3S$ | 260 | 0.9 μ*M* | Human platelets | | 240 |
| 3. | 40828-46-4 | 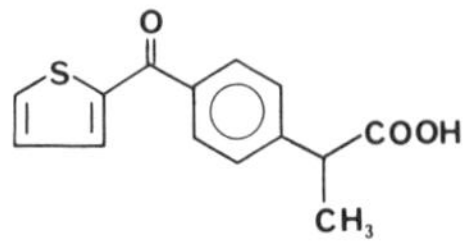 | α-Methyl-4-(2-thienylcarbonyl)-benzeneacetic acid (Suprofen) | $C_{14}H_{12}O_3S$ | 260 | 0.03 μ*M* | SSV | | 241 |
| 4. | 51579-82-9 | 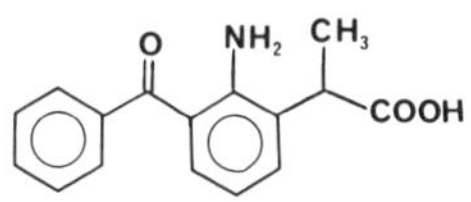 | 2-Amino-3-benzoyl-benzeneacetic acid (Amfenac) | $C_{14}H_{13}NO_3$ | 243 | 0.02 μ*M* | BSV | | 181 |
| 5. | 74103-06-3 | 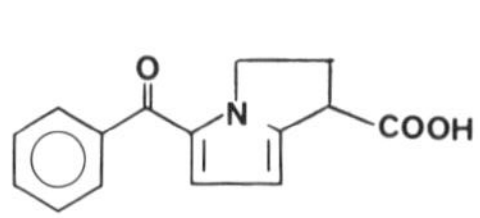 | 5-Benzoyl-2,3-dihydro-1H-pyrrolizine-1-carboxylic acid (Ketorolac) | $C_{15}H_{13}NO_3$ | 255 | 0.26 μ*M*<br>0.19 μ*M* | BSV<br>Platelets | Under clinical development | 242 |
| 6. | 66635-89-0 | 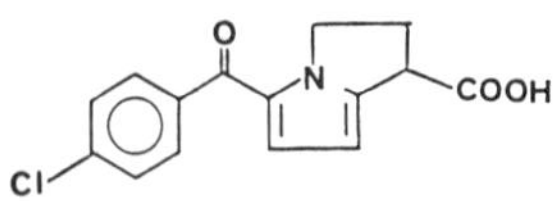 | 5-(4-Chlorobenzoyl)-2,3-dihydro-1H-pyrrolizine-1-carboxylic acid | $C_{15}H_{12}ClNO_3$ | 289.5 | 0.43μ*M*<br>1.1 μ*M* | BSV<br>Platelets | | 242 |

| | | | | | | | | | |
|---|---|---|---|---|---|---|---|---|---|
| 7. | 26171-23-3 | 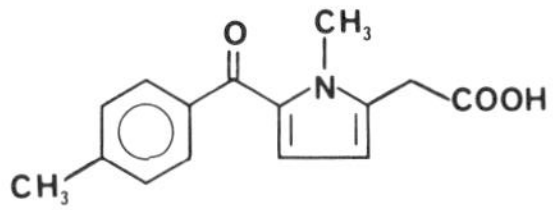 | 1-Methyl-5-(4-methylbenzoyl)-1H-pyrrole-2-acetic acid (Tolmetin) | $C_{15}H_{15}NO_3$ | 257 | 11.7 μ*M*<br>5.4 μ*M* | BSV<br>Mouse fibroblasts | Competitive, reversible | 243 |
| 8. | 33369-36-1 | 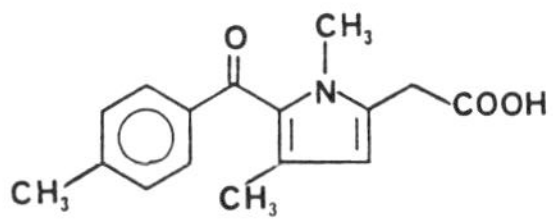 | 1,4-Dimethyl-5-(4-methylbenzoyl)-1H-pyrrole-2-acetic acid | $C_{16}H_{17}NO_3$ | 271 | 7.3 μ*M* | BSV | Competitive, reversible | 243 |
| 9. | 31879-05-7 | 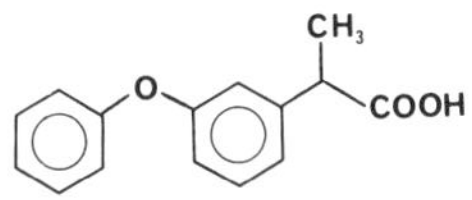 | α-Methyl-3-phenoxybenzeneacetic acid (Fenoprofen) | $C_{15}H_{14}O_3$ | 242 | 2.0 μ*M*<br>4.0 μ*M*<br>9.1 μ*M* | Human synovium<br>Rat platelets<br>Mouse fibroblasts | R-isomer converted to S-isomer *in vivo* | 102, 244, 245 |
| 10. | 15307-86-5 | 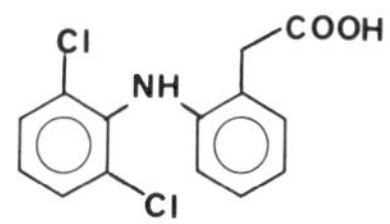 | 2-[2,6-Dichlorophenyl)amino]benzeneacetic acid (Diclofenac) | $C_{14}H_{11}Cl_2NO_2$ | 296 | 0.72 μ*M*<br>0.2 μ*M*<br><br>0.3 μ*M* | BSV<br>Human rheumatoid synovium<br>SSV | Competitive, reversible; inhibits release, enhances uptake of arachidonic acid by lymphocytes | 91, 246, 247, 248 |
| 11. | 53716-49-7 (±)<br>52263-84-0 (+)<br>52263-83-9 (−) | 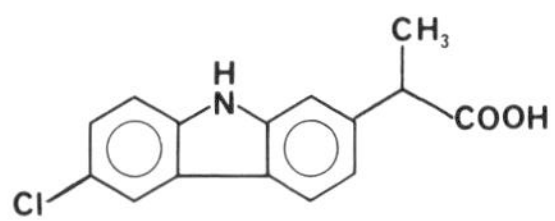 | 6-Chloro-α-methyl-9H-carbazole-2-acetic acid (Carprofen) | $C_{15}H_{11}ClNO_2$ | 272.5 | <br>(±)48 μ*M*<br>(+)31 μ*M*<br>(−)500 μ*M* | BSV<br>BSV<br>BSV | (−) Isomer inactive in platelet aggr. and in *in vivo* anti-inflammatory assays | 249 |
| 12. | 78499-27-1 | 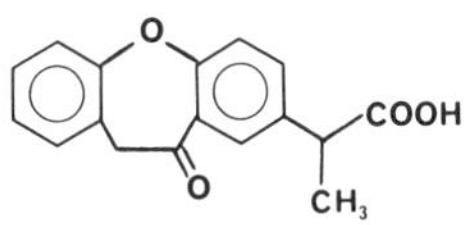 | 2-(8-Methyl-10,11-dihydro-11-oxodibenz[b,f]oxepin-2-yl)propionic acid | $C_{17}H_{14}O_4$ | 282 | 0.78 μ*M* | Rabbit renal medulla | | 250 |

## Table 5 (continued)
## ARYLACETIC ACIDS AND RELATED COMPOUNDS

| Entry no. | Chemical abstracts number[a] | Structure | Chemical name (common name) | Molecular formula | Mol wt | Inhibitory potency[b] | Assay | Comments | Ref. |
|---|---|---|---|---|---|---|---|---|---|
| 13. | 15687-27-1 | 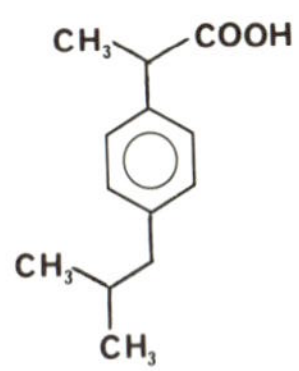 | α-Methyl-4-(2-methylpropyl)-benzeneacetic acid (Ibuprofen) | $C_{13}H_{18}O_2$ | 206 | (±) 84 μ*M*<br>(+) 52 μ*M*<br>(−) 8600 μ*M*<br>1.5 μ*M*<br>1.0 μ*M* | BSV<br>BSV<br>BSV<br>SSV<br>Human synovium | Reversible, competitive; enantiomeric differences not reflected *in vivo* | 105, 163, 251, 252 |
| 14. | 95833-50-4 | 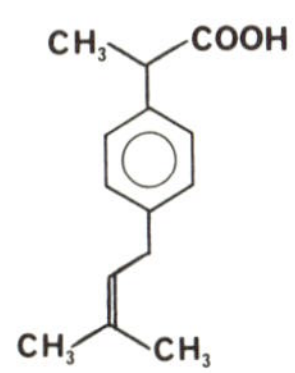 | α-Methyl-4-(3-methyl-2-butenyl)-benzeneacetic acid | $C_{14}H_{18}O_2$ | 218 | $K_i$ 8 μ*M* | BSV | Competitive; equipotent to ibuprofen | 253 |
| 15. | 56983-13-2 | 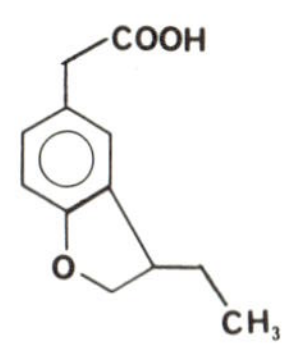 | 2-Ethyl-2,3-dihydro-5-benzofuranyl-acetic acid (Furofenac) | $C_{12}H_{14}O_3$ | 206 | 260 μ*M* | Rat platelets | $IC_{50}$ not altered by preincubation time (0—12 mins) | 254 |
| 16. | 68785-53-5 | 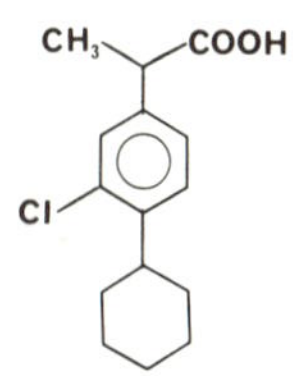 | α-Methyl-3-chloro-4-cyclohexyl-benzeneacetic acid (MK 830) | $C_{15}H_{19}ClO_2$ | 266.5 | 0.2 μ*M* | SSV | Inhibitory activity resides in the (+) isomer | 13 |

| | | | | | | | | | |
|---|---|---|---|---|---|---|---|---|---|
| 17. | 36616-52-1 | 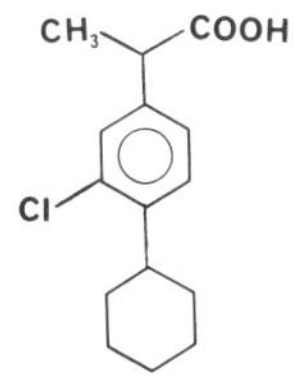 | α,3-Dichloro-4-cyclohexylbenzene-acetic acid (Fenclorac) | $C_{14}H_{16}Cl_2O_2$ | 287 | .05 μ*M*<br>0.01 μ*M* | BSV Human synovium | Reversible, competitive, potency *in vivo* ca. 1/3 indomethacin | 106, 255, 256, 257 |
| 18. | 31793-07-4 | 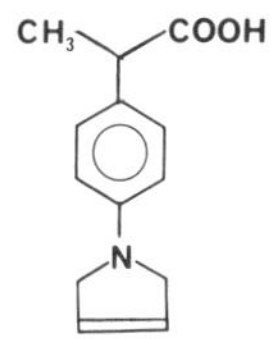 | 3-Chloro-4-(2,5-dihydro-1H-pyrrol-1-yl)-α-methylbenzene acetic acid (Pirprofen) | $C_{13}H_{15}NO_2$ | 217 | 3.5 μ*M*<br>4.2 μ*M*<br>(+)1.2 μ*M*<br>(±)8.3 μ*M* | SSV<br>BSV<br>BSV<br>BSV | Reversible, competitive; activity resides in the (+) enantiomer; not time dependent | 258, 259 |
| 19. | 52651-17-9 | 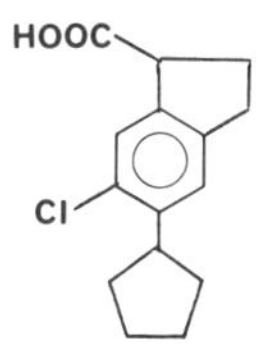 | 1H-Indene-1-carboxylic acid, 6-chloro-5-cyclopentyl-2,3-dihydro | $C_{15}H_{17}ClO_2$ | 264.5 | 1.1 μ*M* | Rabbit renal medulla | | 155 |
| 20. | 31962-05-37 | 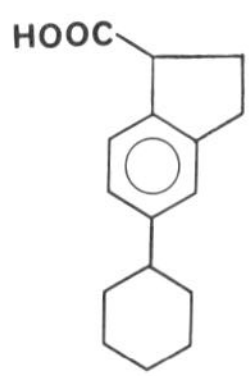 | 1H-Indene-1-carboxylic acid, 5-cyclohexyl-2,3-dihydro | $C_{16}H_{20}O_2$ | 244 | 60 μ*M* | Rabbit renal medulla | Marked loss of inhibitory potency on removing Cl substituents (cf. #21) | 155 |
| 21. | 34148-01-1 | 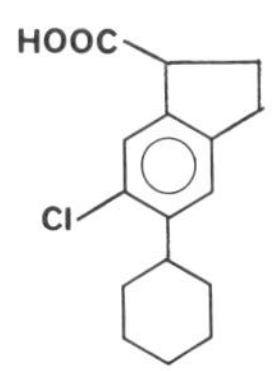 | 6-Chloro-5-cyclohexyl-2,3-dihydro-1H-indene-1-carboxylic acid (Clidanac) | $C_{16}H_{19}ClO_2$ | 278.5 | 2.7 μ*M* | Rabbit renal medulla | S(+) Isomer 5—12× more potent than R (−)isomer, in rats and mice, R and S isomers equipotent in guinea pigs | 155 |

**Table 5 (continued)**
**ARYLACETIC ACIDS AND RELATED COMPOUNDS**

| Entry no. | Chemical abstracts number[a] | Structure | Chemical name (common name) | Molecular formula | Mol wt | Inhibitory potency[b] | Assay | Comments | Ref. |
|---|---|---|---|---|---|---|---|---|---|
| 22. | 80382-23-6 | 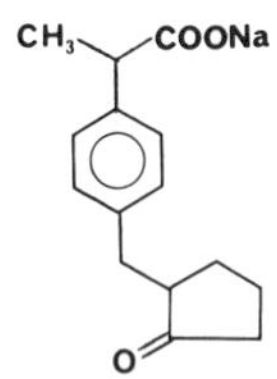 | α-Methyl-4-[(2-oxocyclopentyl)-methyl]-benzene-acetic acid, sodium salt (Loxoprofen) | $C_{15}H_{17}NaO_3$ | 268 | 680 μ*M* | BSV | | 260 |
| 23. | 83648-76-4 | 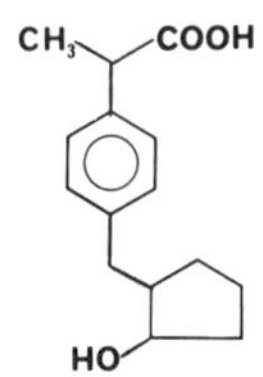 | Benzeneacetic acid 4-[(2-hydroxycyclo-pentyl)methyl, α methyl | $C_{15}H_{20}O_3$ | 248 | 11 μ*M* | BSV | Metabolite of loxoprofen | 260 |
| 24. | 36690-95-6 | 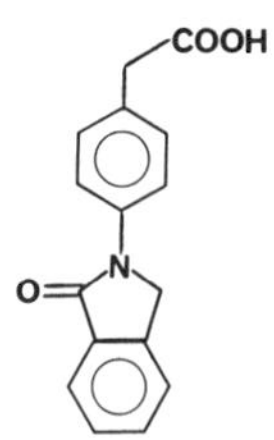 | 4-(1,3-Dihydro-1-oxo-2H-isoindol-2-yl)-benzeneacetic acid | $C_{16}H_{13}NO_3$ | 267 | 35 μ*M* | BSV | | 154 |

| | | | | | | | | | |
|---|---|---|---|---|---|---|---|---|---|
| 25. | 31842-01-0 | 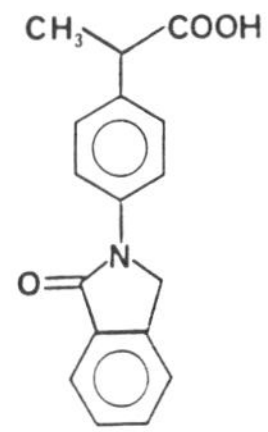 | 4-(1,3-Dihydro-1-oxo-2H-isoindol-2-yl)-α-methylbenzene acetic acid (Indoprofen) | $C_{17}H_{15}NO_3$ | 281 | 25 μ*M* | BSV | Showed greatest *in vivo* potency among No. 24,25,26,2, and 28 | 154 |
| 26. | 63610-08-2 | 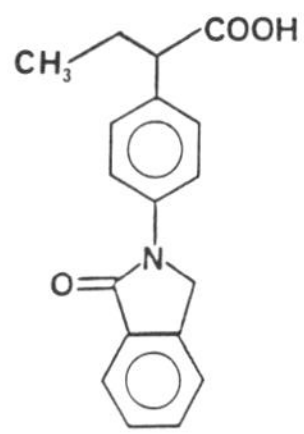 | 4-(1,3-Dihydro-1-oxo-2H-isoindol-2-yl)-α-ethyl-benzeneacetic acid | $C_{18}H_{17}NO_3$ | 295 | 11 μ*M* | BSV | | 154 |
| 27. | 53022-61-0 | 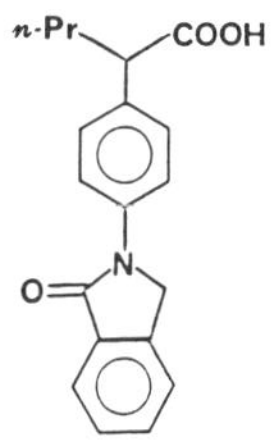 | 4-(1,3-Dihydro-1-oxo-2H-isoindol-2-yl)-α-propyl-benzeneacetic acid | $C_{19}H_{19}NO_3$ | 309 | 5.1 μ*M* | BSV | | 154 |
| 28. | 53022-62-1 | 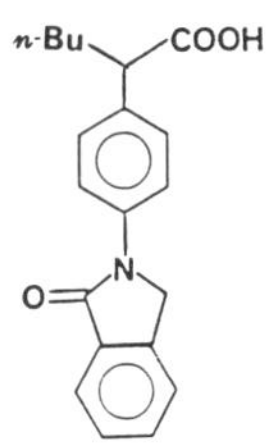 | 4-(1,3-Dihydro-1-oxo-2H-isoindol-2-yl)-α-butyl-benzeneacetic acid | $C_{20}H_{21}NO_3$ | 323 | 2.6 μ*M* | BSV | | 154 |

**Table 5 (continued)**
**ARYLACETIC ACIDS AND RELATED COMPOUNDS**

| Entry no. | Chemical abstracts number[a] | Structure | Chemical name (common name) | Molecular formula | Mol wt | Inhibitory potency[b] | Assay | Comments | Ref. |
|---|---|---|---|---|---|---|---|---|---|
| 29. | 5728-52-9 | 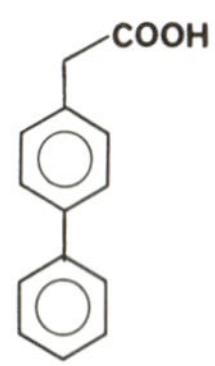 | 1,1′-Biphenyl-4-acetic acid | $C_{14}H_{12}O_2$ | 212 | 2.9 $\mu M$ | Guinea-pig lung | | 261 |
| 30. | 5104-49-4 | 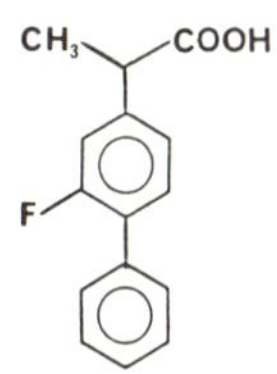 | 2-Fluoro-α-methyl-[1,1′-biphenyl]-4-acetic acid (Flurbiprofen) | $C_{15}H_{13}FO_2$ | 244 | 0.59 $\mu M$<br>0.6 $\mu M$<br><br>0.7 $\mu M$<br>1.5 $\mu M$ | BSV<br>Human rheumatoid synovium<br>SSV<br>Mouse fibroblasts | | 13, 262 |
| 31. | 17969-20-9 | 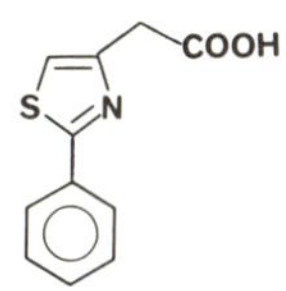 | 2-(4-Chlorophenyl)-4-thiazoleacetic acid (Fenclozic acid) | $C_{11}H_8ClNO_2S$ | 253.5 | 400 $\mu M$ | SSV | | 263 |
| 32. | 60653-25-0 | 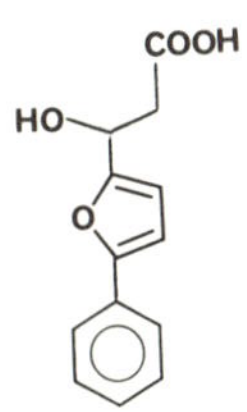 | 5-(4-Chlorophenyl)-β-hydroxy-2-furan-propanoic acid (Orpanixin) | $C_{13}H_{11}ClO_4$ | 266.5 | 1910 $\mu M$ | BSV | *In vivo* anti-inflammatory activity (rat) at 155 mg/kg | 264 |

| | | | | | | | | | |
|---|---|---|---|---|---|---|---|---|---|
| 33. | 36330-85-5 | 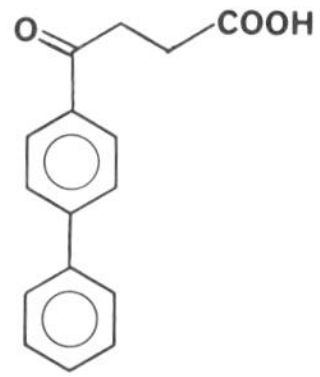 | γ-Oxo-[1,1′-biphenyl]-4-butanoic acid (Fenbufen) | $C_{16}H_{14}O_3$ | 254 | >100 μ*M* | GP lung | Active *in vivo* presumably a prodrug for No. 29 | 261 |
| 34. | 51234-28-7 | 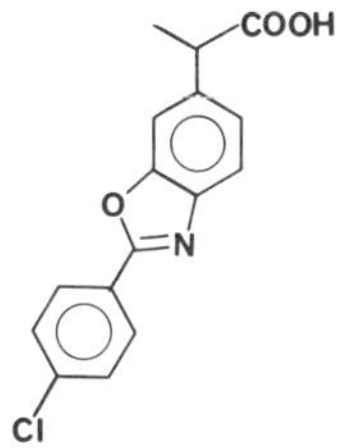 | 2-(4-Chlorophenyl)-α-methyl-5-benzoxazole-acetic acid (Benoxaprofen) | $C_{16}H_{12}ClNO_3$ | 301.5 | 170 μ*M* | BSV | R(−) enantiomer is converted to S(+) *in vivo* | 95, 159, 265 |
| 35. | 22204-53-1 | 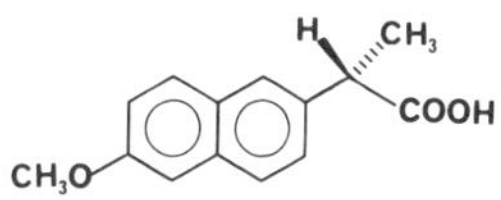 | (+) 6-Methoxy-α-methyl-2-naphth-alene-acetic acid (Naproxen) | $C_{14}H_{14}O_3$ | 230 | 0.8 μ*M*<br>6.1 μ*M*<br>6.8 μ*M* | BSV<br>SSV<br>Mouse fibroblasts | Activity resides in S(+) isomer | 135, 163 |
| 36. | 53-86-1 | 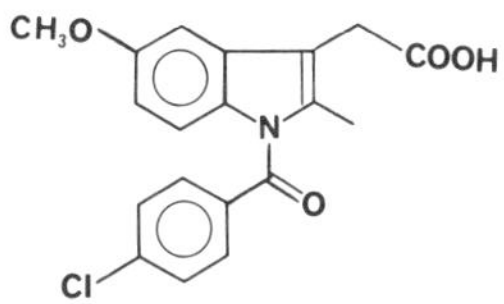 | 1-(4-Chlorobenzoyl)-5-methoxy-2-methyl-1H-indole-3-acetic acid (Indomethacin) | $C_{19}H_{16}ClNO_4$ | 357.5 | ca. 1 μ*M*<br>0.12 μ*M*<br>0.15 μ*M* | Many<br>Fibroblasts<br>Rabbit synovium | Commonly used reference compound, see text and reviews cited | |
| 37. | 16130-32-8 | 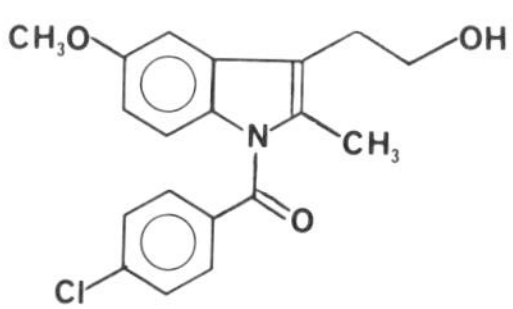 | 1-(4-Chlorobenzoyl)-5-methoxy-2-methyl-1H-indole-3-ethanol | $C_{19}H_{18}ClNO_3$ | 343.5 | 3 μ*M* | SSV | Carboxyl group not needed for inhibitory activity | 13 |

**Table 5 (continued)**
**ARYLACETIC ACIDS AND RELATED COMPOUNDS**

| Entry no. | Chemical abstracts number[a] | Structure | Chemical name (common name) | Molecular formula | Mol wt | Inhibitory potency[b] | Assay | Comments | Ref. |
|---|---|---|---|---|---|---|---|---|---|
| 38. | 38194-50-2 | 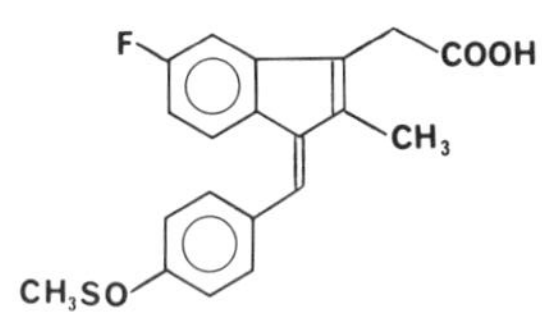 | 5-Fluoro-2-methyl-1-[4-(methylsulphinyl) phenyl]-methylene-1H-indene-3-acetic acid (Sulindac) | $C_{20}H_{17}FO_3S$ | 356 | Inact. | SSV | Inactive pro-drug for No. 39 | 13 |
| 39. | 61812-45-1 | 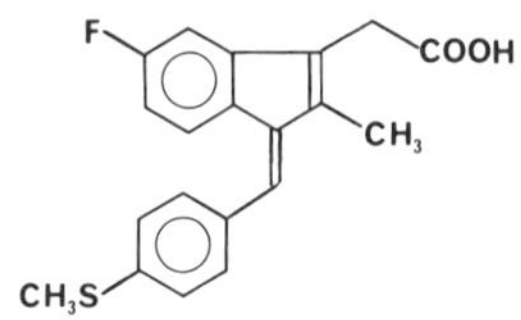 | 5-Fluoro-2-methyl-1-[(4-methylthio)-phenyl]methylene-1H-indene-3-acetic acid | $C_{20}H_{17}FO_2S$ | 340 | 2.2 μ*M*<br>4.1 μ*M*<br>0.45 μ*M* | SSV<br>BSV<br>Human rheumatoid synovium | Metabolite of sulindac (No. 38) | 107 |
| 40. | 78547-34-9 | 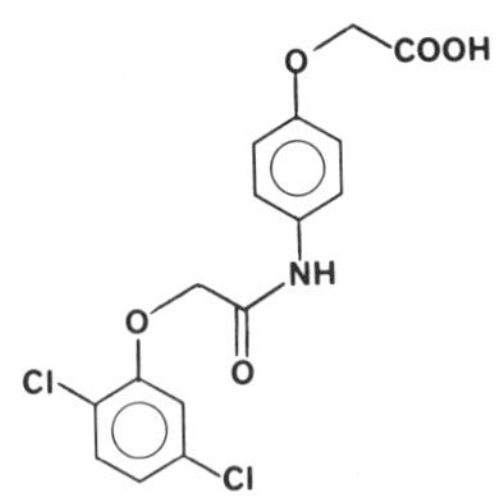 | Acetic acid, [4-[[(2,5-dichlorophenoxy) acetyl]-amino]phenoxy] | $C_{16}H_{13}Cl_2NO_5$ | 370 | 5 μ*M* | BSV | | 266 |
| 41. | 50270-33-2 | 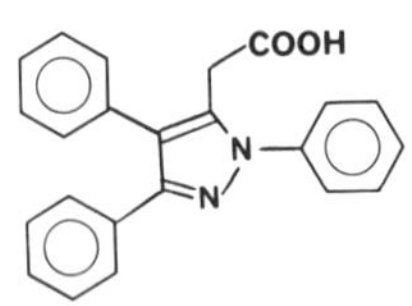 | 1,3,4-Triphenyl-1H-pyrazole-5-acetic acid (Isofezolac) | $C_{23}H_{18}N_2O_2$ | 354 | 0.02 μ*M* | Guinea pig lung | Comparable *in vivo* potency to indomethacin | 267 |

| | | | | | | | | | |
|---|---|---|---|---|---|---|---|---|---|
| 42. | 41340-25-4 | 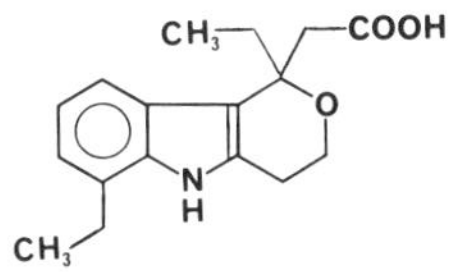 | 1,8-Diethyl-1,3,4,9-tetrahydro-pyrano(3,4-b)indole-1-acetic acid (Etodolic acid) | $C_{17}H_{21}NO_3$ | 287 | (±) 240 μ*M* (+) 120 μ*M* (−)>400 μ*M* | SSV | Racemate is used clinically | 268 |

[a] When available.
[b] $IC_{50}$ unless otherwise stated.

## Table 6
## FENAMIC ACIDS

| Entry no. | Chemical abstracts number[a] | Structure | Chemical name (common name) | Molecular formula | Mol wt | Inhibitory potency[b] | Assay | Comments | Ref. |
|---|---|---|---|---|---|---|---|---|---|
| 1. | 530-78-9 | 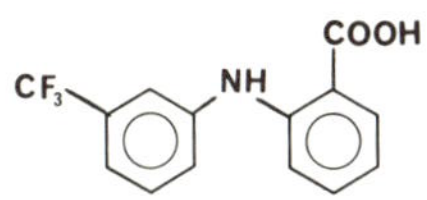 | Benzoic acid,2-[[3-(trifluoromethyl)-phenyl]amino] (Flufenamic acid) | $C_{14}H_{10}F_3NO_2$ | 281 | 11.1 $\mu M$<br>1.7 $\mu M$<br>0.2 $\mu M$<br>2.5 $\mu M$ | BSV<br>BSV<br>Human synovium<br>SSV | Oxygen uptake<br>$PGE_2$ production<br><br>Prostaglandin antagonist | 105, 163, 235 |
| 2. | 4394-00-7 | 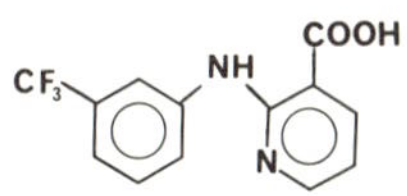 | 3-Pyridinecarboxylic acid, 2-[[3-(trifluoromethyl)-phenyl]-amino] (Niflumic acid) | $C_{13}H_9F_3NO_2$ | 268 | 0.3 $\mu M$<br>1.2 $\mu M$<br>0.11 $\mu M$ | BSV<br>SSV<br>Dog spleen | | 13, 98, 135 |
| 3. | 7220-56-6 | 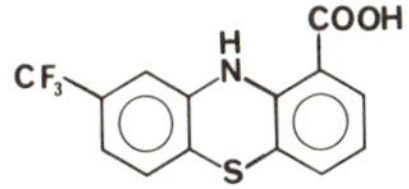 | 10-Phenothiazine-1-carboxylic acid, 8-(trifluoromethyl) (Flutiazin) | $C_{14}H_8F_3NO_2$ | 279 | 75 $\mu M$<br>2 $\mu M$ | BSV<br>SSV | Most potent of a number of tricyclic fenamic acid analogues | 13, 164, 269 |
| 4. | 61-68-7 | 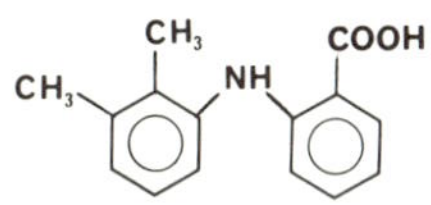 | Benzoic acid 2-[(2,3-dimethyl-phenyl)amino] (Mefenamic acid) | $C_{15}H_{20}NO_2$ | 246 | 0.71 $\mu M$<br>2.1 $\mu M$<br>3.2 $\mu M$<br>1.9 $\mu M$ | Dog spleen<br>SSV<br>BSV<br>Rabbit kidney | Competitive, nonreversible | 90, 163, 234, 258, 270 |
| 5. | 13710-19-5 | 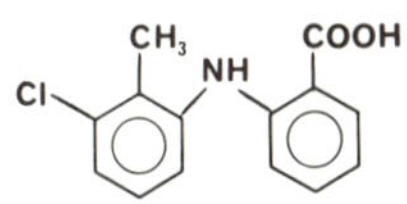 | Benzoic acid,2-[(3-chloro-2-methyl-phenyl)amino] (Tolfenamic acid) | $C_{14}H_{12}ClNO_2$ | 261.5 | 0.64 $\mu M$ | Rabbit kidney | | 271 |

| | | | | | | | | | |
|---|---|---|---|---|---|---|---|---|---|
| 6. | 17737-65-4 | 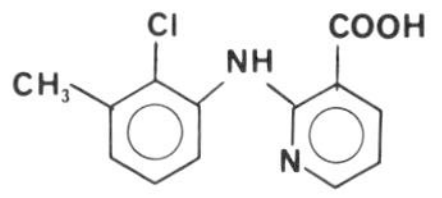 | 3-Pyridinecarboxy-lic acid, 2-[(3-chloro-2-methyl-phenyl)amino] (Clonixin) | $C_{13}H_{11}ClN_2O_2$ | 262.5 | 0.3 μ*M* | BSV | | 135 |
| 7. | 644-62-2 | 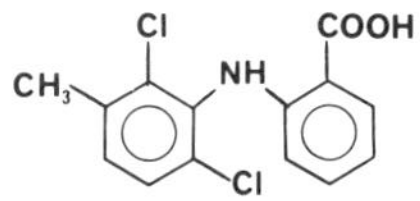 | Benzoic acid,2-[(2,6-dichloro-3-methyl-phenyl)amino] (Meclo-fenamic acid) | $C_{14}H_{11}Cl_2NO_2$ | 296 | 0.1 μ*M*<br>1.4 μ*M*<br>2.6 μ*M* | Dog spleen<br>Rabbit kidney<br>BSV | Competitive, irreversible | 98, 234, 270 |

[a] When available.
[b] $IC_{50}$ unless otherwise stated.

itory potency is also reduced by the introduction of these larger substituents. However, the homologous series of indoprofen analogues (Compounds 24 to 28) indicates the reverse to be true. $IC_{50}$ values decrease as the size of the α-alkyl group is increased, though in this as in many other series, *in vivo* potency is maximal for the α-methyl analogue (Compound 25). The inverse correlation between *in vivo* and *in vitro* potencies was attributed to a greater degree of plasma-protein binding, and thus a lower *in vivo* potency, for the more lipophilic compounds.[154] Measurement of cyclooxygenase inhibition for a number of other homologous series will be needed to determine whether this is a general phenomenon. The introduction of an α-methyl group creates an asymmetric center, and the influence of the absolute stereochemistry of that center on cyclooxygenase-inhibitory potency has been examined in a number of series. One enantiomer was found to be active, the other inactive, for carprofen (Compound 11), ibuprofen (Compound 13), MK 830 (Compound 16), pirprofen (Compound 18), and naproxen (Compound 35). The active enantiomer was found to have S absolute stereochemistry in all cases.[16] The stereospecificity required for cyclooxygenase inhibition is not invariably reflected in the relative potencies of the enantiomers in animal models of inflammation.[155] In humans, stereoselective inversion of the inactive to the active enantiomer has been demonstrated in a number of cases.[156-159]

A variety of substituents (alkyl, cycloalkyl, aryl, aroyl) on the arylacetic acid moiety is compatible with cyclooxygenase-inhibitory activity. Indomethacin, the ancestor of this class of compounds, contains a benzoyl group *meta* to the acetic acid function, and this feature is found in many of the analogues shown in Table 5. The earliest "active site" proposed for these compounds[123,124] (proposals made before the discovery of the cyclooxygenase system) included a hydrogen-bond donor site to which the carbonyl oxygen could bind, and a pocket into which the second aromatic ring could fit, out of the plane of the ring bearing the acetic acid (see earlier section on models of the cyclooxygenase active site). Increased potency, *in vitro* and/or *in vivo,* for compounds bearing substituents (often *ortho* to the inter-annular bond) which would favor non-coplanarity of the two rings, supports this hypothesis (cf. Compounds 7 and 8, 19, and 20).

Most of the compounds in this group are reversible inhibitors of cyclooxygenase. An exception is indomethacin; the irreversible inhibition caused by this compound is not due to acylation of the enzyme with the fairly labile p-chlorobenzoyl group[13] and can be partially restored by prolonged phosphate dialysis.[160] Ibuprofen (Compound 13) is a reversible inhibitor which can protect platelet cyclooxygenase from irreversible inhibition by aspirin.[161]

**Fenamic Acids: (Table 6)**

The anti-inflammatory activity of fenamic (*N*-arylanthranilic) acids was first reported in 1962,[162] and a considerable amount of information on the effect of structural changes on *in vivo* activity in the series has been published.[153] However, cyclooxygenase-inhibitory potencies are available for only a few members of the series. Attempts to relate *in vitro* potencies to anti-inflammatory activity in the rat carragenin paw assay failed to show a correlation[163] (in a later study, better correlation was shown between *in vitro* activity and a combination of *in vivo* potency and partition coefficients for a series of tricyclic flufenamic acid analogues[164]). The simplest molecule which caused significant inhibition of cyclooxygenase was diphenylamine, but *ortho* or *meta* carboxyl groups, especially when combined with a *meta* substituent in the second aromatic ring, caused a considerable increase in inhibitory potency.[134] Compounds in which the NH group linking the two rings was replaced by N–$CH_3$,[165] O, $CH_2$, or S were inactive as cyclooxygenase inhibitors,[135] a finding which supports the proposed interaction between the fenamic acids and cyclooxygenase which was described earlier (see earlier section on models of the cyclooxygenase active site). The fenamic acids can be accommodated in the same receptor-site models as the arylacetic acids. Niflumic acid (Compound 2) and meclofenamic acid (Compound 7) are weak inhibitors of prostaglandin 15-hydroxy dehydrogenase.[166]

**Enolic Acids and Related Compounds: (Table 7)**

Table 7 contains a group of structurally heterogeneous compounds which have in common either the presence of a weakly acidic moiety such as a β-diketone, a β-ketoamide, or a trifluoromethyl sulfonamide, or in the case of the nonacidic antipyrine-like congeners (Compounds 7, 8, and 9), a structural similarity to phenylbutazone. Those compounds which are closest in structure to phenylbutazone are fairly weak inhibitors of cyclooxygenase. The minimal structural requirements are exemplified by 2-phenylindanedione, (Compound 11) a weak inhibitor whose potency is increased almost 100-fold by the addition of *ortho* substituents. It is tempting to ascribe this increase in potency to the twisting of the substituted benzene ring out of the plane of the remainder of the molecule, so as to produce a conformation reminiscent of those required for high-inhibitory potency in the fenamic and arylacetic acid series. However, the structural differences between the compounds of Table 7 and those of Table 5 and 6 are considerable, and it is difficult to see how they could be accommodated in the receptor sites described in Section 4. Nevertheless, many of the compounds are competetive reversible inhibitors, and show similar *in vivo* effects to the cyclooxygenase inhibitors in different chemical classes.

Despite inhibiting the production of PGE and PGF, phenylbutazone (Compound 1) has no effect on the production of PGD and malondialdhyde, and production of $PGF_{2\alpha}$ is actually stimulated.[167,167a] As in other series, the relationships between *in vivo* and *in vitro* potencies are complicated. Replacement of the butyl side-chain of phenylbutazone with a cyclohexyl (Compound 3) results in a considerable loss of potency *in vitro*, but a complete loss of *in vivo* anti-inflammatory activity even at high doses.[168] A comprehensive review of structures and activities of phenylbutazone analogues has appeared.[169] Azapropazone (Compound 7) combines structural features from both phenylbutazone and amidopyrine, and is considerably more potent as a cyclooxygenase inhibitor than either of them. Clinically effective doses of the three compounds do not reflect the large differences in *in vitro* potencies.

The oxicams (Compounds 13 to 16) are among the more potent cyclooxygenase inhibitors, and several members of this series have proceeded to clinical evaluation. The acidic enolic group is essential to their activity; pKa values of 6.3 and 5.6, surprisingly acidic for β-dicarbonyls, presumably due to hydrogen-bonded stabilization of the enolate anion, have been reported.[170] The corresponding enol methyl ethers are less potent cyclooxygenase inhibitors, and substitution in the benzene ring or replacement of the *N*-methyl group with higher alkyl substituents also resulted in reduction in inhibitory potency.[171] The high *in vitro* potencies of sudoxicam and pyroxicam are reflected in daily doses of 20 mg for the treatment of rheumatoid arthritis.[172]

The difluoromethyl sulfonamides 17, 18, and 19 are included in Table 7 because, like phenylbutazone and the oxicams, they are weak organic acids. Their structures are reminiscent of those of the arylacetic acids (Table 5) and, unlike phenylbutazone and the oxicams, can probably be accommodated in some of the proposed cyclooxygenase active-site models (see earlier section). Structure-activity relationships in this series of compounds have been reviewed.[173]

**Phenols, Anti-Oxidants: (Table 8)**

The compounds in Table 8 have as a common feature the presence of a phenolic hydroxyl group; considerable structural diversity exists, however, and the biological activities of several of the compounds are likely to owe as much to their additional structural features as their phenolic character. The ability of phenolic compounds and anti-oxidants to inhibit cyclooxygenase can be readily understood in view of their radical-trapping propensities, and consequent ability to block free-radical chain reactions.[174] Some phenols, particularly those which are readily oxidized to quinones, actually increase the production of cyclooxygenase products, and may prevent the inhibition of cyclooxygenase by indomethacin-like agents.[13,13A]

## Table 7
## ENOLIC ACIDS AND RELATED COMPOUNDS

| Entry no. | Chemical abstracts number[a] | Structure | Chemical name (common name) | Molecular formula | Mol wt | Inhibitory potency[b] | Assay | Comments | Ref. |
|---|---|---|---|---|---|---|---|---|---|
| 1. | 50-33-9 | 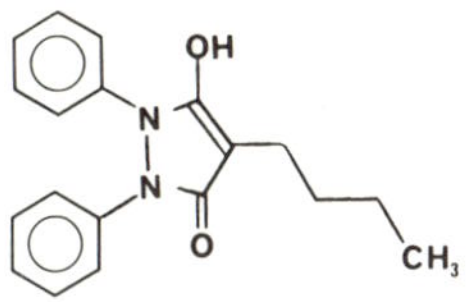 | 3,5-Pyrazolidinedione, 4-butyl-1,2-diphenyl (Phenylbutazone) | $C_{19}H_{20}N_2O_2$ | 308 | 12 μ*M*<br>88 μ*M*<br>15 μ*M* | Mouse fibroblasts<br>BSV<br>Rabbit kidney | Competitive, reversible; no effect on MDA; for other values see References 11 and 13 | 167, 265, 270 |
| 2. | 129-20-4 | 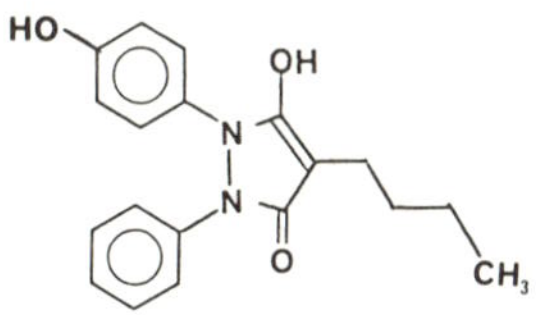 | 3,5-Pyrazolidinedione, 4-butyl-1-(4-hydroxyphenyl)-2-phenyl (Oxyphenbutazone) | $C_{19}H_{20}N_2O_3$ | 324 | $K_i$ 810 μ*M*<br>540 μ*M* | SSV<br>BSV | Competitive, reversible, phenylbutazone metabolite | 91, 270 |
| 3. | 34925-60-5 | 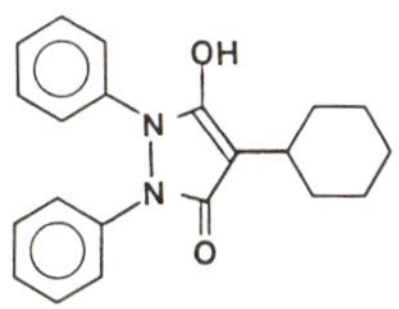 | 3,5-Pyrazolidinedione,4-cyclohexyl-1,2-diphenyl | $C_{21}H_{22}N_2O_2$ | 334 | 240 μ*M* | BSV | No *in vivo* anti-inflammatory activity at 10× dose at which phenylbutazone was active | 168 |
| 4. | 57-96-5 | 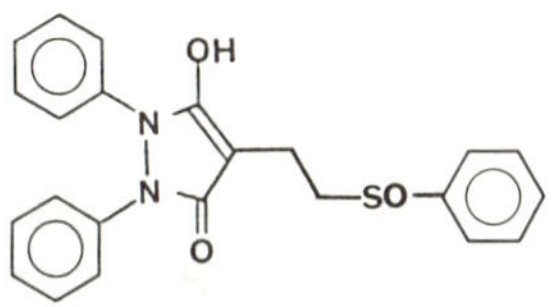 | 3,5-Pyrazolidinedione, 1,2-diphenyl-4-[2-(phenylsulphinyl)ethyl] (Sulfinpyrazone) | $C_{23}H_{20}N_2O_3S$ | 404 | active at 385 μ*M* | Platelet aggr. | Competitive | 272 |

| | | | | | | | | | |
|---|---|---|---|---|---|---|---|---|---|
| 5. | 3736-92-3 | 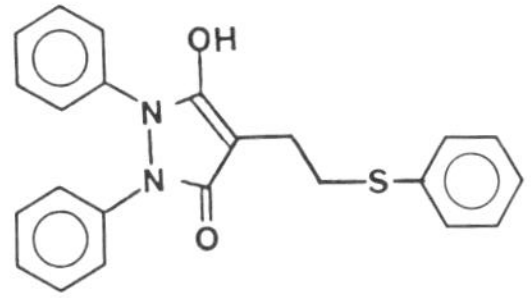 | 3,5-Pyrazolidinedione, 1,2-diphenyl-4-[2-(phenylthio)ethyl] | $C_{23}H_{20}N_2O_2S$ | 388 | active at 26 μ*M* | Platelet aggr. | Competitive; metabolite of sulfinpyrazone | 272 |
| 6. | 68-89-3 | 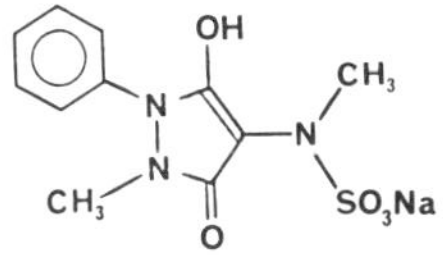 | Methanesulphonic acid, [(2,3-dihydro-1,5-dimethyl-3-oxo-2-phenyl-1H-pyrazol-4-yl)methylamino], sodium salt (Dipyrone) | $C_{12}H_{14}N_3NaO_5S$ | 335 | active at $10^{-4}M$<br>−36% at $10^{-6}M$<br>−68% at $10^{-5}M$ | SSV<br><br>Human skin<br>Mouse fibroblasts | Competitive, inhibits platelet aggregation at $10^{-5}M$ | 273, 274, 246 |
| 7. | 60-80-0 | 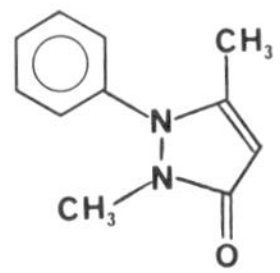 | 3H-Pyrazol-3-one, 1,2-dihydro-1,5-dimethyl-2-phenyl (Antipyrine) | $C_{11}H_{12}N_2O$ | 188 | 4900 μ*M* | BSV | | 275 |
| 8. | 83-07-8 | 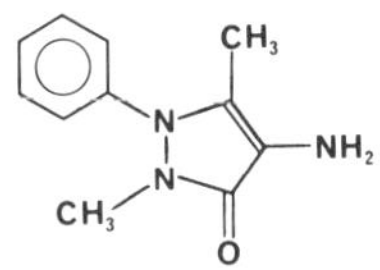 | 3H-Pyrazol-3-one, 4-amino-1,2-dihydro-1,5-dimethyl-2-phenyl (4-Aminoantipyrine) | $C_{11}H_{13}N_3O$ | 203 | 2700 μ*M* | BSV | | 275 |
| 9. | 58-15-1 | 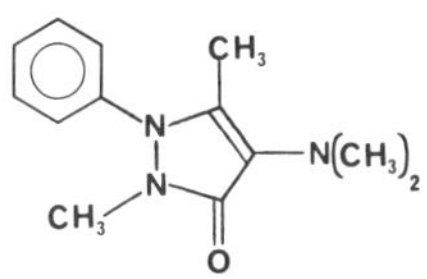 | 3H-Pyrazol-3-one, 4-(dimethylamino)-1,2-dihydro-1,5-dimethyl-2-phenyl (Amidopyrine) | $C_{13}H_{17}N_3O$ | 231 | 966 μ*M*<br>1340 μ*M* | BSV<br>BSV | (Oxygen uptake)<br>($PGE_2$ production) | 235 |
| 10. | 13539-59-8 | 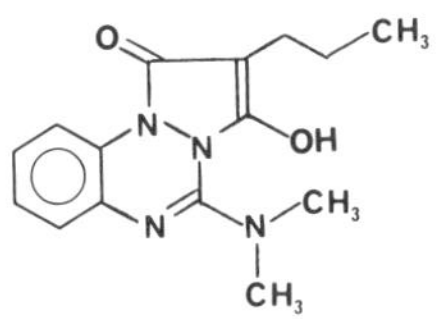 | 1H-Pyrazolo[1,2-a]-benzotriazine-1,3-(2H)dione, 5-dimethyl-amino-9-methyl-2-propyl (Azapropazone) | $C_{15}H_{18}N_4O_2$ | 286 | 3 μM | SSV | Active in man at 800 mg/d | 13 |

**Table 7 (continued)**
**ENOLIC ACIDS AND RELATED COMPOUNDS**

| Entry no. | Chemical abstracts number[a] | Structure | Chemical name (common name) | Molecular formula | Mol wt | Inhibitory potency[b] | Assay | Comments | Ref. |
|---|---|---|---|---|---|---|---|---|---|
| 11. | 83-12-5 | 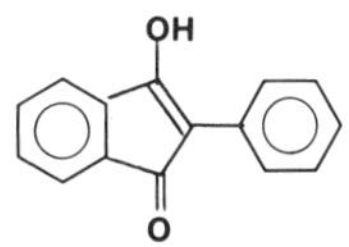 | 1H-Indene-1,3 (2H)-dione,2-phenyl | $C_{15}H_{10}O_2$ | 222 | 480 μM | BSV | | 276 |
| 12. | 55994-28-0 | 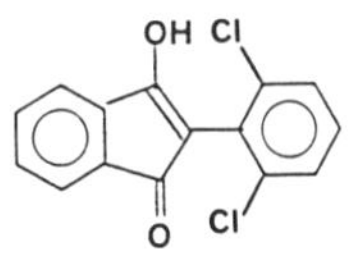 | 1H-Indene-1,3(2H)-dione,2-(2,6-dichlorophenyl) | $C_{15}H_8Cl_2O_2$ | 291 | 6.4 μM | BSV | Potentiating effect of ortho substituents (cf. 11) not reflected in *in vivo* potencies | 276 |
| 13. | 36322-90-4 | 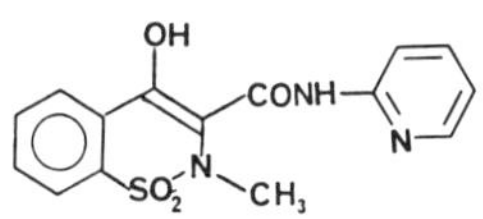 | 2H-1,2-Benzothiazine-3-carboxamide, 4-hydroxy-*N*-2-pyridinyl, 1,1-dioxide (Piroxicam) | $C_{15}H_{13}N_3O_4S$ | 331 | 0.5 μ*M*<br>0.14 μ*M*<br>0.4 μ*M* | Human platelet<br>Mouse fibroblast<br>Rabbit synovium | | 277, 278 |
| 14. | 34042-85-8 | 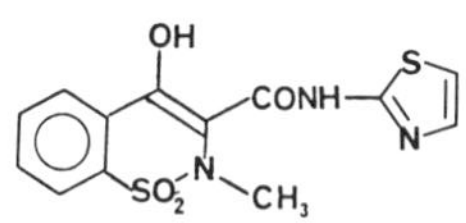 | 2H-1,2-Benzothiazine-3-carboxamide, 4-hydroxy-2-methyl-*N*-2-thiazolyl,1,1-dioxide (Sudoxicam) | $C_{13}H_{11}N_3O_4S_2$ | 337 | 7 μ*M* | SSV | | 13 |
| 15. | 34552-84-6 | 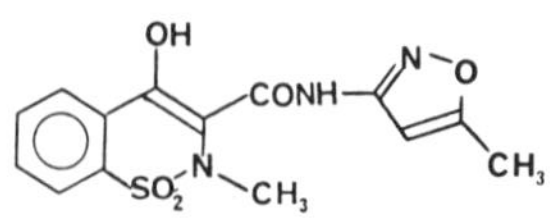 | 2H-1,2-Benzothiazine-3-carboxamide, 4-hydroxy-2-methyl-N-(5-methyl-3-isoxazolyl), 1,1-dioxide (Isoxicam) | $C_{14}H_{13}N_3O_5S$ | 335 | 2 μ*M* | Mouse fibrosarcoma cells | Not a lipoxygenase inhibitor | 279 |

| | | | | | | | | | |
|---|---|---|---|---|---|---|---|---|---|
| 16. | 58904-37-4 | 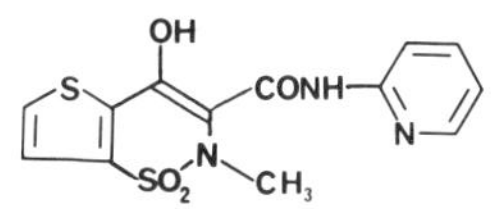 | 2H-Thieno[2,3-e]-1,2-thiazine-3-carboxamide, 4-hydroxy-2-methyl-N-2-pyridinyl,1,1-dioxide (Tenoxicam) | $C_{13}H_{11}N_3O_4S_2$ | 337 | 110 μ*M* | SSV | $PGE_2$ production | 280 |
| 17. | 22736-85-2 | 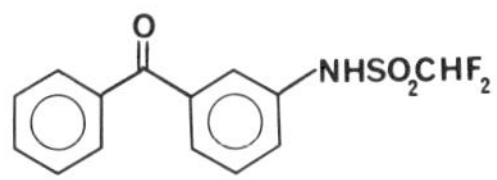 | Methanesulphonamide, *N*-(3-benzoyl-phenyl),1,1-difluoro (Diflumidone) | $C_{14}H_{11}F_2NO_3S$ | 311 | 6 μ*M* | BSV | Competitive | 281 |
| 18. | 22736-86-3 | 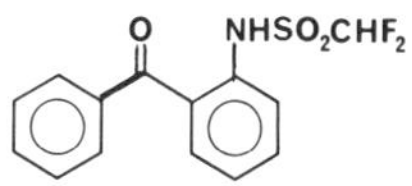 | Methanesulphonamide, *N*-(2-benzoyl-phenyl),1,1-difluoro | $C_{14}H_{11}F_2NO_3S$ | 311 | 5 μ*M* | SSV | Competitive, inhibits arachidonic acid-induced platelet aggregation | 281 |
| 19. | | 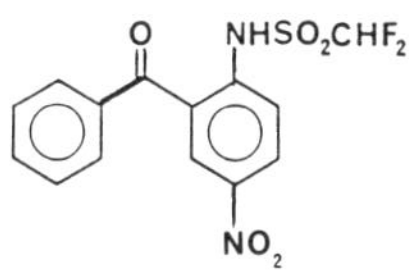 | Methanesulphonamide, *N*-(2-benzoyl-4-nitro-phenyl), 1,1-difluoro | $C_{14}H_{10}F_2N_2O_5S$ | 356 | 25 μ*M* | BSV | More active *in vivo* than diflumidone (No. 16) | 281 |

[a] If available.
[b] $IC_{50}$ unless otherwise stated.

## Table 8
## PHENOLS, ANTI-OXIDANTS

| Entry no. | Chemical abstracts number[a] | Structure | Chemical name (common name) | Molecular formula | Mol wt | Inhibitory potency[b] | Assay | Comments | Ref. |
|---|---|---|---|---|---|---|---|---|---|
| 1. | 103-90-2 | 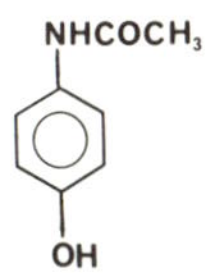 | Acetamide, *N*-(4-hydroxyphenyl) (Acetaminophen) | $C_8H_9NO_2$ | 151 | 893 μ*M* | BSV | More potent an inhibitor of rabbit brain cyclooxygenase, reversible, noncompetitive | 66, 98, 235 |
| 2. | 117-99-7 | 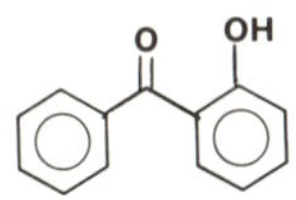 | 2-Hydroxybenzophenone | $C_{13}H_{10}O_2$ | 198 | 3 μ*M* | SSV | | 176 |
| 3. | 6272-38-4 | 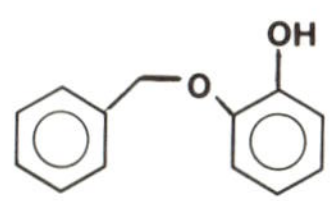 | 2-Benzyloxyphenol | $C_{13}H_{12}O_2$ | 200 | 5 μ*M* | SSV | | 176 |
| 4. | 527-60-6 | 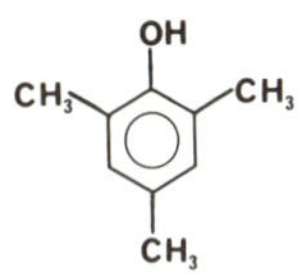 | Phenol, 2,4,6-trimethyl | $C_9H_{12}O$ | 136 | 7 μ*M* | SSV | Electron-donating or lipophilic substituents increased inhibitory potency | 176 |
| 5. | 582-17-2 | 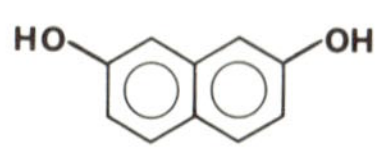 | 2,7-Dihydroxy-naphthalene | $C_{10}H_8O_2$ | 160 | 2.0 μ*M* | BSV | Most active dihydroxy-naphthalene inhibitor, active *in vivo* anti-inflammatory (rat) | 282 |

| | | | | | | | | | |
|---|---|---|---|---|---|---|---|---|---|
| 6. | 305-01-1 | 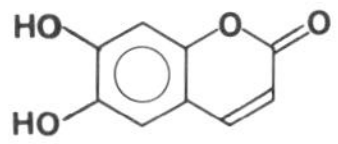  | 2H-1-Benzopyran-2-one, 6,7-dihydroxy | $C_9H_6O_4$ | 178 | active at $10^{-5}M$ | Cercariae | | 283 |
| 7. | 20123-80-2 | 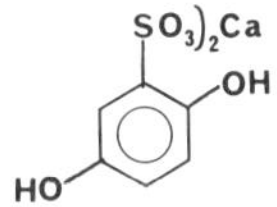  | Benzenesulphonic acid,2,5-dihydroxy, calcium salt | $C_{12}H_{10}CaO_{10}S_2$ | 418 | 101 $\mu M$ | Pregnant human myometrium | | 284 |
| 8. | 481-42-5 | 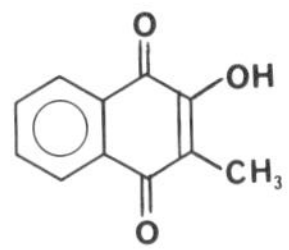  | 2-Methyl-3-hydroxy-naphthoquinone | $C_{11}H_8O_3$ | 188 | −88% at $10^{-3}M$ | Rat renal medulla | More lipophilic analogues showed greater potency | 285 |
| 9. | 153-18-4 | 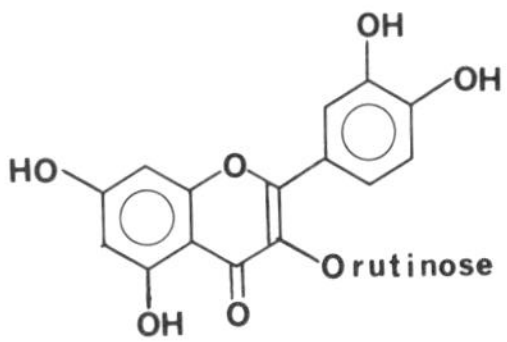  | 3-[[6-0-(6-Deoxy-α-L-mannopyranosyl)-β-D-glucopyranosyl]oxy]-2-(3,4-dihydroxy-phenyl)5,7-dihydroxy-4H-1-benzopyran-4-one (Rutin) | $C_{27}H_{30}O_{16}$ | 610.5 | active at 10 μm | | The aglycone, quercetin, is an inhibitor of both cyclooxygenase and lipoxygenase | 286, 287 |
| 10. | | 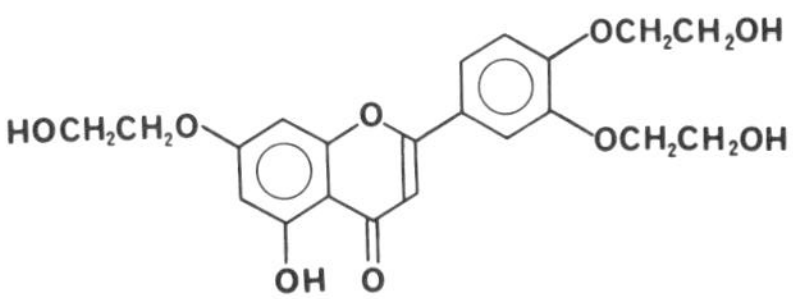  | 4H-1-Benzopyran-4-one, 2-[3,4-di(2-hydroxy-ethoxy)phenyl]-7-(2-hydroxyethoxy)-5-hydroxy | $C_{21}H_{22}O_9$ | 418 | <20 $\mu M$ | Human skin | 7-Mono(hydroxyethyl) compound *increases* prostaglandin production | 178 |
| 11. | 1406-18-4 | 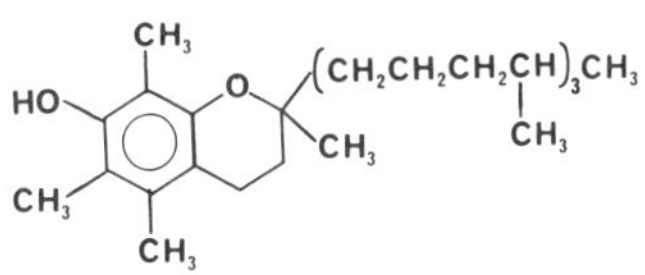  | 2,5,7,8-Tetramethyl-(4′,8′,12′-trimethyltri-decyl)-6-chromanol (Vitamin E) | $C_{29}H_{50}O_2$ | 430 | | Human platelets | Irreversible, time-dependent | 288 |
| 12. | 152-23-4 | 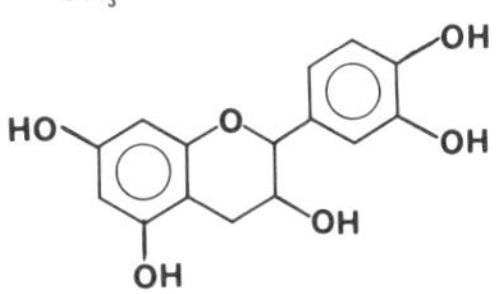  | 2H-1-Benzopyran-3,5,7-triol,2-(3,4-dihydroxy-phenyl),3,4-dihydro ((+) Cyanidanol) | $C_{15}H_{14}O_6$ | 290 | 50 $\mu M$ | Rat renal medulla | Inhibits PGE production *in vivo* (rat), used in treatment of hepatitis | 289 |

## Table 8 (continued)
## PHENOLS, ANTI-OXIDANTS

| Entry no. | Chemical abstracts number[a] | Structure | Chemical name (common name) | Molecular formula | Mol wt | Inhibitory potency[b] | Assay | Comments | Ref. |
|---|---|---|---|---|---|---|---|---|---|
| 13. | | 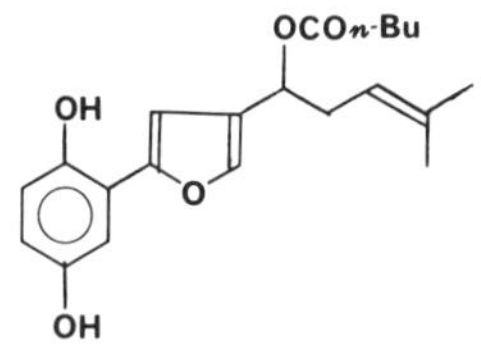 | Pent-3-en-1-ol,1-[2-(2,5-dihydroxyphenyl)-4-furyl-4-methyl, pentanoate | $C_{21}H_{26}O_5$ | 358 | −73% at 6 μ*M* | Rabbit kidney | Isolated from *Arnebia euchroma* | 217 |
| 14. | | 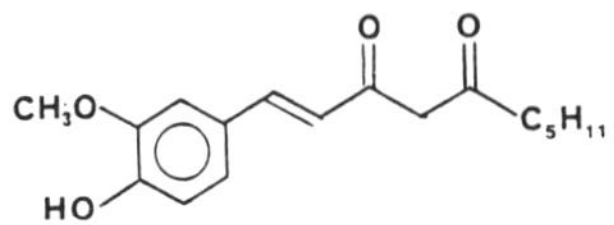 | Dec-1-en-3,5-dione 1-(4-hydroxy-3-methoxy-phenyl [6] Dehydrogingerdione) | $C_{17}H_{20}O_4$ | 290 | 1.0 μ*M* | Rabbit kidney | Extracted from ginger | 290 |
| 15. | | 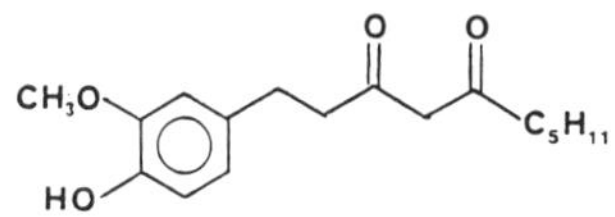 | Decane-3,5-dione,1-(4-hydroxy-3-methoxy-phenyl) ([6] Gingerdione) | $C_{17}H_{20}O_4$ | 288 | 1.6 μ*M* | Rabbit kidney | | 290 |
| 16. | | 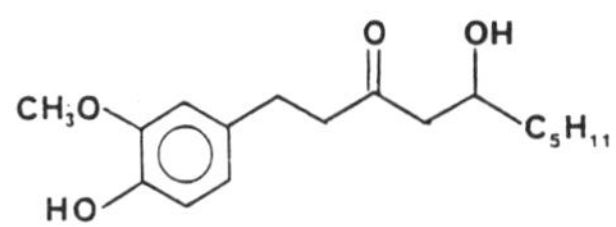 | Decan-3-on-5-ol, 1-(4-hydroxy-3-methoxy-phenyl) ([6] Gingerol) | $C_{17}H_{26}O_4$ | 294 | 5.5 μ*M* | Rabbit kidney | Shows analgesic and antipyretic properties | 290 |
| 17. | 458-37-7 | 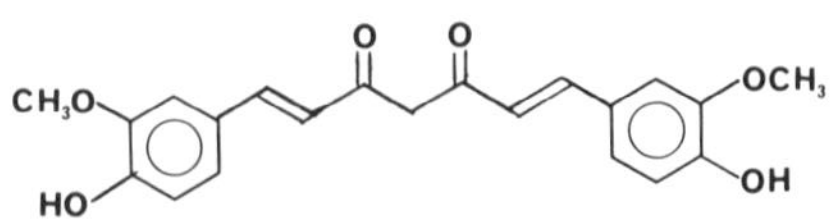 | 1,6-Heptadiene-3,5-dione,1,7-bis(4-hydroxy-3-methoxy-phenyl) (Curcumin) | $C_{21}H_{20}O_6$ | 368 | 100 μ*M* | Monkey platelets | Has anti-inflammatory and antithrombotic effects *in vivo* | 180 |

| | | | | | | | | | | |
|---|---|---|---|---|---|---|---|---|---|---|
| 18. | 91-53-2 | 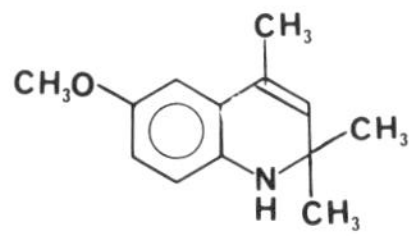 | 6-Ethoxy-1,2-dihydro-2,2,4-trimethylquinoline (Santoquin) | $C_{14}H_{17}NO$ | 215 | 6.5 μ*M* | SSV | | Several antioxidants inhibited both cyclooxygenase and lipooxygenase, santoquin was specific for Co, non-competitive | 291 |
| 19. | 496-74-2 | 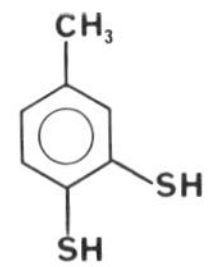 | Toluenc, 3,5-dimercapto | $C_7H_8S_2$ | 156 | 15 μ*M* | SSV | | | 292 |

[a] If available.
[b] $IC_{50}$ unless otherwise stated.

A large number of relatively simple phenols have been examined for cyclooxygenase inhibition. Electron-donating or lipophilic substituents generally were found to increase inhibitory potency. The compounds were noncompetitive reversible inhibitors which did not cause a time-dependent inactivation of the enzyme, in contrast to agents such as indomethacin.[139,175] Acetaminophen (Compound 1) is the most important therapeutic agent among this group of compounds. It is a reversible inhibitor of cyclooxygenase, from which it can be inferred that unlike aspirin it does not act by irreversibly transferring the acetyl group to the enzyme. The *in vitro* inhibitory potency in peripheral tissues is relatively low, but is considerably higher in the brains of mouse, dog, and rabbit, an observation which has been proposed to account for the analgetic/antipyretic rather than anti-inflammatory effects which acetaminophen evokes *in vivo*.[68,98,99]

Relatively simple phenols are used in a number of topical preparations in which anti-inflammatory activity may be an advantage. For example, 2-hydroxybenzophenone (Compound 2) is a constituent of a sunscreen preparation;[176] the *ortho* hydroxyketone moiety in this compound is reminiscent of the β-dicarbonyl enolic acids discussed earlier in the section on enolic acids. A number of polyhydroxylated chromones and flavones are weak inhibitors or even stimulators of cyclooxygenase, and some have also been shown to be inhibitors of lipoxygenase (see the chapter by J. Pfister in this volume). The more active compounds have an *ortho* dihydroxy moiety, and are scavengers of peroxide radical anion, though this property did not correlate with cyclooxygenase inhibition.[177] Hydroxyethylation of free phenolic groups in one instance caused a change from stimulation to inhibition of prostaglandin biosynthesis[178] (Compound 10).

A group of compounds related not only structurally and biogenetically, but also in their origin in natural food flavorings, is included in Table 8. Curcumin (Compound 17) and three closely related compounds extracted from ginger (Compounds 14, 15, and 16) are cyclooxygenase inhibitors which also evince *in vivo* effects attributable to that property. An examination of the chemical constituents of turmeric, which is used in Indian medicine as an anti-inflammatory agent, showed it to contain a variety of compounds. Of the components, only curcumin was found to possess significant activity in animal models of inflammation[179] (cotton pellet granuloma assay, adjuvant arthritis assay) as well as antithrombotic effects.[180] The presence in this group of compounds of enolizable β-diketone groups analogous to those in the enolic acids (Table 7) may contribute to their cyclooxygenase-inhibitory activity.

**Quinazolinediones: (Table 9)**

Unlike the compound classes which have been discussed so far in this section, the quinazolinediones are not acidic. The development of nonacidic cyclooxygenase inhibitors for use in inflammatory disease has received sporadic attention, inspired largely by the hope that, unlike acidic agents, neutral or basic compounds would not accumulate in parietal cells, and would therefore cause less gastrointestinal irritation.[93] Neutral compounds such as the quinazolinediones would be expected to show different pharmacokinetic and tissue-distribution patterns, and the extent of their side effects compared to those of established agents remains to be clarified. The compounds bear some structural resemblances both to phenylbutazone-like compounds and to arylacetic acids, in that they contain two linked aromatic systems which are unlikely to be coplanar. Whether or not this analogy is valid, proquazone is an extremely potent inhibitor of cyclooxygenase. The propionic acid (Compound 3) is one of a group of compounds which were designed as cyclooxygenase inhibitors with structural characteristics of both quinazolinediones and of amfenac (Table 5, Compound 4). Although some compounds of moderate-inhibitory potency resulted, the most potent inhibitor (Compound 3) showed no *in vivo* anti-inflammatory activity.[181]

# Table 9
# QUINAZOLINEDIONES

| Entry no. | Chemical abstracts number[a] | Structure | Chemical name (common name) | Molecular formula | Mol wt | Inhibitory potency[b] | Assay | Comments | Ref. |
|---|---|---|---|---|---|---|---|---|---|
| 1. | 22760-18-5 | 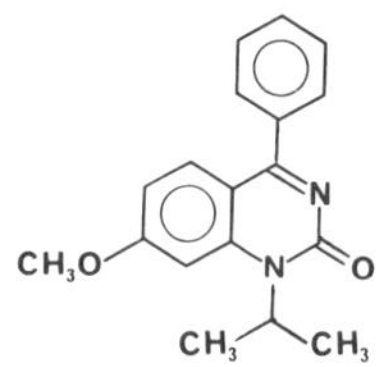 | 2-(1H)Quinazolinone 7-methyl-1(-1-methyl-ethyl)-4-phenyl (Proquazone) | $C_{18}H_{18}N_2O_2$ | 294 | 0.07 $\mu M$ | BSV | | 181 |
| 2. | 33453-23-5 | 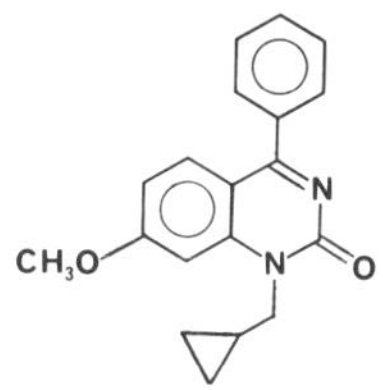 | 2(1H)Quinazolinone, 1-(cyclopropylmethyl)-6-methoxy-4-phenyl (Ciproquazone) | $C_{19}H_{18}N_2O_2$ | 306 | 5 $\mu M$ | BSV | | 293 |
| 3. | 91409-57-3 | 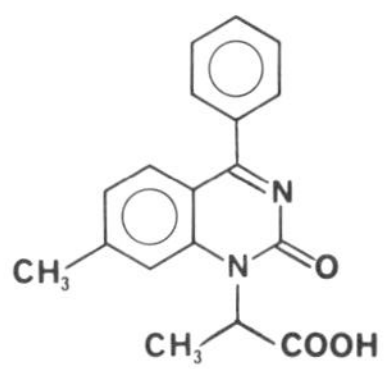 | 1(2H)-Quinazolineacetic acid, α-7-dimethyl-2-oxo-4-phenyl | $C_{18}H_{16}N_2O_3$ | 308 | 300 $\mu M$ | BSV | | 181 |

[a] If available.
[b] $IC_{50}$ unless otherwise stated.

## Table 10
## DIARYL HETEROCYCLES

| Entry no. | Chemical abstracts number[a] | Structure | Chemical name (common name) | Molecular formula | Mol wt | Inhibitory potency[b] | Assay | Comments | Ref. |
|---|---|---|---|---|---|---|---|---|---|
| 1. | 13682-29-6 | 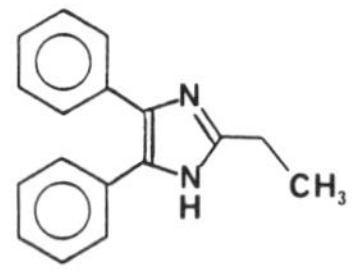 | 1H-Imidazole, 2-ethyl-4,5-diphenyl | $C_{17}H_{16}N_2$ | 248 | 1.0 μ*M* | SSV | | 13 |
| 2. | 36740-73-5 | 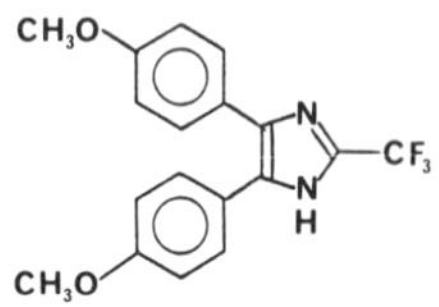 | 1H-Imidazole, 4,5-bis-(4-methoxy-phenyl)-2-(trifluoromethyl) (Flumizole) | $C_{18}H_{15}F_3N_2O_2$ | 348 | 0.2 μ*M*<br>0.7 μ*M* | SSV<br>Goat SV | | 13<br>185 |
| 3. | 30011-11-1 | 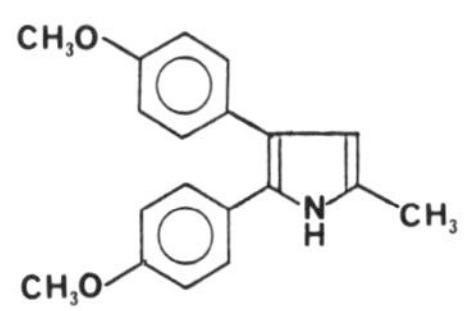 | 1H-Pyrrole, 2,3-bis(4-methoxyphenyl)-5-methyl (Bimetopyrol) | $C_{19}H_{19}NO_2$ | 293 | | SSV | | 13 |
| 4. | 73445-46-2 | 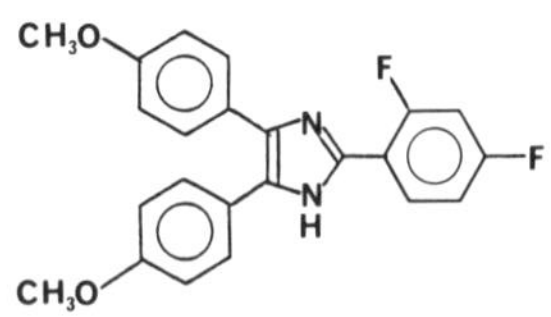 | 1H-Imidazole,2-(2,4-di-fluorophenyl)-4,5-bis(4-methoxyphenyl) (Fenflumizole) | $C_{23}H_{18}F_2N_2O_2$ | 392 | 1.8 μ*M* | BSV | Does not inhibit $TXA_2$ synthetase, inhibits arachidonic acid induced bronchoconstriction (guinea pig) | 184 |

| | | | | | | | | | |
|---|---|---|---|---|---|---|---|---|---|
| 5. | 5034-76-4 | 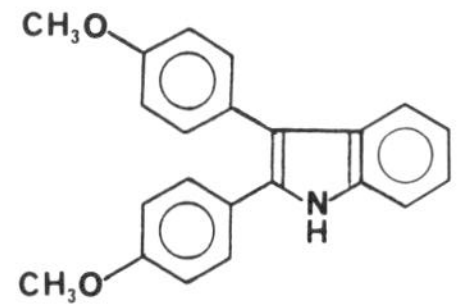 | 1H-Indole,2,3-bis-(4-methoxyphenyl) (Indoxole) | $C_{22}H_{19}NO_2$ | 329 | 1.5 μ*M* | SSV | | 13 |
| 6. | 62894-82-0 | 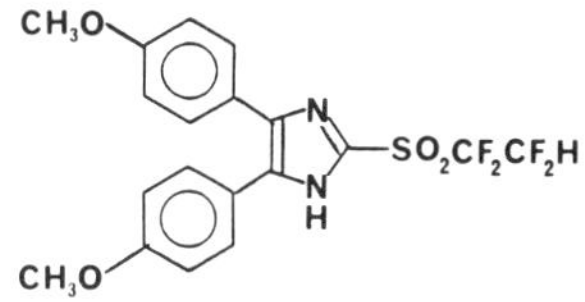 | 1H-Imidazole,4,5-bis(4-methoxyphenyl)-2-[(1,1,2,2-tetrafluoroethyl) sulfonyl] | $C_{19}H_{16}F_4N_2O_4S$ | 444 | 0.14 μ*M* | BSV | | 186 |
| 7. | 62894-89-7 | 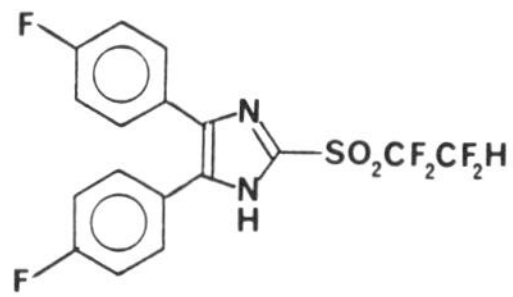 | 1H-Imidazole,4,5-bis(4-fluorophenyl)-2-[(1,1,2,2,-tetrafluoroethyl)sulfonyl] (Tiflamizole) | $C_{17}H_{10}F_6N_2O_2S$ | 420 | 0.4 μ*M* | BSV | | 186 |
| 8. | 21256-18-8 | 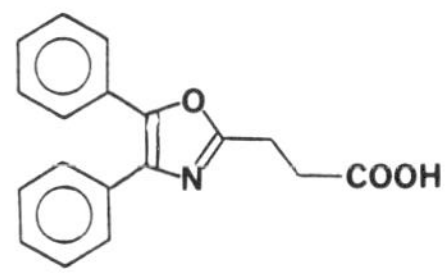 | 2-Oxazolepropanoic acid,4,5-diphenyl (Oxaprozin) | $C_{18}H_{15}NO_3$ | 293 | 124 μ*M* | Rabbit platelets | Anti-inflammatory and antithrombotic *in vivo* | 294 |
| 9. | 18471-20-0 | 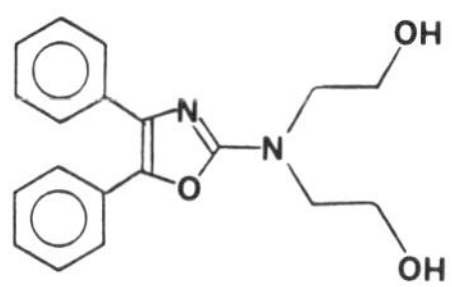 | Ethanol,2,2′[4,5-diphenyl-2-oxazolyl)imino]bis | $C_{19}H_{20}N_2O_3$ | 324 | 6.4 μ*M* | Rat platelet | | 102 |

[a] If available.
[b] $IC_{50}$ unless otherwise stated.

**Diaryl Heterocycles: (Table 10)**

The compounds of Table 10 exhibit considerable structural homogeneity; they have two phenyl rings, usually *para* substituted, attached to a five-membered heterocyclic ring, to which a variety of side-chains are attached. Relatively little has been published about the pharmacology of these compounds though several of them have undergone advanced study as anti-inflammatory agents. Indoxole[182] (Compound 5) was the first compound of this type to undergo clinical evaluation, but proved to have photosensitizing properties which presumably were associated with its extended ultraviolet chromophore.[183] Flumizole (Compound 2) was eight times as potent as indomethacin *in vitro,*[185] and was also more potent in animal models. The compound was active in clinical trials, though the efficacy may have been reduced by poor bioavailability caused by low aqueous solubility,[185] a problem which may affect other members of this group of neutral compounds. Tiflamizole (Compound 7), a du Pont compound which incorporates a tetrafluoroethylene group in the side chain, is a potent inhibitor of cyclooxygenase.[186] The compound showed *in vivo* activity commensurate with the high *in vitro* potency[187] (10× indomethacin in the adjuvant arthritis assay) and had a better therapeutic ratio with respect to gastric ulceration that either pyroxicam, sulindac, or ibuprofen.[188] However, it was chiefly distinguished by extraordinarily long half-lives after oral administration to animals and man. After relatively rapid adsorption, slow fecal elimination occurred with half-lives ranging from 1.6 d in the dog to 11 d in man. After an initial loading dose of 5 mg, appropriate blood levels were maintained in man by a daily dose of 0.25 mg.[189] The slow excretion may indicate that the neutral lipophilic compound is distributed preferentially into lipid regions of the body. The structures of the diaryl heterocycles are such that coplanarity of the three aromatic rings seems unlikely due to interactions between hydrogens at the *ortho* positions relative to the heterocyclic ring. Whether or not this has any relevance to the nonplanar receptor site models is a matter of conjecture. The frequent occurrence of *para* methoxy substituents in the more potent cyclooxygenase inhibitors in this group of compounds may indicate that they act as radical-trapping agents.

**Depsides: (Table 11)**

During attempts to find novel inhibitors of prostaglandin biosynthesis from microbial cultures, a number of cyclooxygenase inhibitors were isolated from *Thielavia terricola,* a fungus isolated from animal dung. The most potent were the tridepsides (esters of phenolic benzoic acids), thielavin A (Compound 3), and thielavin B (Compound 4).[190,191] Although neither compound was effective in inhibiting paw edema in the rat following oral administration, thielavin B (but not thielavin A) produced a significant reduction in paw volume following i.v. administration of a dose of 5 mg/kg. Following this finding, a group of 40 structurally analogous mono- and dibenzenoid esters and acids were examined for similar activities. The dimeric compounds 1 and 2 were found to be potent inhibitors of cyclooxygenase, with $IC_{50}$ values comparable to those for indomethacin.[129,192] Compound 1, 4-*O*-methylcryptochlorophaeic acid, was found to inactivate the molecule in a time-dependent manner, and to be competitive with respect to the substrate arachidonic acid. Monobenzenoid compounds which combine the two halves of Compound 1 were found to be more than two orders of magnitude less potent that the dimeric molecules. Based on these findings, and an X-ray crystal structure for Compound 1, an active-site model for cyclooxygenase was proposed (see earlier section on models of the cyclooxygenase active site). *In vivo* anti-inflammatory activities, if any, of the potent inhibitors 1 and 2 have not been reported.

# Table 11
## DEPSIDES

| Entry no. | Chemical abstracts number[a] | Structure | Chemical name (common name) | Molecular formula | Mol wt | Inhibitory potency[b] | Assay | Comments | Ref. |
|---|---|---|---|---|---|---|---|---|---|
| 1. | 27587-68-4 | 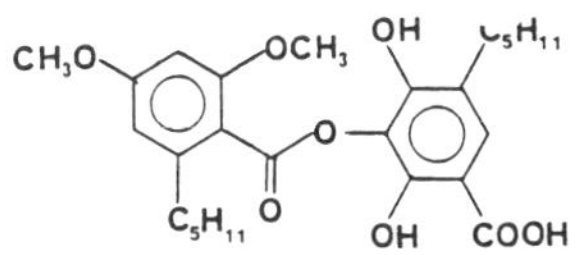 | Benzoic acid, 3-[(2,4-dimethoxy-6-pentylbenzoyl)oxy]-2,4-dihydroxy-5-pentyl (4-O-Methylcryptochlorophaeic acid) | $C_{26}H_{34}O_8$ | 474 | 0.34 μ*M* | Rabbit kidney | Competitive; most potent of a group of 40 analogues | 129, 192 |
| 2. | 2879-80-3 | 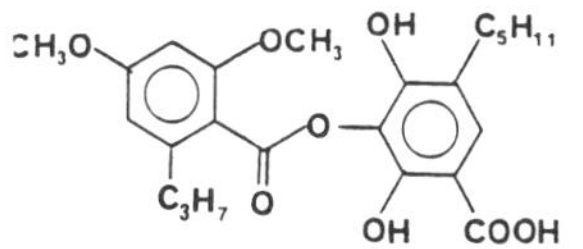 | Benzoic acid,3-[(2,4-dimethoxy-6-propylbenzoyl)oxy]-2,4-dihydroxy-5-pentyl (Merochlorophaeic acid) | $C_{24}H_{30}O_8$ | 446 | 0.43 μ*M* | Rabbit kidney | Monomeric compounds ca. 100× less potent | 129, 192 |
| 3. | 71950-66-8 | 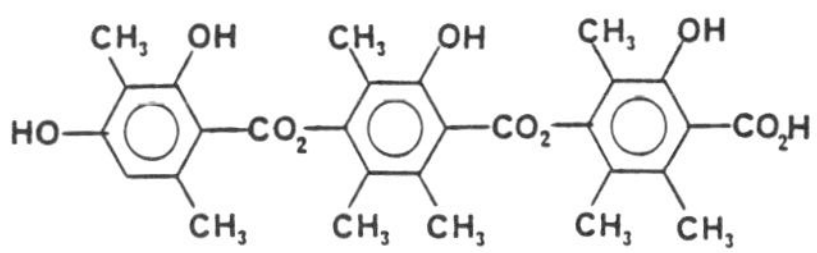 | Benzoic acid,4-[(2,4-dihydroxy-3,6-di-methylbenzoyl)oxy]-2-hydroxy-3,5,6-trimethyl,4-carboxy-3-hydroxy-2,5,6-trimethylphenyl ester (Thielavin A) | $C_{29}H_{30}O_{10}$ | 538 | 12 μ*M* | SSV | Shows no *in vivo* anti-inflammatory activity, p.o. or i.v. | 190, 191 |
| 4. | 71950-67-9 | 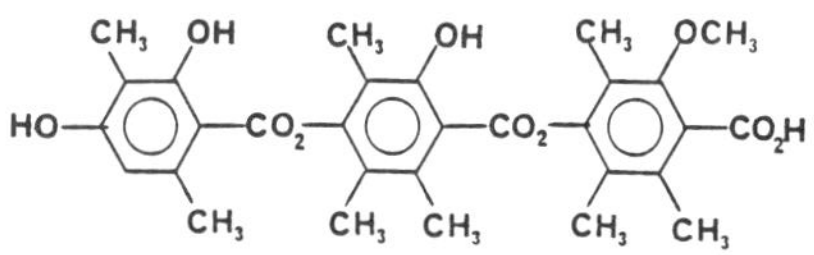 | Benzoic acid,4-[(2,4-dihydroxy-3,6-dimethylbenzoyl)oxy]-2-methoxy-3,5,6-trimethyl,4-carboxy-3-methoxy-2,5,6-trimethylphenyl ester (Thielavin B) | $C_{30}H_{32}O_{10}$ | 552 | 9 μ*M* | SSV | Active at 5 mg/kg, i.v. vs. rat carageenin edema | 190, 191 |

[a] If available.
[b] $IC_{50}$ unless otherwise stated.

## Table 12
## ESTROGENS AND ANTI-ESTROGENS

| Entry no. | Chemical abstracts number[a] | Structure | Chemical name (common name) | Molecular formula | Mol wt | Inhibitory potency[b] | Assay | Comments | Ref. |
|---|---|---|---|---|---|---|---|---|---|
| 1. | 10540-29-1 | 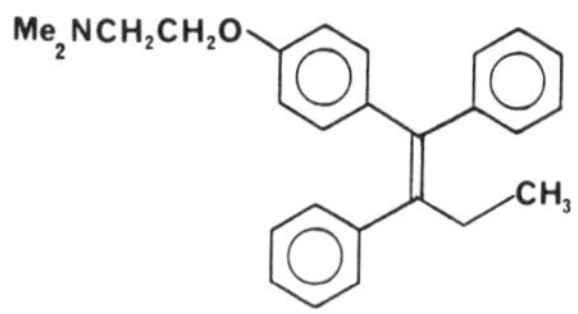 | Ethanamine,2-[4-(1,2-diphenyl-1-butenyl)phenoxy]-*N,N*-dimethyl (Tamoxifen) | $C_{26}H_{29}NO$ | 371 | 2.2 μ*M* −65% at $10^{-4}M$ | BSV Breast tumor | Inhibition of breast tumor PG synthesis was not prevented by estradiol | 193, 195 |
| 2. | 22393-63-1 | 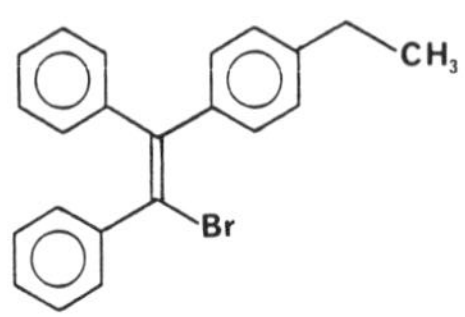 | Benzene,1-(2-bromo-1,2-diphenyl-ethenyl)-4-ethyl (Broparestrol-Z) | $C_{22}H_{19}Br$ | 363 | 7.0 μ*M* | BSV | Estrogen | 195 |
| 3. | 22393-62-0 | 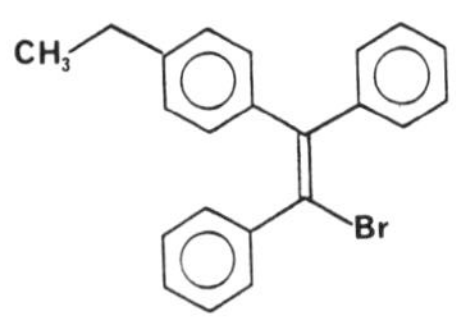 | Benzene, 1-(2-bromo-1,2-diphenylethenyl)-4-ethyl, (E) (Broparestrol-E) | $C_{22}H_{19}Br$ | 363 | 2.8 μ*M* | BSV | Estrogen | 195 |
| 4. | 1845-11-0 | 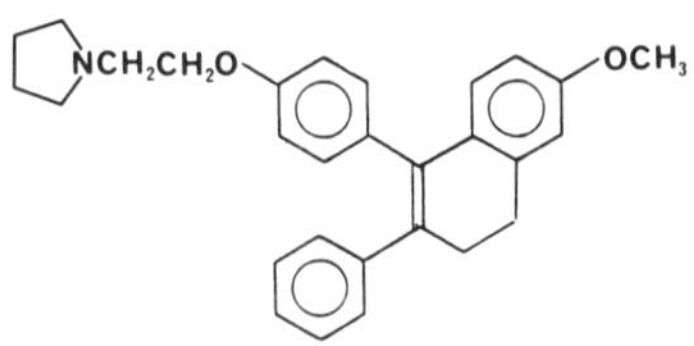 | Pyrrolidine,1-[2-[4-(3,4-dihydro-6-methoxy-2-phenyl-1-naphthalenyl)-phenoxy]ethyl] (Nafoxidine) | $C_{29}H_{31}NO$ | 409 | 2.6 μ*M* | BSV | | 195 |

| | | | | | | | | | |
|---|---|---|---|---|---|---|---|---|---|
| 5. | 911-45-5 | 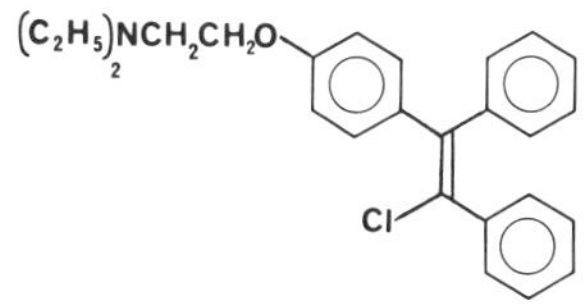 | Ethanamine,2-[4-(2-chloro-1,2-diphenylethenyl)phenoxy]-*N*,*N*-diethyl (Clomiphene) | $C_{26}H_{28}ClNO$ | 377.5 | 1.3 μ*M*,<br>8.0 μ*M* | BSV<br>BSV | | 195<br>295 |
| 6. | 56-53-1 | 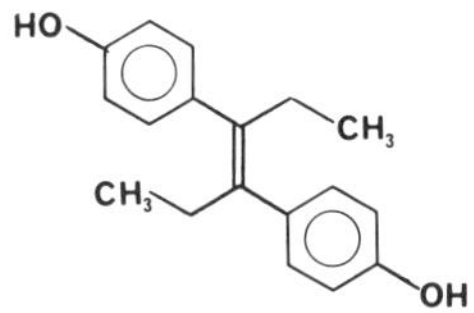 | E-4,4′(1,2-Diethyl-1,2-ethenediyl)-bisphenol (E) (Diethylstilbestrol) | $C_{18}H_{20}O_2$ | 268 | 44 μ*M* | BSV | | 295 |
| 7. | 67-98-1 | 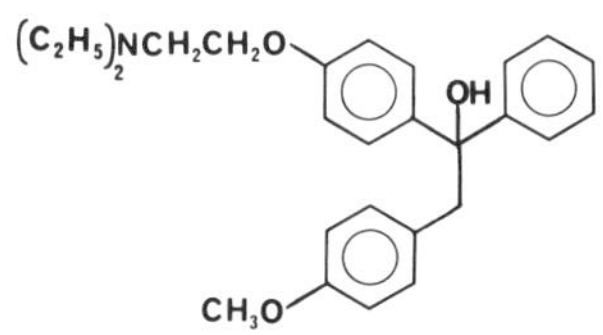 | α-[4-[2(Diethylamino)ethoxy]phenyl]-4-methoxy-α-phenylbenzeneethanol (Ethamoxytriphetol) | $C_{27}H_{33}NO_3$ | 419 | 400 μ*M* | BSV | Marginally active *in vivo* (rat carageenin paw assay) | 295 |
| 8. | 78-41-1 | 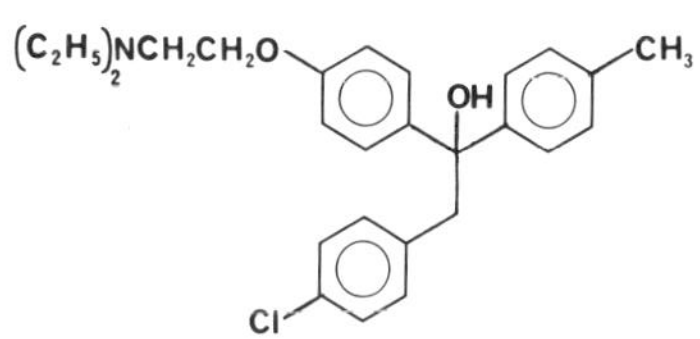 | 4-Chloro-α-[4-[2-(diethylamino)ethoxy]phenyl]α-(4-methylphenyl)benzeneethanol (Triparanol) | $C_{27}H_{32}ClNO_2$ | 438 | 800 μ*M* | BSV | As above | 295 |

[a] If available.
[b] $IC_{50}$ unless otherwise stated.

## Table 13
## TRIPHENYLACRYLONITRILES

| Entry no. | Chemical abstracts number[a] | Structure | Chemical name (common name) | Molecular formula | Mol wt | Inhibitory potency[b] | Assay | Comments | Ref. |
|---|---|---|---|---|---|---|---|---|---|
| 1. | 82925-23-3 | 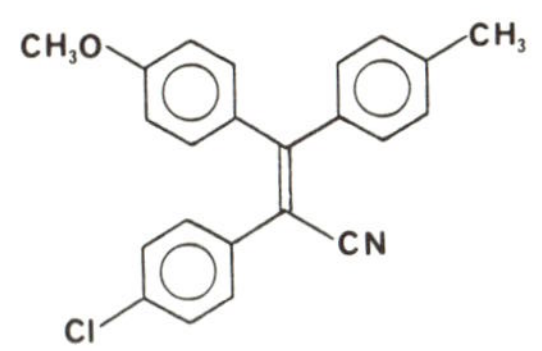 | Benzeneacetonitrile 4-chloro-α-[(4-methoxy-phenyl)(4-methyl-phenyl)-methylene](E) | $C_{23}H_{18}ClNO$ | 359.5 | 0.03 μ*M* | BSV | | 195 |
| 2. | 84836-21-5 | 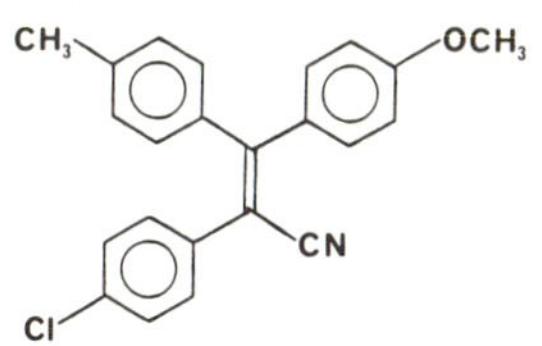 | Benzeneacetonitrile 4-chloro-α-[(4-methoxy-phenyl)(4-methyl-phenyl)-methylene]-(Z) | $C_{23}H_{18}ClNO$ | 359.5 | 0.05 μ*M* | BSV | | 195 |
| 3. | 82925-24-4 | 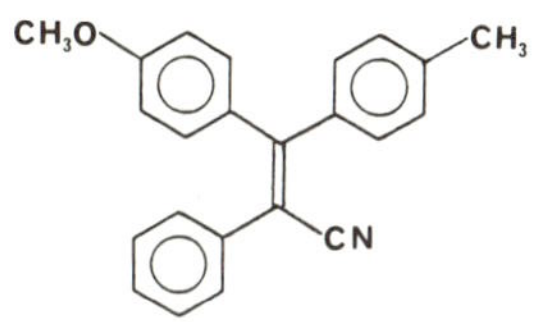 | Benzeneacetonitrile α-[(4-methoxyphenyl)(4-methylphenyl) methylene], (Z) | $C_{23}H_{19}NO$ | 325 | 0.5 μ*M* | BSV | | 195 |
| 4. | 84836-18-0 | 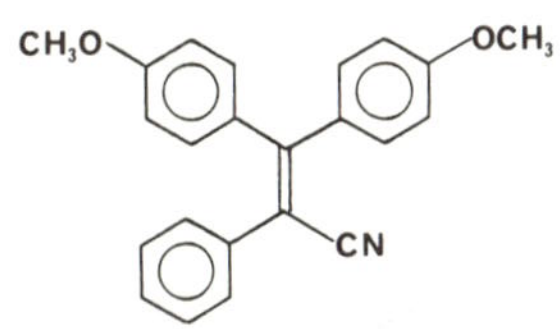 | Benzeneacetonitrile α-[(4-methoxyphenyl)(4-methylphenyl) methylene], (E) | $C_{23}H_{19}NO$ | 325 | 0.6 μ*M* | BSV | | 195 |

| | | | | | | | | |
|---|---|---|---|---|---|---|---|---|
| 5. | 84836-14-6 | 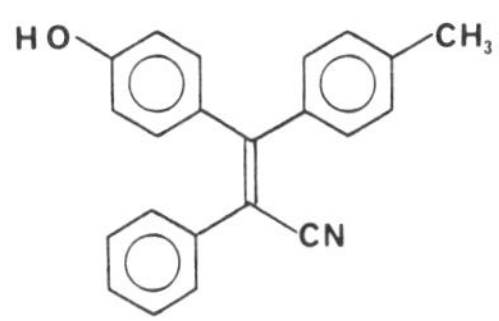 | Benzeneacetonitrile α-[(4-hydroxyphenyl)(4-methylphenyl) methylene], (Z) | $C_{22}H_{17}NO$ | 311 | 0.08 μ*M* | BSV | 195 |
| 6. | 84836-13-5 | 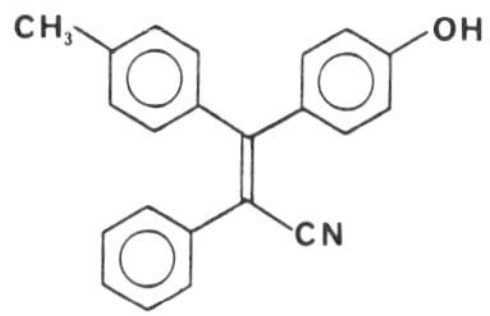 | Benzeneacetonitrile α-[(4-hydroxyphenyl)(4-methylphenyl) methylene], (E) | $C_{22}H_{17}NO$ | 311 | 0.3 μ*M* | BSV | 195 |

[a] If available.
[b] $IC_{50}$ unless otherwise stated.

**Estrogens and Anti-Estrogens: (Table 12)**

The potential advantages of a combined anti-estrogen/cyclooxygenase inhibitor for the treatment of breast tumors have been described,[193,194] though not yet established in practice. Inhibition of cyclooxygenase could reduce prostaglandin-induced bone resorption, and, to the extent that they may be mediated by platelet aggregation, the production of metastases. It is not clear whether the ability of the estrogens and anti-estrogens of Table 11 to inhibit cyclooxygenase at submicromolar concentrations indicates similarities between the estrogen-receptor site and the cyclooxygenase-active site. The inhibition of cyclooxygenase by tamoxifen (Compound 1) was not prevented by estradiol, which itself had no effect. Structural analogies between these compounds and established cyclooxygenase inhibitors are tenuous; they have some features in common with the diaryl heterocycles (see earlier section on enolic acids) and closer resemblances to the triphenyl acrylonitriles (see next section).

**Triphenylacrylonitriles: (Table 13)**

More than 50 compounds of this structural type were screened for cyclooxygenase-inhibitory activity, following the observation that some structurally related estrogens and anti-estrogens had such activity (see previous section). A number of compounds were found to be extremely potent inhibitors, and inhibitory potency was found in some cases to be greatly affected by small structural changes.[195] Thus while the (E) and (Z) isomeric pairs 1 and 2, 3 and 4, were approximately equipotent, the analogous phenols 5 and 6 differed in potency by a factor of ten. The cyano group and the ethylenic bond were necessary for high inhibitory potency. Replacement of the cyano by carboxamide or carboxylic acid resulted in a reduction of one to two orders of magnitude, and hydrogenation of the double bond, while retaining the cyano group, had if anything a more profound effect. Conformational studies using X-ray analysis, NMR spectroscopy, and space-filling models indicated that the active compounds were relatively rigid molecules. Rotation of all the phenyl rings was restricted, and this was particularly true for the β-phenyl group, whose presence was essential for high-inhibitory potency. A parallel was drawn between the out-of-plane orientation of this ring and the nonplanar configuration of indomethacin-type compounds (see earlier sections on models of the cyclooxygenase active site and on arylacetic acids). The observed potentiating effect of the 4-chloro substituent on this ring (cf. Compounds 1 and 3, 2 and 4) supports the analogy with indomethacin. The introduction of the chloro substituent into indomethacin has a potentiating effect which has been proposed to be responsible for the irreversible inhibition of cyclooxygenase.[196]

**Tricyclic Amines: (Table 14)**

The relatively modest inhibition of cyclooxygenase by the lipophilic amines of Table 14 is unlikely to be associated with their more prominent CNS and antimalarial effects. No reduction of prostaglandin levels *in vivo* was detected after administration of chlorpromazine[197] and despite the prolonged administration of several of these agents to large groups of patients, no reports of anti-inflammatory or antirheumatic efficacy for neuroleptics have appeared. However, it is possible that the antipyretic activity of cyproheptadine (Compound 6) is a consequence of the inhibition of cyclooxygenase in the brain, and is independent of anti-serotonin and α-blocking properties.[198]

Mepacrine (Compound 5) has, like other antimalarals, been used for the treatment of rheumatoid arthritis.[199] Although the mechanism by which it acts is unknown, it is unlikely to be due to inhibition of cyclooxygenase, or indeed to remove a similarly weak inhibition of phospholipase $A_2$.[200,201] The inhibition of these enzymes by mepacrine has been ascribed to perturbation of the microsomal membranes in which they are bound[202] and the other compounds in Table 14 may act similarly. It should be noted that psychotropic agents structurally unrelated to those of Table 14, such as meprobamate, diazepam, reserpine, and bromoperidol, are also inhibitors of cyclooxygenase (see the next section).

**Miscellaneous Cyclooxygenase Inhibitors: (Table 15)**

In the preceding 15 sections, there have been indicated some unifying structural features among the various chemical classes of cyclooxygenase inhibitors. Such parallels are necessarily more difficult to draw for the heterogeneous group of compounds in Table 15, and although some similarities to previously described compounds exist, the following comments will mainly provide additional relevant information on individual compounds.

WY-41770 (Compound 1) is a weak inhibitor of cyclooxygenase which produces immunosuppressive and anti-inflammatory effects in animal tests. The compound was especially effective in the adjuvant arthritis assay, and did not produce gastric ulcerations in rats.[203,204] The mechanism of action is unknown but appears not to be due to inhibition of cyclooxygenase. The chromone derivative (Compound 2) inhibits adjuvant-induced arthritis in the rat at a dose of 100 mg/kg, and protects against ovalbumin-induced bronchoconstriction with an $ED_{50}$ of 0.3 mg/kg.[205] The former activity may be related to cyclooxygenase inhibition; the latter, because of the structural similarity between Compound 2 and cromolyn, may indicate that it acts as a mast-cell protector.[206] The pyrazolopyrimidine carboxylates (Compounds 2 and 3), despite having inhibitory potencies comparable to that of indomethacin, exhibit only weak *in vivo* anti-inflammatory activity and produce hypothermia in the rat. The compounds shown were the most potent of over 20 analogues.[207] The pyrimidopurines (Compound 6 and 7) were especially active in long-term anti-inflammatory assays, and had low ulcerogenicity. The unusual isoprene substituent was important for cyclooxygenase inhibition. Further development in this series was precluded because of the production of ocular toxicity.[208] The structure of diazepam (Compound 8) resembles those of the diaryl heterocycles (see earlier section on diaryl heterocycles) and the compound could perhaps be accommodated in the receptor-site models discussed earlier. It is not clear whether cyclooxygenase inhibition is relevant to the mechanism of action of this tranquilizer.[209]

The indole Compounds 9 and 11 are active in anti-inflammatory assays; however, while the *in vivo* activity of nictindole (Compound 9) is believed to be due to cyclooxygenase inhibition,[210] that of the bromomethyl gramine (Compound 11) is believed to be due to antiserotonin properties, since the *in vivo* potencies of a series of analogues appeared to be unrelated to cyclooxygenase inhibition.[211] Neither the benzoylpyrrole[212] (Compound 10) nor the indolenitrile (Compound 12) had significant *in vivo* anti-inflammatory activity, though the latter compound prevented arachidonic-acid-induced diarrhea in mice.[213] Inhibitory potency of a series of 2-phenylbenzisoxazoles (Compounds 14, 15, and 16) was found to be sensitive to substitution on the benzene ring; the p-tolyl derivative (Compound 16) was a potent inhibitor.[13] Information on the *in vivo* biological activities of these compounds, which may have been produced as analogues of the anthelmintic agent thiabendazole (Compound 17) is not available. Thiabendazole is a weak analgetic.[13] Dapsone (Compound 24) has shown efficacy in a rheumatoid arthritis clinical trial,[214,215] which was attributed to inhibition of complement activation rather than of cyclooxygenase. Among the more bizarre structures for which cyclooxygenase inhibition has been reported are a dioxime (Compound 22),[216] which is also an inhibitor of diaryl glycerol lipase, a naturally occurring naphthoquinone (Compound 23),[217] and a *bis*-isonitrile (Compound 27).[218] The latter is an extremely potent inhibitor, but produced no relevant *in vivo* effects at doses up to 50 mg/kg.[218]

## Table 14
## TRICYCLIC AMINES

| Entry no. | Chemical abstracts number[a] | Structure | Chemical name (common name) | Molecular formula | Mol wt | Inhibitory potency[b] | Assay | Comments | Ref. |
|---|---|---|---|---|---|---|---|---|---|
| 1. | 50-53-3 | 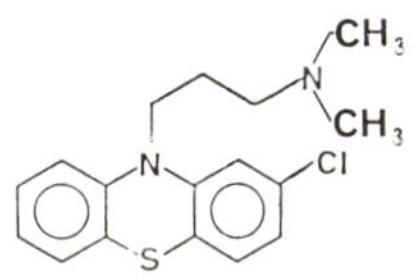 | 10H-Phenothiazine-10-propanamine,2-chloro-*N,N*-dimethyl (Chloropromazine) | $C_{20}H_{24}ClN_3S$ | 373.5 | 330 μ*M* | BSV | Also inhibits bovine brain cyclooxygenase | 200, 296 |
| 2. | 117-89-5 | 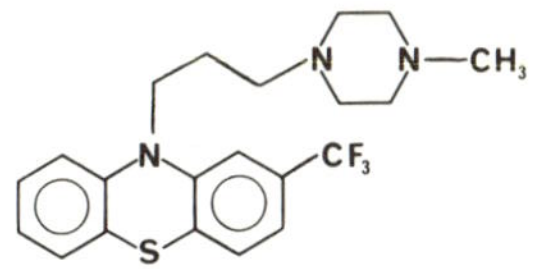 | 10H-Phenothiazine,10-[3-[4-methyl-1-piperazinyl]propyl]2-(trifluoromethyl) (Trifluperazine) | $C_{21}H_{24}F_3N_3S$ | 407 | 400 μ*M* | BSV | | 296 |
| 3. | 69-23-8 | 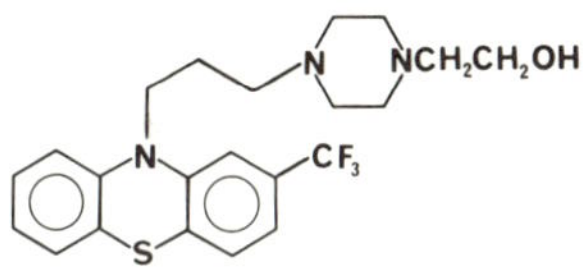 | 1-Piperazineethanol 4-[3-[2-(trifluoromethyl)-10H-phenothiazin-10-yl]-propyl] (Flufenazine) | $C_{22}H_{26}F_3N_3OS$ | 437 | 280 μ*M* | BSV | | 296 |
| 4. | 2709-56-0 | 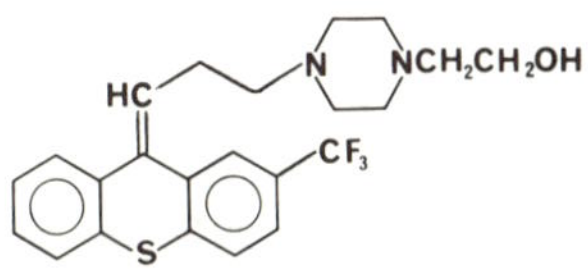 | 1-Piperazineethanol 4-[3-[2-(trifluoromethyl)-9H-thioxan-then-9-ylidene]-propyl] (Flupenthixol) | $C_{23}H_{25}F_3N_2OS$ | 419 | 290 μ*M* | BSV | | 296 |

| | | | | | | | | | |
|---|---|---|---|---|---|---|---|---|---|
| 5. | 83-89-6 | 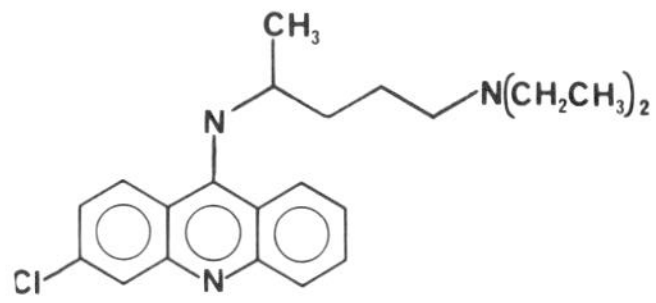 | 1,4-Pentanediamine, *N*4-(6-chloro-2-methoxy-9-acridinyl-*N*1,*N*1,diethyl | $C_{22}H_{28}ClN_3$ | 369.5 | 92% at 50 μ*M*, 22% at 20 μ*M* | Rabbit kidney | Antimalarial, also inhibits Phospholipase $A_2$ | 200 |
| 6. | 129-03-3 | 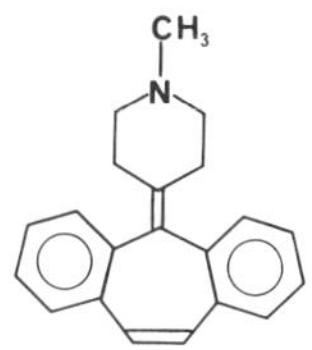 | 4,(5H-Dibenzo[a,d] cyclohepten-5-ylidine)-1-methylpiperidine (Cyproheptadine) | $C_{21}H_{21}N$ | 287 | ca. 10 μ*M* | Bovine cerebral cortex microsomes | Antipyretic; inhibited $PGE_1$-induced pyrexia | 198 |

[a] If available.
[b] $IC_{50}$ unless otherwise stated.

## Table 15
## MISCELLANEOUS

| Entry no. | Chemical abstracts number[a] | Structure | Chemical name (common name) | Molecular formula | Mol wt | Inhibitory potency[b] | Assay | Comments | Ref. |
|---|---|---|---|---|---|---|---|---|---|
| 1. | 4517-99-1 | 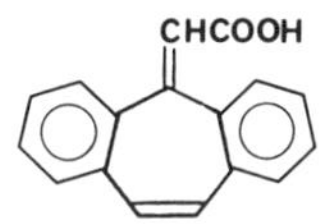 | Acetic acid, 5H-dibenzo[a,d]cyclohept-5-enylidene (WY-41770) | $C_{17}H_{12}O_2$ | 248 | 300 μ*M*<br>21 μ*M* | SSV<br>Mouse peritoneal macrophage | Not a lipoxygenase inhibitor; shows anti-inflammatory & immunosuppressive activity *in vivo* | 203<br>204 |
| 2. | 37456-31-8 | 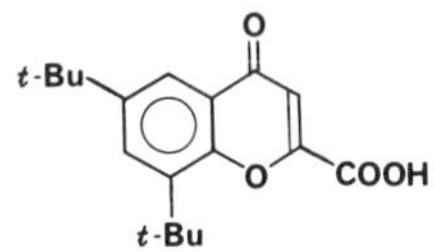 | 6,8-Di-t-butyl-4-oxo-4H-1-benzopyran-2-carboxylic acid (FPL 52791) | $C_{18}H_{22}O_4$ | 302 | −84% at 36 μ*M* | Pig-lung microsomes | Anti-inflammatory, analgesic, and anti-allergic *in vivo* | 205 |
| 3. | 96461-27-7 | 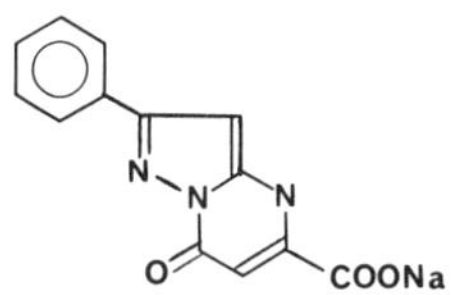 | Pyrazolo[1,5-a]pyrimidine-5-carboxylic acid,4,7-dihydro-7-oxo-2-phenyl (Sodium salt) | $C_{13}H_8N_3NaO_3$ | 277 | 1.63 μ*M* | Guinea-pig lung | *In vivo* anti-inflammatory analgesic; potency comparable to aspirin | 207 |
| 4. | 71509-32-5 | 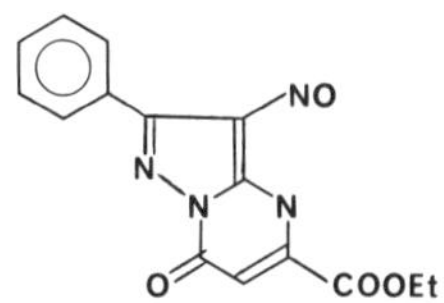 | Pyrazolo[1,5-a]pyrimidine-5-carboxylic acid,4,7-dihydro-3-nitroso-7-oxo-2-phenyl | $C_{14}H_{11}N_4O_3$ | 283 | 0.61 μ*M* | Guinea-pig lung | As above | 207 |
| 5. | | 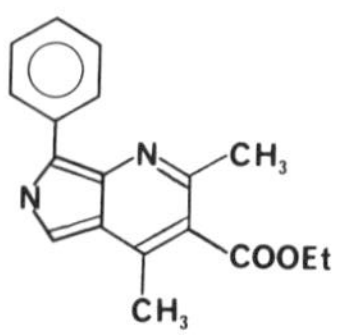 | Pyrrolo[3,4-b]-pyridine-6-carboxlyic acid, 5,7-dimethyl-3-phenyl, ethyl ester | $C_{18}H_{18}N_2O_2$ | 294 | 100% at 100 μ*M* | BSV | Anti-inflammatory activity at 50—100 mg/kg *in vivo* | 298 |

| | | | | | | | | | |
|---|---|---|---|---|---|---|---|---|---|
| 6. | 91297-71-1 | 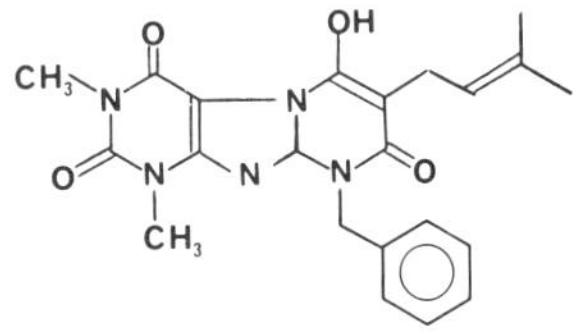 | 1,3-Dimethyl-9-(phenylmethyl)-6-hydroxy-7-(3-methyl-2-butenyl) pyrimido[2,1-f]purine-2,4,8(1H,3H,9H)trione | $C_{22}H_{23}N_5O_4$ | 421 | 2 μ*M* | Rat neutrophil | Weak lipoxygenase inhibitor at 50 μ*M*, *in vivo* anti-inflammatory activity, low ulcerogenic activity | 208 |
| 7. | 91285-56-2 | 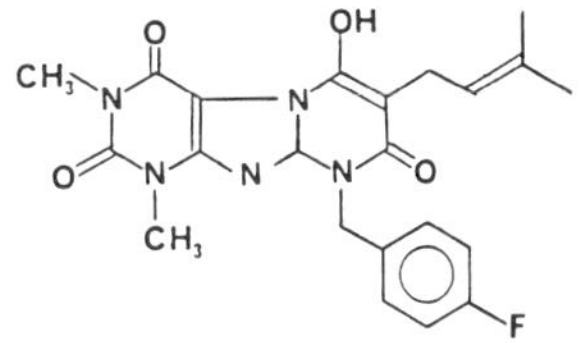 | 1,3-Dimethyl-9-[(4-fluorophenyl)-methyl]-6-hydroxy-7-(3-methyl-2-butenyl)pyrimido[2,1-f]purine-2,4,8(1H,3H,9H)trione | $C_{22}H_{22}FN_5O_4$ | 439 | 4.2 μ*M* | Rat neutrophil | As above | 208 |
| 8. | 439-14-5 | 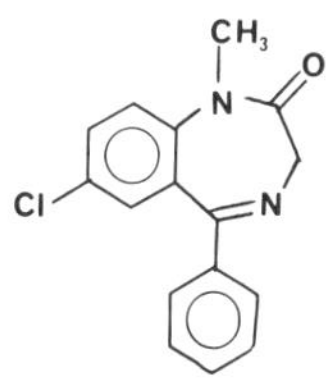 | 2H-1,4-Benzodiazepin-2-one,2-chloro-1,3-dihydro-1-methyl-5-phenyl (Diazepam) | $C_{16}H_{13}ClN_2O$ | 284.5 | 27 μ*M* | BSV | Also an inhibitor of phospholipase A | 209 |
| 9. | 36504-64-0 | 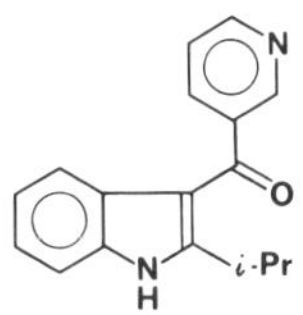 | Methanone,[2,(1-methylethyl)-1H-indol-3-yl]-3-pyridinyl (Nictindole) | $C_{17}H_{16}N_2O$ | 264 | 6 μ*M* | BSV | Anti-inflammatory and analgesic agent | 210 |
| 10. | | 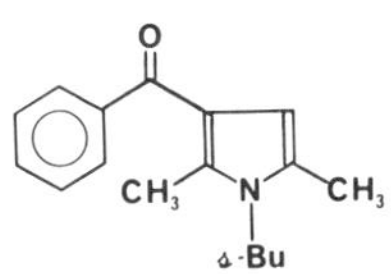 | Pyrrole, 3-benzoyl-2,5-dimethyl-1-(1-methylpropyl) | $C_{17}H_{21}NO$ | 255 | 0.4 μ*M*<br>14 μ*M* | Guinea-pig platelets<br>BSV | Most potent of 103 analogues tested | 212 |

**Table 15 (continued)**
**MISCELLANEOUS**

| Entry no. | Chemical abstracts number[a] | Structure | Chemical name (common name) | Molecular formula | Mol wt | Inhibitory potency[b] | Assay | Comments | Ref. |
|---|---|---|---|---|---|---|---|---|---|
| 11. | 100387-87-9 | 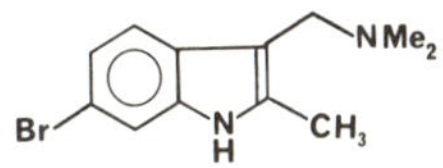 | Indole, 5-bromo-3-(dimethylaminomethyl)-2-methyl | $C_{12}H_{14}BrN_2$ | 266 | 33% at 40 μ*M* | Rat spleen | Anti-inflammatory and analgesic *in vivo*, possibly due to anti-serotonin properties | 211 |
| 12. | 70894-45-0 | 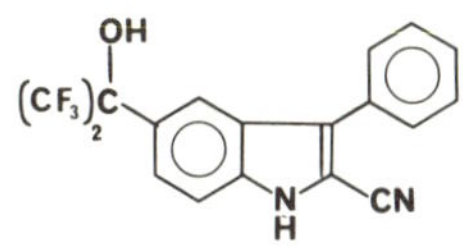 | 3-Phenyl-5-[2,2,2-trifluoro-1-hydroxy-1-(trifluoromethyl)ethyl]indole-2-carbonitrile | $C_{18}H_{10}F_6N_2O$ | 384 | 0.5 μ*M* | BSV | Inhibited platelet aggregation, showed no anti-inflammatory activity, prevented arachidonic acid-induced diarrhea in mice | 213 |
| 13. | 642-78-8 | 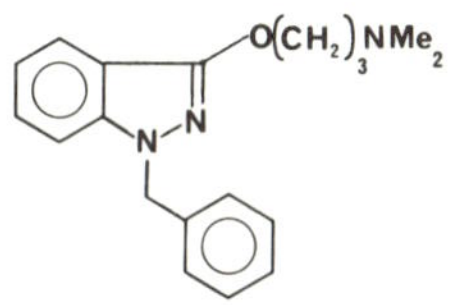 | 1-Propanamine,*N*,*N*-dimethyl-3-[[1-(phenylmethyl)-1H-indazol-3-yl]oxy] (Benzydamine) | $C_{19}H_{23}N_3O$ | 309 | 160 μ*M* | BSV | Analgetic, increases $PGE_2$ production, inhibits $PGF_{2\alpha}$ and $PGD_2$ at high arachidonic acid concentrations | 135 |
| 14. | 833-50-1 | 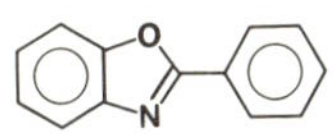 | Benzoxazole,2-phenyl | $C_{13}H_9NO$ | 195 | 50 μ*M* | SSV | | 13 |

| | | | | | | | | | |
|---|---|---|---|---|---|---|---|---|---|
| 15. | 52333-61-6 | 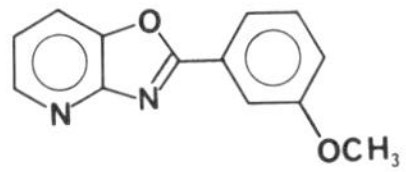 | Oxazolo[4,5-b]pyridine,2-(3-methoxyphenyl) | $C_{13}H_{10}N_2O_2$ | 226 | 5 μ*M* | SSV | | 13 |
| 16. | 52333-81-0 | 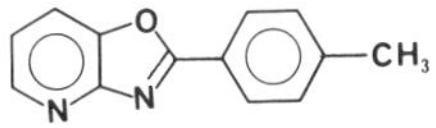 | Oxazolo[4,5-b]pyridine,2-(4-methylphenyl) | $C_{13}H_{10}N_2O$ | 210 | 2.5 μ*M* | SSV | | 13 |
| 17. | 148-79-8 | 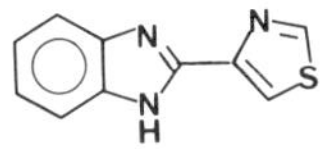 | 1H-Benzimidazole,2-(4-thiazolyl) (Thiabendazole) | $C_{10}H_7N_3S$ | 201 | active at $5 \times 10^{-5}M$ | SSV | Anthelmintic agent, weak analgetic | 13 |
| 18. | 525-82-6 | 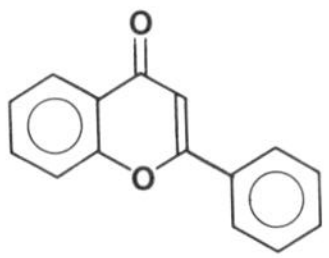 | 4H-1-Benzopyran-4-one,2-phenyl (Flavone) | $C_{15}H_{10}O_2$ | 222 | 100% at 50 μ*M* | Platelet aggr. | Lipoxygenase products were increased | 299 |
| 19. | 21626-89-1 | 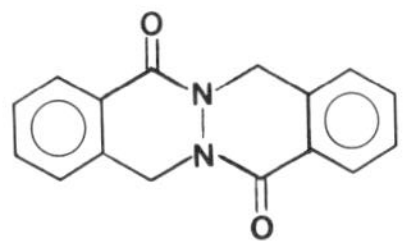 | Phthalazino[2,3-b]phthalazine-5,12-(7H,14H)dione (Diftalone) | $C_{16}H_{12}N_2O_2$ | 264 | 170 μ*M* | BSV | | 300 |
| 20. | 21221-18-1 | 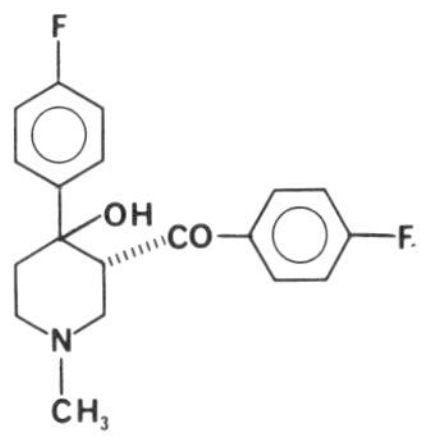 | Methanone,(4-fluorophenyl)[4-(4-fluorophenyl)-4-hydroxy-1-methyl-3-piperidinyl] (Flazolone) | $C_{19}H_{19}F_2NO_2$ | 331 | 350 μ*M* | BSV | Immunomodulator, increases $PGE_2$ production at high substrate concentration | 135 |

**Table 15 (continued)**
**MISCELLANEOUS**

| Entry no. | Chemical abstracts number[a] | Structure | Chemical name (common name) | Molecular formula | Mol wt | Inhibitory potency[b] | Assay | Comments | Ref. |
|---|---|---|---|---|---|---|---|---|---|
| 21. | 10457-90-6 | 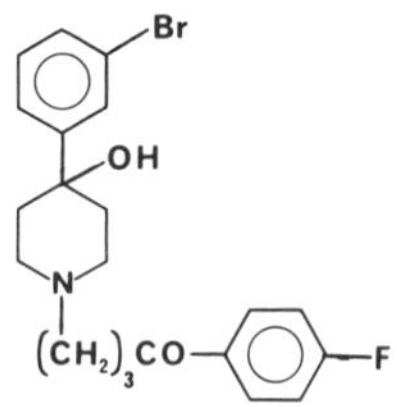 | 1-Butanone,4-[4-(4-bromophenyl)-4-hydroxy-1-piperidino]-4′-fluoro (Bromoperidol) | $C_{21}H_{23}BrFNO_2$ | 420 | 172 μ*M* | BSV | | 296 |
| 22. | 83654-05-1 | 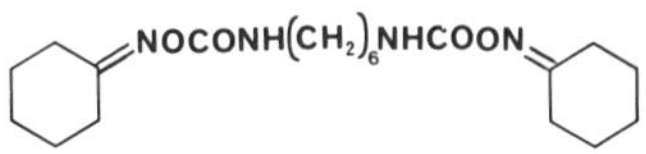 | Cyclohexanone,0,0′-[1,6-hexanediylbis (iminocarbonyl)] dioxime (RHC 80267) | $C_{20}H_{34}N_4O_4$ | 394 | 18 μ*M* | Platelet aggre. | Also inhibits phospholipase C | 216 |
| 23. | 87255-09-2 | 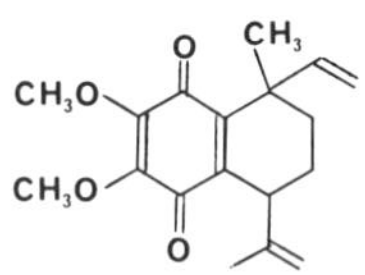 | 1,4-Naphthalenedione,5-ethenyl-5,6,7,8-tetrahydro-2,3-dimethoxy-5-methyl-8-(1-methylethenyl) (Arnebinone) | $C_{18}H_{22}O_4$ | 302 | 25% at 7 μ*M* | Rabbit kidney | Isolated from *Arnebia euchroma* | 217 |
| 24. | 80-08-0 | 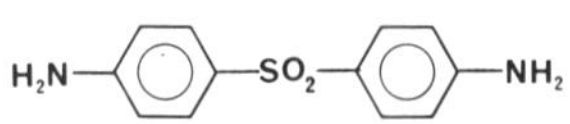 | Benzenamine, 4,4′-sulfonylbis (Dapsone) | $C_{12}H_{12}N_2O_2S$ | 248 | 100 μ*M* | Rat mast cells | Leprostatic; anti-inflammatory anti-rheumatic in clinical trials | 214, 301, 3027 |
| 25. | 57-53-4 | 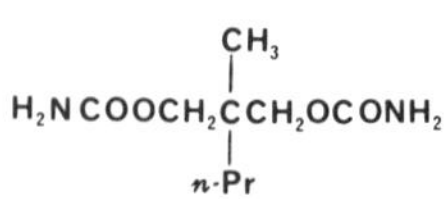 | 1,3-Propanediol,2-methyl-2-propyl, dicarbamate (Meprobamate) | $C_9H_{18}N_2O_4$ | 218 | 370 μ*M* | BSV | | 209 |

| | | | | | | | | |
|---|---|---|---|---|---|---|---|---|
| 26. | 50-55-5 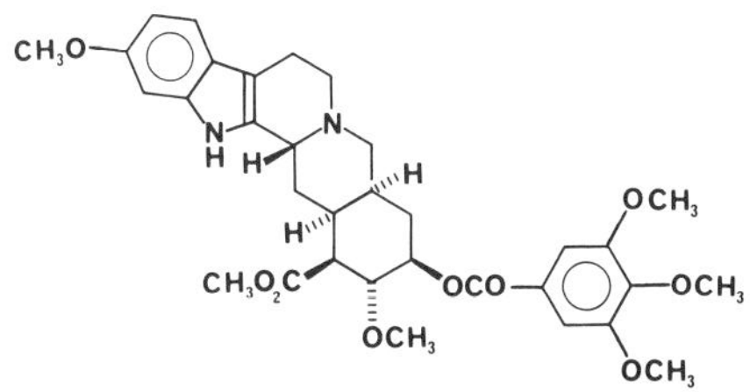 | 11,17α-Dimethoxy-18β-[(3,4,5-trimethoxybenzoyl)oxy]-3β, 20α-yohimban-16β-carboxylic acid methyl ester (Reserpine) | $C_{33}H_{40}N_2O_9$ | 608.7 | 4.8 μ*M* | | | 209 |
| 27. | 19559-24-1 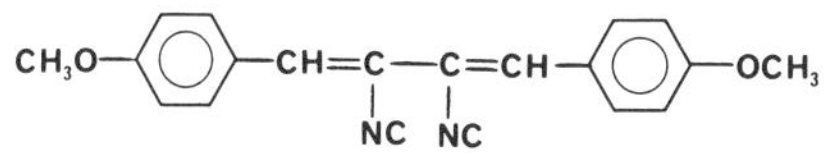 | Phenol,4-[2,3-diisocyano-4-(4-methoxyphenyl)-1,3-butadienyl] (XanthocillinX monomethyl ether) | $C_{20}H_{16}N_2O_2$ | 316 | 0.2 μ*M*<br>20 μ*M* | Rabbit kidney<br>SSV | No *in vivo* anti-inflammatory effects, 50 mg/kg p.o. or 10 mg/kg, i.v. (rat) | 218<br>303 |

[a] If available.
[b] $IC_{50}$ unless otherwise stated.

## REFERENCES


1. **Bergstrom, S., Carlson, L. A., and Oro, L.,** Effect of prostaglandins on catecholamine-induced changes in the free fatty acids of plasma and in blood pressure in the dog, *Acta Physiol. Scand.*, 60, 170, 1964.
2. **Bergstrom, S., Danielsson, H., and Samuelsson, B.,** The enzymatic formation of prostaglandin $E_2$ from arachidonic acid. Prostaglandins and related factors, *Biochim. Biophys. Acta*, 90, 207, 1964.
3. **Dorp, D. A. van, Beerthuis, R. K., Nugteren, D. H., and Vonkeman, H.,** The biosynthesis of prostaglandins, *Biochim. Biophys. Acta*, 90, 204, 1964.
4. **Moncada, S. and Vane, J. R.,** Pharmacology and endogenous roles of prostaglandin endoperoxides, thromboxane $A_2$, and prostacyclin, *Pharmacol. Rev.*, 30, 293, 1979.
5. **Willis, A. L.,** Release of histamine, kinin and prostaglandins during carrageenin-induced inflammation of the rat, in *Prostaglandins, Peptides and Amines*, Mantegazza, P. and Horton, E. W., Eds., Academic Press, London, 1969, 31.
6. **Ferreira, S. H. and Vane, J. R.,** Indomethacin and aspirin abolish prostaglandin release from the spleen, *Nature (London) New Biol.*, 231, 237, 1971.
7. **Smith, J. B. and Willis, A. L.,** Aspirin selectively inhibits prostaglandin production in human platelets, *Nature (London) New Biol.*, 231, 235, 1971.
8. **Vane, J. R.,** Inhibition of prostaglandin synthesis as a mechanism of action for aspirin-like drugs, *Nature (London) New Biol.*, 231, 232, 1971.

8A. **Willis, A. L.,** An enzymatic mechanism for the anti-thrombotic and anti-hemostatic actions of aspirin, *Science*, 183, 325, 1974.

9. **Milton, A. S. and Wendlandt, S.,** Effect on body temperature of prostaglandins of the A, E and F series on injection into the third ventricle of unanaesthetized cats and rabbits, *J. Physiol.*, 218, 325, 1971.
10. **Hamberg, M. and Samuelsson, B.,** Prostaglandin endoperoxides. Novel transformations of arachidonic acid in human platelets, *Proc. Natl. Acad. Sci. U.S.A.*, 71, 3400, 1974.
11. **Samuelsson, B., Hammarstrom, S., Murphy, R. C., and Borgeat, P.,** Leukotrienes and slow reacting substance of anaphylaxis (SRS-A), *Allergy*, 35, 375, 1980.
12. **Flower, R. J.,** Drugs which inhibit prostaglandin biosynthesis, *Pharmacological Rev.*, 26, 33, 1974.
13. **Shen, T. Y.,** Prostaglandin synthetase inhibitors, *Handbook of Experimental Pharmacology*, 30 (2; Anti-inflammatory Drugs), Springer-Verlag, Berlin, 305, 1979.

13A. **Egan, R. W., Gale, P. H., Baptista, E. M., and Kuehl, F. A., Jr.,** Mechanism of prostaglandin hydroperoxidase cooxygenation reactions, *Prog. Lipid Res.*, 20, 173, 1982.

14. **Whittle, B. J. R.,** Prostaglandin synthetase inhibitors. Drugs which affect arachidonic acid metabolism, *Acta Obstet. Gynecol. Scand. Supply.*, 87, 21, 1979.
15. **Chang, J. and Lewis, A. J.,** Prostaglandins and cyclooxygenase inhibitors, *Immunol. Ser.*, 25 (Immune Modulation Agents Their Mechanism), Marcel Dekker, New York, 649, 1984.
16. **Shen, T. Y. and Tischler, A. N.,** Non-steroidal inhibitors of arachidonic acid metabolism, in *Development of Anti-Asthma Drugs*, Buckle, D. R. and Smith, H., Eds., Butterworth, London, 1984, 315.
17. **Christ, E. J. and van Dorp, D. A.,** Comparative aspects of prostaglandin biosynthesis in animal tissues, *Biochim. Biophys. Acta*, 270, 537, 1972.
18. **Christ, E. J. and van Dorp, D. A.,** Comparative aspects of prostaglandin biosynthesis in animal tissue, in *Supplementum to Advances in the Biosciences*, Vol. 9, Bergstrom, S. and Bernhard, S., Eds., Int. Conf. Prostaglandins, Pergamon Press, Brauschweig, 1973, 35.
19. **Destaphano, D. B., Brady, U. E., and Woodall, L. B.,** Partial characterization of prostaglandin synthetase in the reproductive tract of the male house cricket, *Acheta domesticus, Prostaglandins*, 11, 261, 1976.
20. **DeWitt, D. L., Rollins, T. E., Day, J. S., Gauger, J. A., and Smith, W. L.,** Orientation of the active site and antigenic determinants of prostaglandin endoperoxide in the endoplasmic reticulum, *J. Biol. Chem.*, 256, 19375, 1981.
21. **Roth, G. J. and Machuga, E. T.,** Radioimmune assay of human platelet prostaglandin synthetase, *J. Lab. Clin. Med.*, 99, 187, 1982.
22. **Pollard, J. and Flower, R. J.,** Unpublished observations, quoted in Reference 12.
23. **Christ, E. J. and van Dorp, D. A.,** Comparative aspects of prostaglandins, *Adv. Biosci.*, 9, 35, 1972.
24. **Piper, P. J. and Vane, J. R.,** The release of prostaglandins from lung and other tissues, *Ann. N.Y. Acad. Sci.*, 180, 363, 1971.
25. **Ferreira, S. H. and Vane, J. R.,** Prostaglandins: their disappearance from and release into the circulation, *Nature (London)*, 216, 868, 1967.
26. **Salmon, J. A. and Flower, R. J.,** Prostaglandins and related compounds, in *Hormones in Blood*, 3rd ed., Gray, G. and James, V., Eds., Academic Press, London, 1979, 237.
27. **Flower, R. J. and Blackwell, G. J.,** The importance of phospholipase $A_2$ in prostaglandin biosynthesis, *Biochem. Pharmacol.*, 25, 285, 1976.
28. **Kaye, B., Champion, S., and Jacquemin, C.,** A limiting factor in the biosynthesis of prostaglandins in the thyroid, *FEBS Lett.*, 30, 253, 1973.

29. **Kunze, M. and Vogt, W.**, Significance of phospholipase A for prostaglandin production, *Ann. N.Y. Acad. Sci.*, 180, 123, 1971.
30. **Hamberg, M. and Samuelsson, B.**, On the mechanism of the biosynthesis of prostaglandins $E_1$ and $F_{1\alpha}$, *J. Biol. Chem.*, 242, 5336, 1967.
31. **Nugteren, D. H., Beerthuis, R. K., and van Dorp, D. A.**, The enzymic conversion of all-cis 8, 11, 14-eicosatrienoic acid into prostaglandin $E_1$, *Rec. Trav. Chim. Pays Bas*, 85, 405, 1966.
32. **Downing, D. T., Barve, J. A., Gunstone, F. D., Jacobsberg, M., and Lie, K. J.**, Structural requirements of acetylenic fatty acids for inhibition of soybean lipoxygenase and prostaglandin synthetase, *Biochim. Biophys. Acta*, 280, 343, 1972.
33. **Samuelsson, B.**, Biosynthesis of prostaglandins, *Fed. Proc.*, 31, 1442, 1972.
34. **Samuelsson, B.**, On the incorporation of oxygen in the conversion of 8,11,14-eicosatrienoic acid into prostaglandin $E_1$, *J. Am. Chem. Soc.*, 87, 3011, 1965.
35. **Nugteren, D. A. and van Dorp, D. A.**, The participation of molecular oxygen in the biosynthesis of prostaglandins, *Biochim. Biophys. Acta*, 98, 654, 1965.
36. **Ryhage, L. and Samuelsson, B.**, The origin of oxygen incorporation during the biosynthesis of prostaglandin $E_1$, *Biochem. Biophys. Res. Commun.*, 19, 279, 1965.
37. **Hammarstrom, S. and Falardeac, P.**, Resolution of prostaglandin endoperoxide synthetase and thromboxane synthetase of human platelets, *Proc. Natl. Acad. Sci. U.S.A.*, 74, 3691, 1977.
38. **Diczfalusy, U., Falardeau, P., and Hammarstrom, S.**, Conversion of prostaglandin endoperoxides to $C_{17}$-hydroxy acids catalyzed by human platelet thromboxane synthetase, *Fed. Eur. Biochem. Soc. Lett.*, 84, 271, 1977.
39. **Yoshimoto, T., Yamamoto, S., Okuma, M., and Hayaishi, O.**, Solubilization and resolution of thromboxane synthesizing system from microsomes of bovine blood platelets, *J. Biol. Chem.*, 252, 5871, 1977.
40. **Smith, W. L. and Lands, W. E. M.**, Oxygenation of polyunsaturated fatty acids during prostaglandin biosynthesis by sheep seminal vesicle glands, *Biochemistry*, 11, 3276, 1972.
41. **Miyamoto, T., Ogino, N., Yamamoto, S., and Hayaishi, O.**, Purification of prostaglandin endoperoxide synthetase from bovine vesicular gland microsomes, *J. Biol. Chem.*, 251, 2629, 1976.
42. **Miyamoto, T., Yamamoto, S., and Hayaishi, O.**, Prostaglandin synthetase system — resolution into oxygenase and isomerase components, *Proc. Natl. Acad. Sci. U.S.A.*, 71, 3645, 1974.
43. **Maddox, I. S.**, Copper in PG synthesis, *Biochim. Biophys. Acta*, 306, 74, 1973.
43A. **Hamberg, M. and Samuelsson, B.**, Detection and isolation of an endoperoxide intermediate in prostaglandin biosynthesis, *Proc. Natl. Acad. Sci. U.S.A.*, 70, 899, 1973.
44. **Gryglewski, R. J., Bunting, S., Moncada, S., Flower, R. J., and Vane, J. R.**, Arterial walls are protected against deposition of platelet thrombi by a substance (prostaglandin X) which they make from prostaglandin endoperoxides, *Prostaglandins*, 12, 685, 1976.
45. **Nugteren, D. H. and Hazelhof, E.**, Isolation and properties of intermediates in prostaglandin biosynthesis, *Biochim. Biophys. Acta*, 326, 448, 1973.
46. **Pace-Asciak, C. and Nashat, M.**, Catabolism of an isolated, purified intermediate of prostaglandin biosynthesis by regions of the adult rat kidney, *Biochim. Biophys. Acta*, 388, 243, 1975.
47. **Sun, F. F., Chapman, J. P., and McGuire, J. C.**, Metabolism of prostaglandin endoperoxides in animal tissues, *Prostaglandins*, 14, 1055, 1977.
48. **Bergstrom, S.**, Closing remarks, in *Prostaglandin Synthetase Inhibitors*, Robinson, H. J. and Vane, J. R., Eds., Raven Press, New York, 1974, 379.
49. **Vane, J. R.**, Anti-inflammatory drugs and inhibition of prostaglandin synthetase, in *Role Prostaglandins Inflammation*, Proc. Workshop, Lewis, G. P., Ed., Huber, Bern, Switzerland, 1976, 88.
50. **Brune, K.**, Prostaglandins, inflammation and anti-inflammatory drugs, *Eur. J. Inflamm.*, 5, 335, 1982.
51. **Lands, W. E. M.**, Mechanisms of action of anti-inflammatory drugs, *Advances Drug Res.*, 14, 147, 1985.
52. **Whittle, B. J. R., Broughton-Smith, N. K., Moncada, S., and Vane, J. R.**, Actions of prostacyclin ($PGI_2$) and its product 6-oxo-$PGF_{1\alpha}$ on the rat gastric mucosa *in vivo* and *in vitro*, *Prostaglandins*, 15, 955, 1978.
53. **Friedman, W. F., Printz, M. P., and Kirkpatrick, S. E.**, Blockers of prostaglandin synthesis: a novel therapy in the management of the premature human infant with patent ductus arteriosus, in *Advances in Prostaglandin and Thromboxane Research*, Vol. 4, Coceani, F. and Olley, P. M., Eds., Raven Press, New York, 1978, 373.
54. **Gill, J. R., Frolich, J. C., Bowden, R. E., Taylor, A. A., Keiser, H. R., Seyberth, H. W., Oates, J. A., and Bartter, F. C.**, Bartter's syndrome, a disorder characterized by high urinary prostaglandins and a dependence of hyperreninemia on prostaglandin synthesis, *Am. J. Med.*, 61, 43, 1976.
55. **Lewis, R. B. and Shulman, J. D.**, Influence of acetylsalicylic acid, an inhibitor of prostaglandin synthesis on the duration of human gestation and labor, *Lancet, ii*, 1159, 1973.
56. **Pickles, V. R., Hall, W. J., Best, F. A., and Smith, G. N.**, Prostaglandins in endometrium and menstrual fluid from normal and dysmenorrheic subjects, *J. Obstet. Gynaecol. Br. Commonw.*, 72, 185, 1965.
57. **Hong, S. L., Wheless, C. M., and Levine, L.**, Elevated prostaglandin synthetase activity in methylcholanthrene-transformed mouse BALB/3T3, *Prostaglandins*, 13, 271, 1977.

58. **Fitzpatrick, F. A. and Stringfellow, D. A.,** Prostaglandin $D_2$ formation by malignant melanoma cells correlates inversely with cellular metastatic potential, *Proc. Natl. Acad. Sci. U.S.A.,* 76, 1765, 1979.
59. **Bennett, A., Berstock, D. A., and Carroll, M. A.,** Enhanced anti-cancer effect by combining cytotoxic drugs with the prostaglandin synthesis inhibitor flurbiprofen, *Br. J. Pharmacol.,* 74, 208P, 1981.
60. **Bennett, A., Houghton, J., Leaper, D. J., and Stamford, I. F.,** Cancer growth, response to treatment and survival time in mice: beneficial effects of the prostaglandin synthetase inhibitor flurbiprofen, *Prostaglandins,* 19, 179, 1979.
61. **Mamett, L. J.,** Polycyclic aromatic hydrocarbon oxidation during prostaglandin biosynthesis, *Life Sci.,* 29, 531, 1981.
62. **Higgs, G. A., Moncada, S., and Vane, J. R.,** The mode of action of anti-inflammatory drugs which prevent the peroxidation of arachidonic acid, *Clin. Rheum. Dis.,* 6, 675, 1980.
63. **Szczeklik, A., Gryglewski, R. J., and CzerniawskaMysik, G.,** Clinical patterns of hypersensitivity to non-steroidal anti-inflammatory drugs and their pathogenesis, *J. Allerg. Clin. Immunol.,* 60, 276, 1977.
64. **Walker, J. L.,** Interrelationships of SRS-A production and arachidonic acid metabolism in human lung tissue, *Adv. Prostaglandin Thromboxane Res.,* 6, 115, 1980.
65. **Higgs, G. A., Moncada, S., and Vane, J. R.,** The mode of action of anti-inflammatory drugs which prevent the peroxidation of arachidonic acid, in *Antirheumatic Drugs,* Huskisson, E. C., Ed., Praeger, London, 1983, 11.
66. **Higgs, G. A. and Vane, J. R.,** Inhibition of cyclooxygenase and lipoxygenase, *Br. Med. Bull.,* 39, 265, 1983.
67. **Higgs, G. A., Palmer, R. M. J., Eakins, K. E., and Moncada, S.,** Arachidonic acid metabolism as a source of inflammatory mediators and its inhibition as a mechanism of action for anti-inflammatory drugs, *Mol. Aspects Med.,* 4, 275, 1981.
68. **Willis, A. L., Davison, P., Ramwell, P. W., Brocklehurst, W. E., and Smith, J. B.,** Release and actions of prostaglandins in inflammation and fever: inhibition by anti-inflammatory and anti-pyretic drugs, in *Prostaglandins in Cellular Biology,* Ramwell, P. W. and Pharriss, B. B., Eds., Plenum Press, New York, 1972, 227.
69. **Ferreira, S. H.,** Prostaglandins, in *Chemical Messengers of the Inflammatory Process,* Houck, J. C., Ed., Elsevier/North Holland, Amsterdam, 1979, 113.
70. **Trang, L. E., Granström, E., and Lovgren, O.,** Levels of prostaglandin $F_{2\alpha}$ and $E_2$ and thromboxane $B_2$ in joint fluid in rheumatoid arthritis, *Scand. J. Rheumatol.,* 6, 151, 1977.
71. **Brodie, M. J., Hensby, C. N., Parke, A., and Gordon, D.,** Is prostacyclin the major proinflammatory prostanoid in joint fluid? *Life Sci.,* 27, 603, 1980.
72. **Herman, A. G. and Moncada, S.,** Release of prostaglandins and incapacitation after injection of endotoxin in the knee joint of the dog, *Br. J. Pharmacol.,* 53, 465P, 1975.
73. **Higgins, A. J. and Lee, P.,** A bioassay technique for prostaglandin-like activity in equine inflammatory exude, *Br. Vet. J.,* 140, 609, 1984.
74. **Higgins, A. J., Lee, P., and Higgs, G. A.,** The detection of prostaglandin-like activity in equine inflammatory exude — a preliminary report, *Equine Vet. J.,* 16, 71, 1984.
75. **Klein, D. C. and Raisz, L. G.,** Prostaglandins: stimulation of bone resorption in tissue culture, *Endocrinology,* 86, 1436, 1970.
76. **Tashjian, A. M., Shupnik, M. A., Voelkel, E. F., and Levine, L.,** Prostaglandins and bone: skeletal actions of epidermal growth factor and metabolism of endogenous and exogenous arachidonic acid, *Excerpta Med. Int. Congr. Ser.,* Vol. date 1980, 511 (Horm. Control Calcium Metab.) 163, 1981.
77. **Higgs, E. A., Moncada, S., and Vane, J. R.** Inflammatory effects of prostacyclin and 6-oxo-$PGF_{1\alpha}$ in the rat paw, *Prostaglandins,* 16, 153, 1978.
78. **Moncada, S., Ferreira, S. H., and Vane, J. R.,** Prostaglandins, aspirin-like drugs and the oedema of inflammation, *Nature (London),* 246, 217, 1973.
79. **Williams, T. J. and Morley, J.,** Prostaglandins as potentiators of increased vascular permeability in inflammation, *Nature (London),* 246, 215, 1973.
80. **Williams, T. J. and Peck, M. J.,** Role of prostaglandin-mediated vasodilatation in inflammation, *Nature (London),* 270, 530, 1977.
81. **Moncada, S. and Vane, J. R.,** Interactions between anti-inflammatory drugs and inflammatory mediators: a reference to products of arachidonic acid metabolism, *Agents Actions,* (Suppl. 3), 141, 1977.
82. **Vane, J. R.,** Mode of action of aspirin and similar compounds, *J. Allerg. Clin. Immunol.,* 58, 691, 1976.
83. **Willis, A. L. and Cornelson, M.,** Repeated injection of prostaglandin $E_2$ in rat paws induces a chronic swelling and marked decrease in pain threshold, *Prostaglandins,* 3, 353, 1973.
84. **Grant, N. H., Auburn, H. E., and Singer, A. C.,** Correlation between *in vitro* and *in vivo* models in anti-inflammatory drug studies, *Biochem. Pharmacol.,* 20, 2137, 1971.
85. **Glazco, A. J.,** Unpublished observation, quoted in Reference 12.
86. **Prestcott, L. F., Sandor, M., Levin, W., and Conney, A. H.,** The comparative metabolism of phenacetin and N-acetyl-p-aminophenol in man, with particular reference to the kidney, *Clin. Pharmacol. Ther.,* 9, 605, 1968.

87. **Woodbury, D. M.,** Analgesic-antipyretics, anti-inflammatory agents and inhibitors of uric acid synthesis, in *Pharmacological Basis of Therapeutics,* 4th ed., Goodman, L. S. and Gilman, A., Eds., Macmillan, New York, 1970, 314.
88. **Brune, K., Glatt, M., and Graf, P.,** Mechanism of action of anti-inflammatory drugs, *Gen. Pharmacol.,* 7, 27, 1976.
89. **Brune, K., Rainsford, K. D., Wagner, N., and Peskar, B. A.,** Inhibition by anti-inflammatory drugs of prostaglandin production in cultured macrophages, *Naunyn-Schmeidebergs Arch. Pharm.,* 315, 269, 1981.
90. **Flower, R. J., Gryglewski, R., Herbaczynska-Cedro, K., and Vane, J. R.,** Effects of anti-inflammatory drugs on prostaglandin synthesis, *Nature (London),* 238, 104, 1972.
91. **Ziel, R. and Krupp, P.,** The significance of inhibition of prostaglandin synthesis in the selection of non-steroidal anti-inflammatory agents, *Int. J. Clin. Pharmacol.,* 12, 186, 1975.
92. **Brune, K., Gubler, H., and Schweitzer, A.,** Autoradiographic methods for the evaluation of ulcerogenic effects of anti-inflammatory drugs, *Pharmacol. Ther.,* 5, 199, 1979.
93. **Brune, K., Rainsford, N. D., Wagner, K., and Peskar, B. A.,** Inhibition by anti-inflammatory drugs of prostaglandin production in cultured macrophages, *Naunyn-Schmeidebergs Arch Pharm.,* 315, 269, 1981.
94. **Cohen, M. M. and Pollett, J. M.,** Prostaglandin $E_2$ prevents aspirin and indomethacin damage to human gastric mucosa, *Surg. Forum,* 21, 400, 1976.
95. **Cashin, C. H., Dawson, W., and Kitchen, E. A.,** The pharmacology of benoxaprofen (2-[4-chlorophenyl]-α-methyl-5-benzoxazole acetic acid) LRCL3794, a new compound with anti-inflammatory activity apparently unrelated to inhibition of prostaglandin synthesis, *J. Pharm. Pharmacol.,* 29, 330, 1977.
96. **Higgs, G. A. and Mugridge, K. G.,** The effects of carrageenin-induced inflammation of compounds which interfere with arachidonic acid metabolism, *Br. J. Pharmacol.,* 76, 284P, 1982.
97. **Anderson, R., Lukey, P. T., and van Rensburg, C. E. J.,** Effects of benoxaprofen binding to and inactivation of leukoattractants by human polymorphonuclear leukocytes *in vitro, Agents Actions,* 16, 527, 1985.
98. **Flower, R. J. and Vane, J. R.,** Inhibition of prostaglandin biosynthesis, *Biochem. Pharmacol.,* 23, 1439, 1974.
99. **Flower, R. J. and Vane, J. R.,** Inhibition of prostaglandin synthesis in brain explains the antipyretic activity of paracetamol (4-acetamidophenol), *Nature (London),* 240, 410, 1972.
100. **Baenziger, N. L., Dillender, M. J., and Majerus, P. W.,** Cultured human skin fibroblasts and arterial cells produce a labile platelet-inhibitory prostaglandin, *Biochem. Biophys. Res. Commun.,* 78, 294, 1977.
101. **Moncada, S. and Vane, J. R.,** Unstable metabolites of arachidonic acid and their role in haemostasis and thrombosis, *Br. Med. Bull.,* 34, 129, 1978.
102. **Patrono, C., Ciabattoni, G., Greco, F., and Grossi-Belloni, D.,** Comparative evaluations of the inhibitory effects of aspirin-like drugs on prostaglandin production by human platelets and synovial tissue, in *Advances in Prostaglandins and Thromboxane Research,* Vol. 1, Samuelsson, B. and Paoletti, R., Eds., Raven Press, New York, 1976, 125.
103. **Limas, C. J. and Cohn, J. N.,** Isolation and properties of myocardial prostaglandin synthetase, *Cardiovasc. Res.,* 7, 623, 1973.
104. **Bhattacherjee, P. and Eakins, K.,** Inhibition of the PG-synthetase system in ocular tissues by indomethacin, *Pharmacologist,* 15, 209, 1973.
105. **Kantrowitz, F., Robinson, D. R., McCuire, M. B., and Levine, L.,** Corticosteroids inhibit prostaglandin production by rheumatoid synovia, *Nature (London),* 258, 737, 1975.
106. **Crook, D. and Collins, A. J.,** Prostaglandin synthetase activity from human rheumatoid synovial tissue and its inhibition by non-steroidal anti-inflammatory drugs, *Prostaglandins,* 9, 857, 1975.
107. **Steele, L., Hunneyball, I. M., and Bresloff, P.,** Comparison of rheumatoid synovial microsomes and bovine seminal vesicle microsomes for determining the relative potencies of prostaglandin synthetase inhibitors, *J. Pharmacol. Methods,* 5, 341, 1981.
108. **Hansen, H. S.,** 15-Hydroxyprostaglandin dehydrogenase: a review, *Prostaglandins,* 12, 647, 1976.
109. **Flores, A. G. A. and Sharp, G. W. G.,** Endogenous prostaglandins and osmotic water flow in the toad bladder, *Am. J. Physiol.,* 223, 1392, 1972.
110. **Kantor, M. S. and Hampton, M.,** Indomethacin in submicromolar concentrations inhibits cyclic AMP-dependent protein kinase, *Nature (London),* 276, 841, 1978.
111. **Muscoplat, C. C., Klausner, D. J., Brunner, C. J., Sloane, E. D., and Johnson, D. W.,** Regulation of mitogen and antigen-stimulated lymphocyte blastogenesis by prostaglandins, *Infect. Immunol.,* 26, 311, 1979.
112. **Goodwin, J. S., Bankhurst, A. D., and Messner, R. P.,** Suppression of human T-cell mitogenesis by prostaglandin, *J. Exp. Med.,* 146, 1719, 1977.
113. **Sims, T., Clagett, J. A., and Page, R. C.,** Effect of cell concentration and exogenous prostaglandin on the interaction and responsiveness of human peripheral blood lymphocytes, *Clin. Immunol. Immunopathol.,* 12, 150, 1979.

114. **Rao, K. M. K., Schwartz, S. A., and Good, R. A.,** Modulation of the mitogenic response of lymphocytes from young and aged individuals by prostaglandins and indomethacin, *Cell. Immunol.,* 48, 155, 1979.
115. **Odazaki, T., Shimuzu, M., Arbesman, C. E., and Middleton, E.,** Prostaglandin E and mitogenic stimulation of human lymphocytes in serum-free medium, *Prostaglandins,* 15, 423, 1978.
116. **Burcheil, S. W.,** $PGI_2$ and $PGD_2$ effects on cyclic AMP and human T-cell mitogenesis, *Prostaglandins Med.,* 3, 315, 1979.
117. **Novogrodsky, A., Rubin, A. L., and Stezzel, K. H.,** Selective suppression by adherent cells, prostaglandin and cyclic AMP analogues of blastogenesis induced by different mitogens, *J. Immunol.,* 122, 1, 1979.
118. **Kishimoto, R. and Ishizaka, K.,** Regulation of antibody response *in vitro, J. Immunol.,* 116, 534, 1976.
119. **Razin, E., Bauminger, S., and Globerson, A.,** Effect of prostaglandins on phagocytosis of sheep erythrocytes by mouse peritoneal macrophages., *J. Reticuloendothelial Soc.,* 23, 237, 1977.
120. **Oropeza-Rendon, R. L., Speth, V., Hiller, G., Weber, K., and Fischer, H.,** Prostaglandin $E_1$ reversibly induces morphological changes in macrophages and inhibits phagocytosis, *Exp. Cell. Res.,* 119, 365, 1979.
121. **Schnyder, J., Dewald, B., and Baggiolini, M.,** Effects of cyclooxygenase inhibitors and prostaglandin $E_2$ on macrophage activation *in vitro, Prostaglandins,* 22, 411, 1981.
122. **Cantorow, W. D., Cheung, H. T., and Sundharadas, G.,** Effect of prostaglandins on the spreading, adhesion and migration of mouse peritoneal macrophages, *Prostaglandins,* 16, 39, 1978.
123. **Shen, T. Y.,** Synthesis and biological activity of some indomethacin analogs, in *Non-Steroidal Anti-inflammatory Drugs,* Garattini, S. and Dukes, M. N. G., Eds., Excerpta Medica Foundation, Milan, 1964, 13.
124. **Scherrer, R. A., Winder, C. V., and Short, F. W.,** Natl. Med. Symp. Am. Chem. Soc. Div. Med. Chem., Abstr. 11a—11i, 1964.
125. **Shen, T. Y., Ham, E. A., Cirillo, V. J., and Zanetti, M.,** Structure-activity relationship of certain prostaglandin synthetase inhibitors, in *Prostaglandin Synthetase Inhibitors,* Robinson, H. J. and Vane, J. R., Eds., Raven Press, New York, 1974, 19.
126. **Scherrer, R. A.,** Introduction to the chemistry of anti-inflammatory agents, in *Anti-inflammatory Agents, Chemistry and Pharmacology,* Vol. 1, Scherrer, R. A., Ed., Academic Press, New York, 1974, 29.
127. **Gund, P. and Shen, T. Y.,** A model for the prostaglandin synthetase cyclooxygenase site and its inhibition by antiinflammatory arylacetic acids, *J. Med. Chem.,* 20, 1146, 1977.
128. **Appleton, R. A. and Brown, K.,** Conformational requirements at the prostaglandin cyclooxygenase receptor site: a template for designing non-steroidal anti-inflammatory drugs, *Prostaglandins,* 18, 29, 1979.
129. **Sankawa, U., Shibuya, M., Ebizuka, Y., Noguchi, M., Kinoshita, T., Iitaka, Y., Endo, A., and Kitahara, N.,** Depside as potent inhibitor of prostaglandin biosynthesis: a new active site model for fatty acid cyclo-oxygenase, *Prostaglandins,* 24, 21, 1982.
130. **Peterson, D. A., Gerrard, J. M., Rao, G. H. R., Mills, E. L., and White, J. G.,** Interaction of arachidonic acid and heme iron in the synthesis of prostaglandin, in *Advances in Prostaglandin and Thromboxane Research,* Samuelsson, B. and Ramwell, P. W., Eds., Raven Press, New York, 1980, 157.
131. **Bekemeier, H., Böhm, R., Hagen, V., Hannig, E., Henkel, H. J., Hirschelman, R., and Wenzel, U.,** *Agents Actions, (Suppl.)* Trends in Inflammation Research, p. 17, 1982.
132. **Corey, E. J.,** Eicosanoid biosynthesis, (a) seminar at Syntex Corporation, Palo Alto, CA, July 28, 1986, (b) **Corey, E. J.,** Enzymic lipoxygenation of arachidonic acid: mechanism, inhibition and role in eicosanoid biosynthesis, *Pure Appl. Chem.,* 59, 269, 1987.
133. **van der Ouderaa, F. J., Buytenhek, M., Nugteren, D. H., and van Dorp, D. A.,** Purification and characterisation of prostaglandin endoperoxide synthetase from sheep vesicular glands, *Biochim. Biophys. Acta,* 487, 315, 1977.
134. **van der Ouderaa, F. J., Slikkerveer, F. J., Buytenhek, M., and van Dorp, D. A.,** On the haemoprotein character of prostaglandin endoperoxide synthetase, *Biochim. Biophys. Acta,* 572, 29, 1979.
135. **Cushman, D. W. and Cheung, H. S.,** Effect of substrate concentration on inhibition of prostaglandin synthetase of bull seminal vesicles by anti-inflammatory drugs and fenamic acid analogs, *Biochim. Biophys. Acta,* 424, 449, 1976.
136. **Terada, H., Muraoka, S., and Fujita, T.,** Structure-activity relationships of fenamic acids, *J. Med. Chem.,* 17, 330, 1974.
136A. **Tobias, L. D., Vane, F. M., and Paulsrud, J. R.,** The biosynthesis of la,lb-Dihomo-$PGE_2$ and la,lb-Dihomo-$PGF_{2\alpha}$ from acetone-pentane powder of sheep vesicular gland microsomes, *Prostaglandins,* 10, 443, 1975.
136B. **Sprecher, H., Van Rollins, M., Sun, F., Wyche, A., and Needleman, P.,** Dihomo prostaglandins and thromboxanes, *J. Biol. Chem.,* 257, 912, 1982.
137. **Cagen, L. M. and Baer, P. G.,** Adrenic acid inhibits prostaglandin synthesis, *Life Sci.,* 26, 765, 1980.
138. **Lands, W. E. M., Letellier, P. R., Rome, L. H., and van der Hoek, J. Y.,** Modes of inhibiting the prostaglandin synthetic capacity of sheep vesicular gland preparations, *Fed. Proc. Fed. Am. Soc. Exp. Biol.,* 31, 476A, 1972.

139. **Lands, W. E. M., LeTellier, P. R., Rome, L. H., and van der Hoek, J. Y.,** Inhibition of prostaglandin biosynthesis, in *Advances in the Biosciences,* Vol. 9, Bergstrom, S. and Bernhard, S., Eds., Pergamon Press Vieweg, Braunschweig, 1973, 15.
140. **Van der Hoek, J. Y. and Lands, W. E. M.,** Acetylenic inhibitors of sheep vesicular gland oxygenase, *Biochim. Biophys. Acta,* 296, 374, 1973.
141. **Van der Hoek, J. Y.,** The inhibition of the fatty acid cyclooxygenase of sheep vesicular gland by antioxidants, *Biochim. Biophys. Acta,* 296, 382, 1973.
142. **Fretland, D. J. and Cammarata, P. S.,** Comparative diuretic, saluretic, kaliuretic and prostaglandin synthetase inhibitory activity of a competitive inhibitor of prostaglandin synthetase and spironolactone, *Prostaglandins Leukotrienes Med.,* 20, 29, 1985.
142A. **Shaw, J. E., Jessup, S. J., and Ramwell, P. W.,** Prostaglandin-adenylate cyclase relationships, in *Advances in Cyclic Nucleotide Research,* Vol. 1, Paoletti, R., Ed., Raven Press, New York, 1972, 429.
142B. **Willis, A. L.,** Unpublished data, 1972.
143. **Bundy, G. L.,** The synthesis of prostaglandin endoperoxide analogs, *Tetrahedron Lett.,* 1957, 1975.
144. **Corey, E. J., Nicolau, K. C., Machida, C. Y., Malmsten, C. L., and Samuelsson, B.,** Synthesis and biological properties of a 9,11-azaprostanoid: highly active biochemical mimic of prostaglandin endoperoxide, *Proc. Natl. Acad. Sci. U.S.A.,* 72, 3355, 1975.
145. **Corey, E. J., Shibasaki, M., Nicolau, K. C., Malmsten, C. L., and Samuelsson, B.,** Simple stereocontrolled total synthesis of a biologically active analog of the prostaglandin endoperoxides ($PGH_2$, $PGG_2$), *Tetrahedron Lett.,* p. 737, 1976.
146. **Malmsten, C.,** Some biological effects of prostaglandin endoperoxide analogs, *Life Sci.,* 18, 169, 1976.
147. **Harris, D. N., Philipps, M. B., Michel, I. M., Goldenberg, H. J., Steinbacher, T. E., Ogletree, M. L., and Hall, T. E.,** Inhibition of prostaglandin biosynthesis by SQ 28852, a 7-oxabicyclo[2.2.1] heptane analog, *Prostaglandins,* 31, 651, 1986.
148. **Takeguchi, C., Kohno, K., and Sih, S. J.,** Mechanism of prostaglandin biosynthesis. I. Characterisation and assay of bovine prostaglandin synthetase, *Biochemistry,* 10, 2372, 1971.
149. **Bender, A. D., Berkoff, C. E., Groves, W. G., Sofranko, L. M., Wellman, G. R., Liu, J., Begosh, P. P., and Horodniak, J. W.,** Synthesis and biological properties of some novel heterocyclic homoprostanoids, *J. Med. Chem.,* 18, 1094, 1975.
150. **Roth, G. J., Stanford, N., and Majerus, P. W.,** Acetylation of prostaglandin synthetase by aspirin, *Proc. Natl. Acad. Sci. U.S.A.,* 72, 3073, 1975.
151. **McConkey, B., Amos, R. S., Butter, E. P., Crockson, R. A., Crockson, A. P., and Walsh, L.,** Salazopyrin in rheumatoid arthritis, *Agents Actions,* 8, 438, 1978.
152. **Berry, C. N., Hoult, J. R. S., Peers, S. H., and Agback, H.,** Inhibition of prostaglandin 15-hydroxydehydrogenase by sulfasalazine and a novel series of potent analogues, *Biochem. Pharmacol.,* 32, 2863, 1983.
153. **Juby, P. F.,** Aryl and heteroarylalkanoic acids and related compounds, in *Antiinflammatory Agents,* Vol. 1, Scherrer, R. A., Ed., Academic Press, New York, 1974, 92.
154. **Ceserani, R., Ferrari, M., Goldaniga, G., Mioro, E., and Buttinoni, H.,** Role of protein binding and pharmacokinetics in the lack of correlation between *in vitro* inhibition of PG synthetase, and *in vivo* antiinflammatory activity of a homologous series of nonsteroidal antiinflammatory compounds, *Life Sci.,* 21, 223, 1977.
155. **Tamura, S., Kuzuna, S., and Kawai, K.,** Inhibition of prostaglandin biosynthesis by clidanac and related compounds: structural and conformational requirements for PG synthetase inhibition, *J. Pharm. Pharmacol.,* 33, 29, 1981.
156. **Vangeissen, G. J. and Kaiser, D. G.,** GLC determination of ibuprofen (dl-2-(p-isobutylphenyl)propionic acid) enantiomers in biological specimens, *J. Pharm. Sci.,* 64, 798, 1975.
157. **Kaiser, D. G., Vangeissen, G. J., Reischer, R. J., and Wechter, W. J.,** Isomeric inversion of ibuprofen (R)-enantiomer in human, *J. Pharm. Sci.,* 65, 269, 1976.
158. **Lan, S. J., Kripalani, K. J., Dean, A. V., Egli, P., Difazio, L. T., and Schreiber, E. C.,** Inversion of optical configuration of α-methyl-fluorene-2-acetic acid (cycloprofen) in rats and monkeys, *Drug Metab. Dispos.,* 4, 330, 1970.
159. **Bopp, R. J., Nash, J. F., Ridolfo, A. S., and Shepard, E. R.,** Stereoselective inversion of R-(−) benoxaprofen to the (S)-(+) enantiomer in humans, *Drug Metab. Dispos.,* 7, 356, 1979.
160. **Raz, A., Stern, H., and Kenig-Wakshal, R.,** Indomethacin and aspirin inhibition of $PGE_2$ synthesis by sheep seminal vesicle microsomal powder and seminal vesicle slices, *Prostaglandins,* 3, 337, 1973.
161. **Rao, G. H. R., Johnson, G. G., Reddy, K. R., and White, J. G.,** Ibuprofen protects platelet cyclooxygenase from irreversible inhibition by aspirin, *Arteriosclerosis,* 3, 383, 1983.
162. **Winder, C. V., Wax, J., Scotti, L., Scherrer, R. A., Jones, E. M., and Short, F. W.,** Antiinflammatory, antipyretic and antinociceptive properties of *N*-(2,3-xylyl)anthranilic acid (mefanamic acid), *J. Pharm. Exp. Ther.,* 138, 405, 1962.

163. **Ham, E. A., Cirillo, V. J., Zanetti, M., Shen, T. Y., and Kuehl, F. A.,** Mode of action of non-steroidal antiinflammatory agents, in *Prostaglandins in Cellular Biology,* Ramwell, P. W. and Pharriss, B. B., Eds., Plenum Press, New York, 1972, 345.
164. **Horodniak, J. W., Matz, E. D., Walz, D. T., Cramer, R. D., III, Sutton, B. M., Berkoff, C. E., Zarembo, J. E., and Bender, A. D.,** Inhibition of prostaglandin synthetase and carrageenan-induced edema by analogs of flufenamic acid, *Drug Exp. Clin. Res.,* 2, 35, 1977.
165. **Sota, K., Noda, K., Maruyama, H., Fujihara, E., and Nakazawa, M.,** Antiinflammatory activities of related compounds to anthranilic acid. I. On *N*-phenylanthranilic acid derivatives, *Yakugaku Zasshi,* 89, 1392, 1969.
166. **Hansen, E. S.,** Inhibition by indomethacin and aspirin of 15-hydroxy prostaglandin dehydrogenase *in vitro, Prostaglandins,* 8, 95, 1974.
167. **Flower, R. J., Cheung, H. S., and Cushman, D. W.,** Quantitative determination of prostaglandin and malondialdehyde formed by the arachidonate oxygenase system of bovine seminal vesicles, *Prostaglandins,* 4, 325, 1973.
167A. **Stone, K. J., Mather, S. J., and Gibson, P. P.,** Selective inhibition of prostaglandin biosynthesis by gold salts and phenylbutazone, *Prostaglandins,* 10, 241, 1975.
168. **Moser, P., Jaekel, K., Krupp, P., Menasse, R., and Sallman, A.,** Structure-activity relation of analogs of phenylbutazone, *Eur. J. Med. Chem. Chim. Ther.,* 10, 613, 1975.
169. **Lombardino, J. G.,** Enolic acids with anti-inflammatory activity, in *Anti-inflammatory Agents, Chemistry and Pharmacology,* Vol. 1, Scherrer, R. A., Ed., Academic Press, New York, 1974, 129.
170. **Lombardino, J. G. and Wiseman, E. H.,** Sudoxicam and related *N*-heterocyclic carboxamides of 4-hydroxy-2H-1,2-benzothiazine-1,1-dioxide. Potent non-steroidal antiinflammatory agents, *J. Med. Chem.,* 15, 848, 1972.
171. **Lombardino, J. G. and Wiseman, E. H.,** The oxicams: a new class of non-steroidal anti-inflammatory agents, *Trends Pharmacol. Sci.,* 2, 132, 1981.
172. **Wiseman, E. H. and Boyle, J. A.,** Pyroxicam (Feldene) in *Clinics in Rheumatic disease: Anti Rheumatic Drugs II,* Vol. 6, Huskisson, E. C., Ed., Sanders, London, 1980, 585.
173. **Moore, G. G. I.,** Sulfonamides with anti-inflammatory activity, in *Anti-inflammatory Agents, Chemistry and Pharmacology,* Vol. 1, Scherrer, R. A., Ed., Academic Press, New York, 1974, 160.
174. **Lands, W. E. M., Cook, H. W., and Rome, L. H.,** Prostaglandin synthesis: consequences of oxygenase mechanism upon *in vitro* assays of drug effectiveness, *Adv. Prostaglandin Thromboxane Res.,* 1, 7, 1976.
175. **van der Hoek, J. K. and Lands, W. E. M.,** The inhibition of fatty acid oxygenase of sheep vesicular gland by anti-oxidants, *Biochim. Biophys. Acta,* 196, 382, 1973.
176. **Dewhirst, F. E.,** Structure-activity relationships for inhibition of prostaglandin biosynthesis by phenolic compounds, *Prostaglandins,* 20, 209, 1980.
177. **Baumann, J., Wurm, G., and von Bruchhausen, F.,** Inhibition of prostaglandin synthetase by flavonoids and phenolic derivatives in comparison with their peroxide anion radical ($O_2 \cdot ^-$) scavenging properties, *Arch. Pharm.* (Weinheim, Ger.), 313, 330, 1980.
178. **Wurm, G., Baumann, J., and Geres, U.,** Effect of flavonoids on arachidonic acid metabolism, *Dtsch. Apoth-Ztg.,* 122, 2062, 1982.
179. **Arora, R. B., Basu, N., Kapoor, V., and Jain, A. P.,** Anti-inflammatory studies on Curcuma Longa (Turmeric), *Indian J. Med. Res.,* 59, 1289, 1971.
180. **Srivastava, R., Dikshit, M., Srimal, R. C., and Dhawan, B. N.,** Antithrombotic effects of curcumin, *Thromb. Res.,* 40, 413, 1985.
181. **Walsh, D. A., Sleevi, M. C., and Sancilio, L. F.,** Anti-inflammatory activity of *N*-(2-benzoylphenyl)alanine derivatives, *J. Med. Chem.,* 27, 1317, 1984.
182. **Szmuszkovicz, J., Glenn, E. M., Heinzelman, R. V., Hester, J. B., and Youngdale, G. A.,** Synthesis and antiinflammatory activity of 2,3-bis (p-methoxyphenyl)indole and related compounds, *J. Med. Chem.,* 9, 527, 1966.
183. **Shen, T. Y.,** Non-acidic antiarthritic agents, in *Anti-inflammatory Agents, Chemistry and Pharmacology,* Vol. 1, Scherrer, R. A., Ed., Academic Press, New York, 1974, 179.
184. **Corell, T., Hasselman, G., Splawinski, J., and Wojtaszek, B.,** Fenflumizole: interactions with the arachidonic acid cascade, *Acta Pharmacol. Toxicol.,* 53, 297, 1983.
185. **Wiseman, E. H., McIlhenny, H. M., and Bettis, J. W.,** Flumizole, a new non-steroidal anti-inflammatory agent, *J. Pharm. Sci.,* 64, 1469, 1975.
186. Anonymous, Prostaglandin synthetase inhibitors, *Res. Discl.,* 220, 293, 1982.
187. **Hewes, W. E., Rakestraw, D. C., Whitney, C. C., and Vernier, V. G.,** Tiflamizole: effects on rat adjuvant arthritis and the relationship of effects to pharmacokinetics, *Pharmacologist,* 24, 129, 1982.
188. **Schotzberger, G. S., Hewes, W. E., Galbraith, W., and Vernier, V. G.,** Comparative gastrointestinal safety of tiflamizole and standard anti-arthritic drugs in rats, *Pharmacologist,* 24, 129, 1982.
189. **Rakestraw, D. C., Whitney, C. C., and Vernier, V. G.,** Tiflamizole pharmacokinetics, *Pharmacologist,* 24, 129, 1982.

190. **Kitahara, N., Haruyama, H., Hata, T., and Takahashi, S.,** The structures of thielavins A, B and C. Prostaglandin synthetase inhibitors from fungi, *J. Antibiot.*, 36, 599, 1983.
191. **Kitahara, N., Endo, A., Furuya, K., and Takahashi, S.,** Thielavin A and B, new inhibitors of prostaglandin biosynthesis produced by *Thielavin terricola, J. Antibiot.*, 34, 1562, 1981.
192. **Shibuya, M., Edizuka, Y., Noguchi, H., Iitaka, Y., and Sankawa, U.,** Inhibition of prostaglandin biosynthesis by 4-O-methylcryptochlorophaeic acid: synthesis of monomeric arylcarboxylic acids for inhibitory activity testing and X-ray analysis of 4-O-methylcryptochlorophaeic acid, *Chem. Pharm. Bull.*, 31, 407, 1983.
193. **Ritchie, G. A. F.,** The direct inhibition of prostaglandin synthetase of human breast cancer tumor tissue by tamoxifen, *Recent Results Cancer Res.*, 71, 96, 1980.
194. **Powles, T. J., Dowsett, M., Easty, G. C., and Neville, A. M.,** Breast cancer osteolysis, bone metastases and anti-osteolytic effect of aspirin, *Lancet,* p. 608, 1976.
195. **Gilbert, J., Miquel, J. F., Precigoux, G., Hospital, M., Raynaud, J. P., Michel, F., and Crastes de Paulet, A.,** Inhibition of prostaglandin synthetase by di- and triphenylethylene derivatives, *J. Med. Chem.*, 26, 693, 1983.
196. **Rome, L. H. and Lands, W. E. M.,** Structural requirements for time-dependent inhibition of prostaglandin biosynthesis by anti-inflammatory drugs, *Proc. Natl. Acad. Sci. U.S.A.*, 72, 4863, 1975.
197. **Higgs, G. A., Harvey, E. A., Ferreira, S. H., and Vane, J. R.,** The effect of antiinflammatory drugs on the production of prostaglandins *in vivo, Adv. Prostaglandin Thromboxane Res.*, 1, 105, 1976.
198. **Kandasamy, S. B.,** Inhibition of bovine cerebral cortex prostaglandin synthetase by phenoxybenzamine and cyproheptadine *in vitro, Clin. Exp. Pharmacol. Physiol.*, 4, 585, 1977.
199. **Stecher, V. J., Carlson, J. A., Connolly, K. M., and Bailey, D. M.,** Disease-modifying antirheumatic drugs, *Med. Chem. Rev.*, 5, 371, 1985.
200. **Erman, A., Azuri, R., and Raz, A.,** Prostaglandin biosynthesis in rabbit kidney: mepacrine inhibits renomedullary cyclooxygenase, *Biochem. Pharmacol.*, 33, 79, 1984.
201. **Kench, J. G., Seale, J. P., Temple, D. M., and Tennant, C.,** The effects of non-steroidal inhibitors of phospholipase $A_2$ on leukotriene and histamine release from human and guinea pig lung, *Prostaglandins*, 30, 199, 1985.
202. **Raz, A.,** Mepacrine blockage of arachidonate-induced washed platelet aggregation: relationship to mepacrine inhibition of platelet cyclooxygenase, *Thromb. Haemostasis*, 50, 784, 1983.
203. **Carlson, R. P., Datko, L. J., Chang, J., Nielsen, S. T., and Lewis, A. J.,** The antiinflammatory profile of (5H-dibenzo[a,d]cyclohepten-5-ylidene)acetic acid (WY-41770), an agent possessing weak prostaglandin synthetase inhibitory activity that is devoid of gastric side effects, *Agents Actions*, 14, 654, 1984.
204. **Carlson, R. P., Fenichel, R. L., Lewis, A. J., and Wolf, M.,** Method for modulating the immune response with dibenzocycloheptenylidenes, U.S. Patent 4376124, 1981.
205. **Augstein, J., Cairns, H., Chambers, A., Burns, J. W., and Radziwonik, M.,** 6,8-Di-t-butyl-4-oxo-4H-l-benzopyran-2-carboxylic acid: a chromone derivative with anti-allergic, anti-inflammatory and uricosuric activity, *J. Pharm. Pharmacol.*, 28, 919, 1976.
206. **Cox, T. S. G., Beach, J. E., Blair, A. M. J. N., Clarke, A. J., King, J., Lee, T. B., Loveday, D. E. E., Moss, G. F., Orr, T. S. C., Ritchie, J. T., and Sheard, P.,** Disodium cromoglycate (Intal), in *Advances in Drug Research,* Vol. 5, Harper, N. and Simmonds, A., Eds., Academic Press, New York, 1970, 115.
207. **Pirisino, R., Mangano, G., Cepattelli, P., Corrias, M., Ignesti, G., Carla, V., and Pecori Vettori, L.,** Further investigation on the anti-inflammatory activity of some 2-phenylpyrazolo[1,4-a]pyrimidine compounds, *Farmaco Ed. Sci.*, 36, 682, 1981.
208. **Blythin, D. J., Kaminski, J. J., Domalski, M. S., Spitler, J., Solomon, D. M., Conn, D. J., Wong, S. C., Verbiar, L. L., Bober, L. A., Chiu, P. J. S., Watnick, A. S., Siegel, M. I., Hilbert, J. M., and McPhail, A. T.,** Antiinflammatory[2,1-f]purine-2,4,8-(1H,3H,9H)-triones. Atypical nonsteroidal antiinflammatory agents, *J. Med. Chem.*, 29, 1099, 1986.
209. **Kunze, M., Bohn, E., and Barke, G.,** Effects of psychotropic drugs on prostaglandin biosynthesis *in vitro, J. Pharm. Pharmacol.*, 27, 880, 1975.
210. **Gryglewski, R. J.,** Prostaglandin and thromboxane biosynthesis inhibitors, *Naunyn-Schmeidebergs Arch Pharmacol.*, 297 (Suppl. 1) 85, 1977.
211. **Da Settimo, A., Primofiore, G., Ferrarini, P. L., Franzone, J. S., Cirillo, R., and Cravanzola, C.,** Bromo derivatives of gramine. Preparation and pharmacological properties, *Eur. J. Med. Chem. Chim. Ther.*, 18, 261, 1983.
212. **Ohtsu, A., Tanaka, T., Kamimoto, F., Hoshina, K., Kurozumi, S., Naruchi, T., and Hashimoto, Y.,** Structure-activity relationship of novel 3-acylpyrrole derivatives: new inhibitors of platelet aggregation, *J. Pharmacobio-Dyn.*, 3, 589, 1980.
213. **Fahrenholtz, K. E., Silverzweig, M. Z., Germane, N., Crowleg, M. J., Simko, B. A., and Dalton, C.,** 3-Phenyl-5-[2,2,2-trifluoro-1-hydroxy-1-(trifluoromethyl)ethyl] indole-2-carbonitrile, a potent inhibitor of prostaglandin synthetase and of platelet aggregation, *J. Med. Chem.*, 22, 948, 1979.

214. **McConkey, B., Davies, P., Crockson, R. A., Crockson, A. P., Butler, M., and Constable, T. J.,** Dapsone in rheumatoid arthritis, *Rheum. Rehab.*, 15, 230, 1976.
215. **Swinson, D. R., Zloznick, J., and Jackson, L.,** Paper read to the combined meeting of BARR, Heberden Society and PSM, Nottingham, England, 1980.
216. **Oglesby, T. D. and Gorman, R. R.,** The inhibition of arachidonic acid metabolism in human platelets by RHC 80267, a diacylglycerol lipase inhibitor, *Biochim. Biophys. Acta*, 793, 269, 1984.
217. **Xin-Sheng, Y., Ebizuka, Y., Noguchi, H., Kiuchi, F., and Sankawa, U.,** Structure of arnebinone, a novel monoterpenylbenzoquinone with inhibitory effect to prostaglandin biosynthesis, *Tetrahedron Lett.*, 24, 3247, 1983.
218. **Kitahara, N. and Endo, A.,** Xanthocillin A monomethyl ether, a potent inhibitor of prostaglandin biosynthesis, *J. Antibiotics*, 23, 1556, 1981.
219. **Ahern, D. G. and Downing, D. T.,** Inhibition of prostaglandin biosynthesis by eicosa-5,8,11,14-tetraynoic acid, *Biochim. Biophys. Acta*, 210, 456, 1970.
220. **Aiken, J. W.,** Aspirin and indomethacin prolong parturition in rats; evidence that prostaglandins contribute to expulsion of foetus, *Nature (London)*, 240, 21, 1972.
221. **Downing, D. T., Ahern, D. G., and Bachta, M. L.,** Enzyme inhibition by acetylenic compounds, *Biochem. Biophys. Res. Commun.*, 40, 218, 1970.
222. **Fretland, D. J., Flanders, L. E., Borowski, P. T., Palicharia, P., Cammarata, P. S., Hershenson, F. M., Liang, C. D., and Schulz, J. A.,** The long duration, *in vivo*, inhibition of prostaglandin synthetase by 2-methyl-8-cis-12-trans-14-cis-eicosatrienoic acid, *Biochem. Pharmacol.*, 34, 2103, 1985.
223. **Nugteren, D. H.,** Inhibition of prostaglandin biosynthesis by 8-cis, 12-trans, 14-cis-eicosatrienoic acid, *Biochim. Biophys. Acta*, 210, 171, 1970.
224. **Corey, E. J., Shih, C., and Cashman, J. R.,** Docosahexaenoic acid is a strong inhibitor of prostaglandin but not leukotriene synthesis, *Proc. Natl. Acad. Sci. U.S.A.*, 80, 3581, 1983.
225. **Campbell, W. B., Falck, J. R., Okita, J. R., Johnson, A. R., and Callahan, K. S.,** Synthesis of dihomoprostaglandins from adrenic acid (7,10,13,16-docosatetraenoic acid) by human endothelial cells, *Biochim. Biophys. Acta*, 837, 67, 1985.
226. **Batterman, R. C. and Sommer, E. M.,** Fate of gentisic acid in man is influenced by alkalinisation and acidification, *Proc. Soc. Exp. Biol.*, 82, 376, 1973.
227. **Pace-Isciak, C. and Wolfe, L. S.,** Inhibition of prostaglandin synthesis by oleic, linoleic and linolenic acids, *Biochim. Biophys. Acta*, 152, 784, 1968.
228. **Hashimoto, Y., Naito, C., Teramoto, T., Kato, H., Kinoshita, M., Kawamura, M., Hayashi, H., and Oka, H.,** Time-dependent inhibition of the cyclooxygenase pathway by 12-hydroperoxy-5,8,10,14-eicosatetraenoic acid, *Biochem. Biophys. Res. Commun.*, 130, 781, 1985.
229. **Corey, E. J., Wlodawer, P., Samuelsson, B., and Albonico, S. M.,** Selective inhibition of prostaglandin synthetase by a bicyclo[2.2.1]heptene derivative, *J. Am. Chem. Soc.*, 93, 2815, 1971.
230. **Leeney, T. J., Marsham, P. R., Ritchie, G. A. F., and Senior, M. W.,** Inhibitions of prostaglandin biosynthesis. A bicyclo[2.2.1]heptene analogue of '2' series prostaglandins and related derivatives, *Prostaglandins*, 11, 953, 1976.
231. **Ohki, S., Ogino, N., Yamamoto, S., Hayaishi, O., Yamamoto, M., and Hayashi, M.,** Inhibition of prostaglandin endoperoxide synthetase by thiol analogues of prostaglandin, *Proc. Natl. Acad. Sci. U.S.A.*, 74, 144, 1977.
232. **Le Breton, G. C., Hung, S. C., Ghali, N. I., and Venton, D. L.,** 2-(6-Carboxyhexyl)cyclopentanone hexylhydrazone: a potent inhibitor of the blood platelet cyclooxygenase, *Prostaglandins*, 27, 543, 1984.
233. **McDonald-Gibson, R. G., Flack, J. D., and Ramwell, P. W.,** Inhibition of prostaglandin biosynthesis by 7-oxa and 5-oxa-prostaglandin analogues, *Biochem. J.*, 132, 117, 1973.
234. **Blackwell, G. J., Flower, R. J., and Vane, J. R.,** Some characteristics of the prostaglandin synthesizing system in rabbit kidney microsomes, *Biochim. Biophys. Acta*, 398, 178, 1975.
235. **Saeed, S. A., Kendall, P. A., Butt, N. M., and Collier, H. O. J.,** On the mode of action and biochemical properties of antiinflammatory drugs, *Biochem. Soc. Trans.*, 7, 655, 1979.
236. **Majerus, P. W. and Stanford, N.,** Comparative effects of aspirin and diflunisal on prostaglandin synthetase from human platelets and sheep seminal vesicles, *Br. J. Clin. Pharmacol.*, 4(Suppl. 1), 15, 1977.
237. **Sancho, M. J. deC, Vila, L., Garcia, J., Carretero, F., Fabra, A., and Rutlant, M. L.,** Effects of salicylate derivatives on cyclooxygenase. Interaction studies, *Biol. Clin. Hematol.*, 7, 135, 1985.
238. **Jones, M., Fordyce, M. W., Greenwald, L. B., Hannah, J., Jacobs, A., Ruyle, W. V., Walford, G. L., and Shen, T. Y.,** Synthesis and analgesic-antiinflammatory activity of some 4- and 5-substituted heteroarylsalicylic acids, *J. Med. Chem.*, 21, 1100, 1978.
239. **Hawkey, C. J.,** Sulfasalazine and prostaglandin synthesis, *Lancet*, 2, 1342, 1981.
240. **Schroer, K., Neuhaus, V., Ahland, B., Sauerland, S., Kuhn, A., Darius, H., and Bussmann, K.,** Actions of tiaprofenic acid on vascular prostacyclin biosynthesis and thromboxane and 12-HPETE formation of human platelets *in vitro* and *in vivo*, *Rheumatology*, 7 (New Trends Osteoarthritis), 88, 1982.

241. **DeClerck, F., Vermylen, J., and Reneman, R.,** Effects of suprofen, and inhibitor of prostaglandin biosynthesis on platelet function, plasma coagulation and fibrinolysis. *In vivo* experiments, *Arch. Int. Pharmacodyn.*, 217, 68, 1975.
242. **Muchowski, J. M. et al.,** Synthesis and antiinflammatory and analgesic activity of 5-aroyl-1,2-dihydro-3H-pyrrolo[1,2-a]pyrrole-1-carboxylic acids and related compounds, *J. Med. Chem.*, 28, 1037, 1985.
243. **Taylor, R. J. and Salata, J. J.,** Inhibition of prostaglandin synthetase by tolmetin (tolectin, McN-2559) a new non-steroidal anti-inflammatory agent, *Biochem. Pharmacol.*, 25, 2479, 1976.
244. **Patrono, C., Ciavattoni, G., and Gross-Belloni, D.,** *In vitro* and *in vivo* inhibition of prostaglandin synthesis by fenoprofen, a non-steroidal antiinflammatory drug, *Pharmacol. Res. Commun.*, 6, 509, 1974.
245. **Ho, P. P. K. and Esterman, M. A.,** Fenoprofen: inhibitor of prostaglandin synthesis, *Prostaglandins*, 6, 107, 1974.
246. **Muratov, V. K., Varfolomeev, S. D., Igumnova, N. D., Mevkh, A. T., and Churyukanov, V. V.,** Interaction of voltaren and some pyrazolone and aniline derivatives with endoperoxide prostaglandin synthetase, *Farmakol. Toksikol. (Moscow)*, 47, 41, 1984.
247. **Ku, E. C., Lee, W., Kothary, H. V., Kimble, E. F., Liauw, L., and Tjan, J.,** The effects of diclofenac sodium on arachidonic acid metabolism, *Semin. Arthritis Rheum.*, 15, 36, 1985.
248. **Ku, E. C., Wasvary, J. M., and Cash, W. D.,** Diclofenac sodium (GP 45840, Voltaren), a potent inhibitor of prostaglandin synthetase, *Biochem. Pharmacol.*, 24, 641, 1975.
249. **Gaut, Z. N., Baruth, M., Randall, L. O., Ashley, C., and Paulsrud, J. R.,** Stereoisomeric relations among anti-inflammatory activity, inhibition of platelet aggregation and inhibition of prostaglandin synthetase, *Prostaglandins*, 10, 59, 1975.
250. **Nakamura, H., Yokoyama, Y., Motoyoshi, S., Ishii, K., Imazo, C., Seto, Y., Kadokawa, T., and Shimizo, M.,** The pharmacological profile of 2-(8-methyl-10,11-dihydro-11-oxodibenzo[b.f]oxepin-2-yl)propionic acid (AD 1590), a new non-steroidal antiinflammatory agent with potent anti-pyretic activity, *Arzneim.-Forsch.*, 33, 1555, 1983.
251. **Higgs, G. A. and Vane, J. R.,** Inhibition of cyclooxygenase and lipoxygenase, *Br. Med. Bull.*, 39, 265, 1983.
252. **Adams, S. S., Bresloff, P., and Mason, C. G.,** Pharmacological differences between the optical isomers of ibuprofen: evidence for metabolic inversion of the (-) isomer, *J. Pharm. Pharmacol.*, 28, 256, 1976.
253. **Muramatsu, M., Tanaka, M., Fujita, A., Atomo, S., Aihara, M., and Amano, T.,** Inhibition of prostaglandin biosynthesis by a new anti-inflammatory drug, TA-60, *J. Pharmacobio-Dyn.*, 8, 11, 1985.
254. **Corbelli, G. P., Stanzani, L., Mastacchi, R., Barbanti, M., and Montecchi, L.,** Effects of SAS-650 (Furofenac) on malondialdehyde production by platelets, *Agents Actions*, 14, 735, 1984.
255. **Procaccini, R. L., Smyth, R. D., Rush, K., and Reavey-Cantwell, N. H.,** Studies of the inhibition of prostaglandin synthetase by fenclorac, a new nonsteroidal antiinflammatory agent, *Fed. Proc.*, 35, 774, 1976.
256. **Nuss, G. W., Smyth, R. D., Dreder, C. H., Hitchings, M. J., Mir, G. N., and Reavey-Cantwell, N. H.,** Fenclorac, a new nonsteroidal anti-inflammatory agent, *Fed. Proc.*, 35, 774, 1976.
257. **Procaccini, R. L., Smyth, R. D., and Reavey-Cantwell, N. H.,** Studies on the *in vivo* inhibition of prostaglandin synthetase by fenclorac ($\alpha$,m-dichloro-p-cyclohexylphenylacetic acid) and indomethacin, *Biochem. Pharmacol.*, 26, 1051, 1977.
258. **Ku, E. C. and Wasvary, J. M.,** Inhibition of prostaglandin synthetase by pirprofen. Studies with sheep seminal vesicle enzyme, *Biochim. Biophys. Acta*, 384, 360, 1975.
259. **Maier, R., Schweizer, A., and Wilhelmi, G.,** Pharmacological aspects of pirprofen, in *Pirprofen. Treat. Pain Inflamm.*, Proc. Int. Symp., Van der Korst, J. K., Ed., Huber, Bern, Switzerland, 1981, 9.
260. **Matsuda, K., Tanaka, Y., Ushiyama, S., Ohnishi, K., and Yamazaki, M.,** Inhibition of prostaglandin synthesis by 2-[4-(2-oxocyclopentyl-methyl)phenyl]propionate dihydrate (CS-600), a new anti-inflammatory drug, and its active metabolite *in vitro* and *in vivo*, *Biochem. Pharmacol.*, 33, 2473, 1984.
261. **Tolman, E. L., Birnbaum, J. E., Chiccarelli, F. S., Panagides, J., and Slododa, A. E.,** Inhibition of prostaglandin activity and synthesis by fenbufen (a new non-steroidal antiinflammatory agent) and one of its metabolites, *Adv. Prostaglandin Thromboxane Res.*, 1, 133, 1976.
262. **Crook, D., Collins, A. J., and Rose, A. J.,** A comparison of the effects of flurbiprofen on prostaglandin synthetase from human rheumatoid synovium and enzymically active animal tissues, *J. Pharm. Pharmacol.*, 67, 73, 1979.
263. **Ham, E. A., Cirillo, V. J., Zanetti, M., Shen, T. Y., and Kuehl, F. A.,** Mode of action of nonsteroidal antiinflammatory agents *Prostaglandins Cell. Biol.*, Proc. ALZA Conf., Ramwell, P. W., Ed., Plenum, New York, 1972, 345.
264. **Chaung, T. C. and Ellis, K. O.,** Inhibition of prostaglandin synthetase by F-776, a new anti-inflammatory/analgesic compound, *Biochem. Pharmacol.*, 30, 3008, 1981.
265. **Dawson, W.,** Mechanisms of actions of antiinflammatory drugs, *Adv. Prostaglandin Thromboxane Res.*, 8, 1741, 1980.

266. **Ryznerski, Z.,** Synthesis of phenylphenoxyacetamide derivatives; potential anti-inflammatory activity, *Pol. J. Pharmacol. Pharm.*, 32, 403, 1980.
267. **Mizoule, J., Le Fur, G., and Uzan, A.,** Study of two new non-steroid antiinflammatory drugs having a pyrazole structure (LM 22070 and LM 22102), *Arch. Int. Pharmacodyn. Ther.*, 238, 305, 1979.
268. **Demerson, C. A., Humber, L. G., Abraham, N. A., Schilling, G., Martel, R. R., and Pace-Asciak, C.,** Resolution of etodolac and antiinflammatory and prostaglandin synthetase inhibiting properties of the enantiomers, *J. Med. Chem.*, 26, 1778, 1983.
269. **Horodniak, J. W., Matz, E. D., Walz, D. T., Sutton, B. M., Berkoff, C. E., Zarembo, J. E., and Bender, A. D.,** Inhibition of prostaglandin synthetase and carrageenan-induced edema by tricyclic analogs of flufenamic acid, *Res. Comm. Chem. Pathol. Pharmacol.*, 11, 533, 1975.
270. **Ku, E. C. and Waswary, J. M.,** Inhibition of prostaglandin synthetase by SU-21254, *Fed. Proc.*, 32, 3302, 1973.
271. **Lind'en, I. B., Paratainen, J., and Vapaatalo, H.,** Inhibition of prostaglandin biosynthesis by tolfenamic acid *in vitro, Scand. J. Rheumatol.*, 5, 129, 1976.
272. **Del Maschio, A., Livio, M., Cerletti, C., and De Gaetano, G.,** Inhibition of human platelet cyclo-oxygenase by sulfinpyrazone and three of its metabolites, *Eur. J. Pharmacol.*, 101, 209, 1984.
273. **Luethy, C., Multhaupt, O., Oetliker, O., and Perisic, M.,** Differential effect of acetylsalicylic acid and dipyrone on prostaglandin production in human fibroblast cultures, *Br. J. Pharmacol.*, 79, 849, 1983.
274. **Eldor, A., Polliack, G., Vlodavsky, I., and Levy, M.,** Effects of dipyrone on prostaglandin production by human platelets and cultured bovine aortic endothelial cells, *Thromb. Haemostasis*, 49, 132, 1983.
275. **Cohen, D., Corbin, J., Figueroa, J. P., Nathanielsz, P. W., and Mitchell, M. D.,** Inhibition of arachidonic acid metabolism by antipyrine and 4-aminoantipyrine, *Am. J. Obstet. Gynecol.*, 153, 589, 1985.
276. **Van den Berg, G., Bultsma, T., and Nauta, W. T.,** Inhibition of prostaglandin biosynthesis by 2-aryl-1,3-indanediones, *Biochem. Pharmacol.*, 24, 1115, 1975.
277. **Carty, T. J., Stevens, J. S., Lombardino, J. G., Parry, M. J., and Randall, M. J.,** Piroxicam, a structurally novel anti-inflammatory compound. Mode of prostaglandin synthesis inhibition, *Prostaglandins*, 19, 671, 1980.
278. **Carty, T. J., Eskra, J. D., Lombardino, J. G., and Hoffmann, W. W.,** Piroxicam, a potent inhibitor of prostaglandin production in cell culture, *Prostaglandins*, 19, 51, 1980.
279. **Pugsley, T. A., Spencer, C., Boctor, A. M., and Gluckman, M. I.,** Selective inhibition of the cyclooxygenase pathway of the arachidonic acid cascade by the non-steroidal anti-inflammatory drug isoxicam, *Drug Dev. Res.*, 5, 171, 1985.
280. **Bradshaw, D., Cashin, C. H., Kennedy, A. J., and Roberts, N. A.,** Pharmacological and biochemical activities of Tenoxicam (Ro 12-0068), a new non-steroidal anti-inflammatory drug, *Agents Actions*, 15, 569, 1984.
281. **Vigdahl, R. L. and Tukey, R. H.,** Mechanism of action of novel anti-inflammatory drugs diflumidone and R-805, *Biochem. Pharmacol.*, 26, 307, 1977.
282. **Takeguchi, C. and Sih, S. J.,** A rapid spectrophotometric assay for prostaglandin synthetase: application to a study of non-steroidal antiinflammatory agents, *Prostaglandins*, 2, 169, 1972.
283. **Salafsky, B. and Fusco, A. B.,** Schistosoma: cercarial eicosanoid production and penetration response inhibited by esculetin and ibuprofen, *Exp. Parasitol.*, 60, 73, 1985.
284. **Falkay, G. and Kovacs, L.,** Calcium dobesylate (doxium) as a prostaglandin synthetase inhibitor in pregnant human myometrium *in vitro, Experientia*, 40, 190, 1984.
285. **Wurm, G. and Baumann, J.,** Effect of 2-hydroxy-1,4-naphthoquinone derivatives on prostaglandin synthesis. 2. Studies on 1,4-naphthoquinones, *Arzneim.-Forsch.*, 31, 1673, 1981.
286. **Arturson, G. and Jonsson, C. E.,** Stimulation and inhibition of biosynthesis of prostaglandins in human skin by some hydroxyethylated rutinosides, *Prostaglandins*, 10, 941, 1975.
287. **Swies, J., Robak, J., Dabrowski, L., Duniek, Z., Michalska, Z., and Gryglewski, R.,** Antiaggregatory effects of flavonoids *in vivo* and their influence on lipoxygenase and cyclooxygenase *in vitro, Pol. J. Pharmacol. Pharm.*, 36, 455, 1984.
288. **Ali, M., Gudbranson, C. G., and McDonald, J. W. D.,** Inhibition of human platelet cyclooxygenase by alpha-tocopherol, *Prostaglandins Med.*, 4, 79, 1980.
289. **Baumann, J. and von Bruchhausen, F.,** (±) Cyanidanol-3 as inhibitor of prostaglandin synthetase. Studies on renal medulla and liver of the rat *in vitro* and *in vivo, Naunyn-Schmeidebergs Arch Pharmacol.*, 306, 85, 1979.
290. **Kiuchi, F., Shibuya, M., and Sankawa, M.,** Inhibitors of prostaglandin biosynthesis from ginger, *Chem. Pharm. Bull.*, 30, 754, 1982.
291. **Vanderhoek, J. Y. and Lands, W. E. M.,** Inhibition of fatty acid oxygenase of sheep vesicular gland by antioxidants, *Biochim. Biophys. Acta*, 296, 374, 1973.

292. **Miyazawa, K., Iimori, Y., Makino, M., Mikami, T., and Miyasaki, K.,** Effects of some nonsteroidal antiinflammatory drugs and other agents on cyclooxygenase and lipoxygenase activities in some enzyme preparations, *Jpn. J. Pharmacol.,* 38, 199, 1985.
293. **Yanagi, Y. and Komatsu, T.,** Inhibition of prostaglandins biosynthesis by SL-573, *Biochem. Pharmacol.,* 25, 937, 1976.
294. **Goto, G., Muramatsu, M., Hosoda, K., Otomo, S., and Aihara, M.,** The inhibitory effect of oxaprozin, a new nonsteroidal anti-inflammatory drug, on platelet aggregation, *Nippon Yakurigaku Zasshi,* 83, 395, 1984.
295. **Lerner, L. J., Carminati, P., and Schiatti, P.,** Correlation of anti-inflammatory activity with inhibition of prostaglandin synthesis activity of nonsteroidal antiestrogens and estrogens, *Proc. Soc. Exp. Biol. Med.,* 148, 329, 1975.
296. **Sokola, A.,** Effect of neuroleptic drugs on prostaglandin synthetase activity, *Acta Physiol. Pol.,* 32, 333, 1981.
297. **Krupp, P. and Wesp, M.,** Inhibition of prostaglandin synthetase by psychotropic drugs, *Experientia,* 31, 330, 1975.
298. **Tarzia, G., Panzone, G., Carminati, P., Schiatti, P., and Selva, D.,** Synthesis and pharmacological properties of pyrrolo[3,4-d]pyrimidine and pyrrolo[3,4-d]pyridines (I). *Farmaco. Ed. Sci.,* 31, 81, 1976.
299. **Mower, R. L., Landolfi, R., and Steiner, M.,** Inhibition of *in vitro* platelet aggregation and arachidonic acid metabolism by flavone, *Biochem. Pharmacol.,* 33, 357, 1984.
300. **Carminati, P. and Lerner, L. J.,** Effect of diftalone and other non-steroidal antiinflammatory agents on the synthesis of prostaglandins, *Proc. Soc. Exp. Biol. Med.,* 148, 455, 1975.
301. **Ruzicka, T., Wasserman, S. I., Soter, N. A., and Printz, M. P.,** Inhibition of rat mast cell arachidonic acid cyclooxygenase by dapsone, *J. Allerg. Clin. Immunol.,* 72, 365, 1983.
302. **Lewis, A. J., Gemmell, D. K., and Stimson, W. H.,** The anti-inflammatory profile of dapsone in animal models of inflammation, *Agents Actions,* 8, 578, 1978.
303. **Ando, K., Suzuki, S., Takatsuki, K., Arima, K., and Tamura, G.,** A new antibiotic, 1-(p-hydroxyphenyl)-2,3-diisocyano-4-(p-methoxyphenyl)buta-2,3-diene. Isolation and biological properties. (Studies on antiviral and antitumor antibiotics III), *J. Antibiotics,* 21, 587, 1968.
304. **Willis, A. J.,** Personal communication.

# LIPOXYGENASE INHIBITORS

**Jürg R. Pfister and Michael J. Ernest**

## INTRODUCTION

Although the occurrence of lipoxygenases in plants had been known for some time,[1] the discovery of 12-HPETE,[2] the first evidence of lipoxygenase activity in mammalian tissue, was reported as recently as 1974. In the intervening years, remarkable progress has been made in characterizing this alternate arachidonic acid metabolic cascade by elucidating the structure of and synthesizing such lipoxygenase-derived products as $LTA_4$, HPETEs, HETEs, $LTB_4$, the lipoxins, and the peptidoleukotrienes $LTC_4$, $LTD_4$, and $LTE_4$ (formerly known collectively as "slow-reacting substance of anaphylaxis" SRS-A).[3-6] Since these mediators possess varied and potent pharmacological actions,[7,8] inhibition of leukotriene biosynthesis[9-15] may conceivably lead to new therapeutic agents for the treatment of anaphylactic and inflammatory disease states.[16-19]

In this compilation, compounds for which lipoxygenase-inhibitory activity has been demonstrated are listed in tabular form. Inhibition of enzymes involved in subsequent biosynthetic steps of the leukotriene branch of the arachidonic acid cascade, as well as leukotriene antagonists, have not been included. The latter subject is reviewed by Musser et al. in a later chapter in this volume. Since lipoxygenases from different sources have been utilized in crude or purified form or as a whole-cell assay system, discrepancies are often found in regard to the potencies of the inhibitors studied. It is therefore recommended that the original literature be consulted for more detailed information on experimental parameters. No attempt was made to correlate *in vitro* lipoxygenase-inhibition data with *in vivo* pharmacological activities.

The patent literature has not been used as a source for this review, due to the general lack of description of assay procedures. The information contained herein has been broken down into five structural classes (Tables 1 through 5); literature references are provided for each section.

Table 6 presents some of the newer 5-LO inhibitors described over the past 2 years.

## ACKNOWLEDGMENT

The authors would like to thank Gina Costelli and Bertha Harris for typing this manuscript.

**Table 1**
**EICOSANOID ANALOGUES**

| No. | Name | Structure | Mol. formula (Mol. wt) | Biological data |
|---|---|---|---|---|
| 1. | 5,8,11,14-Eicosatetraynoic acid (ETYA) | 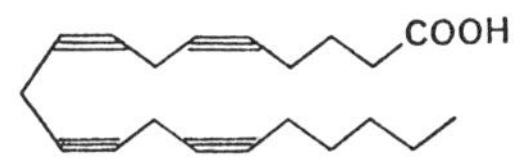 | $C_{20}H_{24}O_2$ (296) | Inhibited soybean 15-LO with $IC_{50}$ values of 2.4 $\mu M$[1] and 125 $\mu M$[2], respectively; at 1 $\mu M$, completely deactivated soybean 15-LO after a preincubation period of 15 min;[3] inhibited rat neutrophil 5-LO ($IC_{50}$ 2.4 $\mu M$),[1] human platelet 12-LO ($IC_{50}$ 0.3 $\mu M$[4] and 4 $\mu M$[5]); inhibited rabbit peritoneal PMNL 15-LO ($IC_{50}$ 0.5 $\mu$g/ml)[6,7] and human leukocyte 15-LO[4] |
| 2. | 4,7,10,13-Eicosatetraynoic acid | 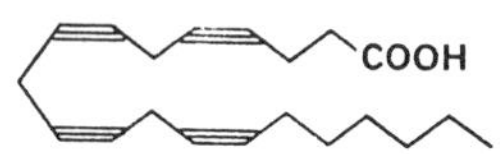 | $C_{20}H_{24}O_2$ (296) | Inhibited human platelet 12-LO ($IC_{50}$ 0.46 $\mu M$[8] and 7.8 $\mu M$[9]) |
| 3. | 5,8,11,14-Heneicosatetraynoic acid | 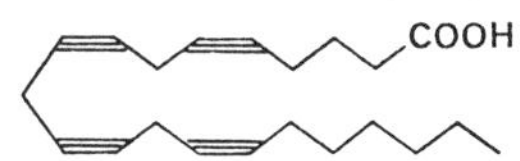 | $C_{21}H_{26}O_2$ (310) | Inhibited human platelet 12-LO ($IC_{50}$ 0.31 $\mu M$)[8] |
| 4. | 5,8,11-Eicosatriynoic acid | 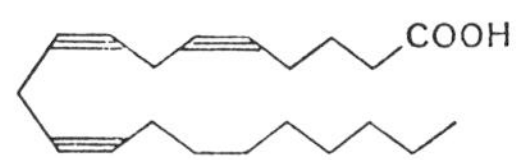 | $C_{20}H_{28}O_2$ (300) | Inhibited soybean 15-LO ($IC_{50}$ 30 $\mu M$)[2] and human platelet 12-LO ($IC_{50}$ 24 $\mu M$)[5] |
| 5. | 9,12-Octadecadiynoic acid | 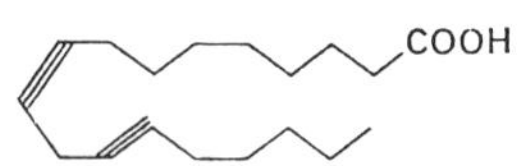 | $C_{18}H_{28}O_2$ (276) | Inhibited soybean 15-LO 68% at 48 $\mu M$[10] |
| 6. | 5,6-Dehydroarachidonic acid | 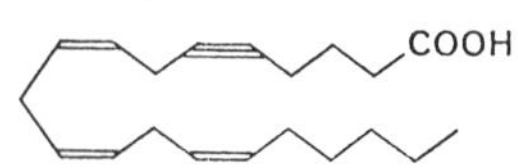 | $C_{20}H_{30}O_2$ (302) | Irreversibly inhibited RBL-1 cell 5-LO in the concentration range 60—140 $\mu M$[11] |
| 7. | 14,15-Dehydroarachidonic acid | 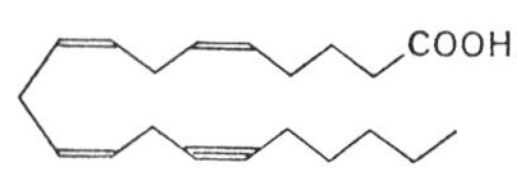 | $C_{20}H_{30}O_2$ (302) | Inhibited soybean 15-LO under aerobic incubation conditions ($IC_{50}$ ~0.6 $\mu M$)[12] |

| | | | | |
|---|---|---|---|---|
| 8. | 4,5-Dehydroarachidonic acid | 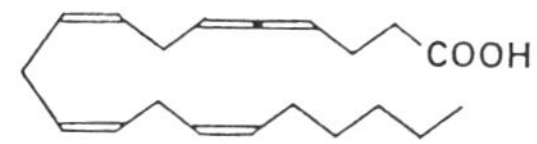 | $C_{20}H_{30}O_2$ (302) | Inhibited RBL-1 cell 5-LO ($IC_{50}$ ~ 10 μ*M*)[13] |
| 9. | 4,5,8-Eicosatrienoic acid |  | $C_{20}H_{34}O_2$ (306) | In a whole cell assay, inhibited human PMNL 5-LO (~ 2 × ETYA)[14] |
| 10. | 5-(1-Heptyl-2,5-cyclo-hexadienyl)-5Z-hexenoic acid methyl ester | 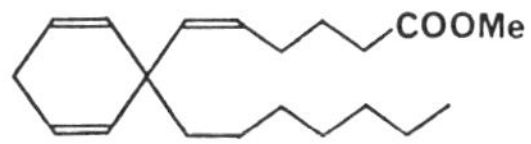 | $C_{20}H_{32}O_2$ (304) | Inhibited RBL-1 cell 5-LO ($IC_{50}$ 120 μ*M*)[15] |
| 11. | 14Z-Eicosaenoic acid (erucic acid) | 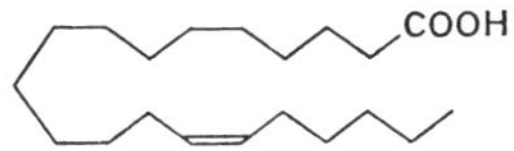 | $C_{20}H_{38}O_2$ (310) | Inhibited soybean 5-LO 40% at 5 μ*M*[16] |
| 12. | *Trans*-5,6-methano-7E,9E,11Z,-14Z-eicosatetraenoic acid (5,6-methanoleukotriene $A_4$) | 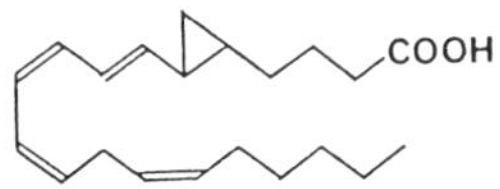 | $C_{21}H_{32}O_2$ (316) | Inhibited guinea pig PMNL 5-LO ($IC_{50}$ 3 μ*M*)[17-19] |
| 13. | *Trans*-5,6-Methano-7E,9E,11Z,-14Z-eicosatetraenoic acid methyl ester (5,6-methanoleukotriene $A_4$ methyl ester) | 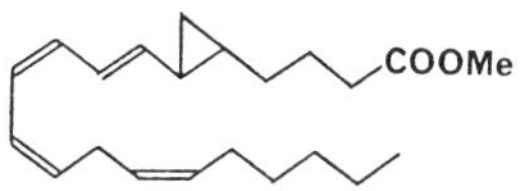 | $C_{22}H_{34}O_2$ (330) | Inhibited 5-LO from cloned mastocytoma P-815, Z-E-6 cells ($IC_{50}$ 18 μ*M*)[20,21] |
| 14. | 5,6-Benzoarachidonic acid | 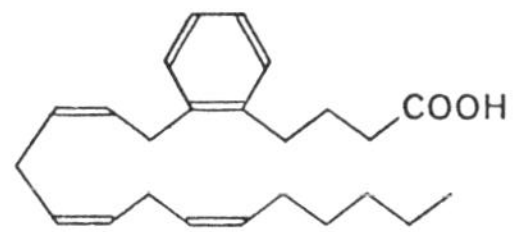 | $C_{24}H_{34}O_2$ (354) | Inhibited 5-HETE formation in intact human PMNLs by 90% at 100 μ*M*[32] |
| 15. | 7,7-Dimethylarachidonic acid | 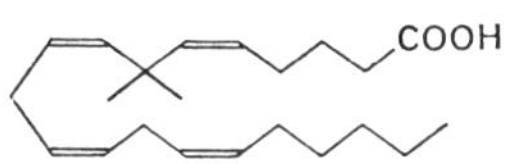 | $C_{22}H_{36}O_2$ (332) | Inhibited 5-LO from RBL-1 cells ($IC_{50}$ ~ 68 μ*M*) and $PLA_2$ ($IC_{50}$ 14 μ*M*;[23,24] stimulated lipoxygenase activity in human PMNLs at 100 μ*M*[22] |
| 16. | 7,7-Dimethyl-5Z,8Z,11Z-eicosatrienoic acid | 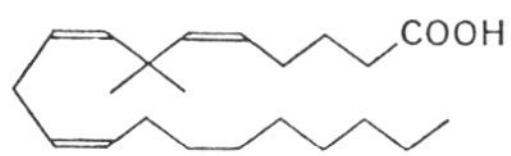 | $C_{22}H_{38}O_2$ (334) | Inhibited RBL-1 cell 5-LO ($IC_{50}$ 100 μ*M*)[25] |
| 17. | 7,7-Dimethyl-5Z,8Z-eicosadienoic acid | 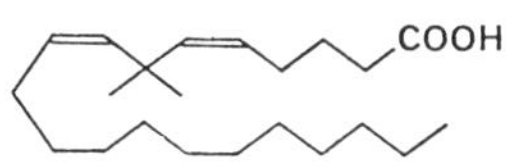 | $C_{22}H_{40}O_2$ (336) | At 50 μ*M*, inhibited 5-LO from RBL-1 cells and human PMNLs by 43% and 26%, respectively[26] |

**Table 1 (continued)**
**EICOSANOID ANALOGUES**

| No. | Name | Structure | Mol. formula (Mol. wt) | Biological data |
|---|---|---|---|---|
| 18. | 10,10-Dimethylarachidonic acid | 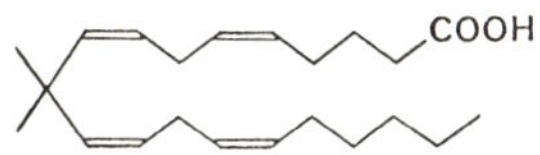 | $C_{22}H_{36}O_2$ (332) | Inhibited RBL-1 cell 5-LO by 42% at 100 μ*M*; inhibited $PLA_2$ ($IC_{50}$ 14 μ*M*);[23,24] stimulated lipoxygenase activity in human PMNLs at 100 μ*M*[22] |
| 19. | 10,10-Dimethyl-5Z,8Z,11Z-eicosatrienoic acid | 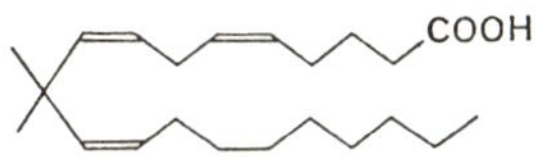 | $C_{22}H_{38}O_2$ (334) | At 100 μ*M*, inhibited RBL-1 cell 5-LO by 40%[25] |
| 20. | 7-Ethanoarachidonic acid | 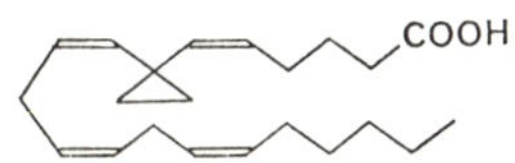 | $C_{22}H_{34}O_2$ (330) | At 100 μ*M*, inhibited guinea-pig leukocyte 5-LO by 34%[19] and RBL-1 cell 5-LO by 86%[27] |
| 21. | 5-Hydroxymethyl-6E,8Z,11Z,-14Z-eicosatetraenoic acid | 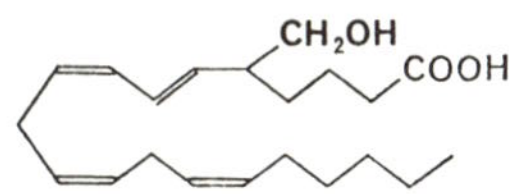 | $C_{21}H_{34}O_3$ (334) | Inhibited guinea-pig PMNL 5-LO ($IC_{50}$ 100 μ*M*)[17-19] |
| 22. | 5-Hydroxy-6E,8Z,11Z,14Z-eicosatetraenoic acid (5-HETE) | 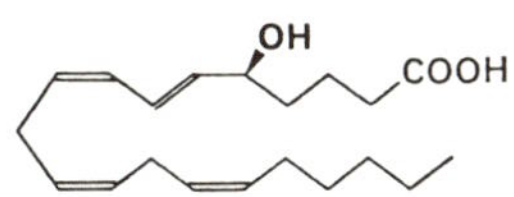 | $C_{20}H_{32}O_3$ (320) | Inhibited rabbit PMNL 5-LO ($IC_{50}$ 14 μ*M*) and 15-LO ($IC_{50}$ 10 μ*M*)[28] |
| 23. | 15-Hydroxy-5Z,8Z,11Z,13E-eicosatetraenoic acid (15-HETE) | 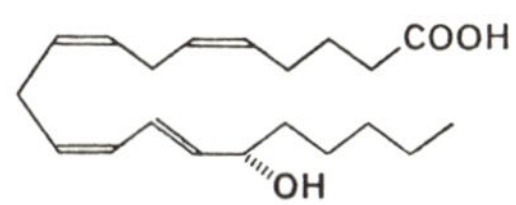 | $C_{20}H_{32}O_3$ (320) | Inhibited rabbit PMNL 5-LO ($IC_{50}$ 6 μ*M*) and rabbit platelet 12-LO ($IC_{50}$ 0.34 μ*M*);[29] inhibited human platelet 12-LO ($IC_{50}$ 8 μ*M*)[30] |
| 24. | 15-Hydroperoxy-5Z,8Z,11Z,13E-eicosatetraenoic acid (15-HPETE) | 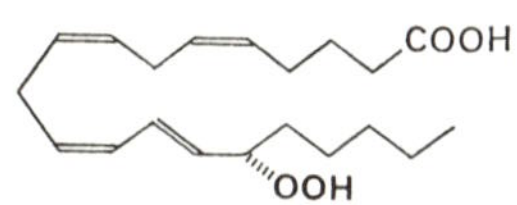 | $C_{20}H_{32}O_4$ (336) | Inhibited human platelet 12-LO ($IC_{50}$ 2.5 μ*M*)[30] and rabbit PMNL 5-LO ($IC_{50}$ 0.95 μ*M*)[28] |
| 25. | 15-Oxo-5Z,8Z,11Z,13E-eicosatetraenoic acid (15-KETE) | 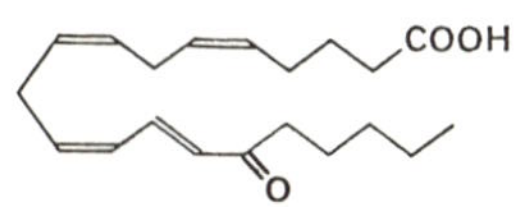 | $C_{20}H_{30}O_3$ (318) | Inhibited rabbit PMNL 5-LO ($IC_{50}$ 1.7 μ*M*)[28] |

| | | | | |
|---|---|---|---|---|
| 26. | 17-Hydroxy-4Z,7Z,10Z,13Z,15E,19Z-docosahexaenoic acid | 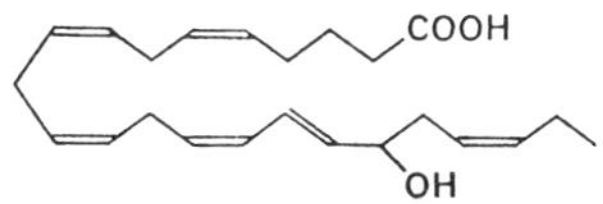 | $C_{22}H_{32}O_3$ (344) | Inhibited human platelet 12-LO ($IC_{50}$ 0.4 $\mu M$)[31] |
| 27. | 5-[1-(2-Hydroxyheptyl)-2,5-cyclohexadienyl]-5Z-hexenoic acid methyl ester | 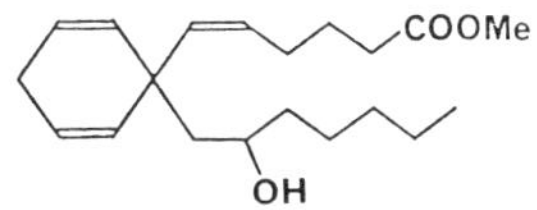 | $C_{20}H_{32}O_3$ (320) | Inhibited RBL-1 cell 5-LO ($IC_{50}$ 6 $\mu M$)[15] |
| 28. | 5-Hydroxamylmethyl-6E,8Z,11Z,14Z-eicosatetraenoic acid | 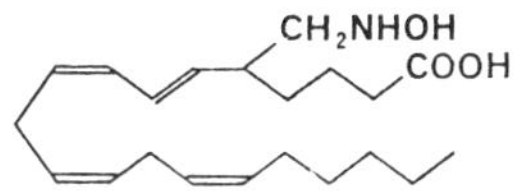 | $C_{21}H_{35}NO_3$ (349) | Inhibited RBL-1 5-LO ($IC_{50}$ 0.19 $\mu M$)[32] |
| 29. | 5-Hydroxamyl-6E,8Z,11Z,14Z-eicosatetraenoic acid | 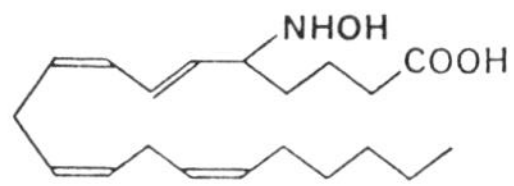 | $C_{20}H_{33}NO_3$ (335) | Inhibited RBL-1 5-LO ($IC_{50}$ 1.4 $\mu M$)[32] |
| 30. | 2-Bromooctadecanoic acid (α-bromostearic acid) | 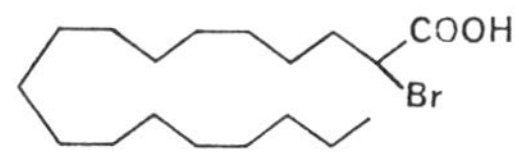 | $C_{18}H_{19}BrO_2$ (347) | At 5 m$M$, inhibited soybean 15-LO by 95%[33] |
| 31. | 6-Oxa-8E,10E,12Z,15Z-heneicosatetraenoic acid (5,6-secoleukotriene $A_4$) | 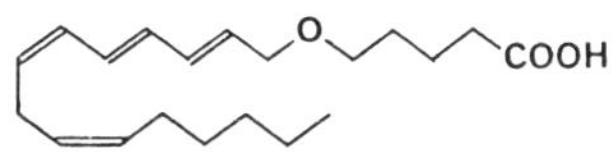 | $C_{20}H_{32}O_3$ (320) | Decreased the formation of $LTB_4$ in human PMNLs[34] |
| 32. | 7,13-Cycloarachidonic acid | 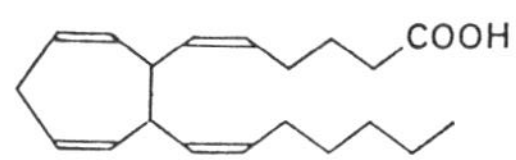 | $C_{20}H_{30}O_2$ (302) | Potent and selective 5-lipoxygenase-inhibitory activity claimed[35] |
| 33. | 7-Thiaarachidonic acid | 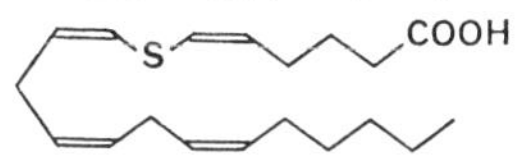 | $C_{19}H_{32}O_2S$ (324) | Inhibited RBL-1 5-LO ($K_I$ 14.2 $\mu M$)[36] |
| 34. | 7-Thia-5z,8-nonadienoic acid |  | $C_8H_{12}O_2S$ (172) | Inhibited RBL-1 5-LO ($K_I$ 6.0 $\mu$M)[36] |
| 35. | 13-Thiaarachidonic acid | 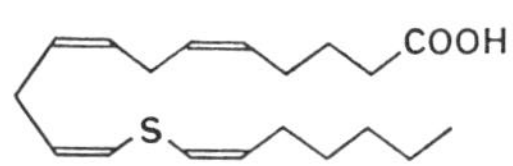 | $C_{19}H_{32}O_2S$ (324) | Inhibited soybean 15-LO[37] |
| 36. | 13-Thia-9Z,11E-octadecadienoic acid | 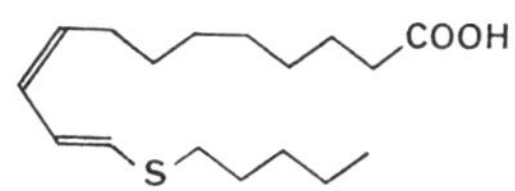 | $C_{17}H_{30}O_2S$ (298) | Inhibited soybean 15-LO ($K_I$ 30 $\mu M$)[38] |

**Table 1 (continued)**
**EICOSANOID ANALOGUES**

| No. | Name | Structure | Mol. formula (Mol. wt) | Biological data |
|---|---|---|---|---|
| 37. | *N*-Hydroxyarachidonamide | 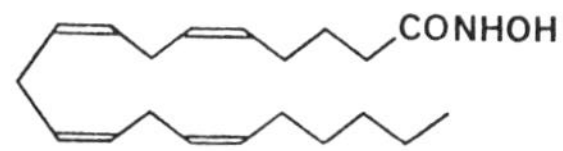 | $C_{20}H_{33}NO_2$ (325) | Inhibited RBL-1 5-LO ($IC_{50}$ 0.1 $\mu M$)[39] |
| 38. | *N*-(3-Hydroxypropyl)-arachidonamide | 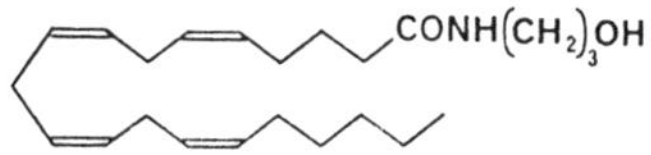 | $C_{23}H_{39}NO_2$ (361) | Inhibited RBL-1 5-LO ($IC_{50}$ 0.03 $\mu M$)[39] |
| 39. | *Cis-N*-(3-methoxy-4-hydroxy-benzyl)oleamide (NE-19550) | 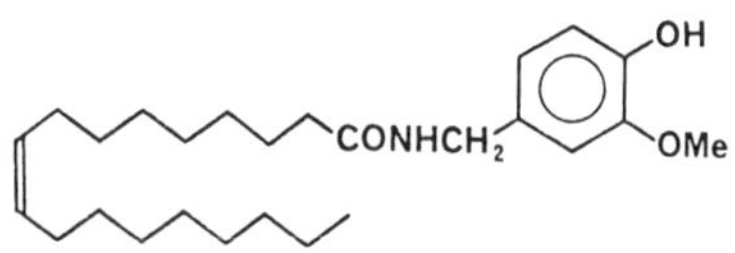 | $C_{26}H_{43}NO_3$ (417) | Inhibited RBL-2H3 5-LO ($IC_{50}$ 0.9 $\mu M$)[40] |
| 40. | N-Octylhydroxylamine |  | $C_8H_{19}NO$ (145) | Inhibited soybean 15-LO[41] |
| 41. | 10-(2,3-Dihydroxybenzoyl-amino)-5Z,8Z-decadienoic acid | 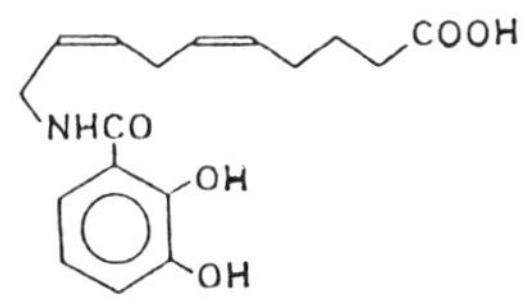 | $C_{17}H_{21}NO_5$ (319) | Inhibited RBL-1 5-LO ($IC_{50}$ 10 $\mu M$)[39] |
| 42. | 6,9-Deepoxy-6,9-phenylimino-$\Delta^{6,8}$-prostaglandin $1_1$ (U60257, piriprosl) | 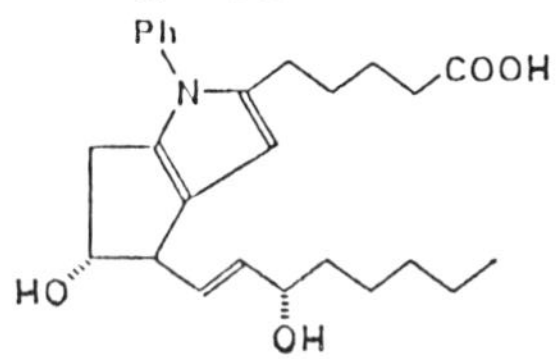 | $C_{26}H_{35}NO_4$ (425) | Inhibited formation of $LTC_4$ due to 5-LO in human eosinophils ($IC_{50}$ 2 $\mu M$);[42] inhibited $LTB_4$ synthesis in human peripheral neutrophils ($IC_{50}$ 1.8 $\mu M$)[43] |
| 43. | 2-(12-Hydroxydodeca-5,10-diynyl)-3,5,6,-trimethyl-1,4-benzoquinone (AA-861) | 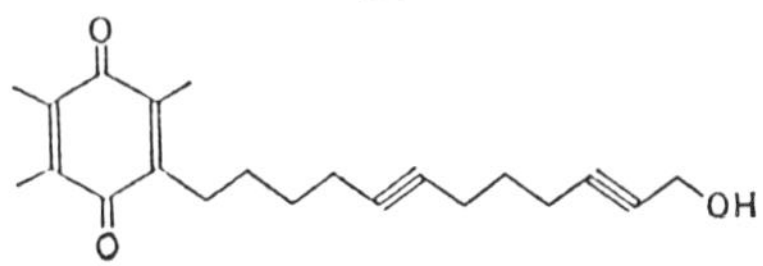 | $C_{21}H_{26}O_3$ (326) | Inhibited 5-LO from rat peritoneal macrophages ($IC_{50}$ 0.03 $\mu M$)[44] and guinea pig PMNL's ($IC_{50}$ 0.8 $\mu M$);[45] inhibited CD-1 mice epidermal 12-LO ($IC_{50}$ 1.9 $\mu M$)[46] |
| 44. | 13-*Cis*-retinoic acid (Ro 4-3780) | 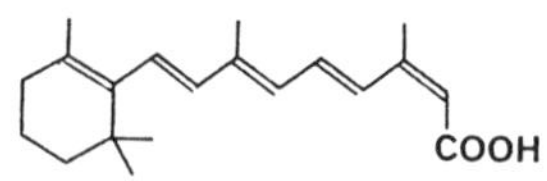 | $C_{20}H_{28}O_2$ (300) | Inhibited RBL-1 5-LO ($IC_{50}$ 9 $\mu M$)[47] |

## REFERENCES TO TABLE 1


1. **Chang, J., Skowronek, M. D., Cherney, M. L., and Lewis, A. J.,** Differential effects of putative lipoxygenase inhibitors on arachidonic acid metabolism in cell-free and intact cell preparations, *Inflammation,* 8, 143, 1984.
2. **Verrando, P., Shroot, B., Ortonne, J. P., and Hensby, C. N.,** Relative potencies of several nonsteroidal anti-inflammatory drugs against soya bean 15-lipoxygenase, *Br. J. Dermatol.,* 109 (Suppl. 25), 120, 1983.
3. **Downing, D. T., Ahern, D. G., and Bachta, M.,** Enzyme inhibition by acetylenic compounds, *Biochem. Biophys. Res. Commun.,* 40, 218, 1970.
4. **Salari, H., Braquet, P., and Borgeat, P.,** Comparative effects of indomethacin, acetylenic acids, 15-HETE, nordihydroguaiaretic acid and BW 755C on the metabolism of arachidonic acid in human leukocytes and platelets, *Prostaglandins Leukotrienes Med.,* 13, 53, 1984.
5. **Hammarstrom, S.,** Selective inhibition of platelet n-8 lipoxygenase by 5,8,11-eicosatriynoic acid, *Biochim. Biophys. Acta,* 487, 517, 1977.
6. **Narumiya, S., Salmon, J. A., Cotter, F. H., Weatherley, B. C., and Flower, R. J.,** Arachidonic acid 15-lipoxygenase from rabbit peritoneal polymorphonuclear leukocytes, *J. Biol. Chem.,* 256, 9583, 1981.
7. **Narumiya, S. and Salmon, J. A.,** Arachidonic acid 15-lipoxygenase from rabbit peritoneal polymorphonuclear leukocytes, *Methods Enzymol.,* 86, 45, 1982.
8. **Wilhelm, T. E., Sankarappa, S. K., Van Rollins, M., and Sprecher, H.,** Selective inhibitors of platelet lipoxygenase: 4,7, 10, 13-eicosatetraynoic acid and 5,8,11,14-heneicosatetraynoic acid, *Prostaglandins,* 21, 323, 1981.
9. **Sun, F. F., McGuire, J. C., Morton, D. R., Pike, J. E., Sprecher, H., and Kunau, W. H.,** Inhibition of platelet arachidonic acid 12-lipoxygenase by acetylenic acid compounds, *Prostaglandins,* 21, 333, 1981.
10. **Downing, D. T., Barve, J. A., Gunstone, F. D., Jacobsberg, F. R., and Jie, M. L. K.,** Structural requirements of acetylenic fatty acids for inhibition of soybean lipoxygenase and prostaglandin synthetase, *Biochim. Biophys. Acta,* 280, 343, 1972.
11. **Corey, E. J., Lansbury, P. T., Jr., Cashman, J. R., and Kantner, S. S.,** Mechanism of the irreversible deactivation of arachidonate 5-lipoxygenase by 5,6-dehydroarachidonate, *J. Am. Chem. Soc.,* 106, 1501, 1984.
12. **Corey, E. J., and Park, H.,** Irreversible inhibition of the enzymic oxidation of arachidonic acid to 15-hydroperoxy-5,8,11-Z,13-E-eicosatetraenoic acid (15-HPETE) by 14,15-dehydroarachidonic acid, *J. Am. Chem. Soc.,* 104, 1750, 1982.
13. **Corey, E. J., Kantner, S. S. and Lansbury, P. T., Jr.,** Irreversible inhibition of the leukotriene pathway by 4,5-dehydroarachidonic acid, *Tetrahedron Lett.,* 24, 265, 1983.
14. **Patterson, J. W., Pfister, J. R., Wagner, P. J., and Murthy, D. V. K.,** Synthesis of 4,5,8-eicosatrienoic acids, *J. Org. Chem.,* 48, 2572, 1983.
15. **Sipio, W. J.,** 1,1-Disubstituted-2,5-cyclohexadienes: selective inhibitors of 5-lipoxygenase, *Tetrahedron Lett.,* 26, 2039, 1985.
16. **St. Angelo, A. J. and Ory, R. L.,** Lipoxygenase inhibition by naturally occurring monoenoic fatty acids, *Lipids,* 19, 34, 1984.
17. **Arai, Y., Konno, M., Shimoji, K., Konishi, Y., Niwa, H., Toda, M., and Hayashi, M.,** Synthesis of (±)-carba analogs of 5-HPETE and leukotriene $A_4$, unstable intermediates of slow-reacting substance (SRS), *Chem. Pharm. Bull.,* 30, 379, 1982.
18. **Arai, Y., Toda, M., and Hayashi, M.,** Synthesis of (±)-carba analogs of 5-HPETE and leukotriene $A_4$, *Adv. Prostaglandin Thromboxane Leukotriene Res.,* 11, 169, 1983.
19. **Arai, Y., Shimoji, K., Konno, M., Konishi, Y., Okuyama, S., Iguchi, S., Hayashi, M., Miyamoto, T., and Toda, M.,** Synthesis and 5-lipoxygenase inhibitory activities of eicosanoid compounds, *J. Med. Chem.,* 26, 72, 1983.
20. **Koshihara, Y., Murota, S., Petasis, N., and Nicolaou, K. C.,** Selective inhibition of 5-lipoxygenase by 5,6-methano- leukotriene $A_4$, a stable analog of leukotriene $A_4$, *FEBS Lett.,* 143, 13, 1982.
21. **Koshihara, Y., Murota, S., and Nicolaou, K. C.,** 5,6-Methanoleukotriene $A_4$: a potent, specific inhibitor for 5-lipoxygenase, *Adv. Prostaglandin Thromboxane Leukotriene Res.,* 11, 163, 1983.
22. **Pfister, J. R., and Murthy, D. V. K.,** Synthesis of three potential inhibitors of leukotriene biosynthesis, *J. Med. Chem.,* 26, 1099, 1983.
23. **Cohen, N., Weber, G., Banner, B. L., Welton, A. F., Hope, W. C., Crowley, H., Anderson, W. A., Simko, B. A., O'Donnell, M., Coffey, J. W., Fiedler-Nagy, C., and Batula-Bernardo, C.,** Analogs of arachidonic acid methylated at C-7 and C-10 as inhibitors of leukotriene biosynthesis, *Prostaglandins,* 27, 553, 1984.
24. **Welton, A. F., Hope, W. C., Fielder-Nagy, C., Batula-Bernardo, C., and Coffey, J. W.,** Analogs of arachidonic acid methylated at C-7 and C-10 inhibit leukotriene biosynthesis and phospholipase $A_2$ activity, *Prostaglandins,* 27, 649, 1984.

25. **Perchonock, C. D., Finkelstein, J. A., Uzinskas, I., Gleason, J. G., Sarau, H. M., and Cieslinski, L. B.,** Dimethyleicosatrienoic acids: inhibitors of the 5-lipoxygenase enzyme, *Tetrahedron Lett.*, 24, 2457, 1983.
26. **Ackroyd, J., Manro, A., Scheinmann, F., Appleton, R. A., and Bantick, J. R.,** Synthesis and 5-lipoxygenase inhibitory activity of 7,7-dimethyleicosa-5Z,8Z-dienoic acid, *Tetrahedron Lett.*, 24, 5139, 1983.
27. **Nicolaou, K. C., Petasis, N. A., Li, W. S., Ladduwahetty, T., Randall, J. L., Webber, S. E., and Hernandez, P. E.,** Ethanoarachidonic acids. A new class of arachidonic acid cascade modulators, *J. Org. Chem.*, 48, 5400, 1983.
28. **Vanderhoek, J. Y., Bryant, R. W., and Bailey, J. M.,** Regulation of leukocyte and platelet lipoxygenases by hydroxyeicosanoids, *Biochem. Pharmacol.*, 31, 3463, 1982.
29. **Vanderhoek, J. Y., Bryant, R. W., and Bailey, J. M.,** 15-Hydroxy-5,8,11,13-eicosatetraenoic acid from polymorphonuclear leukocytes. A potent inhibitor of the leukotriene pathway, *J. Biol. Chem.*, 255, 10064, 1980.
30. **Vanderhoek, J. Y., Bryant, R. W., and Bailey, J. M.,** 15-Hydroxy-5,8,11,13-eicosatetraenoic acid. A potent and selective inhibitor of platelet lipoxygenase, *J. Biol. Chem.*, 255, 5996, 1980.
31. **Mitchell, P. D., Hallam, C., Hemsley, P. E., Lord, G. H., and Wilkinson, D.,** Inhibition of platelet 12-lipoxygenase by hydroxy-fatty acids, *Biochem. Soc. Trans.*, 12, 839, 1984.
32. **Kerdesky, F. A. J., Holms, J. H., Schmidt, S. P., Dyer, R. D., and Carter, G. W.,** Eicosatetraenehydroxamates: inhibitors of 5-lipoxygenase, *Tetrahedron Lett.*, 26, 2143, 1985.
33. **Zakut, R., Grossman, S., Pinsky, A., and Wilchek, M.,** Evidence for an essential methionine residue in lipoxygenase, *FEBS Lett.*, 71, 107, 1976.
34. **Patterson, J. W., Jr. and Murthy, D. V. K.,** Synthesis of (8E,10E,12Z,15Z)-6-oxaheneicosa-8,10,12,15-tetraenoic acid, secoleukotriene $A_4$, *J. Org. Chem.*, 48, 4413, 1983.
35. **Nicolaou, K. C. and Webber, S.,** Synthesis of 7,13-bridged arachidonic acid analogues, *J. Chem. Soc. Chem. Commun.*, 350, 1984.
36. **Corey, E. J., Cashman, J. R., Eckrich, T. M., Corey, D. R.,** A new class of irreversible inhibitors of leukotriene biosynthesis, *J. Am. Chem. Soc.*, 107, 713, 1985.
37. **Corey, E. J., D'Alarcao, M., and Kyler, K. S.,** Synthesis of new lipoxygenase inhibitors 13-thia- and 10-thia-arachidonic acids, *Tetrahedron Lett.*, 26, 3919, 1985.
38. **Funk, M. O., Jr. and Alteneder, A. W.,** A new class of lipoxygenase inhibitor. Polyunsaturated fatty acids containing sulfur, *Biochem. Biophys. Res. Commun.*, 114, 937, 1983.
39. **Corey, E. J., Cashman, J. R., Kantner, S. S., and Wright, S. W.,** Rationally designed, potent competitive inhibitors of leukotriene biosynthesis, *J. Am. Chem. Soc.*, 106, 1503, 1984.
40. **Brand, L. M., Skare, K. L., Loomans, M. E., Skoglund, M. L., Tai, H. H., Chiabrando, C., and Fanelli, R.,** NE-19550, an anti-inflammatory/analgesic agent with a novel mechanism, *Fed. Proc. Fed. Am. Soc. Exp. Biol.*, 45, 334, 1986.
41. **Clapp, C. H., Banerjee, A., and Rotenberg, S. A.,** Inhibition of soybean lipoxygenase 1 by N-alkylhydroxylamines, *Biochemistry*, 24, 1826, 1985.
42. **Cromwell, O., Shaw, R. J., Walsh, G. M., Mallett, A. I., and Kay, A. B.,** Inhibition of leukotriene $C_4$ and $B_4$ generation by human eosinophils and neutrophils with the lipoxygenase pathway inhibitors U60257 and BW 755C, *Int. J. Immunopharmacol.*, 7, 775, 1985.
43. **Sun, F. F. and McGuire, J. C.,** Inhibition of human neutrophil arachidonate 5-lipoxygenase by 6,9-deepoxy-6,9-(phenylimino)-$\Delta^{6,8}$-prostaglandin $I_1$ (U-60257), *Prostaglandins*, 26, 211, 1983.
44. **Ashida, Y., Saijo, T., Kuriki, H., Makino, H., Terao, S., and Maki, Y.,** Pharmacological profile of AA-861, a 5-lipoxygenase inhibitor, *Prostaglandins*, 26, 955, 1983.
45. **Yoshimoto, T., Yokoyama, C., Ochi, K., Yamamoto, S., Maki, Y., Ashida, Y., Terao, S., and Shiraishi, M.,** 2,3,5-Trimethyl-6-(12-hydroxy-5,10-dodecadiynyl)-1,4-benzo-quinone (AA861), a selective inhibitor of the 5-lipoxygenase reaction and the biosynthesis of slow-reacting substance of anaphylaxis, *Biochim. Biophys. Acta*, 713, 470, 1982.
46. **Nakadate, T., Yamamoto, S., Aizu, E., and Kato, R.,** Inhibition of mouse epidermal 12-lipoxygenase by 2,3,5-trimethyl-6-(12-hydroxy-5,10-dodecadiynyl)-1,4-benzoquinone (AA861), *J. Pharm. Pharmacol.*, 37, 71, 1985.
47. **Fiedler-Nagy, C., Hamilton, J. G., Batula-Bernardo, C., and Coffey, J. W.,** Inhibition of Δ5-lipoxygenase (Δ5-LO), Δ12-lipoxygenase (Δ12-LO) and prostaglandin endoperoxide synthase (PES) by selected retinoids (vitamin A derivatives), *Fed. Proc. Fed. Am. Soc. Exp. Biol.*, 42, 919, 1983.

**Table 2**
**POLYPHENOLS**

| No. | Name | Structure | Mol. formula (Mol. wt) | Biological data |
|---|---|---|---|---|
| 1. | 1,5-Dihydroxynaphthalene | 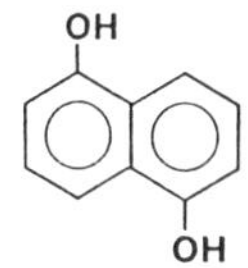  | $C_{10}H_8O_2$ (160) | Inhibited soybean 15-LO with an $IC_{50}$ value of 20 $\mu M$[1] |
| 2. | 2,3-Dihydroxynaphthalene |   | $C_{10}H_8O_2$ (160) | Inhibited soybean 15-LO ($IC_{50}$ 60 $\mu M$)[1] |
| 3. | 1,8,9-Trihydroxyanthracene (Anthralin) | 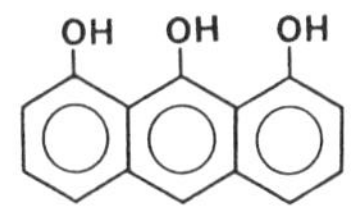  | $C_{14}H_{10}O_3$ (226) | Inhibited soybean 15-LO ($IC_{50}$ 86 $\mu M$);[2] inhibited 12-LO from mouse epidermal homogenates ($IC_{50}$ 50 $\mu M$) and human platelets ($IC_{50}$ 10 $\mu M$)[3] |
| 4. | 2,3-*Bis*-(3,4-dihydroxybenzyl)butane (nordihydro-guaiaretic acid, NDGA) | 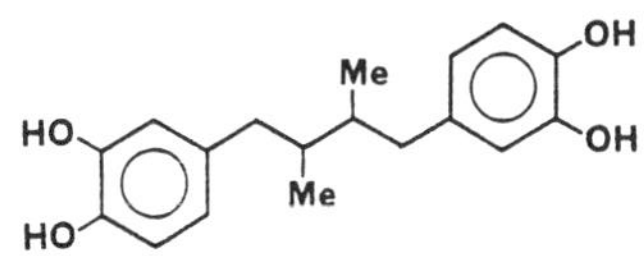  | $C_{16}H_{18}O_4$ (274) | Inhibited 5-LO from rat neutrophils ($IC_{50}$ 1.0 $\mu M$),[4] rat PMNLs ($IC_{50}$ 2.4 $\mu M$,[5] and human leukocytes ($IC_{50}$ 0.3 $\mu M$);[6] inhibited 12-LO from rat platelets ($IC_{50}$ 3.7 $\mu M$),[5] mouse epidermis ($IC_{50}$ 5.5 $\mu M$),[7] and intact human platelets ($IC_{50}$ 17 $\mu M$),[8] inhibited soybean 15-LO with $IC_{50}$ values of 3.6 $\mu M$,[4] ~ 5 $\mu M$,[9] and 10 $\mu M$[10] |
| 5. | 3-(3,4-Dihydroxyphenyl)-2-propenoic acid (caffeic acid) | 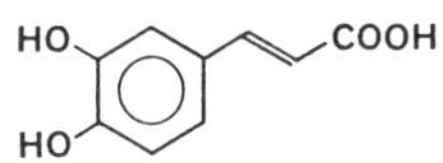  | $C_9H_8O_4$ (180) | Inhibited 5-LO from mouse mastocytoma P-815 cells ($IC_{50}$ 3.7 $\mu M$)[11,12] |
| 6. | 3-(3,4-Dihydroxyphenyl)-2-propenoic acid methyl ester (caffeic acid methyl ester) | 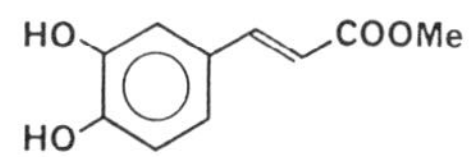  | $C_{10}H_{10}$ $O_4$ (194) | Inhibited 5-LO from mouse mastocytoma P-815 cells ($IC_{50}$ 0.48 $\mu M$)[13] |

## Table 2 (continued)
## POLYPHENOLS

| No. | Name | Structure | Mol. formula (Mol. wt) | Biological data |
|---|---|---|---|---|
| 7. | 3-(3,4-Dihydroxyphenyl)-*N*-(4-hydroxyphenyl)-2-propenamide (TMK 911) | 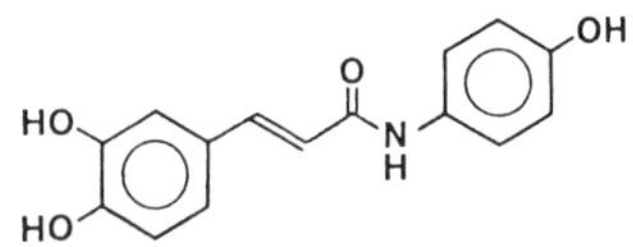 | $C_{15}H_{13}NO_4$ (271) | Inhibited 5-LO from mouse mastocytoma P-815 cells ($IC_{50}$ 0.2 $\mu M$)[12] |
| 8. | 3-(3,4-Dihydroxyphenyl)-*N*-(5-chloro-2-hydroxyphenyl)-2-propenamide (TMK 920) | 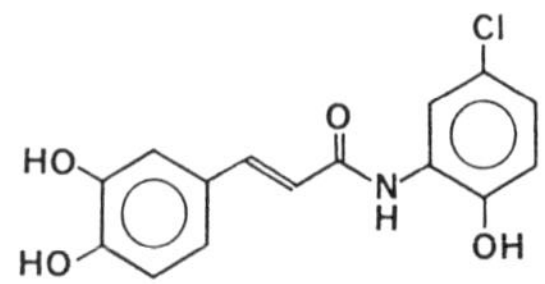 | $C_{15}H_{12}ClNO_4$ (306.5) | Inhibited 5-LO from mouse mastocytoma P-815 cells ($IC_{50}$ 0.2 $\mu M$)[12] |
| 9. | 3,4-Dihydroxychalcone | 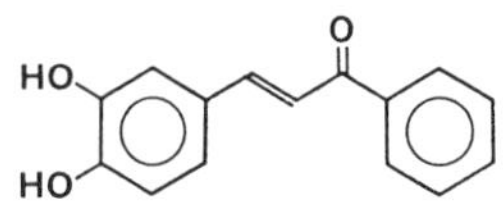 | $C_{15}H_{12}O_3$ (240) | Inhibited mouse epidermal 12-LO ($IC_{50}$ 0.3 $\mu M$)[14] |
| 10. | 6,7-Dihydroxycoumarin (esculetin) | 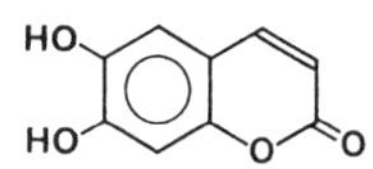 | $C_9H_6O_4$ (178) | Inhibited 5-LO from cloned mastocytoma P-815 cells ($IC_{50}$ 4 $\mu M$)[15] and human PMNLs ($IC_{50}$ 0.4 $\mu M$);[16] inhibited 12-LO from mastocytoma cells ($IC_{50}$ 2.5 $\mu M$)[15] and rat platelets ($IC_{50}$ 0.65 $\mu M$)[17] |
| 11. | 3,4,5-Trihydroxybenzoic acid propyl ester (propyl gallate) | 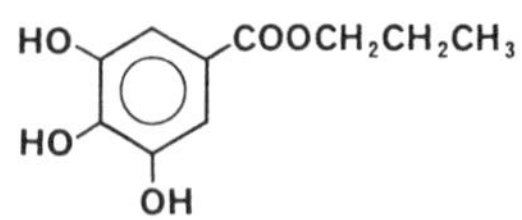 | $C_{10}H_{12}O_5$ (212) | Inhibited soybean 15-LO by 26% at a concentration of 200 $\mu M$;[18] inhibited human platelet 12-LO ($IC_{50}$ 90 $\mu M$)[8] |
| 12. | Tannic acid | | $C_{76}H_{52}O_{46}$ (1701) | Noncompetitively inhibited soybean 15-LO ($IC_{50}$ 0.75 $\mu M$)[19] |
| 13. | 3′,4′-Dihydroxyflavone | 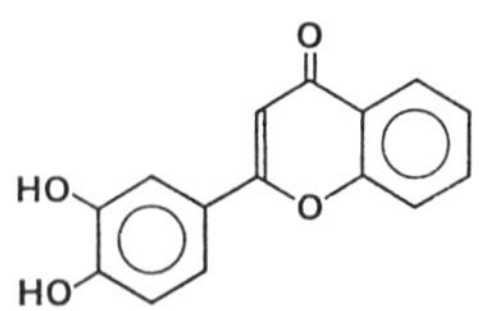 | $C_{15}H_{10}O_4$ (254) | Inhibited soybean 15-LO ($IC_{50}$ 33 $\mu M$) |

| | | | | |
|---|---|---|---|---|
| 14. | 5,6,7-Trihydroxyflavone (baicalein) | 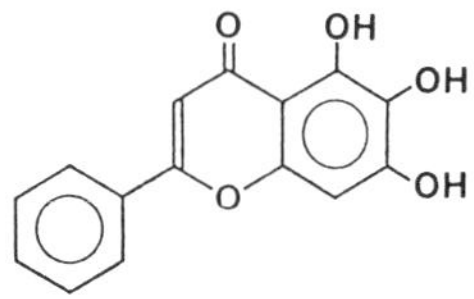 | $C_{15}H_{10}O_5$ (270) | Selectively inhibited rat platelet 12-LO ($IC_{50}$ 0.12 $\mu M$)[20] |
| 15. | 5,7-Dihydroxy-3′,4′,6-trimethoxyflavone (eupatilin) | 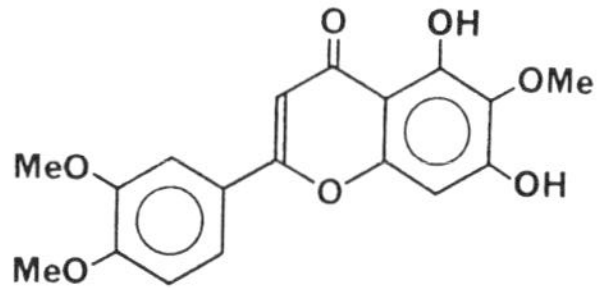 | $C_{18}H_{16}O_7$ (344) | Inhibited mastocytoma P-815 cell derived 5-LO ($IC_{50}$ 14 $\mu M$)[11] |
| 16. | 3′,4′,5-Trihydroxy-6,7-dimethoxyflavone (cirsiliol) | 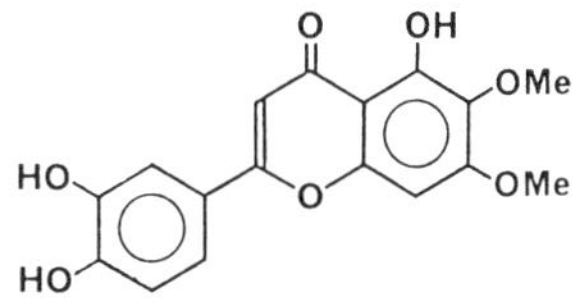 | $C_{17}H_{14}O_7$ (330) | Inhibited RBL-1 cell 5-LO ($IC_{50}$ 0.1 $\mu M$) and 12-LO from bovine platelets and porcine leukocytes ($IC_{50}$ ~ 1 $\mu M$)[21,22] |
| 17. | 3,3′,4′,5,7-Pentahydroxyflavone (quercetin) | 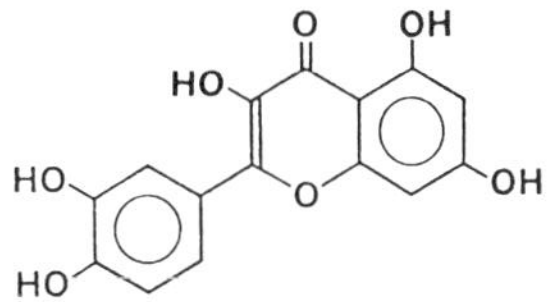 | $C_{15}H_{10}O_7$ (302) | Inhibited 5-LO from rat neutrophils ($IC_{50}$ 3.2 $\mu M$)[4] and RBL-1 cells ($IC_{50}$ 0.2 $\mu M$);[23] inhibited mouse epidermal 12-LO with $IC_{50}$ values of 1.4 $\mu M$[7] and 1.3 $\mu M$;[24] human platelet 12-LO was inhibited with an $IC_{50}$ of 4—5 $\mu M$;[23] inhibited soybean 5-LO ($IC_{50}$ 3.2 $\mu M$[4] and 2—3 $\mu M$[25]) |
| 18. | 4′,6,7-Trihydroxyisoflavan | 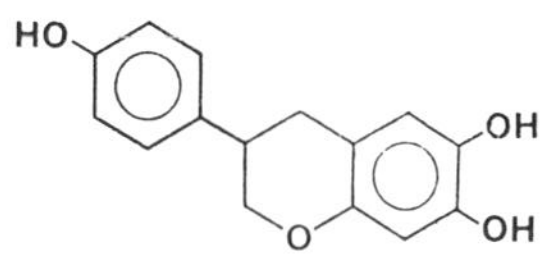 | $C_{15}H_{14}O_4$ (258) | Inhibited human PMNL 5-LO ($IC_{50}$ 1.6 $\mu M$) and human platelet 12-LO ($IC_{50}$ 22 $\mu M$)[26] |
| 19. | 2,2′-*Bis*-(8-formyl-1,6,7-trihydroxy-5-isopropyl-3-methylnaphthalene (gossypol) | 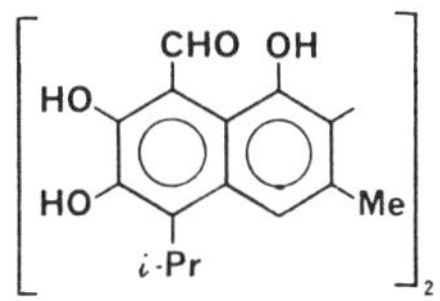 | $C_{30}H_{30}O_8$ (518) | Inhibited RBL-1 cell 5-LO ($IC_{50}$ 0.3 $\mu M$) and 12-LO ($IC_{50}$ 0.7 $\mu M$)[27] |

**Table 2 (continued)**
**POLYPHENOLS**

| No. | Name | Structure | Mol. formula (Mol. wt) | Biological data |
|---|---|---|---|---|
| 20. | 6-Chloro-2,3-dihydroxy-1,4-naphthoquinone | 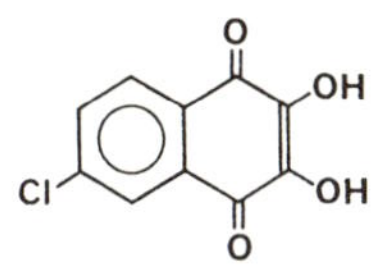 | $C_{10}H_5ClO_4$ (224.5) | Inhibited mouse epidermal 12-LO ($IC_{50}$ 25 $\mu M$)[3] |

**REFERENCES TO TABLE 2**


1. **Baumann, J., Bruchausen, F. V., and Wurm, G.,** Flavonoids and related compounds as inhibitors of arachidonic acid peroxidation, *Prostaglandins,* 20, 627, 1980.
2. **Sircar, J. C. and Schwender, C. F.,** Antipsoriatic drugs as inhibitors of soybean lipoxygenase. A possible mode of action, *Prostaglandins Leukotrienes Med.,* 11, 373, 1983.
3. **Bedord, C. J., Young, J. M., and Wagner, B. M.,** Anthralin inhibition of mouse epidermal arachidonic acid lipoxygenase *in vitro, J. Invest. Dermatol.,* 81, 566, 1983.
4. **Chang, J., Skowronek, M. D., Cherney, M. L., and Lewis, A. J.,** Differential effects of putative lipoxygenase inhibitors on arachidonic acid metabolism in cell-free and intact cell preparations, *Inflammation,* 8, 143, 1984.
5. **Miyazawa, K., Iimori, Y., Makino, M., Mikami, T., and Miyasaka, K.,** Effects of some nonsteroidal anti-inflammatory drugs and other agents on cyclooxygenase and lipoxygenase activities in some enzyme preparations, *Jpn. J. Pharmacol.,* 38, 199, 1985.
6. **Salari, H., Braquet, P., and Borgeat, P.,** Comparative effects of indomethacin, acetylenic acids, 15-HETE, nordihydroguaiaretic acid and BW 775C on the metabolism of arachidonic acid in human leukocytes and platelets, *Prostaglandins Leukotrienes Med.,* 13, 53, 1984.
7. **Nakadate, T., Yamamoto, S., Satoshi, A., and Kato, R.,** Inhibition of 12-O-tetradecanoylphorbol-13-acetate-induced increase in vascular permeability in mouse skin by lipoxygenase inhibitors, *Jpn. J. Pharmacol.,* 38, 161, 1985.
8. **Van Wauwe, J. and Goossens, J.,** Effects of antioxidants on cyclooxygenase and lipoxygenase activities in intact human platelets: comparison with indomethacin and ETYA, *Prostaglandins,* 26, 725, 1983.
9. **Alcaraz, M. J. and Hoult, J. R. S.,** Effects of hypolaetin-8-glucoside and related flavonoids on soybean lipoxygenase and snake venom phospholipase $A_2$, *Arch. Int. Pharmacodyn. Ther.,* 278, 4, 1985.
10. **Yasumoto, K., Yamamoto, A., and Mitsuda, H.,** Soybean lipoxygenase. IV. Effect of phenolic antioxidants on lipoxygenase reaction, *Agr. Biol. Chem.,* 34, 1162, 1970.
11. **Koshihara, Y., Neichi, T., Murota, S., Lao, A., Fujimoto, Y., and Tatsuno, T.,** Selective inhibition of 5-lipoxygenase by natural compounds isolated from Chinese plant, Artemisia rubripes Nakai, *FEBS Lett.,* 158, 41, 1983.
12. **Murota, S. and Koshihara, Y.,** New lipoxygenase inhibitors isolated from Chinese plants. Development of new anti-allergic drugs, *Drugs Exp. Clin. Res.,* 11, 641, 1985.
13. **Koshihara, Y., Neichi, T., Murota, S., Lao, A., Fujimoto, Y., and Tatsuno, T.,** Caffeic acid is a selective inhibitor for leukotriene biosynthesis, *Biochim. Biophys. Acta,* 792, 92, 1984.

14. **Nakadate, T., Aizu, E., Yamamoto, S., and Kato, R.,** Effect of chalcone derivatives on lipoxygenase and cyclooxygenase activities of mouse epidermis, *Prostaglandins,* 30, 357, 1985.
15. **Neichi, T., Koshihara, Y., and Murota, S.,** Inhibitory effect of esculetin on 5-lipoxygenase and leukotriene biosynthesis, *Biochim. Biophys. Acta,* 753, 130, 1983.
16. **Panossian, A. G.,** Inhibition of arachidonic acid 5-lipoxygenase of human polymorphonuclear leukocytes by esculetin, *Biomed. Biochim. Acta,* 43, 1351, 1984.
17. **Sekiya, K., Okuda, H., and Arichi, S.,** Selective inhibition of platelet lipoxygenase by esculetin, *Biochim. Biophys. Acta,* 713, 68, 1982.
18. **Panganamala, R. V., Miller, J. S., Gwebu, E. T., Sharma, H. M., and Cornwell, D. G.,** Differential inhibitory effects of vitamin E and other antioxidants on prostaglandin synthetase, platelet aggregation and lipoxidase, *Prostaglandins,* 14, 261, 1977.
19. **Goswami, S. K. and Kinsella, J. E.,** Inhibitory effects of tannic acid and benzophenone on soybean lipoxygenase and ram seminal vesicle cyclooxygenase, *Prostaglandins Leukotrienes Med.,* 17, 223, 1985.
20. **Sekiya, K. and Okuda, H.,** Selective inhibition of platelet lipoxygenase by baicalein, *Biochem. Biophys. Res. Commun.,* 105, 1090, 1982.
21. **Yoshimoto, T., Furukawa, M., Yamamoto, S., Horie, T., and Watanabe-Kohno, S.,** Flavonoids: potent inhibitors of arachidonate-5-lipoxygenase, *Biochem. Biophys. Res. Commun.,* 116, 612, 1983.
22. **Yamamoto, S., Yoshimoto, T., Furukawa, M., Horie, T., and Watanabe-Kohno, S.,** Arachidonate 5-lipoxygenase and its new inhibitors, *J. Allerg. Clin. Immunol.,* 74, 349, 1984.
23. **Hope, W. C., Welton, A. F., Fiedler-Nagy, C., Batula-Bernardo, C., and Coffey, J. W.,** *In vitro* inhibition of the biosynthesis of slow reacting substance of anaphylaxis (SRS-A) and lipoxygenase activity *in vitro, Biochem. Pharmacol.,* 32, 367, 1983.
24. **Kato, R., Nakadate, T., Yamamoto, S., and Sugimura, T.,** Inhibition of 12-O-tetradecanoylphorbol 13-acetate-induced tumor promotion and ornithine decarboxylase activity by quercetin: possible involvement of lipoxygenase inhibition, *Carcinogenesis,* 4, 1301, 1983.
25. **Takahama, U.,** Inhibition of lipoxygenase-dependent lipid peroxidation by quercetin: mechanism of antioxidative function, *Phytochemistry,* 24, 1443, 1985.
26. **Kuhl, P., Shiloh, R., Jha, H., Murawski, U., and Zilliken, F.,** 6,7,4′-Trihydroxyisoflavan: a potent and selective inhibitor of 5-lipoxygenase in human and porcine peripheral blood leukocytes, *Prostaglandins,* 28, 783, 1984.
27. **Hamasaki, Y. and Tai, H. H.,** Gossypol, a potent inhibitor of arachidonate 5- and 12-lipoxygenases, *Biochim. Biophys. Acta,* 834, 37, 1985.

## Table 3
## PHENOLS

| No. | Name | Structure | Mol. formula (Mol. wt) | Biological data |
|---|---|---|---|---|
| 1. | 2-Aminophenol | 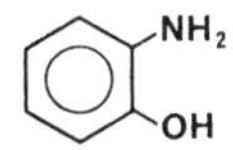 | $C_6H_7NO$ (109) | Inhibited cytosolic PMNL 5-LO ($IC_{50}$ 15 $\mu M$)[1] |
| 2. | 2-Amino-4-(phenylthio)-phenol | 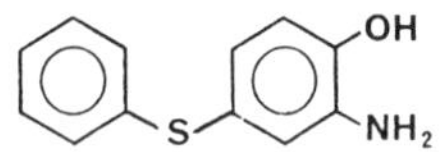 | $C_{12}H_{11}NOS$ (217) | Inhibited cytosolic PMNL 5-LO ($IC_{50}$ 0.4 $\mu M$)[1] |
| 3. | 2-Amino-6-(4-chlorophenyl-hydroxymethyl)-4-t-butyl-phenol | 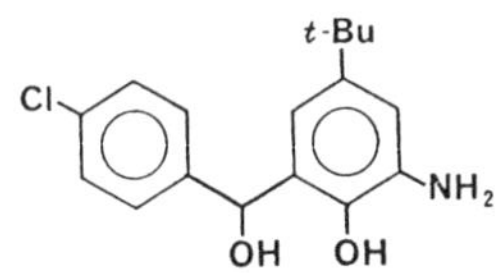 | $C_{17}H_{20}ClNO_2$ (305.5) | Inhibited cytosolic PMNL 5-LO ($IC_{50}$ 3 $\mu M$)[1] |
| 4. | 2,6-Di-t-butyl-4-methyl-phenol (BHT) | 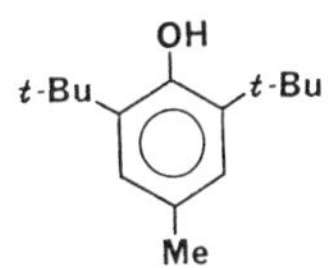 | $C_{15}H_{24}O$ (220) | At 0.01 $\mu M$, inhibited soybean 15-LO by 58%[2] |
| 5. | 2,6-Di-t-butyl-4-(2-thenoyl)-phenol (R-830) | 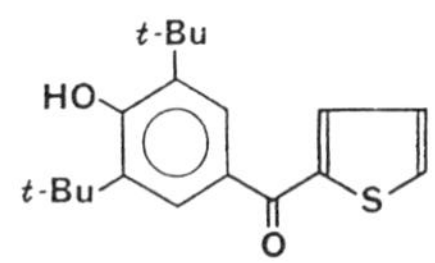 | $C_{19}H_{24}O_2S$ (316) | Inhibited guinea-pig lung lipoxygenase ($IC_{50}$ ~ 20 $\mu M$)[3] |
| 6. | 2-(3,5-Di-t-butyl-4-hydroxy-benzylidene)butyrolactone (KME-4) | 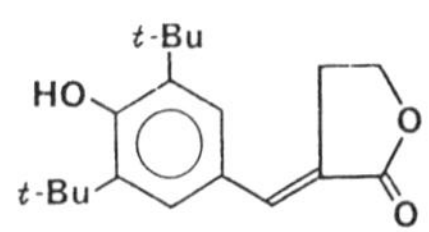 | $C_{19}H_{26}O_3$ (302) | Inhibited RBL-1 5-LO ($IC_{50}$ 1.3 $\mu M$)[4] and cytosolic guinea-pig PMNL 5-LO ($IC_{50}$ 0.85 $\mu M$);[5] platelet 12-LO was not affected up to 100 $\mu M$[5] |
| 7. | Sulfasalazine | 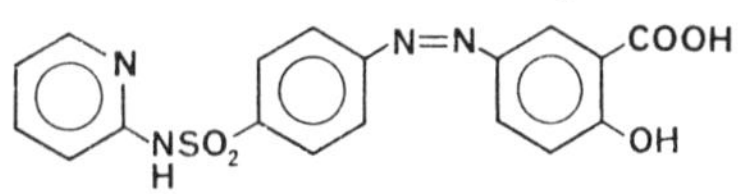 | $C_{18}H_{14}N_4O_5S$ (398) | Inhibited soybean 15-LO ($IC_{50}$ 66.2 $\mu M$);[6] inhibited synthesis of lipoxygenase products by human colonic mucosa[7] |

| | | | | |
|---|---|---|---|---|
| 8. | 5-Aminosalicylic acid | 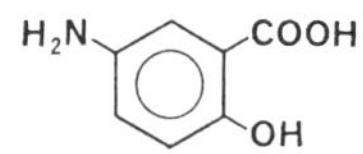 | $C_7H_7NO_3$ (153) | Inhibited soybean 15-LO ($IC_{50}$ 170 $\mu M$)[6] |
| 9. | 5-Acetylaminosalicylic acid | 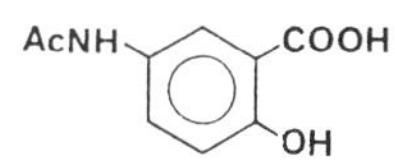 | $C_9H_9NO_4$ (195) | Inhibited soybean 15-LO ($IC_{50}$ 250 $\mu M$)[8] |
| 10. | α-Tocopherol (vitamin E) | 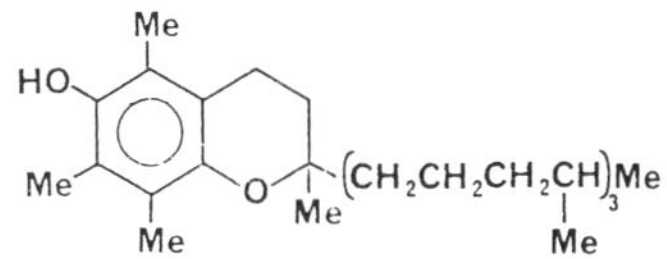 | $C_{29}H_{50}O_2$ (430) | Inhibited soybean 15-LO by 45% at 0.3 $\mu M$[2] and human platelet 12-LO by 12% at 20 $\mu M$[9] |
| 11. | 6-Hydroxy-2,5,7,8-tetra-methylchroman-2-carboxylic acid (Trolox C) | 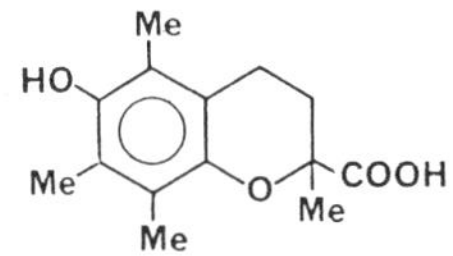 | $C_{14}H_{18}O_4$ (250) | Inhibited soybean 15-LO by 43% at 20 $\mu M$[2] |
| 12. | 7-[3-(4-Acetyl-3-hydroxy-2-propylphenoxy)-2-hydroxypropoxy]-8-propylchromone-2-carboxylic acid (FPL 55712) | 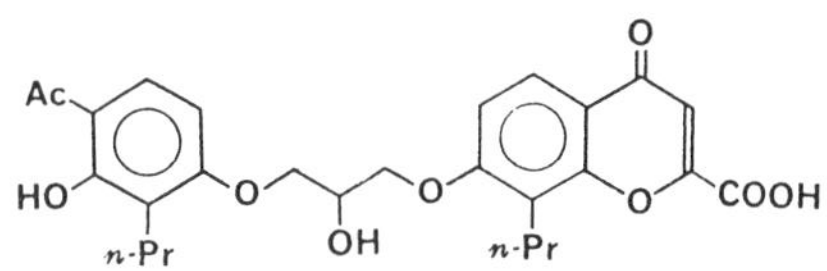 | $C_{27}H_{30}O_9$ (498) | Inhibited RBL-1 5-LO ($IC_{50}$ 20.6 $\mu M$)[10] |
| 13. | Mycophenolic acid | 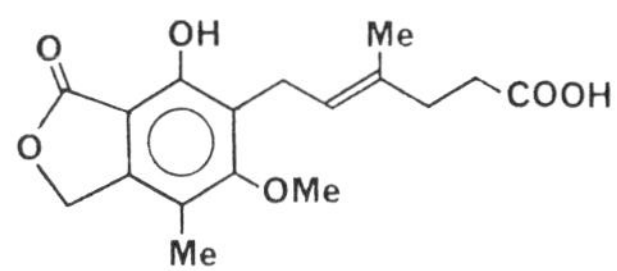 | $C_{17}H_{20}O_6$ (320) | Inhibited soybean 15-LO ($IC_{50}$ 55 $\mu M$)[11] |
| 14. | 2-Aminomethyl-4-t-butyl-6-iodophenol (MK 447) | 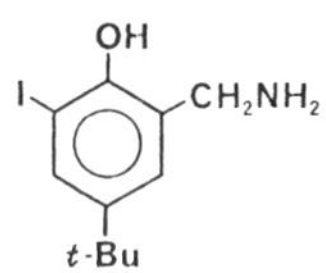 | $C_{11}H_{16}INO$ (305) | Inhibited rat PMNL 5-LO ($IC_{50}$ 86 $\mu M$)[12] |

## REFERENCES TO TABLE 3


1. **Miyamoto, T. and Obata, T.,** New inhibitors of 5-lipoxygenase, *Excerpta Med. Int. Congr. Ser.,* 623, 78, 1983.
2. **Panganamala, R. V., Miller, J. S., Gwebu, E. T., Sharma, H. M., and Cornwell, D. G.,** Differential inhibitory effects of vitamin E and other antioxidants on prostaglandin synthetase, platelet aggregation and lipoxidase, *Prostaglandins,* 14, 261, 1977.
3. **Moore, G. G. I. and Swingle, K. F.,** 2,6-Di-tert-butyl-4-(2′-thenoyl)phenol (R-830): a novel nonsteroidal antiinflammatory agent with antioxidant properties, *Agents Actions,* 12, 674, 1982.
4. **Hidaka, T., Hosoe, K., Ariki, Y., Takeo, K., Yamashita, T., Katsumi, I., Koudo, H., Yamashita, K., and Watanabe, K.,** Pharmacological properties of a new antiinflammatory compound, α-(3,5-di-tert-butyl-4-hydroxybenzylidene)-γ-butyrolactone (KME-4), and its inhibitory effects on prostaglandin synthetase and 5-lipoxygenase, *Jpn. J. Pharmacol.,* 36, 77, 1984.
5. **Hidaka, T., Takeo, K., Hosoe, K., Katsumi, I., Yamashita, T., and Watanabe, K.,** Inhibition of polymorphonuclear leukocyte 5-lipoxygenase and platelet cyclooxygenase by α-(3,5-di-tert-butyl-4-hydroxybenzylidene)-γ-butyrolactone (KME-4), a new anti-inflammatory drug, *Jpn. J. Pharmacol.,* 38, 267, 1985.
6. **Sircar, J. C., Schwender, C. F., and Carethers, M. E.,** Inhibition of soybean lipoxygenase by sulfasalazine and 5-aminosalicylic acid: a possible mode of action in ulcerative colitis, *Biochem. Pharmacol.,* 32, 170, 1983.
7. **Hawkey, C. J., Boughton-Smith, N. K., and Whittle, B. J. R.,** Modulation of human colonic arachidonic acid metabolism by sulfasalazine, *Dig. Dis. Sci.,* 30, 1161, 1985.
8. **Allgayer, H., Eisenburg, J., and Paumgartner, G.,** Soybean lipoxygenase inhibition: studies with the sulfasalazine metabolites N-acetylaminosalicylic acid, 5-aminosalicylic acid and sulfapyridine, *Eur. J. Clin. Pharmacol.,* 26, 449, 1984.
9. **Gwebu, E. T., Trewyn, R. W., Cornwell, D. G., and Panganamala, R. V.,** Vitamin E and the inhibition of platelet lipoxy-genase, *Res. Commun. Chem. Pathol. Pharmacol.,* 28, 361, 1980.
10. **Casey, F. B., Appleby, B. J., and Buck, D. C.,** Selective inhibition of the lipoxygenase metabolic pathway of arachidonic acid by the SRS-A antagonist, FPL 55712, *Prostaglandins,* 25, 1, 1983.
11. **Sircar, J. C. and Schwender, C. F.,** Antipsoriatic drugs as inhibitors of soybean lipoxygenase. A possible mode of action, *Prostaglandins Leukotrienes Med.,* 11, 373, 1983.
12. **Carlson, R. P., O'Neill-Davis, L., Chang, J., and Lewis, A. J.,** Modulation of mouse ear edema by cyclooxygenase and lipoxygenase inhibitors and other pharmacologic agents, *Agents Actions,* 17, 197, 1985.

## Table 4
## AZINES AND HETEROCYCLES

| No. | Name | Structure | Mol. formula (Mol. wt) | Biological data |
|---|---|---|---|---|
| 1. | Phenylhydrazine | 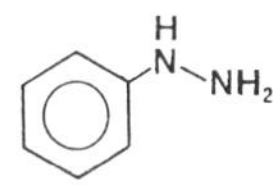 | $C_6H_8N_2$ (108) | Inhibited soybean 15-LO ($IC_{50}$ 0.33 $\mu M$) and prostaglandin generation by bovine seminal-vesicle microsome ($IC_{50}$ 1.3 $\mu M$)[1] |
| 2. | Acetone phenylhydrazone | 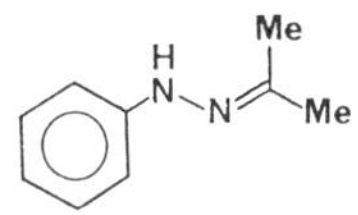 | $C_9H_{12}N_2$ (148) | Inhibited rat PMNL 5-LO ($IC_{50}$ 4.84 $\mu M$);[2] inhibited rat and human platelet 12-LO with $IC_{50}$ values of 8.07 $\mu M$[2] and 2.3 $\mu M$;[3] inhibited soybean 15-LO ($IC_{50}$ 0.12 $\mu M$[2] and 1 $\mu M$[4]) |
| 3. | Acetonylacetone *bis*-phenyl-hydrazone | 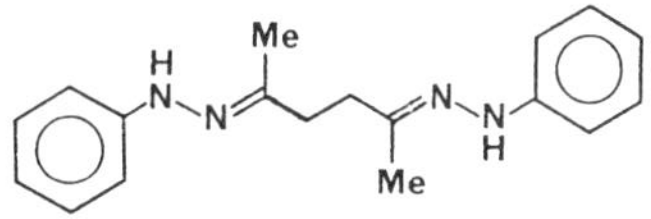 | $C_{18}H_{22}N_4$ (294) | Inhibited soybean 15-LO ($IC_{50}$ 0.19 $\mu M$)[5] |
| 4. | 4-Formylpyridine 3,4-dichlorophenylhydrazone | 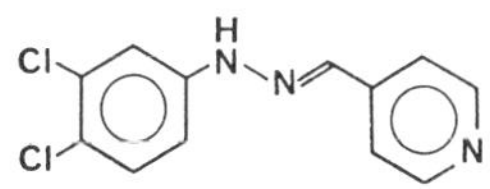 | $C_{12}H_9Cl_2N_3$ (266) | Inhibited soybean 5-LO ($IC_{50}$ 0.01 $\mu M$) and human platelet 12-LO ($IC_{50}$ 140 $\mu M$)[6] |
| 5. | 4-Acetylpyridine 3-chlorophenylhydrazone | 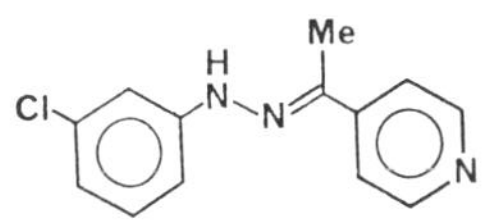 | $C_{13}H_{12}ClN_3$ (245.5) | Inhibited soybean 15-LO ($IC_{50}$ 0.25 $\mu M$) and human platelet 12-LO ($IC_{50}$ 0.14 $\mu M$)[6] |
| 6. | *N*-Phenylbenzamidrazone (CBS-1114) | 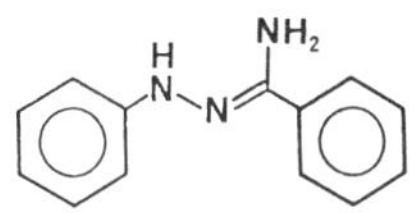 | $C_{13}H_{13}N_3$ (211) | Inhibited rabbit PMNL 5-LO and platelet cyclooxygenase ($IC_{50}$ ~ 15 $\mu M$)[7] |
| 7. | 1-Phenyl-3-pyrazolidone (Phenidone) | 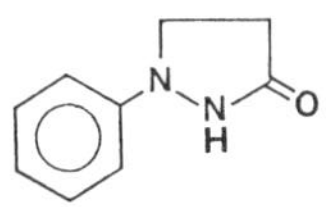 | $C_9H_{10}N_2O$ (162) | Inhibited soybean 15-LO with $IC_{50}$ values of 0.09 $\mu M$[8] and 7.2 $\mu M$;[2] inhibited 5-LO from rat neutrophils ($IC_{50}$ 12 $\mu M$)[8] and rat PMNLs ($IC_{50}$ 24 $\mu M$);[2] inhibited rat platelet 12-LO ($IC_{50}$ 66 $\mu M$)[2] and horse platelet 12-LO ($IC_{50}$ 50 $\mu$g/ml);[9] in the latter case, the $IC_{50}$ for cyclooxygenase inhibition was determined as 63 $\mu$g/ml[9] |

## Table 4 (continued)
## AZINES AND HETEROCYCLES

| No. | Name | Structure | Mol. formula (Mol. wt) | Biological data |
|---|---|---|---|---|
| 8. | 3-Amino-1-[3-(trifluoromethyl)phenyl]-2-pyrazoline (BW 755C) | 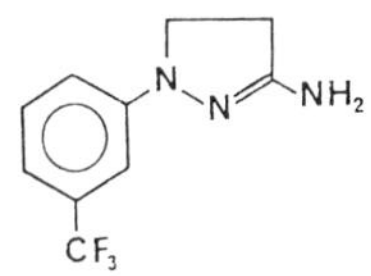 | $C_{10}H_{10}F_3N_3$ (229) | Inhibited horse platelet 12-LO ($IC_{50}$ 1.7 μg/ml) and cyclooxygenase ($IC_{50}$ 0.72 μg/ml);[10] inhibited rat neutrophil 5-LO ($IC_{50}$ 43 μ*M*) and soybean 15-LO ($IC_{50}$ 0.1 μ*M*);[8] inhibited rabbit peritoneal PMNL 15-LO ($IC_{50}$ 20 μg/ml);[11] inhibited $LTB_4$ synthesis in stimulated human PMNLs ($IC_{50}$ 8 μ*M*)[12] |
| 9. | 3-Propylamino-1-[3-(trifluoromethyl)phenyl]-2-pyrazoline | 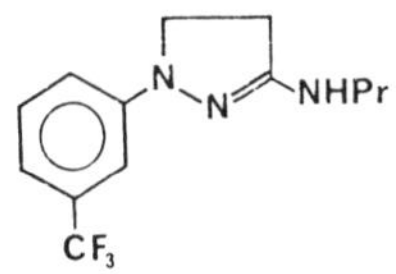 | $C_{13}H_{16}F_3N_3$ (271) | Inhibited 5-LO from rabbit peritoneal leukocytes ($IC_{50}$ 0.04 μ*M*)[13] |
| 10. | 1-[(2-(β-naphthyloxy)ethyl]-3-methyl-2-pyrazoline-5-one (nafazatrom, Bay g 6575) | 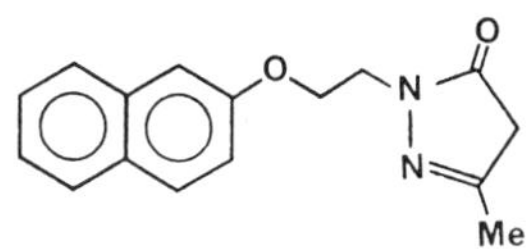 | $C_{16}H_{16}N_2O_2$ (268) | Inhibited the formation of 5-HETE and 12-HETE by B16a cells ($IC_{50}$ 3 μ*M*);[14] at 10 μg/ml, decreased formation of 5-HETE in human PMNLs by 44%, whereas 15-HETE production was increased[15] |
| 11. | 5-Methyl-3-pyrazole-carboxylic acid phenylhydrazide | 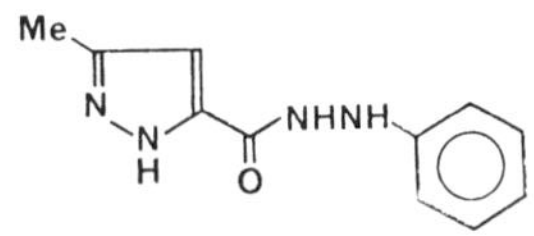 | $C_{11}H_{12}N_4O$ (216) | Inhibited soybean 15-LO ($IC_{50}$ 0.17 μ*M*)[16] |
| 12. | 2-Acetylthiophene 2-thiazolylhydrazone (CBS-1108) | 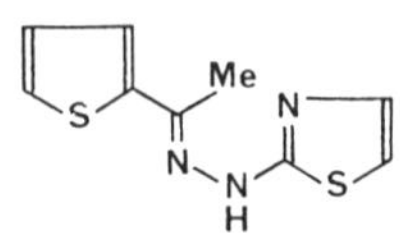 | $C_9H_9N_3S_2$ (223) | Inhibited rabbit peritoneal PMNL 5-LO ($IC_{50}$ 2 μ*M*), platelet 12-LO ($IC_{50}$ 9 μ*M*), and cyclooxygenase ($IC_{50}$ 2 μ*M*);[17] inhibited croton-oil-induced rat-ear edema ($IC_{50}$[16] μg/ml)[18] |

| | | | | |
|---|---|---|---|---|
| 13. | *N*-Cyclohexyl-*N'*-4-2-methyl-quinolyl)-*N''*-2-thiazolyl-guanidine (timegadine, SR 1368) | 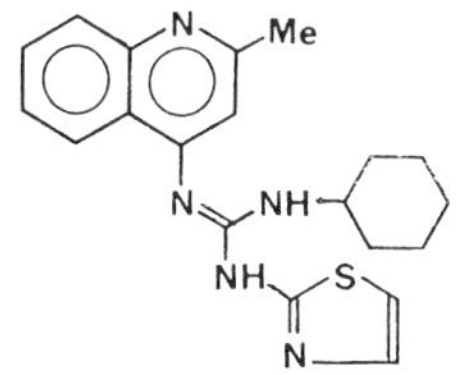 | $C_{20}H_{23}N_5S$ (365) | Inhibited horse-platelet cytosolic 12-LO ($IC_{50}$ 100 μ*M*); prostaglandin synthetase from several tissues was potently inhibited ($IC_{50}$ 0.005 to 20 μ*M*)[19] |
| 14. | *N*-(1,2,4-Triazol-3-yl)-p-chlorophenylsulfenamide (Bay 0 8278) | 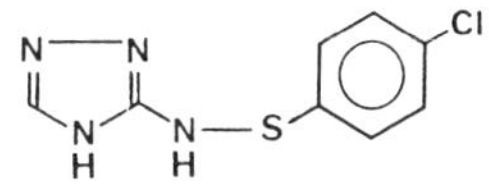 | $C_7H_7ClN_4S$ (214.5) | Inhibited the formation of LO products in rabbit and human PMNLs at concentrations of 1—10 μg/ml[20] |
| 15. | 2-Methyl-1,2-*bis*-(3-pyridyl)-1-propanone (metyrapone) | 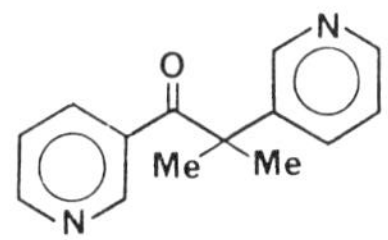 | $C_{14}H_{14}N_2O$ (226) | Inhibited soybean 15-LO ($IC_{50}$ 150—200 μ*M*); known inhibitor of cytochrome P-450[21] |
| 16. | 6-Ethoxy-2,2,4-trimethyl-1,2-dihydroquinoline (ethoxyquin) | 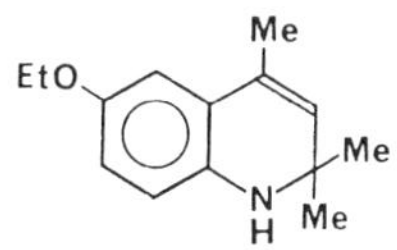 | $C_{14}H_{19}NO$ (217) | Inhibited rat PMNL 5-LO ($IC_{50}$ 25.3 μ*M*); no activity against platelet 12-LO up to 1500 μ*M*)[2] |
| 17. | 2-Phenyl-1,2-benzoiso-selenazol-3-one (ebselen, PZ 51) | 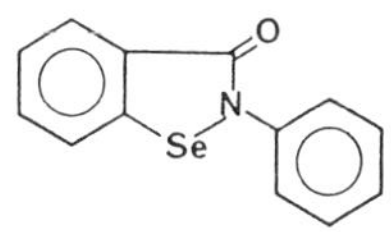 | $C_{13}H_9NOSe$ (274) | Inhibited rat PMNL 5-LO ($IC_{50}$ 20 μ*M*)[22] |
| 18. | 2-(4-Chlorophenyl)-α-methyl-5-benzoxazole-acetic acid (benoxaprofen) | 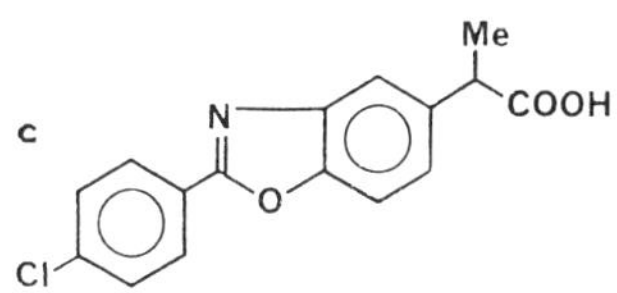 | $C_{16}H_{12}ClNO_3$ (301.5) | At 20 μg/ml, inhibited rabbit PMNL induced 5-HETE formation by 66%;[23] did not affect human platelet 12-LO at concentrations up to 300 μ*M*;[24] inhibited $LTB_4$ formation by ionophore-stimulated human neutrophils ($IC_{50}$ 36 μ*M*)[12,25] |
| 19. | 2,4-Diamino-7-methyl-pyrazolo[1,5-a]1,3,5-triazine (LA 2851) | 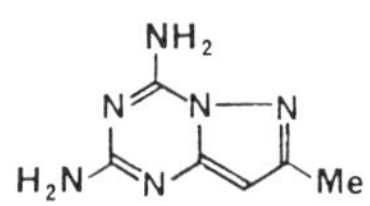 | $C_6H_8N_6$ (164) | Inhibited platelet 12-LO and ionophore-induced SRS-A formation in perfused guinea-pig lungs[26] |

**Table 4**
**AZINES AND HETEROCYCLES**

| No. | Name | Structure | Mol. formula (Mol. wt) | Biological data |
|---|---|---|---|---|
| 20. | 2-Chloro-10-(3-dimethyl-aminopropyl)phenothiazine (chlorpromazine) | 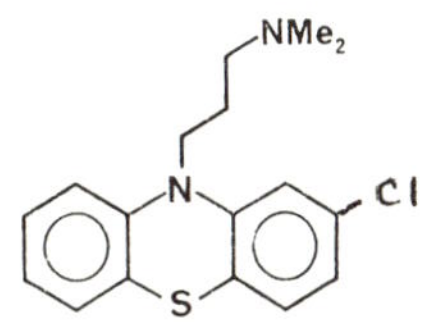 | $C_{17}H_{19}ClN_2S$ (318.5) | Inhibited soybean 15-LO ($IC_{50}$ 50—150 μ*M*)[27] |
| 21. | Trans-2,3b,4,5,7,8b,9,10-octahydronaphtho[1,2-c:-5,6-c]dipyrazole (LC-6) | 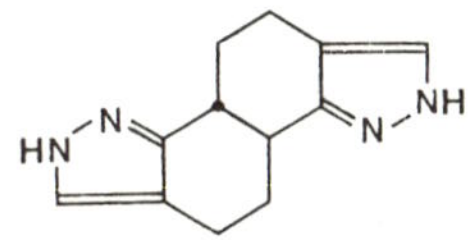 | $C_{12}H_{14}N_4$ (214) | Inhibited soybean 15-LO ($IC_{50}$ 60 μ*M*) and histamine release induced by various mediators[28] |

**REFERENCES TO TABLE 4**


1. **Robak, J. and Duniec, Z.,** The influence of phenylhydrazine in cyclooxygenase and lipoxidase activities, in *Proc. Int. Symp. Prostaglandins Thromboxanes Cardiovasc. Syst.*, 3rd. Foerster, W., Ed., Pergamon, Oxford, England, 1981, 341.
2. **Miyazawa, K., Iimori, Y., Makino, M., Mikami, T., and Miyasaka, K.,** Effects of some non-steroidal anti-inflammatory drugs and other agents on cyclooxygenase and lipoxygenase activities in some enzyme preparations, *Jpn. J. Pharmacol.*, 38, 199, 1985.
3. **Sun, F. F., McGuire, J. C., Wallach, D. P., and Brown, V. R.,** Study on the property and inhibition of human platelet arachidonic acid 12-lipoxygenase, *Adv. Prostaglandin Thromboxane Res.*, 6, 111, 1980.
4. **Baumann, J. and Wurm, G.,** Soybean lipoxygenase-1 inhibition by ketone hydrazones, *Agents Actions,* 12, 360, 1982.
5. **Baumann, J., Wurm, G., and Baumann, I.,** Interactions of a variety of lipoxygenase inhibitors with a supplementary binding site on soybean lipoxygenase, *Agents Actions,* 16, 63, 1985.
6. **Wallach, D. P. and Brown, V. R.,** A novel preparation of human platelet lipoxygenase. Characteristics and inhibition by a variety of phenyl hydrazones and comparisons with other lipoxygenases, *Biochim. Biophys. Acta,* 663, 361, 1981.
7. **Coquelet, C., Conduzorgues, J. P., Bertez, C., Bonne, C., and Sincholle, D.,** CBS-1114, *Drugs Fut.*, 9, 102, 1984.
8. **Chang, J., Skowronek, M. D., Cherney, M. L., and Lewis, A. J.,** Differential effects of putative lipoxygenase inhibitors on arachidonic acid metabolism in cell-free and intact cell preparations, *Inflammation,* 8, 143, 1984.
9. **Blackwell, G. J. and Flower, R. J.,** 1-Phenyl-3-pyrazolidone: an inhibitor of cyclooxygenase and lipoxygenase pathways in lung and platelets, *Prostaglandins,* 16, 417, 1978.
10. **Higgs, G. A., Flower, R. J., and Vane, J. R.,** A new approach to anti-inflammatory drugs, *Biochem. Pharmacol.*, 28, 1959, 1979.

11. **Narumiya, S., Salmon, J. A., Cottee, F. H., Weatherley, B. C., and Flower, R. J.,** Arachidonic acid 15-lipoxygenase from rabbit peritoneal polymorphonuclear leukocytes. Partial purification and properties, *J. Biol. Chem.*, 256, 9583, 1981.
12. **Salmon, J. A., Tilling, L. C., and Moncada, S.,** Evaluation of inhibitors of eicosanoid synthesis in leukocytes: possible pitfall of using the calcium ionophore A23187 to stimulate 5′-lipoxygenase, *Prostaglandins,* 29, 377, 1985.
13. **Copp, F. C., Islip, P. J., and Tateson, J. E.,** 3-N-Substituted-amino-1-[3-(trifluoromethyl)phenyl]-2-pyrazolines have enhanced activity against arachidonate 5-lipoxygenase and cyclooxygenase, *Biochem. Pharmacol.*, 33, 339, 1984.
14. **Honn, K. V. and Dunn, J. R.,** Nafazatrom (Bay g 6575) inhibition of tumor cell lipoxygenase activity and cellular proliferation, *FEBS Lett.*, 139, 65, 1982.
15. **Mardin, M., Busse, W. D.,** Effect of nafazatrom on the lipoxygenase pathways in PMN leukocytes and RBL-1 cells, *Prostaglandins Ser.*, Vol. 3 (Leukotrienes Other Lipoxygenase Prod.), 263, 1983.
16. **Tihanyi, E., Feher, O., Gal, M., Janaky, J., Tolnay, P., and Sebestyen, L.,** Pyrazolecarboxylic acid hydrazides as anti-inflammatory agents. New selective lipoxygenase inhibitors, *Eur. J. Med. Chem. Chim. Ther.*, 19, 433, 1984.
17. **Bertez, C., Miquel, M., Coquelet, C., Sincholle, D., and Bonne, C.,** Dual inhibition of cyclooxygenase and lipoxygenase by 2-acetylthiophene 2-thiazolylhydrazone (CBS-1108) and effect on leukocyte migration *in vivo, Biochem. Pharmacol.*, 33, 1757, 1984.
18. **Sincholle, D., Bertez, C., Legrand, A., Conduzorgues, J. P., and Bonne, C.,** Anti-inflammatory activity of a dual inhibitor of cyclooxygenase and lipoxygenase pathways, CBS-1108 (2-acetylthiophene-2-thiazolylhydrazone), *Arzneim. Forsch.*, 35, 1260, 1985.
19. **Ahnfelt-Roenne, I. and Arrigoni-Martelli, E.,** A new anti-inflammatory compound, timegadine (N-cyclohexyl-N″-[2-methylquinolyl]-N′-2-thiazolylguanidine), which inhibits both prostaglandin and 12-hydroxy-eicosatetraenoic acid (12-HETE) formation, *Biochem. Pharmacol.*, 29, 3265, 1980.
20. **Mardin, M., Busse, W. D., Gruetzmann, R., and Rochels, R.,** Improvement of corneal epithelial repair by Bay 08276, a novel lipoxygenase inhibitor and anti-inflammatory agent, *Arch. Pharmacol.*, 322 (Suppl. R), 114, 1983.
21. **Pretus, H. A., Ignarro, L. J., Easley, H. E., and Feigen, L. P.,** Inhibition of soybean lipoxygenase by SKF 525-A and metyrapone, *Prostaglandins,* 30, 591, 1985.
22. **Safayhi, H., Tiegs, G., and Wendel, A.,** A novel biologically active seleno-organic compound. V. Inhibition by ebselen (PZ 51) of rat peritoneal neutrophil lipoxygenase, *Biochem. Pharmacol.*, 34, 2691, 1985.
23. **Dawson, W., Boot, J. R., Harvey, J., and Walker, J. R.,** The pharmacology of benoxaprofen with particular reference to effects on lipoxygenase product formation, *Eur. J. Rheumatol. Inflammation,* 5, 61—68, 1982.
24. **Harvey, J., Parish, H., Ho, P. P. K., Boot, J. R., and Dawson, W.,** The preferential inhibition of 5-lipoxygenase product formation by benoxaprofen, *J. Pharm. Pharmacol.*, 35, 44, 1983.
25. **Salmon, J. A., Higgs, G. A., Tilling, L., Moncada, S., and Vane, J. R.,** Mode of action of benoxaprofen, *Lancet,* 1 (8381), 848, 1984.
26. **Guillaume, M. and Lakatos, C.,** LA 2851, A new bronchodilator and anti-allergic compound which inhibits slow-reacting substance formation, *Prostaglandins Ser.*, 3(Leukotrienes Other Lipoxygenase Prod.), 332, 1983.
27. **Robak, J. and Duniec, Z.,** The influence of chlorpromazine on lipoxidases, *Biochim. Biophys. Acta,* 620, 59, 1980.
28. **Magro, A. M. and Hurtado, I.,** The orally active antiallergic compound, LC-6 (trans-2,3b,4,5,7,8b,9,10-octahydronaphtho[1,2-c:5,6-c]dipyrazole) inhibits the arachidonate lipoxygenase enzyme, *J. Immunopharmacol.*, 5, 191, 1983.

## Table 5
## MISCELLANEOUS

| No. | Name | Structure | Mol. formula (Mol. wt) | Biological data |
|---|---|---|---|---|
| 1. | Acetylsalicylic acid (Aspirin) | 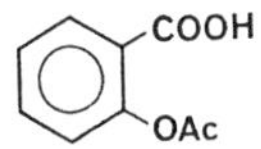 | $C_9H_8O_3$ (180) | Inhibited the formation of lipoxygenase products from carrageenin pleural exudate neutrophils;[1] inhibited human platelet 12-LO[2,3] |
| 2. | Toluene-3,4-dithiol | 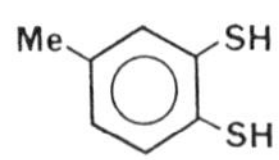 | $C_7H_8S_2$ (156) | Inhibited rat PMNL 5-LO ($IC_{50}$ 24.4 $\mu M$), rat platelet 12-LO ($IC_{50}$ 20 $\mu M$), and soybean 15-LO ($IC_{50}$ 219 $\mu M$)[4] |
| 3. | Diphenyldisulfide | 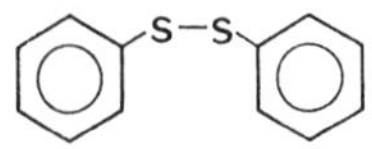 | $C_{12}H_{10}S_2$ (218) | Inhibited 5-LO from the soluble fraction of sonified RBL-1 cells ($IC_{50}$ 1.5 $\mu M$);[5] inhibited $LTC_4$ formation in intact cells ($IC_{50}$ 20 $\mu M$)[6] |
| 4. | Ethylenediaminetetraacetic acid (EDTA) |  | $C_{10}H_{16}N_2O_8$ (292) | Inhibited human platelet 12-LO ($IC_{50}$ 7.6 $\mu M$)[7] |
| 5. | 2,2-Diphenylvaleric acid diethylaminoethyl ester (SKF 525-A) | 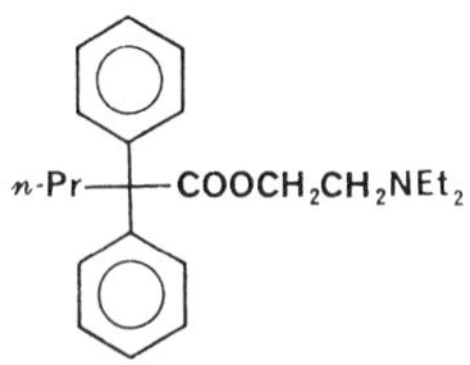 | $C_{23}H_{31}NO_2$ (353) | Inhibited soybean 15-LO ($IC_{50}$ 40 $\mu M$); known inhibitor of cytochrome P-450[8] |

## REFERENCES TO TABLE 5

1. **Siegel, M. I., McConnell, R. T., Porter, N. A., Selph, J. L., Truax, J. F., Vinegar, R., and Cuatrecasas, P.,** Aspirin-like drugs inhibit arachidonic acid metabolism via lipoxygenase and cyclooxygenase in rat neutrophils from carrageenan pleural exudates, *Biochem. Biophys. Res. Commun.*, 92, 688, 1980.
2. **Siegel, M. I., McConnell, R. T., and Cuatrecasas, P.,** Aspirin-like drugs interfere with arachidonate metabolism by inhibition of the 12-hydroperoxy-5,8,10,14-eicosatetraenoic acid peroxidase activity of the lipoxygenase pathway, *Proc. Natl. Acad. Sci. U.S.A.*, 76, 3774, 1979.
3. **Eynard, A. R., Galli, G., Tremoli, E., Maderna, P., Magni, F., and Paoletti, R.,** Aspirin inhibits platelet 12-hydroxy-eicosatetraenoic acid formation, *J. Lab. Clin. Med.*, 107, 73, 1986.
4. **Miyzawa, K., Iimori, Y., Makino, M., Mikami, T., and Miyasaka, K.,** Effects of some nonsteroidal anti-inflammatory drugs and other agents on cyclooxygenase and lipoxygenase activities in some enzyme preparations, *Jpn. J. Pharmacol.*, 38, 199, 1985.
5. **Egan, R. W., Tischler, A. N., Baptista, E. M., Ham, E. A., Soderman, D. D., and Gale, P. H.,** Specific inhibition and oxidative regulation of 5-lipoxygenase, *Adv. Prostaglandin, Thromboxane, Leukotriene Res.*, 11, 151, 1983.
6. **Egan, R. W. and Gale, P. H.,** Inhibition of mammalian 5-lipoxygenase by aromatic disulfides, *J. Biol. Chem.*, 260, 11554, 1985.
7. **Greenwald, J. E., Alexander, M. S., Fertel, R. H., Beach, C. A., Wong, L. K., and Bianchine, J. R.,** Role of ferric iron in platelet lipoxygenase activity, *Biochem. Biophys. Res. Commun.*, 96, 817, 1980.
8. **Pretus, H. A., Ignarro, L. J., Ensley, H. E., and Feigen, L. P.,** Inhibition of soybean lipoxygenase by SKF 525-A and metyrapone, *Prostaglandins*, 30, 591, 1985.

## Table 6
## NEWER INHIBITORS

| No. | Name | Structure | Mol. formula (Mol. wt) | Biological data |
|---|---|---|---|---|
| 1. | 5-(4-Chlorophenyl)-N-hydroxyl-1-(4-methoxyphenyl)-N-methyl-IH-pyrazole-3-propanamide (tepoxalin) | 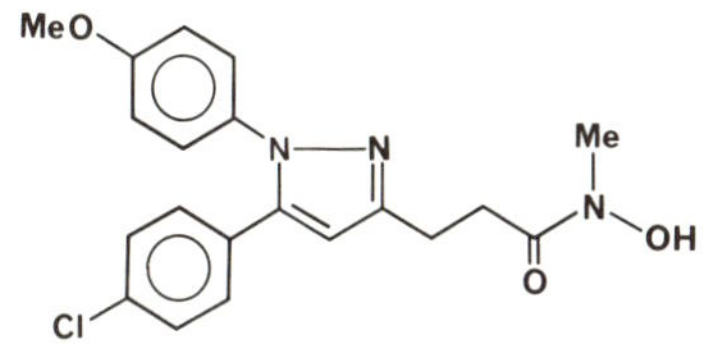 | $C_{20}H_{20}N_3O_3Cl$ 385.5 | Inhibited 5-LO in PMNL ($IC_{50}$ 0.8 $\mu M$) and RBL-1 cell cytosol ($IC_{50}$ 0.2 $\mu M$); inhibited platelet 12-LO ($IC_{50}$ 1—10 $\mu M$)[1] |
| 2. | N-(4-Methoxyphenyl)-1-phenyl-IH-pyrazol-3-amine (FPL-62,064) | 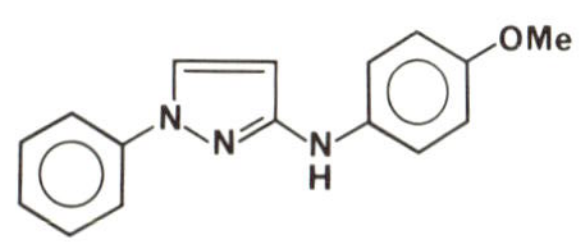 | $C_{16}H_{15}N_3O$ 265 | Inhibited RBL-1 cell cytosol 5-LO ($IC_{50}$ 4 $\mu M$)[2] |
| 3. | N-Methoxy-3-(3,5-di-tert-butyl-4-hydroxybenzylidene)pyrrolidin-2-one (E-5110) | 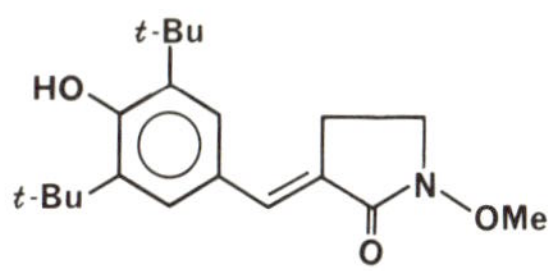 | $C_{20}H_{29}NO_3$ 331 | Inhibited 5-LO in PMNL ($IC_{50}$ 0.2 $\mu M$) and RBL-1 cell cytosol ($IC_{50}$ 0.9 $\mu M$)[3] |
| 4. | 3-(3,5-Di-tert-butyl-4-hydroxyanilino)benzoic acid (S-26431) | 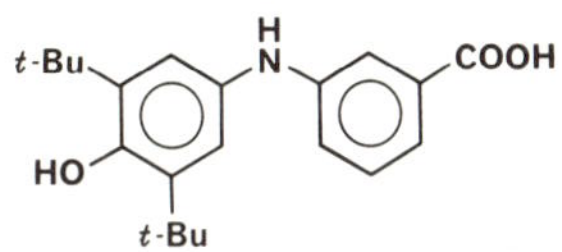 | $C_{21}H_{27}NO_3$ 341 | Inhibited 5-LO activity in RBL-1 cell cytosol ($IC_{50}$ 1.2 $\mu M$), human leukocytes ($IC_{50}$ 8.3 $\mu M$) and guinea pig lung homogenate ($IC_{50}$ 0.4 $\mu M$)[4] |
| 5. | N-(3-Phenoxycinnamyl)-acetohydroxamic acid (BW A4C) | 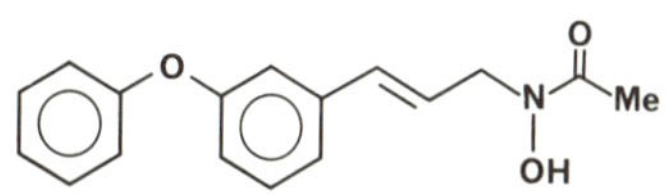 | $C_{17}H_{17}NO_3$ 283 | Inhibited leukocyte 5-LO ($IC_{50}$ 0.1 $\mu M$); orally active in rats; inhibited leukocyte 12-LO/15-LO ($IC_{50}$ 3.3 $\mu M$)[5] |
| 6. | N-Hydroxy-N-[1-[4-(phenylmethoxy)phenyl]ethyl] acetamide (A-63162) | 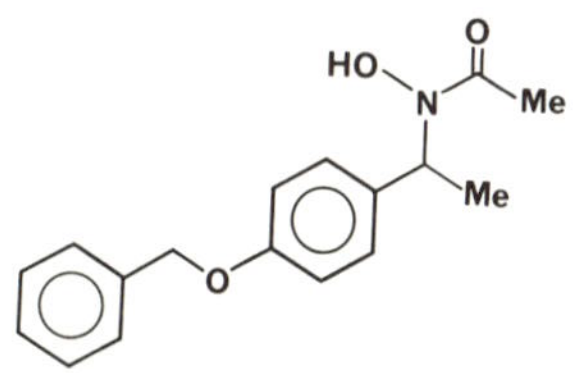 | $C_{17}H_{19}NO_3$ 285 | Inhibited RBL-1 cell cytosol 5-LO ($IC_{50}$ 0.4 $\mu M$); orally active in rats[6] |

| | | | |
|---|---|---|---|
| 7. Methyl 2-[(3,4-dihydro-3,4-dioxo-1-naphthalenyl)amino]benzoate (CGS 8515) | 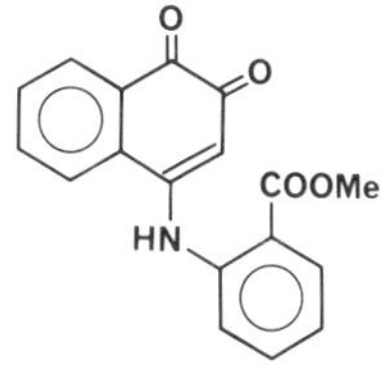 | $C_{18}H_{13}NO_4$ 307 | Inhibited 5-LO in PMNL (rat $IC_{50}$ 4 μ*M*; human $IC_{50}$ 0.8 μ*M*) and rat lung ($IC_{50}$ < 1 μ*M*); orally active in rats; less active against 12-LO and 15-LO[7] |
| 8. 1-Acetoxy-2-n-butyl-4-methoxy-naphthalene (U-66,858) | 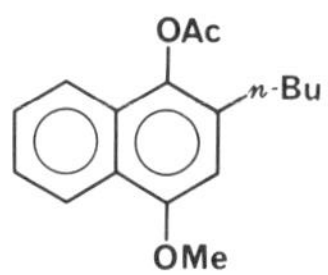 | $C_{17}H_{20}0_3$ 272 | Inhibited rat leukocyte 5-LO ($IC_{50}$ 0.1 μg/ml)[8] |
| 9. 2-[(1-Naphthalenyloxy)methyl]-quinoline (Wy-47,288) | 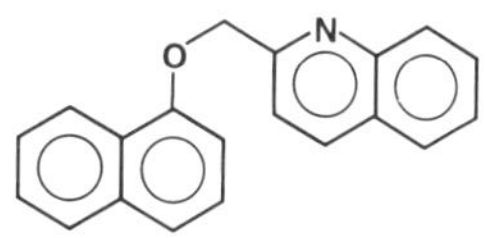 | $C_{20}H_{15}NO$ 285 | Inhibited 5-LO in rat PMNL ($IC_{50}$ 0.4 μ*M*) and mouse macrophages ($IC_{50}$ 0.2 μ*M*)[9] |
| 10. 1,1,1-Trifluoro-N-[3-(2-quinolinylmethoxy)phenyl]methane sulfonamide (Wy-48,252) | 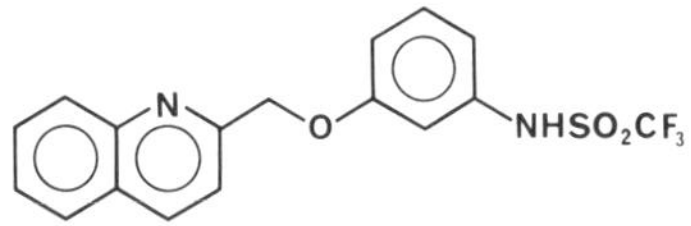 | $C_{17}H_{13}N_2O_3SF_3$ 382 | Inhibited 5-LO activity in rat PMNL ($IC_{50}$ 2—5 μ*M*), human PMNL (5—10 μ*M*) and mouse macrophages ($IC_{50}$ 4 μ*M*). No effect on 12-LO and 15-LO[10] |
| 11. 4-[Hydroxy-[3-(2-quinolinylmethoxy)phenyl]amino]-4-oxobutanoic acid, methyl ester (Wy-45,911) | 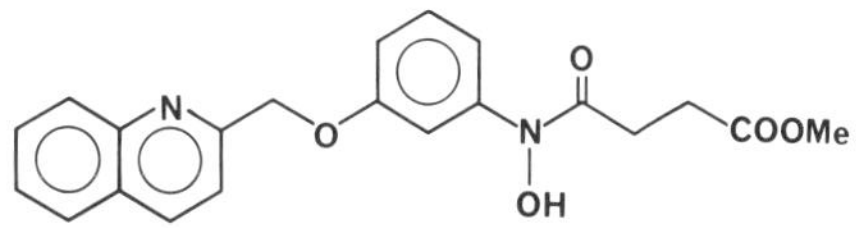 | $C_{21}H_{20}N_2O_5$ 380 | Inhibited 5-LO in rat PMNL ($IC_{50}$ 1.4 μ*M*) and mouse macrophages ($IC_{50}$ 0.5 μ*M*); inhibited rabbit platelet 12-LO ($IC_{50}$ 2.7 μ*M*)[11] |
| 12. N-Hydroxy-N-methyl-7-propoxy-2-naphthalene-ethanamine (QA 208-199) | 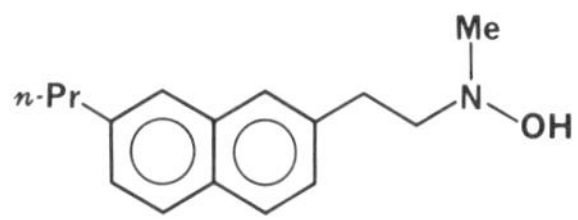 | $C_{16}H_{21}NO$ 243 | Inhibited 5-LO, 12-LO, and 15-LO in psoriatic skin homogenate ($IC_{50}$ < 10 μ*M*)[12] |
| 13. 3,7-Dimethyloxy-4-phenyl-N-(IH-tetrazol-5-yl)-4H-furo[3,2-b]-indole-2-carboxamide (C1-922) | 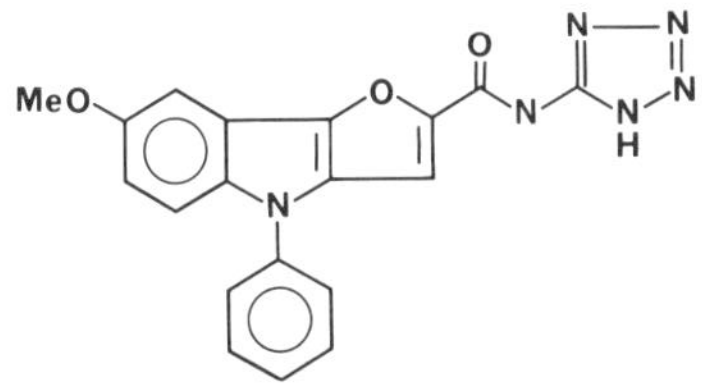 | $C_{19}H_{14}N_6O_3$ 374 | Inhibited 5-LO activity in guinea pig lung homogenate ($IC_{50}$ 1.5 μ*M*)[13] |

## Table 6 (continued)
## NEWER INHIBITORS

| No. | Name | Structure | Mol. formula (Mol. wt) | Biological data |
|---|---|---|---|---|
| 14. | 2,3-Dihydro-6-[3-(2-hydroxy-methyl)-phenyl-2-propenyl]-5-benzofuranol (L-651,896) | 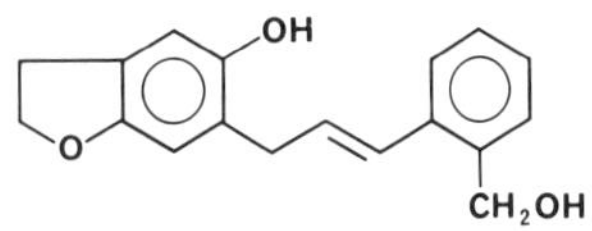 | $C_{18}H_{18}O_3$ 282 | Inhibited 5-LO activity in RBL-1 cells ($IC_{50}$ 0.1 $\mu M$), human PMNL ($IC_{50}$ 0.4 $\mu M$), and mouse macrophages ($IC_{50}$ 0.1 $\mu M$)[14] |
| 15. | 7-Chloro-2-[(4-methoxy-phenyl)-methyl]-3-methyl-5-propyl-benzofuranol (L-656,224) | 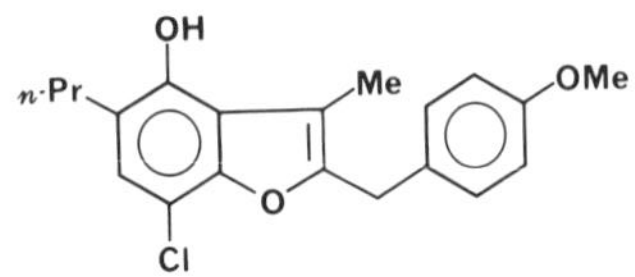 | $C_{20}H_{21}O_3Cl$ 344.5 | Inhibited 5-LO activity in rat and human leukocytes ($IC_{50}$ 18—240 n$M$) as well as the crude human leukocyte and purified porcine leukocyte enzyme ($IC_{50}$ 0.4 $\mu M$); relatively inactive against 12- and 15-LO[15] |
| 16. | 3-Hydroxy-5-trifluoromethyl-N-(2-(2-thienyl)-2-phenyleth-enyl)-benzo[b]thiophene-2-carboxamide (L-652,343) | 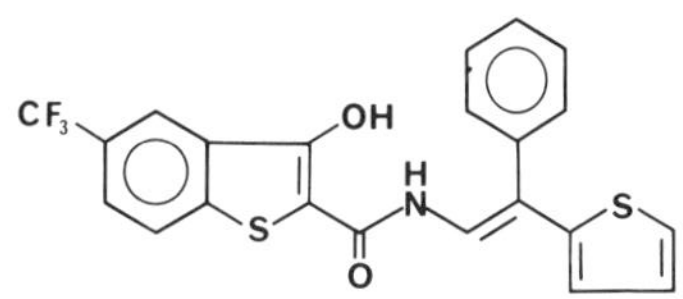 | $C_{22}H_{14}NO_2S_2F_3$ 445 | Inhibited 5-LO activity in RBL-1 cells ($IC_{50}$ 2 $\mu M$), rat PMNL ($IC_{50}$ 0.6 $\mu M$), and human PMNL ($IC_{50}$ 0.6 $\mu M$)[16] |
| 17. | 5-Chloro-2,3-dihydro-2-oxo-3-(2-thienylcarbonyl)-indole-1-carboxamide (CP-66,248) | 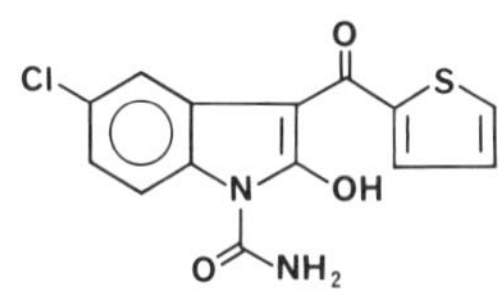 | $C_{14}H_9N_2O_3SCl$ 320.5 | Inhibited 5-LO activity in RBL-1 cell cytosol ($IC_{50}$ 13 $\mu M$), rat PMNL ($IC_{50}$ 5 $\mu M$), and human PMNL ($IC_{50}$ 13 $\mu M$)[17] |
| 18. | 5-(4-Pyridyl)-6-(4-fluoro-phenyl)-2,3-dihydromi-dazo[2,1-b]thiazole (SKF-86002) | 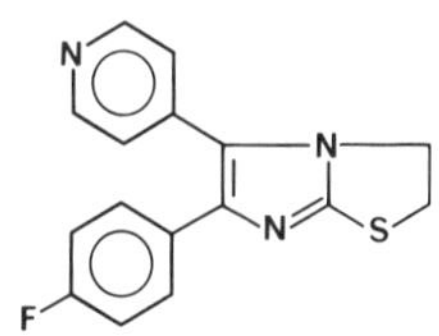 | $C_{16}H_{12}N_3SF$ 297 | Inhibited 5-LO in PMNL ($IC_{50}$ 20 $\mu M$), monocytes ($IC_{50}$ 20 $\mu M$), RBL-1 cells ($IC_{50}$ 40 $\mu M$) and RBL-1 cell cytosol ($IC_{50}$ 10 $\mu M$)[18] |

| | | | | |
|---|---|---|---|---|
| 19. | 4-Bromo-2,7-dimethoxy-3H-phenothiazine-3-one (L-651,392) | 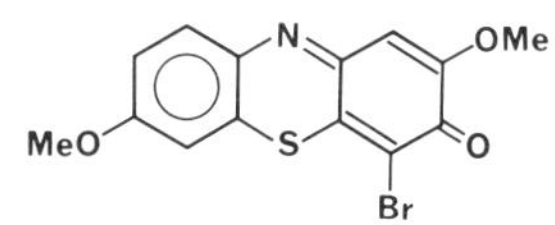 | $C_{14}H_{10}NO_3SBr$ 352 | Inhibited 5-LO activity in rat PMNL ($IC_{50}$ 60 n*M*), human PMNL ($IC_{50}$ 260 n*M*), and mouse macrophages ($IC_{50}$ 250 n*M*)[19] |

## REFERENCES TO TABLE 6


1. **Argentieri, D. C., Ritchie, D. M., Tolman, E. L., Ferro, M. P., Wachter, M. P., Mezick, J. A., and Capetola, R. J.,** Topical and *in vitro* pharmacology of tepoxalin (ORF 20,485) — a new dual cyclooxygenase/lipoxygenase inhibitor, *Fed. Am. Soc. Exp. Biol. J.*, 2, A369, 1988.
2. **Blackham, A., Griffiths, R. J., Norris, A. A., Wood, B. E., Li, S. W., Halla, P. D., Mitchell, P. D., and Mann, J.,** FPL-62,064: a novel dual inhibitor of arachidonic acid metabolism in skin, *Br. J. Pharmacol.*, 95, 536P, 1988.
3. **Shirota, H., Kobayashi, S., Terato, K., Sakuma, Y., Yamada, K., Ikuta, H., Yamagishi, Y., Yamatsu, I., and Katayama, K.,** Effect of the novel anti-inflammatory agent N-methoxy-3-(3,5,di-tert-butyl-4-hydroxybenzylidene)pyrrolidin-2-one on *in vitro* generation of some inflammatory mediators, *Arzneim.-Forsch.*, 37, 936, 1987.
4. **Hammerbeck, D. M., Bell, R. L., Stelzer, V. L., Heghinian, K., Reiter, M. J., Scherrer, R. A., Rustad, M. A., Hupperts, A. M., and Swingle, K. F.,** Effect of a new selective 5-lipoxygenase inhibitor in biochemical and pharmacological models for the inhibition of acute hypersensitivity reactions, *Ann. N.Y. Acad. Sci.*, 524, 398, 1988.
5. **Tateson, J. E., Randall, R. W., Reynolds, C. H., Jackson, W. P., Bhattacherjee, P., Salmon, J. A., and Garland, L. G.,** Selective inhibition of arachidonate 5-lipoxygenase by novel acetohydroxamate acids: biochemical assessment *in vitro* and *ex vivo*, *Br. J. Pharmacol.*, 94, 528, 1988.
6. **Summers, J. B., Gunn, B. P., Martin, J. G., Martin, M. B., Mazdiyasni, H., Stewart, A. O., Young, P. R., Bouska, J. B., Goetze, A. M., Dyer, R. D., Brooks, D. W., and Carter, G. W.,** Structure-activity analysis of a class of orally active hydroxamic acid inhibitors of leukotriene biosynthesis, *J. Med. Chem.*, 31, 1960, 1988.
7. **Ku, E. C., Raychaudhuri, A., Ghai, G., Kimble, E. F., Lee, W. H., Colombo, C., Dotson, R., Oglesby, T. D., and Walsey, J. W. F.,** Characterization of CGS 8515 as a selective 5-lipoxygenase inhibitor using *in vitro* and *in vivo* models, *Biochim. Biophys. Acta*, 959, 332, 1988.
8. **Johnson, H. G., and Stout, B. K.,** Activity of a novel hydroquinone inhibitor of leukotriene synthesis (U-66,858) in the Rhesus monkey *Ascaris* reactor, *Int. Arch. Allergy Appl. Immunol.*, 87, 204, 1988.
9. **Carlson, R. P., O'Neill-Davis, L., Calhoun, W., Datko, L. J., Kreft, A. F., Musser, J. H., and Chang, J.,** Pharmacology of Wy-47,288, a topically active 5-lipoxygenase/cyclooxygenase inhibitor, *Pharmacologist*, 29(3), 138, 1987.
10. **Chang, J., Borgeat, P., Schleimer, R. P., Musser, J., Marshall, L. A., and Hand, J. M.,** Wy-48,252 (1,1,1-trifluoro-N-[3-(2-quinolinylmethoxy) phenyl] methane sulfonamide), an orally active leukotriene antagonist: effects on arachidonic acid metabolism in various inflammatory cells, *Eur. J. Pharmacol.*, 148, 131, 1988.
11. **Chang, J., Musser, J. H., and Hand, J. M.,** Effect of a novel leukotriene $D_4$ antagonist with 5-lipoxygenase and cyclooxygenase inhibitory activity, on leukotriene $D_4$ — and antigen-induced bronchoconstriction in the guinea pig, *Int. Arch. Allergy Appl. Immunol.*, 86, 48, 1988.
12. **Schnyder, J., Hunziker, Th., Strasser, M., Richardson, B., and Krebs, A.,** Reduction of lipoxygenase products in psoriatic skin homogenates by QA 208-199, *Arch. Dermatol. Res.*, 278, 494, 1986.
13. **Robichaud, L. J., Stewart, S. F., and Adolphson, R. L.,** CI-922 — a novel, potent anti-allergic compound. I. Inhibition of mediator release *in vitro*, *Int. J. Immunopharmac.*, 9, 41, 1987.

14. **Bonney, R. J., Davies, P., Dougherty, H., Egan, R. W., Gale, P. H., Chang, M., Hammond, M., Jensen, N., MacDonald, J., Thompson, K., Zambias, R., Opas, E., Meurer, R., Pacholok, S., and Humes, J. L.,** Biochemical and biological activities of 2,3-dihydro-6-[3-(2-hydroxymethyl)phenyl-2-propenyl]-5-benzofuranol (L-651,896), a novel topical antiinflammatory agent, *Biochem. Pharmacol.*, 36, 3885, 1987.
15. **Belanger, P., Maycock, A., Guindon, Y., Bach, T., Dollob, A. L., Dufresne, C., Ford-Hutchinson, A. W., Gale, P. H., Hopple, S., Lau, C. K., Letts, L. G., Luell, S., McFarlane, C. S., MacIntyre, E., Meurer, R., Miller, D. K., Piechuta, H., Riendeau, D., Rokach, J., Rouzer, C., and Scheigetz, J.,** L-656-224 (7-chloro-2-[(4-methoxy-phenyl)methyl]-3-methyl-5-propyl-4-benzofuranol): a novel, selective, orally active 5-lipoxygenase inhibitor, *Can. J. Physiol. Pharmacol.*, 65, 2441, 1987.
16. **Tischler, A., Bailey, P., Dallob, A., Witzel, B., Durette, P., Rupprecht, K., Allison, D., Dougherty, H., Humes, J., Ham, E., Bonney, R., Egan, R., Gallager, T., Miller, D., and Goldenberg, M.,** L-652,343: a novel dual 5-lipoxygenase/cyclooxygenase inhibitor, *Adv. Prostaglandin Thromboxane Leukotriene Res.*, 16, 63, 1986.
17. **Moilanen, E., Alanko, J., Asmawi, M. Z., and Vapaatalo, H.,** CP-66,248, a new antiinflammatory agent, is a potent inhibitor of leukotriene $B_4$ and prostanoid synthesis in human polymorphonuclear leukocytes *in vitro, Eicosanoids,* 1, 35, 1988.
18. **Griswold, D. E., Marshall, P. J., Webb, E. F., Godfrey, R., Newton, J., DiMartino, M. J., Sarau, H. M., Gleason, J. G., Poste, G., and Hanna, N.,** SKF-86002: a structurally novel antiinflammatory agent that inhibits lipoxygenase- and cyclooxygenase-mediated metabolism of arachidonic acid, *Biochem. Pharmacol.*, 36, 3463, 1987.
19. **Guindon, Y., Girard, Y., Maycock, A., Ford-Hutchinson, A. W., Atkinson, J. G., Belanger, P. C., Dallob, A., DeSousa, D., Dougherty, H., Egan, R., Goldenberg, M. M., Ham, E., Fortin, R., Hamel, P., Hamel, R., Lau, C. K., Leblanc, Y., McFarlane, C. S., Piechuta, H., Therien, M., Yoakim, C., and Rokach, J.,** L-651,392: a novel, potent and selective 5-lipoxygenase inhibitor, *Adv. Prostaglandin Thromboxane Leukotriene Res.*, 17, 554, 1987.

## ABBREVIATIONS USED IN THE TABLES

| | |
|---|---|
| ETYA | Eicosatetraynoic acid |
| 5-HETE | 5-Hydroxyeicosatetraenoic acid |
| 12-HETE | 12-Hydroxyeicosatetraenoic acid |
| 15-HETE | 15-Hydroxyeicosatetraenoic acid |
| LO | Lipoxygenase |
| 5-LO | 5-Lipoxygenase |
| 12-LO | 12-Lipoxygenase |
| 15-LO | 15-Lipoxygenase |
| $LTB_4$ | Leukotriene $B_4$ |
| $LTC_4$ | Leukotriene $C_4$ |
| $PLA_2$ | Phospholipase $A_2$ |
| PMNL | Polymorphonuclear leukocyte |
| RBL | Rat basophilic leukemia |
| SRS-A | Slow-reacting substance of anaphylaxis |

## REFERENCES

1. **Veldink, G. A., Vliegenthart, J. F. G., and Boldingh, J.,** Plant lipoxygenases, *Prog. Chem. Fats Other Lipids,* 15, 131, 1977.
2. **Hamberg, M. and Samuelsson, B.,** Prostaglandin endoperoxides. Novel transformations of arachidonic acid in human platelets, *Proc. Natl. Acad. Sci. U.S.A.,* 71, 3400, 1974.
3. **Corey, E. J.,** Chemical studies on slow reacting substances/leukotrienes, *Experientia,* 38, 1259, 1982.
4. **Rokach, J. and Adams, J.,** Synthesis of leukotrienes and lipoxygenase products, *Acc. Chem. Res.,* 18, 87, 1985.
5. **Burka, J. F.,** The products of the lipoxygenase pathway of arachidonic acid metabolism, *N. Engl. Soc. Allerg. Proc.,* 2, 62, 1981.
6. **Taylor, G. W. and Morris, H. R.,** Lipoxygenase pathways, *Br. Med. Bull.,* 39, 219, 1983.
7. **Kreutner, W. and Siegel, M. I.,** Biology of leukotrienes, *Annu. Rep. Med. Chem.,* 19, 241, 1984.
8. **Piper, P. J.,** Pharmacology of leukotrienes, *Br. Med. Bull.,* 39, 255, 1983.
9. **Cashman, J. R.,** Leukotriene biosynthesis inhibitors, *Pharm. Res.,* 253, 1985.
10. **Bach, M. K.,** Inhibitors of leukotriene synthesis and action, in *The Leukotrienes,* Chakrin, L. W. and Bailey, D. M., Eds., Academic Press, Orlando, 1984, Chap. 6.
11. **Bailey, D. M. and Chakrin, L. W.,** Arachidonate lipoxygenase, *Annu. Rep. Med. Chem.,* 16, 213, 1981.
12. **Bailey, D. M. and Casey, F. B.,** Lipoxygenase and the related arachidonic acid metabolites, *Annu. Rep. Med. Chem.,* 17, 203, 1982.
13. **Higgs, G. A. and Vane, J. R.,** Inhibition of cyclooxygenase and lipoxygenase, *Br. Med. Bull.,* 39, 265, 1983.
14. **Musser, J. H., Kreft, A. F., and Lewis, A. J.,** Pulmonary and anti-allergy agents, *Annu. Rep. Med. Chem.,* 19, 93, 1984.
15. **Musser, J. H., Kreft, A. F., and Lewis, A. J.,** Pulmonary and anti-allergy agents, *Annu. Rep. Med. Chem.,* 20, 71, 1985.
16. **Higgs, G. A. and Flower, R. J.,** Anti-inflammatory drugs and the inhibition of arachidonate lipoxygenase, *Prostaglandins Res. Stud. Ser.,* 1(SRS-A Leukotrienes), 197, 1981.
17. **Bhattacherjee, P. and Eakins, K. E.,** Lipoxygenase products: mediation of inflammatory responses and inhibition of their formation, in *The Leukotrienes,* Chakrin, L. W. and Bailey, D. M., Eds., Academic Press, Orlando, 1984, Chap. 8.
18. **Higgs, G. A.,** The effects of lipoxygenase inhibitors in anaphylactic and inflammatory responses *in vivo, Prostaglandins Leukotrienes Med.,* 13, 89, 1984.
19. **Higgins, A. J.,** The biology, pathophysiology and control of eicosanoids in inflammation, *J. Vet. Pharmacol. Ther.,* 8, 1, 1985.

# SELECTIVE INHIBITORS OF THROMBOXANE SYNTHETASE*

**Keith A. M. Walker**

## INTRODUCTION

The discovery of thromboxane $A_2$ ($TxA_2$) in 1975[1] and of prostacyclin ($PGI_2$) in 1976[2,3] heralded a new era in prostaglandin research.[4] Indeed, one authority in the field once proposed that all previous research had been devoted to the biologically useless side products of these two agents. The elucidation of the conversion of arachidonic acid to the endoperoxides $PGG_2$ and $PGH_2$ (see Scheme 1), and thence to either thromboxane (especially in platelets) or prostacyclin (endothelial cells), immediately suggested the possibility of redirecting the metabolism of arachidonic acid towards prostacyclin, if specific inhibitors of thromboxane synthetase could be found.[5,6] It was suggested by various authors that an overproduction of thromboxane $A_2$ (or a hypersensitivity to this agent) might be involved in such disease states as stroke, thrombus formation, angina, Raynaud's syndrome, platelet hyperaggregability, myocardial infarction, cerebral vasospasm, shock, septicemia, graft rejection, asthma, atherosclerosis, and diabetes, among others. It was also proposed[6,7] by Moncada and Vane that endoperoxides released by platelets were converted to the antiaggregatory prostacyclin ($PGI_2$) by vascular walls, preventing platelet adhesion and aggregation unless injury occurred. Although it is now believed that endoperoxides are only released from platelets when thromboxane synthetase is inhibited,[8] conversion of excessive amounts of thromboxanes, produced in response to a stimulus, to the beneficial prostacyclin would offer an advantage not possible with cyclooxygenase inhibitors.** (Unfortunately, recent work seems to suggest that prostacyclin formation *in vivo* is not altered when thromboxane synthesis is inhibited.[10]) Specific inhibition of thromboxane formation would seem to offer both a diagnostic tool to determine the level of involvement of thromboxane in a variety of settings, or the potential of treating various pathological states to which this agent contributed.

## THROMBOXANE-SYNTHETASE INHIBITORS

Agents which inhibited the enzyme thromboxane synthetase were quickly found, most notably imidazole, L8027 (nictindole), N-0164, benzydamine, and 9,11-azoprostadienoic acid (see tables below), although these early agents were soon shown to have other activities, e.g., towards cyclooxygenase, or antagonism of other arachidonate metabolites. However, elaboration of these leads, and the later lead of pyridine and its homologues quickly led to more specific inhibitors. All thromboxane-synthetase inhibitors of interest to date still fall within the two classes heralded by these early leads: endoperoxide analogues and azoles (imidazoles and pyridines).

Endoperoxide analogues in general show complex structure-activity relationships in giving (unpredictably) either thromboxane-agonist activity, thromboxane-synthetase inhibition, and even prostacyclin-agonist activity, or mixed activities, with opposite effects occasionally observed in different tissues. This no doubt results from the close structural similarity between endoperoxide ($PGH_2$) and thromboxane $A_2$ which share a common receptor on platelets, at least. Presumably, this receptor is quite similar to the cavity in the enzyme thromboxane synthetase. Because of the agonist activities these molecules possess in some tissues, no endoperoxide analogues are being further developed as thromboxane-synthetase inhibitors.

* See tables at end of chapter.

** Although many attempts have been made to achieve the same effect with "low-dose" aspirin, no realization of this concept has been demonstrated.[9]

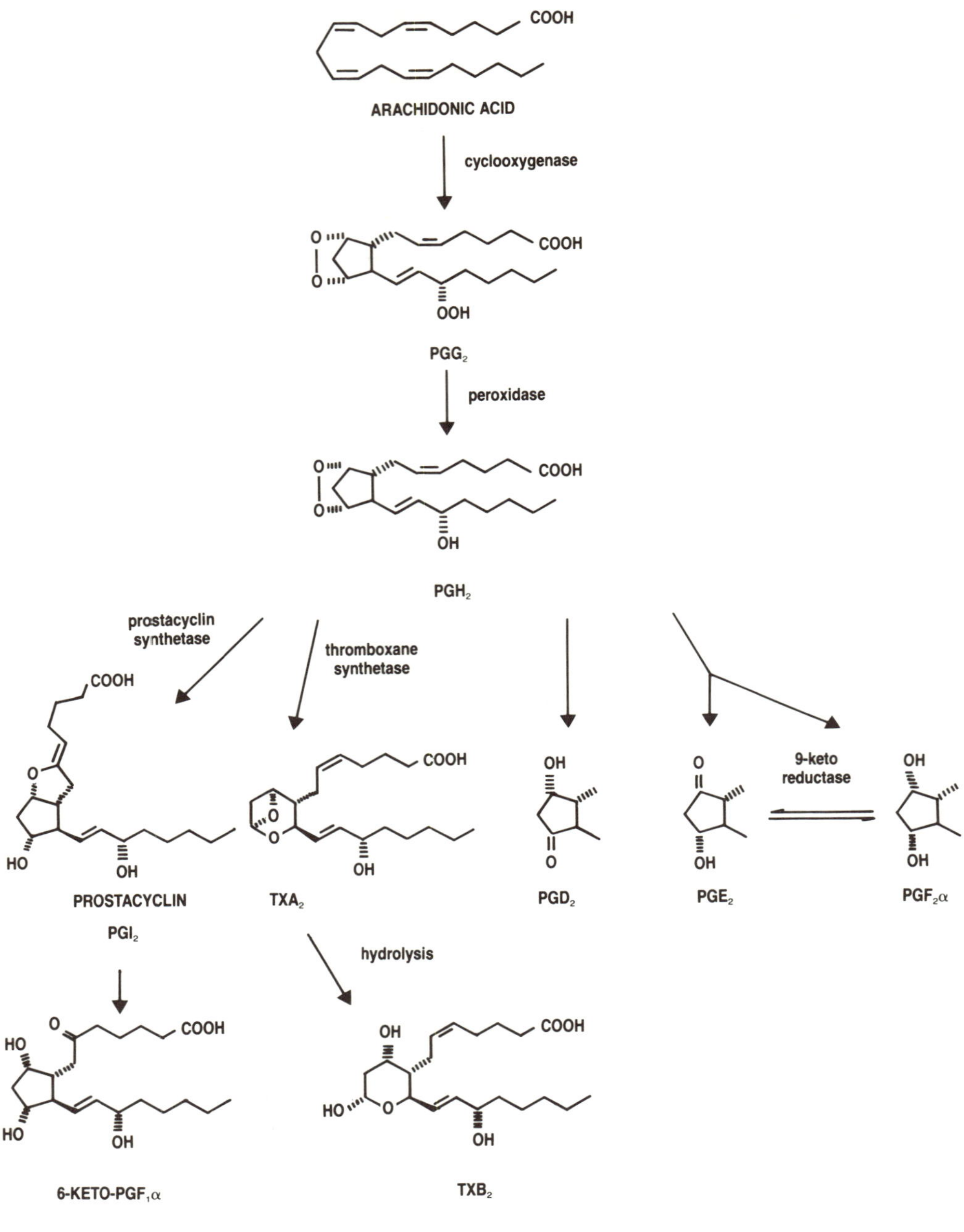


Scheme I

However, elaboration of the imidazole lead quickly led to more potent compounds with insignificant effects on cyclooxygenase or prostacyclin synthetase. Increasing the chain length of a 1-alkyl group was shown to increase activity,[11] whereas attachment of a carboxyl group on this chain, at a position presumably corresponding to that in $PGH_2$, greatly enhanced selectivity towards $TxA_2$ synthetase.[12] Similar elaborations were made in the pyridine series.

It was suggested very early on that thromboxane synthetase might be a metalloprotein, possibly containing an iron (heme).[12] Other workers came to similar conclusions based on the activity of metyrapone (a cytochrome P-450 inhibitor), on the structure-activity relationships which require an unhindered basic nitrogen meta to the side chain (imidazole or 3-pyridyl), and on mechanistic considerations.[13] Binding of the endoperoxide to a metal site in the enzyme followed by bond reorganization could readily give $TxA_2$, and indeed it has been shown by Ullrich and others that thromboxane synthetase is a cytochrome P-450 enzyme[14] and binds with inhibitors in the manner expected.[15] Tight binding of an azole nitrogen to the vacant metal-coordination site effectively inhibits $TxA_2$ formation. It has long been known that simple imidazoles[16] and pyridines[16a] inhibit the heme-containing cytochrome P-450 enzymes. Many of the other biological activities of 1-alkylimidazoles are readily accommodated by a mechanism based on inhibition of such enzymes, e.g., sterol 14-demethylation in ergosterol-synthesis inhibitors, inhibition of side-chain cleavage and hydroxylation in the biosynthesis of testosterone and hydrocortisone, etc. Given such considerations, selectivity for a particular enzyme will depend on lipophilicity, shape, transport, and binding of the particular inhibitor.

## MEASUREMENT OF INHIBITORY ACTIVITY

Various methods have been developed for the measurement of thromboxane $A_2$ in biological systems. Perhaps that most commonly used is radioimmunoassay for the stable metabolite $TxB_2$. Radioisotopic thin-layer chromatography (TLC) of products derived from labeled arachidonic acid is also widely used. Both these methods measure the $TxB_2$ accumulated in the system over a period of time, rather than the concentrations of the short-lived ($t_{1/2} \sim 30$ sec) $TxA_2$ present at a given moment. Direct measurement of $TxA_2$ is made by bioassay using the contraction of a perfused arterial strip and different time intervals to distinguish $TxA_2$ from the longer lasting endoperoxides ($t_{1/2} \sim 5$ min). More recently GC-MS has been used for more accurate measurement. Levels of $PGI_2$ are determined similarly, either as the stable metabolite 6-keto-$PGF_{1\alpha}$, or by bioassay or GC-MS. Care must be taken in collecting samples to avoid artifactual generation of $TxA_2$ or $PGI_2$, and many earlier determinations should be interpreted with caution. This is particularly true for levels determined by radioimmunoassay, where cross-reactivity may also give misleading results. It has been shown that $PGI_2$ is commonly overestimated by widely used analytical methods, the true levels (by GC-MS) actually being remarkably low.[17,18] The $IC_{50}$s obtained by different workers for a given inhibitor are sometimes quite variable and care should be taken in making comparisons. The analytical method used is given in the tables in parentheses.

It will be apparent that simple reduction of thromboxane levels in a biological system will not necessarily indicate effects on thromboxane synthetase, but may be due to (for instance) inhibition of a phospholipase that releases arachidonic acid, inhibition of cyclooxygenase, receptor blockade, membrane stabilization, and effects on calcium flux. The criteria for demonstrating specific effects on thromboxane synthetase have been eloquently stated by Gorman.[19] To be properly classified as a specific inhibitor, a compound should be capable of inhibiting both the production of $TxA_2$ *and* HHT from $PGH_2$ (or arachidonic acid), with simultaneous elevation of $PGD_2$, $PGE_2$, and (if a source of prostacyclin synthetase is present) $PGI_2$. This level of investigation has not always been performed for compounds claimed to be inhibitors.

## BIOLOGICAL ACTIVITY — MODELS, CLINICAL TRIALS

As perusal of the tables will show, inhibitors of thromboxane synthetase have been examined in a remarkably diverse number of biological models, both *in vitro* and *in vivo*. Yet in spite of the apparent effectiveness of these compounds in many *in vivo* models, there remains no convincing demonstration of benefit in any human disease state, with the possible exception of pregnancy-induced hypertension and glomerulonephritis (and the latter has since been discredited[20]). However, close examination will show that most of the human clinical trials reported to date had no successful counterpart in an animal model, and in some cases such as stable angina or Raynaud's syndrome, the possible involvement of thromboxane was only speculative. Conversely, those disease states where animal models suggest a potential for beneficial effect, e.g., myocardial infarction, toxic shock, or tumor metastasis, have not been addressed in the clinic.

Although $TxA_2$-synthesis inhibitors have been shown to reduce $TxA_2$ in man, much has been made of the failure of these inhibitors to prevent aggregation *ex vivo* in blood from certain individuals. With these "nonresponders", the relative proportion of $PGD_2$ resulting from unused endoperoxide is claimed to be lower than in "responders". Such experiments run in the absence of a source of prostacyclin synthetase and in PRP have little relevance to the *in vivo* situation, since endoperoxides build up *in vitro* and may themselves cause platelet aggregation (see references to dazoxiben in Table 1).

Thromboxane-synthetase inhibitors would seem to be ideally suited for chronic use, since they have been shown to be relatively nontoxic and have insignificant effects on hemodynamic parameters. Their use with other agents such as thromboxane antagonists, prostacyclin-stimulating agents, lipoxygenase inhibitors, and phosphodiesterase inhibitors is also a possibility.

## SCOPE OF THE REVIEW

This review covers the literature through summer 1986 with an addendum through 1988, and is not intended to be exhaustive. No attempt has been made to cover the extensive patent literature. In chemical papers where large series of analogues are presented, only representative structures are included unless additional biology is available. Also excluded are compounds in which inhibition of platelet aggregation or thromboxane synthesis is attributable to other mechanisms such as cyclooxygenase or phospholipase inhibition, prostacyclin-agonist activity, thromboxane antagonism, etc. However several well-known drugs in which thromboxane-synthesis inhibition may or may not contribute to activity have been included in Table 4. Where appropriate, references to the chemical synthesis of certain compounds in the tables have been appended to the compound name.

## ACKNOWLEDGMENT

The author wishes to acknowledge the patience and skill of Gina Costelli, Bert Harris, and Robin Mann in the typing of this manuscript, Ishtiaq Mahmud for administrative assistance, and Mike Randall and Valerie Alabaster of Pfizer Corp. for providing some of the literature used.

## ADDENDUM

Additional thromboxane-synthetase inhibitors have been described since the completion of this review. Several series of alkylimidazoles related to Compounds 16 and 17 in Table 1 were also shown to have antihypertensive activity in the SHR along with potent TX inhibitory activity.[21,22] RS-5186, a potent inhibitor with an extended duration of action,[23] reduced the infarct size and PMN infiltration in a canine coronary occlusion-reperfusion model[24] and partially protected mitochondrial function in ischemic canine myocardium.[25] Survival following coronary occlusion and reperfusion was increased in the rabbit.[26] Y-19018, an analogue of Y-20811 (Compound 49, Table 1), showed beneficial effects on crescentic-type anti-glomerular basement membrane nephritis in rats.[27] SC 38249 (an analogue of Compounds 40 and 41 in Table 1) possesses antiaggregatory properties not wholly attributable to inhibition of platelet $TxA_2$ formation.[28] The effects of SC-38249 on aggregatory responses in blood and PRP from four species have been compared.[29] RO 23-3423, a pyridoquinazoline, decreased mean systemic arterial pressure and systemic vascular resistance in endotoxemic sheep.[30] A series of hydrazinopyridazinoindoles was shown to be both thromboxane synthetase inhibitors and hypertensive agents.[31]

CV-4151 (Compound 19, Table 2) has been shown to be a $TxA_2$-$PGH_2$ receptor antagonist in addition to being a Tx synthetase inhibitor.[32] Similar properties are reported[33] for the related new compound R-68,070, which reduces cerebral infarct size in a photochemically induced stroke model in SHR[34] and decreases electrically induced thrombus mass in the dog coronary artery.[35]

Picotamide (Compound 16, Table 4) is also claimed to inhibit Tx synthesis and to block Tx receptors[36] and was shown to improve survival in endotoxin-induced lethality.[37] Other new compounds reported to be in preclinical or clinical development include FCE-22178[36] and S-84-9440[36] (structures not published), as well as DP-1904 (Compound 38, Table 1, being studied for angina pectoris[38]) and CGS-14854.[36,39] A series of antiallergy agents having $TxA_2$ synthetase inhibitory activity has been described.[40]

Recent studies on ozagrel (OKY-046)[41,42] (Compound 22, Table 1) and dazmegrel[43] (Compound 28, Table 1) have been reviewed.

The long acting inhibitor CGS-12970 (Compound 17, Table 2) showed beneficial effects in acute myocardial ischemia when combined with an angiotensin-converting enzyme inhibitor, in contrast to either compound alone.[44] CGS-12970 also normalized platelet half-life in hypercholesterolemic rabbits with once-daily dosing in contrast to the shorter acting dazoxiben.[45] However, this compound did not protect against canine sudden coronary death[46] or acute cyclosporin A nephrotoxicity.[47] CGS-13080 (Compound 47, Table 1) potentiated the beneficial effects of t-Pa in cats subjected to myocardial ischemia followed by reperfusion[48] and improved coronary blood flow after streptokinase-induced thrombolysis.[49] Combination with a phosphodiesterase inhibitor was beneficial in preventing thrombin-induced sudden death in rabbits.[50,51]

Recent work with U-63,557A (Compound 13, Table 2) has shown reduction in human neutrophil superoxide generation in the presence of platelets[52] and decreased neutrophil accumulation in infarcted rat myocardium.[53] (Neutrophil accumulation in infarcted dog myocardium is also reduced by OKY-046.[54]) Graft patency was improved and platelet deposition on artificial grafts in dogs was decreased by U-63,557A,[55] and beneficial effects in an ovine model of pregnancy-induced hypertension[56] and C5a-induced bronchoconstriction in guinea-pigs[57] were reported. In furosemide-treated rats, U-63,557A increased plasma renin activity and urinary 6-keto-$PGF_{1\alpha}$ excretion rates,[58] whereas OKY-1581 (Compound 11c, Table 2) increased the urine output and the sodium excretion rate.[59] OKY-1581 also influences the development of hydronephrotic atrophy after complete unilateral ureteral obstruction in rats.[60]

The effect of thromboxane synthetase inhibition in kidney models (acute glomerulonephritis in rats,[61] acute renal artery hypertension,[62] and renal preservation[63]) has been studied with dazmegrel (UK-38,485) with disappointing results. However, recovery of stunned canine myocardium was enhanced, in contrast to the effect of the Tx receptor antagonist BM-13505.[64]

Recent work on ozagrel (OKY-046) has focused heavily on models of kidney disease and function. Examples not cited in the above reviews[41,42] include the study of autoimmune glomerulonephritis in rats (increased survival, decreased proteinurea),[65] Dahl-S rats (amelioration of lesions),[66] unilateral ureteral obstruction in rabbits (no effect on the late decrease in renal blood flow),[67] nephritis of the NZB/W $F_1$ mouse (no effect on mortality or proteinurea)[68] and aminonucleoside nephritic rats (early decrease in proteinurea only).[69] Ozagrel has also been studied in nonazotemic cirrhotic patients with ascites (increased inulin clearance),[70] and in SHR (no effect on hypertension development)[71] and diabetic rats.[72] The fall in renal blood flow was prevented and glomerular filtration rate preserved in endotoxin-induced acute renal failure in rats by dazoxiben[73] (Compound 20, Table 1).

In studies relevant to atherosclerosis, ozagrel reduced atherosclerotic changes in cholesterol fed rats,[74] dazmegrel reduced foam cell lesions in hypercholesterolemic rabbits,[75] and OKY-1581 reduced serum triglycerides and cholesterol in rats.[76]

In a mechanistic study, the differing response of human subjects to thromboxane synthetase inhibition (see dazoxiben, Table 1) was shown to depend essentially on the relative sensitivity of adenylate cyclase to activating stimuli, with insensitivity leading to continued platelet activation.[77]

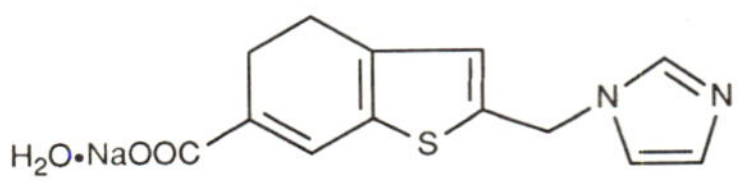


RS-5186

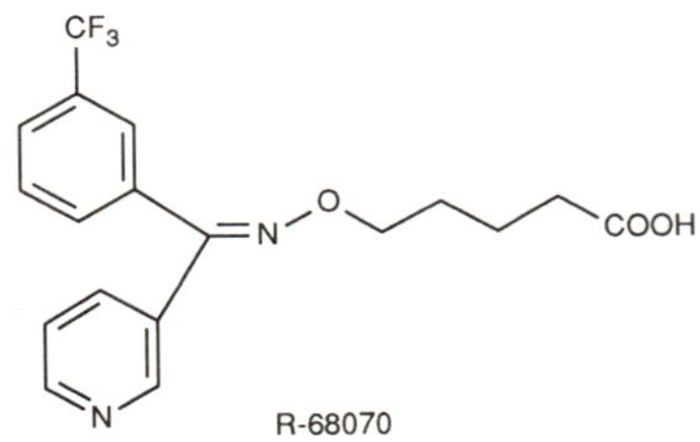


R-68070

## ABBREVIATIONS USED IN THE TABLES

| | |
|---|---|
| AA | Arachidonic acid |
| ADP | Adenosine diphosphate |
| b.i.d. | *bis in die* (twice daily) |
| BSVM | Bovine seminal vesicle microsomes |
| c-AMP | Cyclic adenosine 3′,5′-monophosphate |
| c-GMP | Cyclic guanosine 3′,5′-monophosphate |
| CHD | Congestive heart disease |
| CK | Creatine kinase |
| CP/CPK | Creatine phosphate/creatine phosphokinase |
| $CTA_2$ | Carbathromboxane $A_2$ |
| FMLP | N-Formyl-methionyl-leucyl-phenylalanine |
| GC/MS | Gas chromatography/mass spectrometry |
| GPC | Glycero-3-phosphocholine |
| i.g. | Intragastric |
| i.m. | Intramuscular |
| i.p. | Intraperitoneal |
| i.v. | Intravenous |
| ↑ | Increase |
| HETE | 12-L-Hydroxy-5,8,10,14-eicosatetraenoic acid |
| HHT | 12-L-Hydroxy-5,8,10-heptadecatrienoic acid |
| HPETE | 12-L-Hydroperoxy-5,8,10,14-eicosatetrae-noic acid |
| 5-HT | 5-Hydroxytryptamine (serotonin) |
| HSV | *Herpes simplex* virus |
| LPS | Lipopolysaccharide |
| $LTD_4/E_4$ | Leukotriene $D_4$ or $E_4$ |
| MDA | Malondialdehyde |

| | |
|---|---|
| MDF | Myocardial depressant factor |
| MI | Myocardial infarction |
| MS | Mass spectrometry |
| NaAA | Sodium arachidonate |
| PAF | Platelet-activating factor |
| PG | Prostaglandin |
| PHA | Phytohemagglutinin |
| PMA | Phorbol myristate acetate |
| PMN | Polymorphonuclear (cell) |
| p.o. | *per os* (orally) |
| PPP | Platelet-poor plasma |
| PRP | Platelet-rich plasma |
| q.i.d. | *quarter in die* (four times a day) |
| RIA | Radioimmunoassay |
| RSV(M) | Ram seminal-vesicle microsomes |
| RTLC | Radioisotopic thin-layer chromatography |
| S.A.H. | Subarachnoid hemorrhage |
| s.c. | Subcutaneous |
| SHR | Spontaneously hypertensive rat |
| t.i.d. | *ter in die* (three times daily) |
| SRS(A) | Slow-reacting substance (of anaphylaxis) |
| SSVM | Sheep seminal-vesicle microsomes |
| TLC | Thin-layer chromatography |
| Tx | Thromboxane |
| W.B.C. | White blood cell |
| ZAP | Zymosan-activated plasma complement |

## REFERENCES


1. **Hamberg, M., Svensson, J., and Samuelsson, B.,** Thromboxanes: a new group of biologically active compounds derived from prostaglandin endoperoxides, *Proc. Natl. Acad. Sci. U.S.A.*, 72, 2994, 1975.
2. **Moncada, S., Gryglewski, R., Bunting, S., and Vane, J. R.,** An enzyme isolated from arteries transforms prostaglandin endoperoxides to an unstable substance that inhibits platelet aggregation, *Nature (London)*, 263, 663, 1976.
3. **Johnson, R. A., Morton, D. R., Kinner, J. H., Gorman, R. R., McGuire, J. C., Sunn, F. F., Whittaker, N., Bunting, S., Salmon, J., Moncada, S., and Vane, J. R.,** The chemical structure of prostaglandin X (Prostacyclin), *Prostaglandins*, 12, 915, 1976.
4. **Moncada, S. and Vane, J. R.,** Pharmacology and endogenous roles of prostaglandin endoperoxides, thromboxane $A_2$, and prostacyclin, *Pharmacol. Rev.*, 30, 293, 1979.
5. **Nijkamp, F. P., Moncada, S., White, H. L., and Vane, J. R.,** Diversion of prostaglandin endoperoxide metabolism by selective inhibition of thromboxane $A_2$ biosynthesis in lung, spleen or platelets, *Eur. J. Pharmacol.*, 44, 179, 1977.
6. **Moncada, S. and Vane, J. R.,** Unstable metabolites of arachidonic acid and their role in haemostasis and thrombosis, *Brit. Med. Bull.*, 34, 129, 1978.
7. **Moncada, S. and Vane, J. R.,** Arachidonic acid metabolites and the interactions between platelets and blood-vessel walls, *N. Engl. J. Med.*, 300, 1142, 1979.
8. **Needleman, P., Wyche, A., and Raz, A.,** Platelet and blood vessel arachidonate metabolism and interactions, *J. Clin. Invest.*, 63, 345, 1979.
9. **Fitzgerald, G. A., Oates, J. A., Hawiger, J., Maas, R. L., Roberts, L. J., II, Lawson, J. A., and Brash, A. R.,** Endogenous biosynthesis of prostacyclin and thromboxane and platelet function during chronic administration of aspirin in man, *J. Clin. Invest.*, 71, 676, 1983.
10. **Carey, F. and Haworth, D.,** Thromboxane synthetase inhibition: implications for prostaglandin endoperoxide metabolism. II. Testing the "redirection hypothesis" in an acute intravenous challenge model, *Prostaglandins*, 31, 47, 1986.

11. **Tai, H.-H. and Yuan, B.,** On the inhibitory potency of imidazole and its derivatives on thromboxane synthetase, *Biochem. Biophys. Res. Commun.*, 80, 236, 1978.
12. **Yoshimota, T., Yamamoto, S., and Hayaishi, O.,** Selective inhibition of prostaglandin endoperoxide thromboxane isomerase by 1-carboxyalkylimidazoles, *Prostaglandins*, 16, 529, 1978.
13. **Cross, P. E. and Dickenson, R. P.,** The design of selective thromboxane synthetase inhibitors, *Spec. Publ. R. Soc. Chem.*, 50, 268, 1984.
14. **Haurand, M. and Ullrich, V.,** Isolation and characterization of thromboxane synthetase from human platelets as a cytochrome P-450 enzyme, *J. Biol. Chem.*, 260, 15059, 1985.
15. **Hecker, M., Haurand, M., Ullrich, V., and Terao, S.,** Spectral studies on structure-activity relationships of thromboxane synthase inhibitors, *Eur.J. Biochem.*, 157, 217, 1986.
16. **Rogerson, T. D., Wilkinson, C. F., and Hetarski, K.,** Steric factors in the inhibitory interaction of imidazoles with microsomal enzymes, *Biochem. Pharmacol.*, 26, 1039, 1977.
16a. **Schenkman, J. B., Remmer, H., and Eastabrook, R. W.,** Spectral studies of drug interaction with hepatic microsomal cytochrome, *Mol. Pharmacol.*, 3, 113, 1967.
17. **Pedersen, A. K., Watson, M. L., and FitzGerald, G. A.,** Inhibition of thromboxane biosynthesis in serum: limitations of the measurement of immunoreactive 6-Keto-$PGF_{1\alpha}$, *Thromb. Res.*, 33, 99, 1983.
18. **Chiabrando, C., Castagnoli, M. N., Noseda, A., Fanelli, R., Rajtar, G., Cerletti, C., and de Gaetano, G.,** Comparison of radioimmunoassay and high-resolution gas chromatography mass spectrometry for the quantitative determination of serum thromboxane $B_2$ and 6-Keto-$PGF_{1\alpha}$ after pharmacological blockade of thromboxane synthetase, *Prostaglandins Leukotrienes Med.*, 16, 79, 1984.
19. **Gorman, R. R.,** Biochemical and pharmacological evaluation of thromboxane synthetase inhibitors, *Adv. Prostaglandin Thromboxane Res.*, 6, 417, 1980.
20. **FitzGerald, G. A., Reilly, I. A. G., and Pederson, A. K.,** The biochemical pharmacology of thromboxane synthase inhibition in man, *Circulation*, 72, 1194, 1985.

## ADDITIONAL REFERENCES

21. **Press, J. B., Wright, W. B., Jr., Chan, P. S., Haug, M. F., Marsico, J. W., and Tomcufcik, A. S.,** Thromboxane synthetase inhibitors and antihypertensive agents. 3. *N*-[(1*H*-Imidazol-1-yl)alkyl]-heteroaryl amides as potent enzyme inhibitors, *J. Med. Chem.*, 30, 1036, 1987.
22. **Wright, W. B., Jr., Tomcufcik, A. S., Chan, P. S., Marsico, J. W., and Press, J. B.,** Thromboxane synthetase inhibitors and antihypertensive agents. 4. *N*-[(1*H*-Imidazol-1-yl)alkyl] derivatives of quinazoline-(2,4)(1*H*,3*H*)-diones, quinazolin-4(3*H*)-ones, and 1,2,3-benzotriazin-4(3*H*)-ones, *J. Med. Chem.*, 30, 2277, 1987.
23. **Ushiyama, S., Ito, T., Asai, F., Oshima, T., Terada, A., Matsuda, K., and Yamazaki, M.,** RS-5186, a novel thromboxane synthetase inhibitor with a potent and extended duration of action, *Thromb. Res.*, 51, 507, 1988.
24. **Yoki, Y., Hieda, N., Okumura, K., Hashimoto, H., Ito, T., Ogawa, K., and Satake, T.,** Myocardial salvage by a novel thromboxane $A_2$ synthetase inhibitor in a canine coronary occlusion-reperfusion model, *Arzneim-Forsch.*, 38, 224, 1988.
25. **Ogawa, T., Hieda, N., Sugiyama, S., Toki, Y., Ito, T., Ogawa, K., Satake, T., and Ozawa, T.,** Effect of a novel thromboxane $A_2$ synthetase inhibitor on ischemia-induced mitochondrial dysfunction in canine hearts, *Arzneim-Forsch.*, 38, 228, 1988.
26. **Ito, T., Nagasawa, T., Shimada, Y., Ushiyama, S., Matsuda, K., and Oshima, T.,** Protective effect of RS-5186, a novel thromboxane synthetase inhibitor, on ischemic myocardial injury, *Jpn. J. Pharmacol.*, 46(Suppl.), 280P, 1988.
27. **Suzuki, Y., Tsukushi, Y., Ito, M., and Nagamatsu, T.,** Antinephretic effect of Y-19018, a thromboxane A synthetase inhibitor, or crescentic-type anti-GBM nephritis in rats, *Jpn. J. Pharmacol.*, 45, 177, 1987.
28. **Lad, N., Honey, A. C., Lunt, D. O., Booth, R. F. G., Westwick, J., Manley, P. W., and Tuffin, D. P.,** Effect of SC 38249, a novel substituted imidazole on platelet aggregation *in vitro* and *in vivo*, *Thromb. Haemostasis*, 59, 164, 1988.
29. **Lad, N., Lunt, D. O., and Tuffin, D. P.,** The effect of thromboxane $A_2$ synthesis inhibitors on platelet aggregation in whole blood, *Thromb. Res.*, 46, 555, 1987.
30. **Morel, D. R., Huttemeier, P. C., Skoskiewicz, M. J., Nguyenduy, T., Melvin, C., Robinson, D. R., and Zapol, W. M.,** Dose-dependent effects of a pyridoquinazoline thromboxane synthetase inhibitor on arachidonic acid metabolites and hemodynamics during *E. Coli* endotoxemia in anesthetized sheep, *Prostaglandins*, 33, 879, 1987.
31. **Monge, A., Parrado, P., Font, M., and Fernández-Alvarez, E.,** Selective thromboxane synthetase inhibitors and antihypertensive agents. New derivatives of 4-hydrazino-5*H*-pyridazino[4,5-*b*]-indole, 4-hydrazino[4,5-*a*]indole, and related compounds, *J. Med. Chem.*, 30, 1029, 1987.

32. **Imura, Y., Terashita, Z., Shibouta, Y., and Nishikawa, K.,** The thromboxane $A_2$/prostaglandin endoperoxide receptor antagonist activity of CV-4151, a thromboxane $A_2$ synthetase inhibitor, *Eur. J. Pharmacol.*, 147, 359, 1988.
33. **De Clerck, F., Van de Wiele, R., Xhonneux, B., Van Gorp, L., and Janssen, P. A. J.,** Platelet $TxA_2$ synthetase inhibition and $TxA_2$/prostaglandin endoperoxide receptor blockade combined in one molecule (R 68070), *Thromb. Haemostasis*, 58, 181, 1987.
34. **Van Reempts, J., Van Deuren, B., Borgers, M., and De Clerck, F.,** R 68070, a combined $TxA_2$-synthetase/$TxA_2$-prostaglandin endoperoxide receptor inhibitor, reduces cerebral infarct size after photochemically initiated thrombosis in spontaneously hypertensive rats, *Thromb. Haemostasis*, 58, 182, 1987.
35. **Van de Water, A., Xhonneux, R., and De Clerck, F.,** Antithrombotic effect in canine coronary arteries of a combined $TxA_2$ synthetase/$TxA_2$-prostaglandin endoperoxide receptor inhibitor (R 68070), *Thromb. Haemostasis*, 58, 180, 1987.
36. **Tarr, I.,** After aspirin, the new antithrombotics for AMI, *SCRIP*, No. 1305, 26, 1988.
37. **Matera, G., Chisari, M., Altavilla, D., Foca, A., and Cook, J. A.,** Selective thromboxane synthetase inhibition by picotamide and effects on endotoxin-induced lethality, *Proc. Soc. Exp. Biol. Med.*, 187, 58, 1988.
38. **Anon.,** Daiichi's TX synthetase inhibitor, *SCRIP*, No. 1277, 26, 1988.
39. **Robson, R. D., Liauw, L., Tjan, J., Sakane, Y., and Ku, E.,** Modulation of leucotriene production by thromboxane synthetase inhibition, *Fed. Proc. Fed. Am. Soc. Exp. Biol.*, 43, 1038, 1984.
40. **Tilley, J. W., Levitan, P., Lind, J., Welton, A. F., Crowley, H. J., Tobias, L. D., and O'Donnel, M.,** *N*-(Heterocyclic alkyl)pyrido[2,1-*b*]quinazoline-8-carboxamides as orally active antiallergy agents, *J. Med. Chem.*, 30, 185, 1987.
41. **Anon.,** Ozagrel sodium, *Drugs Fut.*, 13, 382, 1988.
42. **Anon.,** OKY-046, *Drugs Fut.*, 12, 405, 1987.
43. **Anon.,** Dazmagrel, *Drugs Fut.*, 11, 982, 1986.
44. **Bitterman, H., Lefer, D. J., and Lefer, A. M.,** Additive beneficial effects of two inhibitors of vasoconstrictor mediators in acute myocardial ischemia, *Proc. Soc. Exp. Biol. Med.*, 185, 262, 1987.
45. **Butler, K. D., Butler, P. A., Shand, R. A., Ambler, J., and Wallace, R. B.,** Prolongation of platelet survival in hypercholesterolemic rabbits by CGS-12970 (3-methyl-2-(3-pyridyl)-1-indoleoctanoic acid), *Thromb. Res.*, 45, 751, 1987.
46. **Kitzen, J. M., Lynch, J. J., Uprichard, A. C. G., Venkatesh, N., and Lucchesi, B. R.,** Failure of thromboxane synthetase inhibition to protect the postinfarcted heart against the induction of ventricular tachycardia and sudden coronary death, *Pharmacology*, 37, 171, 1988.
47. **Smeesters, C., Chaland, P., Giroux, L., Moutquin, J. M., Etienne, P., Douglas, F., Corman, J., St. Louis, G., and Daloze, P.,** Prevention of acute cyclosporin A nephrotoxicity by a thromboxane synthetase inhibitor, *Transplant. Proc.*, 20(2,Suppl.2), 80, 1988.
48. **Lefer, A. M., Mentley, R., and Sun, J.-Z.,** Potentiation of myocardial salvage by tissue type plasminogen activator in combination with a thromboxane synthetase inhibitor in ischemic cat myocardium, *Circ. Res.*, 63, 621, 1988.
49. **Gallas, M. T. and Lucchesi, B. R.,** Thromboxane synthetase inhibition with CGS-13080 improves coronary blood flow after streptokinase-induced thrombolysis, *Am. Heart J.*, 113, 1345, 1987.
50. **Smith, E. F., III and Egan, J. W.,** Comparison of the effects of a thromboxane synthetase inhibitor or prostacyclin in combination with a phosphodiesterase inhibitor for prevention of experimental thrombosis and sudden death in rabbits, *J. Pharmacol. Exp. Ther.*, 241, 855, 1987.
51. **Smith, E. F., III and Olson, R. W.,** Synergism between a phosphodiesterase inhibitor and modulators of thromboxane formation in thrombin-induced sudden death in rabbits, *Prog. Clin. Biol. Res.*, 242, 241, 1987.
52. **Mehta, J. L., Lawson, D., and Mehta, P.,** Modulation of human neutrophil superoxide production by the selective thromboxane synthetase inhibitor U-63,557A, *Life Sci.*, 43, 923, 1988.
53. **Wargovich, T. J., Mehta, J., Nichols, W. W., Ward, M. B., Lawson, D., Franzini, D., and Conti, C. R.,** Reduction in myocardial neutrophil accumulation and infarct size following administration of thromboxane inhibitor U-63,557A, *Am. Heart J.*, 114, 1078, 1987.
54. **Mullane, K. M. and Fornabaio, D.,** Thromboxane synthetase inhibitors reduce infarct size by a platelet-dependent, aspirin-sensitive mechanism, *Circ. Res.*, 62, 668, 1988.
55. **Huntsman, W. T., Miett, T. O., and Cronenwett, J. L.,** Effect of a selective thromboxane synthetase inhibitor on arterial graft patency and platelet deposition in dogs, *Arch. Surg. (Chicago)*, 122, 887, 1987.
56. **Keith, J. C., Jr., Thatcher, C. D., and Shaub, R. G.,** Beneficial effects of U-63,557A, a thromboxane synthetase inhibitor, in an ovine model of pregnancy-induced hypertension, *Obstet. Gynecol.*, 157, 199, 1987.
57. **Regal, J. F.,** Role of arachidonate metabolites in C5a-induced bronchoconstriction, *J. Pharmacol. Exp. Ther.*, 246, 542, 1988.

58. **Datar, S., McCauley, F. A., and Wilson, T. W.,** Testing of "redirection hypothesis" of prostaglandin metabolism in the kidney, *Prostaglandins*, 33, 275, 1987.
59. **Ramwell, P. W.,** Implication of thromboxane in frusemide diuresis in rats, *Clin. Sci.*, 71, 647, 1986.
60. **Huland, H., Brenger, B., Gonnermann, D., and Schaefer, H.,** Influence of thromboxane $A_2$ inhibition on the development of hydronephrotic atrophy, *Urol. Int.*, 41, 422, 1986.
61. **Cook, H. T., Cattell, V., Smith, J., Salmon, J. A., and Moncada, S.,** Effect of a thromboxane synthetase inhibitor on eicosanoid synthesis and glomerular injury during acute unilateral glomerulonephritis in the rat, *Clin. Nephrol.*, 26, 195, 1986.
62. **Jackson, E. K., Goto, F., Uderman, H. D., Workman, R. J., Herzer, W. A., Fitzgerald, G. A., and Branch, R. A.,** Effects of thromboxane synthase inhibitors on renal function, *Naunyn-Schmiedeberg's Arch. Pharmacol.*, 337, 183, 1988.
63. **Nghiem, D. D., Elkadi, M. H., Southard, J. H., Brubacher, M., Scott, D., and Smith, T.,** Renal preservation by prostaglandins and alkaline buffers: a comparative study, *Transplant. Proc.*, 18(5, Suppl.4), 113, 1986.
64. **Farber, N. E. and Pieper, G. M.,** Lack of involvement of thromboxane $A_2$ in postischemic recovery of stunned myocardium, *Circulation*, 78, 450, 1988.
65. **Papanikolaou, N., Hatziantoniou, C., and Gkika, E. L.,** Effect of the thromboxane $A_2$ synthetase inhibitor OKY-046 and evening primrose oil (efamol) on mercuric chloride induced autoimmune glomerulonephrits in brown Norway rats, *Prog. Clin. Biol. Res.*, 242, 43, 1987.
66. **Yamashita, W., Ito, Y., Weiss, M. A., Ooi, B. S., and Pollak, V. E.,** A thromboxane synthetase antagonist ameliorates progressive renal disease of Dahl-S rats, *Kidney Int.*, 33, 77, 1988.
67. **Loo, M. H., Marion, D. N., Vaughan, E. D., Jr., Felsen, D., and Albanese, C. T.,** Effect of thromboxane inhibition on renal blood flow in dogs with complete unilateral ureteral obstruction, *J. Urol. (Baltimore)*, 136, 1343, 1986.
68. **Clark, W. F., Parbtani, A., McDonald, J. W. D., Taylor, N., Reid, B. D., and Kreeft, J.,** The effects of a thromboxane synthetase inhibitor, a prostacyclin analog and $PGE_1$ on the nephritis of the NZB/W $F_1$ mouse, *Clin. Nephrol.*, 28, 288, 1987.
69. **Suzuki, S., Akama, H., Kume, K., Higuchi, E., Kamiyama, S., Suzuki, J., Ohara, N., Yugeta, E., Kato, K., and Suzuki, H.,** Effects of the selective thromboxane $A_2$ synthetase inhibitor, OKY-046, on proteinuria of aminoglycoside nephrotic rats, *Jpn. J. Nephrol.*, 30, 341, 1988.
70. **Gentilini, P., Laffi, G., Meacci, E., La Villa, G., Cominelli, F., Pinzani, M., and Buzzelli, G.,** Effects of OKY-046, a thromboxane-synthase inhibitor, on renal function in nonazotemic cirrhotic patients with ascites, *Gastroenterology*, 94, 1470, 1988.
71. **Tanno, M., Abe, K., Yasujima, M., Kudo, K., Sato, M., Kasai, Y., Kozuki, M., Takeuchi, K., Omata, K., and Yoshinaga, K.,** The prostaglandin-thromboxane system in the development of hypertension in young spontaneously hypertensive rats, *J. Hypertens.*, 4(Suppl.3), S395, 1986.
72. **Omoto, A., Katayama, S., Inaba, M., Maruno, Y., Watanabe, T., Kawazu, S., and Ishii, J.,** Effect of thromboxane $A_2$ synthesis inhibition on renal renin release and protein excretion in diabetic rats, *Jpn. J. Nephrol.*, 30, 305, 1988.
73. **Badr, K. F., Kelley, V. E., Rennke, H. G., and Brenner, B. M.,** Roles for thromboxane $A_2$ and leukotrienes in endotoxin-induced acute renal failure, *Kidney Int.*, 30, 474, 1986.
74. **Rin, K., Nakagawa, M., and Ijichi, H.,** Effects of antiplatelet agents on platelet $TxA_2$ and vascular $PGI_2$ generation in cholesterol fed rats, *Ketsueki to Myakkan*, 18, 232, 1987; *Chem. Abstr.*, 108, 68662w, 1988.
75. **Skrinska, V. A., Konieczkowski, M., Gerrity, R. G., Galang, C. F., and Rebec, M. V.,** Suppression of foam cell lesions in hypercholesterolemic rabbits by inhibition of thromboxane $A_2$ synthesis, *Arteriosclerosis (Dallas)*, 8, 359, 1988.
76. **Watanabe, T., Utsugi, M., Mitsukawa, M., Suga, T., and Fujitani, H.,** Hypolipidemic effect and enhancement of peroxisomal β-oxidation in the liver of rats by sodium (E)-3-(4-(3-pyridylmethyl)phenyl)-2-methylpropenoate (OKY-1581), a potent inhibitor of $TxA_2$ synthetase, *J. Pharmacobio-Dyn.*, 9, 1023, 1986.
77. **Gresele, P., Blockmans, D., Deckmyn, H., and Vermylen, J.,** Adenylate cyclase activation determines the effect of thromboxane synthase inhibitors on platelet aggregation *in vitro*. Comparison of platelets from responders and nonresponders, *J. Pharmacol. Exp. Ther.*, 246, 301, 1988.

**Table 1**
**IMIDAZOLES**

| No. | Name of compound | Structure | Formula (mol wt) | Biological activity |
|---|---|---|---|---|
| 1. | Imidazole | 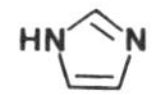 | $C_3H_4N_2$ (68) | Inhibited the conversion of $PGG_2$ and $PGH_2$ to $TxA_2$ by human- or horse-platelet microsomes, $IC_{50}$ 22 μg/ml (bioassay),[1] and the conversion of $PGH_2$ to $TxB_2$ by human-platelet microsomes, $IC_{50}$ $1.5 \times 10^{-4}$ *M* (RTLC).[2] Cyclooxygenase was affected only above 200 μg/ml.[1]<br>Inhibited $TxA_2$ synthesis in rabbit PRP induced by collagen, $IC_{50}$ 235 μ*M* (bioassay);[3] and from AA in dog PRP, $IC_{50}$ 5 m*M*, with enhanced $PGE_2$ and $PGF_{2\alpha}$ production (RIA).[4]<br>In human-platelet suspensions, 140 μg/ml imidazole inhibited production of $TxA_2$ but not aggregation due to AA, $PGH_2$, collagen, or thrombin (bioassay). $PGE_2$ formation from AA was not inhibited.[5,6] In a similar study, 10 m*M* increased the production of $PGF_{2\alpha}$, $PGE_2$, and $PGD_2$ and decreased $TxB_2$ and HHT synthesis from AA in resuspended human platelets (RTLC).[7,8] Similarly, in washed human platelets, imidazole reduced $TxB_2$ synthesis from AA (100—400 μg/ml imidazole) or $PGH_2$ (50—200 μg/ml imidazole) without preventing aggregation ($PGE_2\uparrow$).[9] However, in human PRP, 100—400 μg/ml delayed aggregation due to AA ($PGE_2\uparrow$) while 200 μg/ml blocked $PGH_2$-induced aggregation.[9,10] It should be noted that significant $TxB_2$ was still formed in each of the experiments involving washed platelets or PRP (RIA).[9] $TxB_2$ synthesis was also inhibited during mechanically induced aggregation of human PRP ($PGE_2\uparrow$), again with no correlation between aggregation and $TxB_2$ synthesis.[11] In lysed human platelets, imidazole inhibited the synthesis of $TxB_2$ from AA, $IC_{50}$ $5.5 \times 10^{-4}$ *M*, with increases in $PGF_{2\alpha}$ (RTLC).[12] |

**Table 1 (continued)**
**IMIDAZOLES**

| No. | Name of compound | Structure | Formula (mol wt) | Biological activity |
|---|---|---|---|---|
| | | | | Infusion of 50— 75 μg/ml of imidazole through isolated guinea-pig lung or cat spleen inhibited $TxA_2$ production from AA, with an increase in PGs, mainly $PGF_{2\alpha}$ (bioassay).[12] |
| | | | | Imidazole increased the force of contraction of isolated rabbit atria (7.3 m*M*) and intact dog hearts (50 mg).[13] |
| | | | | In isolated, perfused, sensitized guinea-pig hearts, 100 μg/ml decreased $TxB_2$ and increased $PGD_2$ and $PGF_{2\alpha}$ release during cardiac anaphylaxis after antigenic challenge. Coronary-flow reduction was not diminished in contrast to isoproterenol 1 μg/min (RIA-TLC).[14] |
| | | | | In cats, infusion at 25 mg/kg/h inhibited the plasma $TxB_2$ rise during myocardial ischemia (coronary artery occlusion) (RIA). All indices of ischemic damage indicated significant myocardial protection (S-T segment, plasma CPK, and myocardial CPK activity and amino nitrogen content).[15] In dogs, 30 mg/kg i.v. attenuated the decrease in myocardial lactate extraction (but not the depression in high-energy phosphates) following coronary-artery ligation.[16] |
| | | | | However, the effect of imidazole in reducing myocardial-infarct size in rats with ligation of the left coronary artery was not reproduced by the selective thromboxane-synthetase inhibitor dazoxiben, suggesting a mechanism not involving inhibition of thromboxane synthetase.[17] |
| | | | | Reperfusion arrythymias in dogs following acute myocardial ischemia were not prevented by infusion of imidazole, even though arterial $TxB_2$ was lowered (RIA).[18] |

In an AA-induced thrombosis model in rabbits, the median effective dose of imidazole 60 min before challenge was 12.8 mg/kg, i.p.[19] AA-induced mortality in mice was reduced by pretreatment (2 h) with 300 mg/kg, p.o.[20] In an *E. coli* rat septic-shock model, 30 mg/kg i.p. blocked $TxA_2$ production (and raised $PGI_2$) without improving survival (RIA).[21] However, 30 mg/kg, i.p. 60 min before challenge with *Salmonella enteritidis* toxin (20 mg/kg, i.v.) in rats suppressed plasma $TxB_2$ (but not PGE) elevation and reduced mortality (RIA).[22] In cats, 25 mg/kg/h infusion 30 min after i.v. *E. coli* endotoxin injection reduced the severity of the shock (mean arterial blood pressure, cathepsin D and MDF) without a significant reduction of $TxB_2$ (RIA).[23] In rabbits, imidazole (20 mg/kg) did not prevent hypotension, leukopenia, hyperglycemia, or acidosis during *E. coli* endotoxin infusion for 2 h.[24]

Cobra-venom-factor-induced rat-paw edema was inhibited at 50 mg/kg p.o.[25]

In normal and saline-loaded rats, imidazole, 15 mg/kg i.p. increased the sodium excretion rate and decreased renal $TxB_2$ excretion (RIA).[26] However, other workers found a reduction in sodium excretion rate and urine volume in saline-loaded rats.[27] Rats were partially protected from acute renal failure induced by i.m. injection of glycerol by 15 mg/kg imidazole, i.p. 1 h before and 30 mg/kg, i.p. immediately after challenge.[28]

In isolated toad urinary bladders, imidazole inhibited the increased thromboxane synthesis and water flow stimulated by vasopressin with increases in PGE synthesis (RIA).[29]

Bone resorption from rat fetal calvaria *in vitro* in the presence or absence of parathyroid extract was inhibited by 0.1 mg/ml imidazole.[30]

## Table 1 (continued)
## IMIDAZOLES

| No. | Name of compound | Structure | Formula (mol wt) | Biological activity |
|---|---|---|---|---|
| | | | | The adherence of human platelets to collagen (collagen/Sepharose® column) was increased by incubation with $5 \times 10^{-4}$ *M*.[31] However, *E. coli* LPS-induced adherence of human PMNs to nylon was suppressed (31%) by 5.9 m*M* imidazole.[32] |
| | | | | No protection was found against increased bronchial histamine sensitivity due to sequential histamine challenges (aerosol) in guinea pigs at 10 mg/kg i.p.[33] In rats, the increase in tracheal-mucous gel thickness induced by i.v. SRS challenge was prevented by imidazole (10 mg/kg, i.v.) with decreased plasma $TxB_2$ levels.[34] In isolated, ventilated, perfused rabbit lungs, the increase in pulmonary arterial pressure induced by AA (130—260 μ*M*) was inhibited by imidazole at 0.88 m*M*.[35] In isolated sheep lungs perfused with autologous blood, imidazole (5 m*M*) reduced the changes in $TxB_2$, pulmonary arterial pressure, lung lymph flow, and platelet count.[36] |
| | | | | The inhibition of guinea-pig peritoneal macrophage migration by migration-inhibitory factor was reversed by 1.25—2.5 m*M* imidazole.[37] |
| | | | | Lectin-induced mitogenesis of human lymphocytes was inhibited, as was $TxB_2$ synthesis.[38,39] |
| | | | | Insulin secretion in the glucose-perfused isolated rat pancreas was inhibited at 100—1000 μ*M*.[40] |
| | | | | The salt of imidazole with salicylic acid (ITF 182) is claimed to be a selective inhibitor of thromboxane synthetase[41] and has been studied as an antiinflammatory agent.[42,42a] A potential beneficial effect in cerebral vasospasm has also been suggested.[43] |
| 2. | 1-Methylimidazole | 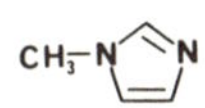 | $C_4H_6N_2$ (82) | Inhibited the conversion of $PGG_2$ to $TxA_2$ by horse or human-platelet microsomes, $IC_{50}$ 15 μg/ml (bioas- |

| | | | | |
|---|---|---|---|---|
| | | | | say).[1] Inhibited $TxB_2$ synthesis in human-blood mononuclear cells at 30 μg/ml with increases in $PGE_2$ (RIA). Some decrease in $PGE_2$ production, but no inhibition of mitogen-stimulated proliferation, was observed at 300 μg/ml.[44]<br>Inhibited *in vitro* bone resorption from rat fetal calvaria, in the presence or absence of parathyroid extract, at 0.1 mg/ml.[30] |
| 3. | 1-Butylimidazole | 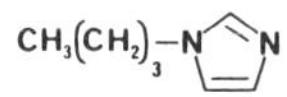 | $C_7H_{12}N_2$ (124) | Inhibited the conversion of $PGH_2$ to $TxB_2$ by human-platelet microsomes, $IC_{50}$ 0.5 μ*M* (RIA),[45] and bovine-platelet microsomes, $IC_{50}$ 9.8 μ*M* (RTLC), with no effect on PG endoperoxide synthetase.[46]<br>In horse-platelet lysates, the conversion of AA to $TxB_2$ was inhibited, $IC_{50}$ 40 μ*M*, with no effect on HETE synthesis, and with stimulation of $PGE_2$, $PGF_{2\alpha}$ and $PGD_2$ synthesis up to 1 m*M*. Similarly, the conversion of $PGH_2$ to $TxB_2$ was inhibited by a 100,000 g fraction of horse-platelet lysates, $IC_{50}$ 0.42 m*M* (RTLC).[47]<br>The aggregation of whole rabbit blood by AA or collagen was prevented by 8 μ*M* with increased 6-keto-$PGF_{1\alpha}$ concentrations (TLC-RIA).[48] $TxA_2$ synthesis by rabbit PRP induced by collagen was inhibited, with an $IC_{50}$ of 26 μ*M* (bioassay).[3]<br>In human-platelet suspensions, 5 m*M* prevented aggregation due to AA, epinephrine, and low-dose collagen but not high-dose collagen, ADP, or thrombin.[49] The aggregation of human platelets induced by $PGH_2$ was also prevented, $IC_{50}$ 3.5 μ*M*.[47]<br>Ineffective in reducing thrombus formation induced in the hamster cheek pouch by electrical stimulation followed by topical ADP at doses where serum $TxB_2$ production was reduced.[50]<br>In isolated, ventilated, perfused rabbit lungs, the increase in pulmonary arterial pressure induced by ionophore A23187 (2—3 μ*M*) was inhibited by 0.6—1.2 m*M*.[35] |

**Table 1 (continued)**
**IMIDAZOLES**

| No. | Name of compound | Structure | Formula (mol wt) | Biological activity |
|---|---|---|---|---|
| | | | | The yield of viruses (e.g., HSV-1) hosted by human lung fibroblasts *in vitro* was reduced by 5 μg/ml.[51]<br>In the glucose-perfused, isolated rat pancreas, insulin secretion was inhibited by 1000 μ*M*. In diabetic rats, weight gain, food consumption, and insulin levels were decreased by 86 mg/kg p.o. daily.[40] |
| 4. | 1-Pentylimidazole | 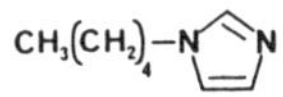 | $C_8H_{14}N_2$ (138) | Inhibited the conversion of $PGH_2$ to $TxB_2$ by human-platelet microsomes, $IC_{50}$ 0.19 μ*M* (RIA).[45] |
| 5. | 1-Hexylimidazole | 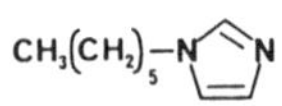 | $C_9H_{16}N_2$ (152) | Inhibited the conversion of $PGH_2$ to $TxB_2$ by bovine-platelet microsomes, $IC_{50}$ 7.6 μ*M*, with inhibition of PG endoperoxide synthetase at higher concentrations (RTLC).[46] |
| 6. | 1-Octylimidazole | 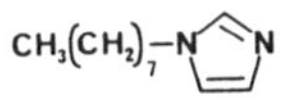 | $C_{11}H_{20}N_2$ (180) | Inhibited the conversion of $PGH_2$ to $TxB_2$ by bovine-platelet microsomes, $IC_{50}$ 5.3 μ*M*, with inhibition of PG endoperoxide synthetase at higher concentrations (RTLC).[46]<br>The formation of $PGD_2$, $PGE_2$, and $PGF_{2\alpha}$ from AA in isolated human platelets in the presence of 1-octylimidazole was further increased by calmodulin.[52,53] |
| 7. | 1-Nonylimidazole | 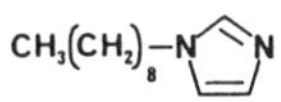 | $C_{12}H_{22}N_2$ (194) | Inhibited the conversion of $PGH_2$ to $TxB_2$ by human-platelet microsomes, $IC_{50}$ 0.01 μ*M* (RIA).[45]<br>Antagonized AA-induced platelet aggregation in guinea-pig PRP at 25—100 μ*M*, but did not inhibit $TxA_2$ synthesis at doses which blocked aggregation. Blocked $TxA_2$ synthesis in rabbit and human PRP and washed guinea-pig platelets (bioassay),[54] and $TxA_2$ synthesis in rabbit PRP induced by collagen, $IC_{50}$ 94 μ*M* (bioassay).[3]<br>AA-initiated bronchoconstriction, thrombocytopenia, and hypotension in guinea pigs was not inhibited by 8 mg/kg, i.v.[54] |

| | | | | |
|---|---|---|---|---|
| 8. | 1-Cyclooctyl-methylimidazole | 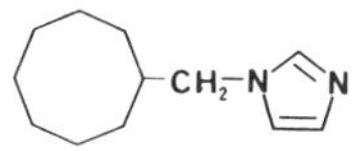 | $C_{12}H_{20}N_2$ (192) | Respiratory distress and death in cats injected with rabbit blood were prevented by 6 mg/kg i.v. Rises in $TxB_2$ were attenuated with fivefold increases in circulating 6-oxo-$PGF_{1\alpha}$. Elevations in cardiovascular pressure were reduced.[55] |
| 9. | 1-Benzylimidazole | 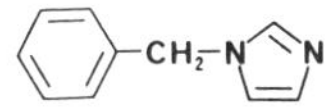 | $C_{10}H_{10}N_2$ (158) | Inhibited the conversion of $PGH_2$ to $TxB_2$ by human-platelet microsomes, $IC_{50}$ 0.25 $\mu M$ (RIA),[45] and $TxB_2$ synthesis from AA in washed dog platelets, $IC_{50}$ 100 $\mu M$ (RTLC).[56] AA-induced platelet shape change and potentiation of ADP aggregation with low AA concentrations in dog PRP was inhibited by 1—10 $\mu M$.[56]<br>The aggregation response of rabbit PRP to 0.2 m$M$ AA was reduced 50% by 0.9 m$M$, with an 84% decrease in $TxA_2$ production (RIA).[57] In rabbit sera following oral (10 or 20 mg/kg) or i.v. (10 mg/kg) administration, inhibition of thromboxane synthesis (70—80%) was associated with increased formation of $PGE_2$ (~ 50% of available endoperoxides) and 6-keto-$PGF_{1\alpha}$ (2—5%).[58]<br>Platelet accumulation on damaged abdominal aorta in rabbits following acute injury was reduced by 10—30 mg/kg i.v.[57] In isolated rabbit ventricular strips, $6.3 \times 10^{-5}$ $M$ increased contractile force by 100%. In intact cats, 0.5 mg/kg, i.v. increased cardiac output by 30—40%.[59] In dogs, 10 mg/kg i.v. increased systemic arterial pressure for 30 min and altered platelet sensitivity for $\geq$4 h. Hematocrit and platelet counts increased significantly.[56]<br>The canine-stomach vasoconstrictor response to AA injections (using a 30 sec delay coil) was inhibited 50% by prior infusion of 50 $\mu M$ benzylimidazole into the delay coil.[60]<br>In rabbits with bovine-serum albumin-induced immune-complex glomerulonephritis, benzylimidazole lessened proteinuria, normalized platelet aggregation, and reduced neutrophil infiltration, mononuclear-cell proliferation, and fibrin deposition.[61] |

## Table 1 (continued)
## IMIDAZOLES

| No. | Name of compound | Structure | Formula (mol wt) | Biological activity |
|---|---|---|---|---|
| | | | | The increased adhesiveness of human PMNs to nylon induced by *E. coli* LPS was suppressed (83%) by 0.2 m*M*. Increased $TxB_2$ synthesis was blocked (RIA).[32] The lectin-stimulated mitogenesis and thromboxane synthesis in human lymphocytes was inhibited by 0.5 m*M*.[38,39] In a mouse macrophage-like cell line, the synthesis of $TxB_2$ and HHT from exogenous AA was inhibited, $IC_{50}$ 9.5 μ*M* (RTLC).[62] |
| 10. | 1-(2-Isopropylphenyl) imidazole | 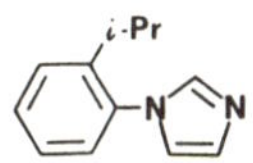 | $C_{12}H_{14}N_2$ (186) | Inhibited the conversion of $PGH_2$ to $TxB_2$ by human-platelet microsomes, $IC_{50}$ 0.04 μ*M* (RIA).[45]<br>Insulin secretion in the isolated rat pancreas was decreased by 10 μ*M*, whereas in diabetic rats the weight gain, food consumption, and insulin levels were reduced by 42—77 mg/kg p.o. daily.[40] |
| 11. | 1-(3-Phenyl-2-propenyl)-1*H*-imidazole (SQ 80,338) | 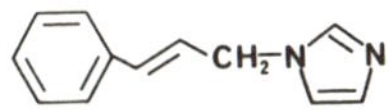 | $C_{12}H_{12}N_2$ (184) | Inhibited thromboxane synthesis from AA by human-platelet lysates, $IC_{50}$ 30 μ*M* (RTLC), with tenfold increases in both $PGE_2$ and $PGF_{2\alpha}$ at 250 μ*M*. Inhibited aggregation of human PRP induced by AA, $IC_{50}$ 30 μ*M*, and the second wave of epinephrine-induced aggregation, $IC_{50}$ 48 μ*M*, but not the primary phase of ADP- or epinephrine-induced aggregation. Collagen-induced aggregation was inhibited 10% at 100 μ*M*.[63]<br>In anesthetized guinea pigs, inhibited bronchoconstriction induced by AA at 0.3—3 mg/kg i.v. and by bradykinin in the presence of β-blockade at 3—10 mg/kg i.v., but not that due to histamine or antigen (ovalbumin) at 3—10 mg/kg i.v.[63,64] However, repeated doses of 10 mg/kg i.p. 4 min before challenge did depress the response to sequential histamine challenges (aerosol) after 4—5 doses.[33] |

| | | | | |
|---|---|---|---|---|
| | | | | AA-induced $TxA_2$ synthesis in an isolated, perfused, guinea-pig lung was reduced by 10 μg/ml (bioassay).[64] |
| 12. | 4-(1-Imidazolyl)acetophenone (RO-22-3581) | 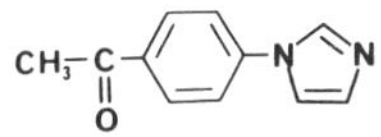 | $C_{11}H_{10}N_2O$ (186) | In sheep, 30 mg/kg i.v., 30 min before 1 μg/kg endotoxin infusion reduced both pulmonary hypertension and increases in plasma and lymph TxB concentrations (RIA). Peak 6-keto-$PGF_{1\alpha}$ concentrations were raised.[65]<br>In spontaneously hypertensive rats (SHR), 100 mg/kg s.c. reduced serum $TxB_2$ by 89% and 41% at 3 and 24 h (RIA). 100 mg/kg daily from age 4 to 10 weeks reduced the development of hypertension in SHR (systolic blood pressure 155 mmHg vs 185 for controls).[66]<br>In glucose-fed diabetic rats, weight gain, food consumption, and insulin levels were inhibited by 60—113 mg/kg, p.o. daily. Cadaver lipids, but not cadaver protein were reduced.[40] |
| 13. | 7-(1-Imidazolyl)heptanoic acid (7-IHA) | 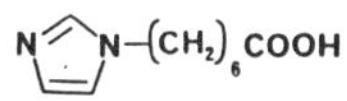 | $C_{10}H_{16}N_2O_2$ (196) | Inhibited the conversion of $PGH_2$ to $TxB_2$ by bovine-platelet microsomes, $IC_{50}$ 0.5 μ*M* (RTLC),[46] and the synthesis of $TxB_2$ from AA in human PRP, $IC_{50}$ 1.9 μ*M* (RIA), with no effect on cyclooxygenase.[67] Inhibited the aggregation of rabbit PRP induced by AA, $IC_{50}$ 1.1 μ*M*, and collagen, $IC_{50}$ 3.3 μ*M*;[68] and human PRP induced by AA, $IC_{50}$ 1.35 m*M*,[67] 2.5 μ*M*.[68]<br>In rats, 30 mg/kg, i.v. 30 min prior to *Salmonella enteritidis* injection (20 mg/kg) improved the survival rate and prevented plasma $TxB_2$ elevation. Thrombocytopenia was reduced.[69]<br>Vasopressin-stimulated water flow and $TxB_2$ synthesis in an isolated toad urinary bladder was inhibited by 10—100 μ*M* without affecting PGE synthesis (RIA).[70] |
| 14. | 1-(7-Carboxyheptyl)imidazole [8-(1-imidazolyl)octanoic acid] | 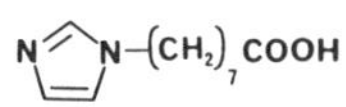 | $C_{11}H_{18}N_2O_2$ (210) | Inhibited the conversion of $PGH_2$ to $TxB_2$ by bovine-platelet microsomes, $IC_{50}$ 0.14 μ*M* (RTLC), with no inhibition of PG endoperoxide synthetase. Most potent of a series.[46] |

## Table 1 (continued)
## IMIDAZOLES

| No. | Name of compound | Structure | Formula (mol wt) | Biological activity |
|---|---|---|---|---|
| | | | | Inhibited $TxA_2$ synthesis induced by collagen in rabbit PRP, $IC_{50}$ 0.6 μ*M* (bioassay),[3] and in rat PRP, $IC_{50}$ 2.0 μ*M* (RIA), with no inhibition of aggregation at even higher concentrations (up to 200 m*M*) which abolished $TxA_2$ formation.[71]<br>Inhibited aggregation of rabbit PRP induced by AA or collagen, $IC_{50}$ 0.81 μ*M*.[68] High-dose collagen-induced aggregation of rabbit PRP was only partly inhibited by carboxyheptylimidazole alone, but was abolished by combination with CP/CPK. $PGH_2$-induced aggregation was only partially inhibited.[3]<br>In human PRP, aggregation induced by AA was inhibited, $IC_{50}$ 0.69 μ*M*,[68] but 10 m*M* reduced aggregation by collagen only by 20%, even though $TxB_2$ synthesis was inhibited over 90%.[71]<br>In rats, 10 mg/kg, p.o. prolonged tail-bleeding time and inhibited *ex vivo* $TxB_2$ production induced by collagen, but not thrombin-induced aggregation. No inhibition of Arthus-induced thrombocytopenia or thrombus formation on implanted cotton thread was observed at 30 mg/kg, p.o.[72] Platelet $TxB_2$ production stimulated by i.v. collagen (100 μg/kg) was inhibited (54%) by 30 mg/kg p.o. Circulating plasma 6-keto $PGF_{1\alpha}$ increased fourfold (RIA), and thrombocytopenia was partially inhibited.[73,74]<br>Ineffective in reducing thrombus formation in a hamster cheek-pouch model.[50]<br>I.P. injection in C57 BL/6J mice reduced metastasis from tail-vein-injected B16a cells and spontaneous metastasis from s.c. B16a and Lewis lung carcinoma tumors.[75] |
| 15. | 1-(8-Aminooctyl)-imidazole | 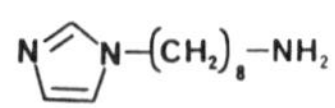 | $C_{11}H_{21}N_3$ (195) | Inhibited the aggregation of rabbit PRP by AA, $IC_{50}$ 0.08 μ*M*, and collagen, $IC_{50}$ 0.33 μ*M*; and the ag- |

| | | | | |
|---|---|---|---|---|
| | | | | gregation of human PRP by AA, $IC_{50}$ 0.25 $\mu M$.[68] |
| 16. | 1-[8-(4-chlorobenzoylamino)octyl]imidazole | 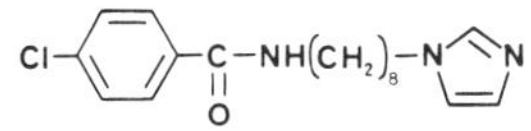 | $C_{18}H_{24}ClN_3O$ (334) | Inhibited the synthesis of $TxB_2$ from endogenous AA in resuspended rat (SHR) platelets, $IC_{50}$ 0.1 $\mu M$.[76] |
| 17. | 2-[4-(1*H*-Imidazol-1-yl)-butyl]-1*H*-isoindole-1,3(2*H*)-dione | 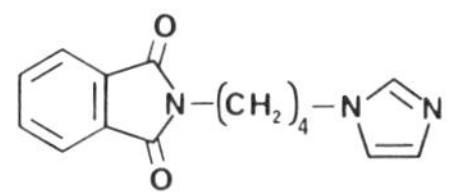 | $C_{15}H_{15}N_3O_2$ (269) | Inhibited the synthesis of $TxB_2$ from endogenous AA in resuspended rat (SHR) platelets, $IC_{50}$ 2 $\mu M$, with no inhibition of $PGI_2$ synthesis in guinea-pig aortic rings (RIA).<br>This compound also has antihypertensive properties, lowering blood pressure in SHR at 30 and 100 mg/kg, p.o., and in two-kidney one clip Goldblatt renal hypertensive dogs at 5—30 mg/kg.[77] |
| 18. | 1-(7-Carboxy-7-methyl-2-octynyl)imidazole | 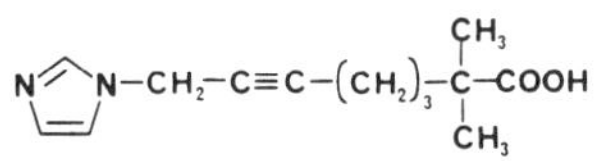 | $C_{13}H_{18}N_2O_2$ (234) | Inhibited the synthesis of $TxB_2$ from $PGH_2$ by a rabbit-platelet suspension, $IC_{50}$ 9 n$M$ (RTLC), with no effect on cyclooxygenase or prostacyclin synthetase ($IC_{50} \gg 100$ $\mu M$).[78] |
| 19. | 4-[(1*H*-Imidazol-1-yl)methylphenoxy]acetic acid [UK-38,322] | 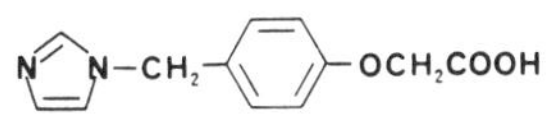 | $C_{12}H_{12}N_2O_3$ (232) | Inhibited the synthesis of $TxB_2$ from $PGH_2$ by human-platelet microsomes, $IC_{50}$ $3.1 \times 10^{-8}$ $M$ (RIA), with no activity against $PGI_2$ synthetase, cyclooxygenase, or steroid 11β-hydroxylase.[79] |
| 20. | 4-[2-(1*H*-Imidazol-1-yl)ethoxy]benzoic acid (Dazoxiben; UK-37,248)[81] | 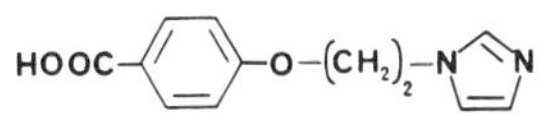 | $C_{12}H_{12}N_2O_3$ (232) | Inhibited $TxB_2$ synthesis from $PGH_2$ by a human-platelet microsomal preparation, $IC_{50}$ $3 \times 10^{-9}$ $M$, with no effect on $PGH_2$ synthesis (ram seminal-vesicle microsomes) and 30% inhibition of $PGI_2$ synthesis (pig-aortic microsomes) at $10^{-4}$ $M$ (RIA).[82,83] Inhibited conversion of AA to $TxB_2$ by rabbit PRP, $IC_{50}$ $7.6 \times 10^{-6}$ $M$ (RIA),[82] and human PRP, $IC_{50}$ 0.6 $\mu M$ (RIA);[84] the anti-aggregation response being enhanced (rabbit PRP) in the presence of pig-aortic microsomes as a source of $PGI_2$ synthetase, or by increasing incubation times.[85] In human PRP the inhibition of $TxB_2$ production was accompanied by increased $PGE_2$, $PGD_2$, and $PGF_{2\alpha}$ (GC-MS).[86]<br>Collagen-induced aggregation of rabbit platelets was only minimally inhibited but serotonin release was reduced by ~40%.[87] Inhibited aggregation of human PRP by threshold collagen, $IC_{50}$ $4.8 \times 10^{-6}$ $M$,[82] |

**Table 1 (continued)**
**IMIDAZOLES**

| No. | Name of compound | Structure | Formula (mol wt) | Biological activity |
|---|---|---|---|---|
| | | | | and $TxB_2$ synthesis in human whole blood stimulated by collagen at 10 $\mu M$ with increased $PGE_2$ and 6-keto-$PGF_{1\alpha}$ production (RIA).[88] Aggregation of human PRP by 2 μg/ml collagen in the presence of 40 $\mu M$ dazoxiben showed inhibition of $TxB_2$ production (>95%) and 20-fold increases in $PGD_2$, $PGE_2$, and $PGF_{2\alpha}$ (GC-MS).[89] In clotting human whole blood, $TxB_2$ production was inhibited, $IC_{50}$ 0.3 μg/ml, with enhanced $PGE_2 > PGF_{2\alpha} >$ 6-keto-$PGF_{1\alpha}$ production.[90] Thrombin-induced 12-HPETE formation in washed human platelets was inhibited (81%) at 100 $\mu M$.[91] In sheep lymphocytes challenged with ZAP, dazoxiben completely inhibited $TxB_2$ production. However 0.1—1.0 mg/ml had no effect on leukocyte aggregation in whole blood.[92] Inhibited $TxA_2$ synthesis from AA in an isolated rabbit-lung preparation ($5 \times 10^{-7}$ $M$ infusion) with stimulation of $PGI_2$, $PGE_2$, and $PGF_{2\alpha}$ synthesis (bioassay), and inhibited $TxB_2$ production in rabbits (0.3 mg/kg i.v.) and dogs (1 mg/kg p.o.) (RIA).[82] In isolated perfused guinea-pig lungs, $TxA_2$ release in response to AA or bradykinin injections was inhibited with enhanced prostacyclin synthesis (RIA).[93] $LD_{50} >$ 1500 mg/kg p.o. in rats and mice,[94] with no toxicity at 6 months in rats and dogs at high doses.[94,95] |
| | | | | In humans, oral doses (50—200 mg) inhibited serum $TxB_2$ production (peak at 1 h) with biological $t_{1/2}$ of 5—6 h (RIA). No clinically relevant changes in heart rate or blood pressure, and no side effects were observed.[96] Oral doses of 200 mg raised serum 6-keto-$PGF_{1\alpha}$ and completely inhibited platelet aggregation due to AA but not ADP,[97] whereas doses of 25—200 mg did not suppress aggregation due to |

PAF (in PRP) or collagen (PRP or whole blood). Urinary prostacyclin excretion (as 2,3-dinor-6-keto-$PGF_{1\alpha}$) and bleeding time were increased.[98-100] ADP-induced aggregation showed inhibition of the second wave of aggregation and pronounced disaggregation when rat aortic or human cord endothelial cells were added to the PRP of atherosclerotic patients given dazoxiben.[101]

A dose of 100 mg reduced the maximal rate of collagen-induced aggregation in human PRP after 1 h and prolonged bleeding time 53%. Plasma 6-keto-$PGF_{1\alpha}$ was increased by 40% at 24 h.[102] In human whole blood, dazoxiben (100 $\mu M$) had no effect on aggregation induced by AA, ADP, adrenaline, or thrombin, and only partially inhibited that due to collagen.[103] In clotting whole blood from humans following 5—200 mg oral doses, $PGE_2$ and $PGF_{2\alpha}$ levels were increased as well as 6-keto-$PGF_{1\alpha}$ (due to leukocytes) (RIA).[85,102]

In PRP from human volunteers, concentrations of dazoxiben above those inhibiting $TxB_2$ synthesis inhibit AA-induced aggregation[84] and the release reaction[104] in some subjects (''responders'') but not others (''nonresponders''). Similar platelet behavior was found both after oral ingestion of dazoxiben (200 mg) or following *in vitro* incubation of PRP with dazoxiben for each individual tested.[104] The platelets of ''nonresponders'' were also less sensitive to the effects of aspirin[104a] and the phosphodiesterase inhibitor AH-P 719[104b] in preventing aggregation and the release reaction induced by AA. The anti-aggregation effect of dazoxiben was prevented by SQ 22536 (an inhibitor of adenylate cyclase), N0164 (a $PGD_2$ antagonist), and $PGE_2$ (in responders), and potentiated by $PGD_2$, prolonged incubation, or serum albumin (in nonresponders).[84,105-108] In washed human platelets, dazoxiben (1—20 $\mu M$) enhanced the shape change, aggregation, and serotonin release induced

**Table 1 (continued)**
**IMIDAZOLES**

| No. | Name of compound | Structure | Formula (mol wt) | Biological activity |
|---|---|---|---|---|
| | | | | by exogenous or endogenous (collagen, $H_2O_2$, or MeHgCl stimulated) AA while inhibiting $TxB_2$ formation (RIA). Albumin or human PPP abolished the potentiating effect of dazoxiben, presumably by converting accumulating $PGH_2$ to $PGD_2$.[109] Dazoxiben (10 μ*M*) potentiates the anti-aggregatory effects of $PGI_2$ (and $PGD_2$) on AA-induced aggregation of human platelets.[110] The combination of dazoxiben (200 mg p.o.) and low doses of aspirin (20 mg p.o.) in humans abolished aggregation induced by threshold NaAA (6/6) whereas aspirin (1/6) or dazoxiben (1/3 at 1 h, 0/3 at 24 h) alone were ineffective.[111] The release reaction induced by ADP or adrenalin was significantly lowered by the combination.[104] |
| | | | | Combination of dazoxiben with a Tx receptor antagonist or $PGI_2$ caused marked potentiation of the latter compounds as inhibitors of human-platelet aggregation induced by AA or ADP (second wave), but not U-46619 (a stable endoperoxide analogue).[112] Similarly, combination with the Tx-receptor antagonist BM 13.177 synergistically inhibited collagen-induced aggregation of whole blood, using a challenge where dazoxiben alone was ineffective. Enhancement of 6-keto-$PGF_{1\alpha}$ production in PRP in the presence of endothelial cells was not diminished.[113] Dazoxiben alone did not prevent the release of serotonin from washed human-platelet suspensions stimulated by AA, whereas BM 13.177 alone was highly effective ($IC_{50}$ 0.1 μ*M*).[114] Combinations of dazoxiben (4—200 μ*M*) with phosphodiesterase inhibitors showed synergistic inhibition of aggregation of human PRP by collagen or AA but not ADP, 9,11-azo- |

$PGH_2$ or 1-alkyl-2-acetyl-GPC.[115] Similar synergy was found between dazoxiben and the phosphodiesterase inhibitor AH-P 719 in inhibition of human-platelet behavior induced by AA. Levels of platelet cAMP were higher than with either agent alone.[104b] However, in healthy volunteers, combination of dipyridamole (which inhibits phosphodiesterase) with dazoxiben did not show any synergistic inhibition of platelet aggregation.[116]

The constriction of rabbit pulmonary-artery strips by carbocyclic thromboxane $A_2$ ($CTA_2$), a thromboxane agonist, was inhibited (80%) by 3.7 $\mu M$ dazoxiben; no effect on $CTA_2$-induced constriction of cat coronary arteries was found at concentrations up to 37 $\mu M$.[117] Caused inhibition of $TxB_2$ synthesis by human pulmonary arteries and veins with an increase in 6-keto-$PGF_{1\alpha}$ at $1 \times 10^{-4} M$ (RIA).[118]

Platelet adhesion to isolated rabbit-aortic subendothelium[119] or damaged rabbit aorta[87] was reduced, but adhesion of rabbit PRP to collagen-coated glass was not prevented.[87,119]

In rats, 3 mg/kg p.o. inhibited $TxB_2$ production, but not the thrombocytopenia, caused by i.v. collagen (100 $\mu$g/kg) with redirection to 6-keto-$PGF_{1\alpha}$.[73]

In cats, 3 mg/kg i.v. induced the release of $PGI_2$ into arterial blood with disaggregation of platelet clumps on blood-superfused collagen strips.[120]

In rabbits, 10 mg/kg completely abolished local $TxB_2$ production stimulated by a nylon thread in the jugular vein with increases in 6-keto-$PGF_{1\alpha}$ (RIA).[121]

In an experimental thrombus model in rats (exposure of the coronary artery to cold, pressure, and an additional flow reduction), 2 or 10 mg/kg i.v. produced the same reduction in thrombus weight as treatment with aspirin (0.4 or 4 mg/kg).[122] Similarly in rabbits, 2 mg/kg i.v. reduced platelet accumulation on carotid arteries after electrical stimulation. In unstimulated animals, $TxB_2$ production was almost totally

**Table 1 (continued)**
**IMIDAZOLES**

| No. | Name of compound | Structure | Formula (mol wt) | Biological activity |
|---|---|---|---|---|
| | | | | inhibited with 3.5-fold increase in 6-keto-$PGF_{1\alpha}$ (RIA).[123] Thrombus formation due to silver nitrate was also reduced.[124] However, in another study in rabbits, neither the frequency of jugular-vein thrombosis (following endothelial damage and a flow restriction) nor arteriolar microembolism (following laser injury) were reduced by dazoxiben infusion.[125] |
| | | | | In sheep, infusion of dazoxiben significantly reduced local thromboxane production, thrombus weight, and platelet accumulation, and improved patency following insertion of human umbilical vein in the carotid artery.[125] |
| | | | | In open-chest dogs, 4 mg/kg prolonged the time required for occlusive thrombi to form at sites of electrical injury in coronary arteries 3-fold with decreased venous $TxB_2$.[126] Vasodilation induced by AA was potentiated.[126,127] |
| | | | | In a cyclic-flow variation (CFV) model, induced by constriction of the canine coronary artery, 2.5 mg/kg i.v. reduced the frequency of CFVs or abolished them entirely, presumably by alteration of the formation and dislodgment of thrombi.[128,129] $TxB_2$ levels in the aorta and distal to the stenosis were returned to control levels without affecting $PGI_2$ synthesis (RIA).[129] |
| | | | | In cats, 5 mg/kg/h infusion protected against acute myocardial ischemia induced by coronary-artery occlusion. The S-T segment was restored and the rise in creatine-kinase activity and circulating $TxB_2$ (RIA) prevented.[130] However, in a similar study, the extent of cellular damage on *reperfusion* of the ischemic myocardium was not modified, and platelet |

count remained depressed, in contrast to the effects of iloprost (a $PGI_2$ analogue).[131,132] In rats, moderate protection was seen following coronary-artery ligation and reperfusion at 3, 10 mg/kg, i.v. but not at 20 mg/kg, i.v.[133] In greyhounds, 2 mg/kg i.v. markedly increased survival (7/8) following coronary artery reperfusion relative to controls (1/8).[134,135]

In doses up to 20 mg/kg, i.v., dazoxiben did not prevent arrhythmias induced by ouabain (dog), $CaCl_2$, or acotine (rat), or thevitin (guinea pig).[133]

In patients with coronary-artery disease, 200 mg p.o. abolished the increase in arterial $TxB_2$ at the onset of angina with no effect on coronary hemodynamics.[136-138] Dazoxiben 200 mg q.i.d. for 7 d[139] or 21 d[140-142] was of no benefit in patients with stable angina (attack rate or exercise time) in two studies; however, one 100 mg dose increased the atrial pacing time to angina in another.[143] In a similar study, a single 200 mg dose orally reduced the ST depression during atrial pacing and increased the postpacing myocardial lactate extraction while aspirin had no effect. Some 60% of patients in both the dazoxiben and aspirin groups experienced less pain.[144] In patients with unstable angina, 100 or 200 mg t.i.d. for 7 d appeared to result in fewer episodes of angina.[145] In a further study, no benefit of dazoxiben 100 mg t.i.d. for 7 d was found in patients with CHD.[146] In a comparison with verapamil, dazoxiben (100 mg t.i.d. for 2 weeks) inhibited the increase in serum $TxB_2$ during exercise to angina, without clinical effect, whereas verapamil caused highly significant prolongation of exercise time in the absence of effects on serum $TxB_2$. *Plasma $TxB_2$ and 6-keto-$PFG_{1\alpha}$ levels were unaltered* in both cases and remained normal.[147] Dazoxiben-induced potentiation of $PGI_2$ synthesis by leukocytes in blood from angina patients (100 mg dose) was comparable to that in healthy individuals (RIA). $PGE_2$ increased 7×, $PGF_{2\alpha}$ 5.5×.[148]

**Table 1 (continued)**
**IMIDAZOLES**

| No. | Name of compound | Structure | Formula (mol wt) | Biological activity |
|---|---|---|---|---|
| | | | | In dogs with temporary (3 h) splanchnic-artery occlusion, dazoxiben, 5 mg/kg i.v. decreased the number of animals progressing to shock.[149] In rats, 30 mg/kg i.v. reduced the mortality and splanchnic infarction due to endotoxic shock induced by i.v. *S. enteritidis* endotoxin (with reduced $TxB_2$ and 6-keto-$PGF_{1\alpha}$ [RIA]),[150,151] but not mortality due to *E. coli* endotoxin.[152] In cats, 5 mg/kg i.v. markedly reduced increases in pulmonary arterial hypertension induced by *E. coli* endotoxin (2 mg/kg i.v.) without affecting increases in intratracheal pressure.[153] In mini-pigs, a 7 mg/kg bolus prevented the early rise in blood pressure and plasma $TxB_2$ (RIA) following *E. coli* endotoxin, but failed to modify the subsequent fall in blood pressure, pre-kallikrein levels, or WBC, and platelet counts.[154] Similarly, in goats, dazoxiben (25 mg/kg then 10 mg/kg/h infusion) prevented plasma $TxB_2$ elevations due to *E. coli* endotoxin (1 μg/kg) and ameliorated the adverse hemodynamic consequences, but did not prevent lung permeability changes.[155,156] The elevated pulmonary-arterial pressure and elevated plasma $TxB_2$ concentrations induced by thrombin infusion in rats were reduced by 4 mg/kg, i.v.[157] In mice, AA-induced mortality was reduced by 50 and 100 mg/kg, p.o. 2 h before challenge.[20] In rabbits, 1—2 mg/kg i.v. protected against sudden death induced by AA injection (but not 9,11-azo $PGH_2$). Vasospasm, elevations in plasma $TxB_2$ (RIA) and pulmonary-artery thrombosis were prevented.[82,158,159] Additionally, dazoxiben appeared to be a specific *Tx-receptor antagonist* in rabbit pulmonary arter- |

ies.[158] Sudden death in rabbits due to i.v. injection of PAF was also prevented by 2.5 mg/kg, i.v. dazoxiben (15 min before challenge). Increased plasma $TxB_2$ was abolished and decreases in mean arterial blood pressure were attenuated.[160] In anesthetized rabbits, 10 mg/kg infusion partially inhibited the thrombocytopenia and hypotension induced by i.v. thrombin but not that caused by collagen, Paf-acether, or ADP.[160a] In perfused rabbit lungs, the increase in pulmonary-artery pressure due to infusion of *t*-BuOOH or AA was attenuated, and $TxB_2$ synthesis abolished.[161] In anesthetized dogs, dazoxiben (5 mg/kg, i.v.) was more effective in preventing AA-induced changes in pulmonary airway resistance or dynamic lung compliance than an equal dose of the thromboxane-receptor antagonist SK&F 88046.[162] The increase in (i.v.) free fatty-acid-induced alveolar surfactant (disatd. phophatidylcholine) content was blocked by 2 mg/kg i.v., and survival rate increased.[163]

In sheep, 10 mg/kg then 4 mg/kg/h infusion prevented $TxB_2$ increase due to thrombin infusion with increased 6-keto-$PGF_{1\alpha}$, and prevented the increase in pulmonary vascular permeability.[164] In another study, dazoxiben prevented the decrease in leukocyte counts during pulmonary microembolism induced by thrombin and attenuated the increased lymph flow.[165] In awake sheep prepared with lung lymph fistulas, $TxB_2$ generation, and the increase in pulmonary vascular pressures and pulmonary lymph flow resulting from $LTD_4$ infusion were prevented.[166] In anesthetized sheep, dazoxiben inhibited the systemic arterial $pO_2$ decrease and $TxA_2$ release due to injections of zymosan-activated plasma. The hypertensive response and increased lung lymph flow were unaltered.[167]

In 7 patients with adult respiratory-distress syndrome, a bolus dose of 1.5 mg/kg, i.v. had no effect on pul-

**Table 1 (continued)**
**IMIDAZOLES**

| No. | Name of compound | Structure | Formula (mol wt) | Biological activity |
|---|---|---|---|---|
| | | | | monary hemodynamics, but caused a moderate increase in arterial oxygen pressure.[168] |
| | | | | In guinea pigs, 5 mg/kg, i.v. suppressed $LTD_4$-induced bronchoconstriction, and blocked plasma $TxB_2$ production without affecting 6-keto $PGF_{1\alpha}$.[169] |
| | | | | *In vitro* inhibition of $TxB_2$ synthesis in rat-kidney glomeruli was less sensitive ($IC_{50}$ 1.6 μg/ml) than in rat whole blood ($IC_{50}$ 0.32 μg/ml), and was not accompanied by changes in $PGE_2$, $PGF_{2\alpha}$, and 6-keto $PGF_{1\alpha}$ (RIA). Similarly, after oral administration in humans (1.5, 3.0 mg/kg), there was no evidence of redirection of renal endoperoxide, even though urinary $TxB_2$ production was reduced. This is in contrast to results obtained *ex vivo* where inhibition of $TxB_2$ production in clotting whole blood leads to enhanced $PGE_2$, $PGF_{2\alpha}$, and 6-keto-$PGF_{1\alpha}$ production.[90] |
| | | | | In patients with severe pregnancy-induced hyptension, dazoxiben was of possible benefit in 2/4 cases.[170] However, in patients with hepatorenal syndrome, dazoxiben (400—600 mg/d) was of no benefit, even though urinary $TxB_2$ was decreased up to ~75%. Urinary $PGE_2$, 6-keto-$PGF_{1\alpha}$ and creatinine clearence were unaltered.[171] |
| | | | | In healthy volunteers, 200 mg p.o. abolished arterial and venous vasoconstriction in the forearm produced by cold stimulation, this effect being negated by aspirin.[172] In a second, open study, dazoxiben (200 mg., p.o. 1 h before challenge) abolished the vasoconstriction in one group of volunteers ("responders"), but not others ("non-responders"), correlating precisely with the response of PRP from individual subjects to NaAA-induced aggregation |

following *in vitro* or oral dazoxiben. The effect of dazoxiben on vasoconstriction in responders was abolished by high-dose (but not low-dose) aspirin.[173] Similarly, in patients with Raynaud's phenomenon and healthy volunteers, treatment with 4 doses of dazoxiben (100 mg t.i.d.) reduced the fall in finger blood flow due to cold challenge.[174] In a repeat study, skin blood flow at rest and during cold challenge was not affected in patients or normal subjects; however recovery was more rapid in dazoxiben-treated patients and normal subjects.[175] In a double-blind, placebo-controlled study, dazoxiben (200 mg) did not affect the changes in cutaneous vascular resistance and arterial blood pressure induced in healthy humans by immersion of feet in ice.[176]

In double-blind studies in patients with Raynaud's phenomenon (fingers), dazoxiben (100 mg q.i.d.) for 2 weeks,[177] 3 weeks,[178] or 12 weeks[175] did not improve blood flow or symptoms. Similarly other investigators found dazoxiben (100 mg, p.o., q.i.d. for 2 weeks) to be ineffective in the treatment of Raynaud's phenomenon, in contrast to the calcium channel blocker nifedipine.[179] The elevated β-thromboglobulin levels in these patients were normalized by nifedipine, but not by dazoxiben.[180] However, in another study, patients treated for 6 weeks showed significant clinical improvement (8/11) but no change in skin temperature.[181]

In healthy volunteers, dazoxiben, 200 mg, p.o. did not affect euglobulin fibrinolytic activity or tissue-type plasminogen activator antigen level induced by 10 min of venous occlusion.[182]

In patients with peripheral vascular disease, short term treatment (100 mg t.i.d. × 3 d) reduced $TxB_2$ levels (86%) (RIA) but not β-thromboglobulin levels, without adverse effects.[183]

In patients with severe peripheral vascular disease associated with ischemic rest pain, 100 mg t.i.d. for 1

**Table 1 (continued)**
**IMIDAZOLES**

| No. | Name of compound | Structure | Formula (mol wt) | Biological activity |
|---|---|---|---|---|
| | | | | month showed initial improvement in 6/8 (pain relief) and long-term benefit in 3/4 survivors of this group.[184] However, dazoxiben was ineffective in 4 patients with peripheral artery disease.[185] In patients with chronic occlusive arterial disease (intermittent claudication), 100 mg i.v. gave a modest increase in muscle tissue $pO_2$ in 2/4 patients.[186] |
| | | | | In the blood-perfused mesentery of the rat, dazoxiben (10 μmol/l) inhibited constrictor responses to nerve stimulation, and to injected noradrenaline, and vasopressin. The inhibition was abolished by indomethacin, and was attributed to diversion of endoperoxides to other prostaglandins.[187] |
| | | | | Dazoxiben (1 μg/ml) slightly but significantly inhibited mitogen-induced proliferation of human lymphocytes. $TxB_2$ production was inhibited, and that of $PGE_2$ enhanced (RIA).[188] The activity of human natural cytotoxic cells and NK cells against HSV-infected cells and K562 cells respectively was inhibited by concentrations of $10^{-10}$—$10^{-8}M$ and above.[189] |
| | | | | In allergic patients and volunteers, 3 doses of 100 mg at 4-h intervals enhanced immediate but inhibited late cutaneous allergic reactions due to allergen challenge.[190] |
| | | | | In migraine patients treated with dazoxiben, 100 mg q.i.d. for 3 months, attack frequency was reduced by >50% in 7/16 cases, and increased in another 7. The clinical response correlated with the response (or lack of response) of plasma $TxB_2$ levels after 3 months.[191] |
| | | | | Dazoxiben did not prevent human-platelet deposition |

| | | | | |
|---|---|---|---|---|
| | | | | on Dacron arterial grafts *in vitro* or *ex vivo*.[192] Similarly, in baboons, 50 mg/kg orally did not prevent platelet deposition on Dacron vascular grafts.[193] Doses of 20—100 mg/kg, p.o. daily were also ineffective in prevention of platelet consumption by thrombogenic arteriovenous cannulae.[193,194] The antithrombotic effects of dipyridamole and sulfinpyrazone were not potentiated by dazoxiben, in contrast to potentiation by aspirin.[194]<br>The survival of pig renal xenografts in rabbits was *decreased* by i.v. dazoxiben (2 × 5 mg/kg).[195] However, infusion into the renal artery of 3-d renal allografts in rats decreased urinary $TxB_2$ excretion, and improved renal blood flow and glomerular filtration rate, although these were not restored to control values.[196] Similar results were found in hydronephrotic rat kidneys (from unilateral ureteral obstruction).[197]<br>In osteoblast-rich cells from newborn rat calvaria, dazoxiben *inhibited* $PGE_2$ and $PGI_2$ production with half maximal inhibition at $\sim 10^{-7}M$.[198]<br>No reduction of platelet activation during dialysis.[199]<br>For a study of analogues of dazoxiben, see Reference 79. For structure-activity relationships in this series, see Reference 80. |
| 21. | 4-[3-(1-imidazolyl)-propyl]benzoic acid | 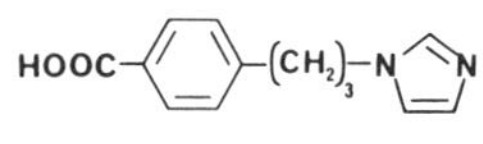 | $C_{13}H_{14}N_2O_2$ (230) | Inhibited the synthesis of $TxB_2$ from $PGH_2$ by a rabbit-platelet suspension, $IC_{50}$ 5 n$M$ (RTLC), with no effects on cyclooxygenase or prostacyclin synthetase ($IC_{50} \geqslant 100\ \mu M$).[78] |
| 22. | *E*-3-[4-(1-imidazolyl)-methylphenyl]prop-2-enoic acid (OKY-046)[78] (ozagrel) | 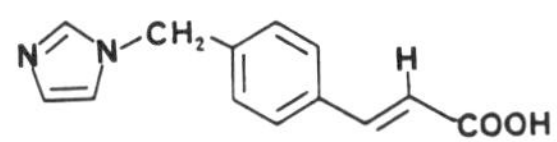 | $C_{13}H_{12}N_2O_2$ (228) | Inhibited the synthesis of $TxB_2$ from $PGH_2$ by a rabbit-platelet suspension, $IC_{50}$ 11 n$M$,[78] and by homogenates from human ($IC_{50}$ 4 n$M$), rabbit ($IC_{50}$ 4 n$M$), dog ($IC_{50}$ 0.26 $\mu M$) and guinea pig ($IC_{50}$ 2.4 $\mu M$) washed platelets (RTLC), with no effects on cyclooxygenase or prostacyclin synthetase at concentrations up to 1 m$M$.[199a] Inhibition of $TxA_2$ production in rat peritoneal cells was accompanied by increased |

**Table 1 (continued)**
**IMIDAZOLES**

| No. | Name of compound | Structure | Formula (mol wt) | Biological activity |
|---|---|---|---|---|
| | | | | 6-keto-$PGF_{1\alpha}$ production at concentrations $\geq 1$ $\mu M$.[199a] |
| | | | | Inhibited AA- or collagen-induced aggregation and $TxA_2$ synthesis in rabbit PRP without affecting PG synthesis (bioassay). No inhibition of ADP, thrombin, or ionophore A-23187-induced aggregation *in vitro* but did inhibit ADP-induced platelet aggregation *in vivo*.[200,201] Prolonged bleeding time in rats.[201] Attenuated the contractile responses due to bronchoactive agents (histamine, serotonin creatinine sulfate, acetylcholine chloride, bradykinin, and $PGF_{2\alpha}$) in guinea-pig tracheal strips and potentiated isoproterenol, salbutamol, and $PGE_2$-induced relaxation. Reduced $TxA_2$ and increased 6-keto-$PGF_{1\alpha}$ production from AA in isolated perfused guinea-pig lung lobes.[202] |
| | | | | Blocked thrombus formation in carotid artery induced by $AgNO_3$ or pronase and inhibited the increase in plasma $TxB_2$ with elevation of 6-keto-$PGF_{1\alpha}$.[201] No prevention of aortal intimal thickening after mechanical injury in rabbits.[203] |
| | | | | In open-chest dogs, 1 mg/kg prevented significant increases in $TxB_2$ and lactate release (but not increases in 6-keto-$PGF_{1\alpha}$) following coronary-artery ligation. Coronary venous blood flow was not reduced, in contrast to indomethacin-treated dogs.[204,205] In a similar study, 3 mg/kg/h infusion decreased the infarct size in dogs with acute myocardial infarction (ligation), and affected levels of 6-keto-$PGF_{1\alpha}$, $TxB_2$ and the ischemic myocardial noradrenaline content.[206] |
| | | | | The number of ventricular extrasystoles during coronary-artery occlusion in dogs and the incidence of |

ventricular arrythmias following reperfusion was reduced by infusion of OKY-046 (5 mg/kg, 2 mg/kg/h).[207] Treatment with 3 mg/kg, i.v. both 10 min before coronary-artery occlusion and 5 min before reperfusion significantly reduced mortality in dogs. Plasma CPK-MB, the formation and size of myocardial infarcts, and plasma $TxB_2$ in the coronary sinus were inhibited.[208]

In patients with effort angina, treatment with OKY-046 resulted in prolongation of exercise time and atrial pacing time, with improved clinical responses (open study).[209] In patients with vasospastic angina, OKY-046 (400 mg/d, orally) had no effect on the number or length of ischemic episodes over a 3-d period, in spite of decreased plasma $TxB_2$ and increased serum 6-keto-$PGF_{1\alpha}$. Chest pain and nitroglycerine use were unchanged.[210]

In beagles with a partially constricted coronary artery, 20 mg/kg i.v. eliminated the cyclical reduction of flow in 5/7 animals.[211] In a hind-limb ischemia/reperfusion model in dogs, pretreatment with OKY-046 lowered platelet and lymph $TxB_2$ after reperfusion and maintained the lymph/plasma ratio below untreated controls.[212]

Protected rabbits from sudden death due to NaAA injection,[199a,201,213,214] and prevented the rise in $TxB_2$ with enhancement of 6-keto-$PGF_{1\alpha}$ levels.[201,213,214] Similarly, sudden death induced by i.v. PAF was fully inhibited by pretreatment with 1 mg/kg, i.v. OKY-046, with only modest changes in mean arterial blood pressure and no increase in plasma $TxB_2$ (RIA).[160] The endotoxin-induced decrease in platelet count and increased plasma $TxB_2$ in rabbits were inhibited by 10 mg/kg, i.v. with enhanced 6-keto-$PGF_{1\alpha}$.[215] However, the granulocytopenia, thrombocytopenia, and pulmonary leukostasis induced by nonviable *Streptococcus pneumoniae* injection in rabbits were not altered by 30 mg/kg, i.v. although

**Table 1 (continued)**
**IMIDAZOLES**

| No. | Name of compound | Structure | Formula (mol wt) | Biological activity |
|---|---|---|---|---|
| | | | | the elevation of $TxB_2$ was blocked and circulating levels of 6-keto-$PGF_{1\alpha}$ were elevated.[216] Prevented the increase in intratracheal pressure in an air-embolism model in dogs, with no effect on systemic blood pressure. Plasma $TxB_2$ increase was prevented.[217] In a model of anaphylactic shock, induced by infusion of *Ascaris* antigen in dogs, the fall in systemic pressure and rise in blood $TxB_2$ were inhibited, but the increases in tracheal pressure and blood leukotriene levels were not altered.[218] |
| | | | | In sheep, a 5 mg/kg bolus attenuated the initial rise in pulmonary artery pressure and pulmonary vascular resistence due to infusion of thrombin. Increases in both $TxB_2$ and 6-keto-$PGF_{1\alpha}$ were inhibited.[219] The early pulmonary hypotension and increases in $TxB_2$ levels following *E. coli* endotoxin infusion in sheep were prevented by pretreatment with OKY-046. There was little effect on lung lymph balance during the late period.[220] In contrast, the pulmonary arterial-pressure increase in sheep resulting from air infusion into the pulmonary artery was not prevented.[221] |
| | | | | OKY-046 had no effect on pleural fluid accumulation or 6-keto-$PGF_{1\alpha}$ or $PGD_2$ levels in pleural fluids in response to intrapleural injection of PMA in rats, even though $TxB_2$ was reduced completely (RIA). In contrast, indomethacin suppressed fluid accumulation and reduced the above metabolites to basal levels.[222] In a model of acute lung injury induced by PMA in blood-perfused isolated dog-lung lobes, OKY-046 ($7 \times 10^{-4}$ *M*) pretreatment blocked permeability changes and attenuated the increased vascular resistance.[222a] PAF-induced bronchoconstriction and air- |

way hyperresponsiveness (to acetylcholine aerosol) in dogs was inhibited by OKY-046. The increase in neutrophil recovery in bronchoalveolar lavage fluid was not altered.[223] Similar results were found in ragweed antigen-[223a] $LTB_4$-[224] and ozone-induced[225,226] hyperresponsiveness.

Experimentally induced cerebral vasospasm was not reversed by infusion of 50 μg/kg/min for 2 h (dogs)[227] or by 30—60 mg/kg i.v. (cats).[228] However, in a similar study in dogs, transorbital administration of 0.05 or 0.5 μg of OKY-046 at the same time as intracisternal injection of autologous blood suppressed the cerebral vasospasm, with inhibition of the decrease in regional blood flow at the higher dose. The increase in cerebrospinal $TxB_2$ was significantly reduced by 0.5 μg, with slight increases in 6-keto-$PGF_{1\alpha}$.[228a] The incidence of cerebral infarction induced by injection of NaAA into the internal carotid artery of rabbits was decreased by pretreatment with OKY-046, 0.3 mg/kg,i.v.[199a] In patients with ruptured cerebral aneurysm, continuous infusion of OKY-046 decreased $TxB_2$ and seemed to prevent cerebral vasospasm.[229]

In patients with ischemic cerebrovascular disease and healthy volunteers, a 100-mg oral dose decreased urinary $TxB_2$ and eliminated that produced by stimulation of platelets (PRP), with increased urinary 6-keto-$PGF_{1\alpha}$ (RIA).[230] The effect of OKY-046 on AA-induced aggregation was different in each subject and there was only slight inhibition of collagen-induced aggregation. Pretreatment with low dose aspirin (0.1—0.25 mg/kg/d) for 1 month before dosing with 100 mg OKY-046 resulted in an additional inhibitory effect.[231]

OKY-046 enhanced sodium excretion and fractional sodium excretion in normal and saline-loaded rats. In a model of acute renal failure induced by glycerol, the reduction in Na excretion and creatinine clear-

**Table 1 (continued)**
**IMIDAZOLES**

| No. | Name of compound | Structure | Formula (mol wt) | Biological activity |
|---|---|---|---|---|
| | | | | ance was partially prevented and the fractional excretion of Na was increased.[232] In a model of renal ischemia in the rat, ischemia-induced $TxB_2$ synthesis was blocked whereas 6-keto-$PGF_{1\alpha}$ levels rose threefold. OKY-046 prevented tubular necrosis, in contrast to ibuprofen.[233]<br>Treatment of spontaneously hypertensive rats with 20 mg/kg for 100 d ameliorated the development of hypertension in one study,[234] whereas 18 mg/kg/d administered to 43-d-old SHR lowered blood pressure after 1 week but not after 2 weeks in another.[235]<br>In patients with essential hypertension, 600 mg/d or 400 mg bolus did not change blood pressure, but potentiated the hypotensive effect of the angiotensin-I-converting enzyme inhibitor SQ 14,255.[236]<br>Gastric mucosal erosion in rats under water-immersion stress was inhibited by OKY-046, with concurrent increases in mucosal blood flow and increased acid output.[237]<br>Chronic administration (10 mg/kg and 100 mg/kg, b.i.d., p.o.) to rabbits on high-lipid diets accelerated $PGI_2$ production from endogenous and exogenous AA in the aorta, even in the absence of platelets.[208]<br>For the general pharmacology of OKY-046, see References 238-240. |
| 23. | *E*-3-[4-(1-Imidazolyl)-methylphenyl]-2-methyl-prop-2-enoic acid.[78] | 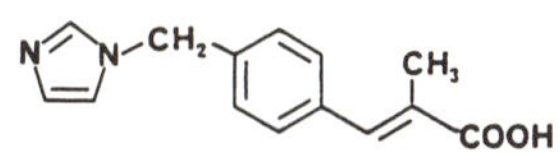 | $C_{14}H_{14}N_2O_2$ (242) | Inhibited the synthesis of $TxB_2$ from $PGH_2$ by a rabbit-platelet suspension, $IC_{50}$ 4 n*M* (RTLC), with no effect on cyclooxygenase or prostacyclin synthetase ($IC_{50} \geqslant 100\ \mu M$).[78] |
| 24. | 5-[2-(1-Imidazolyl)-ethoxy]thiophene-2-carboxylic acid (LG 82-4-00) | 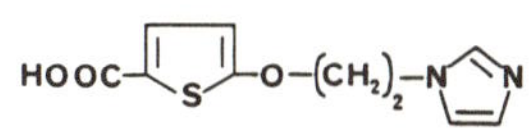 | $C_{10}H_{10}N_2O_3S$ (238) | Inhibited $TxB_2$ synthesis in thrombin-stimulated washed human platelets, $IC_{50}$ 1.1 $\mu M$, and aggregation and $TxB_2$ synthesis ($IC_{50}$ 6 $\mu M$) in human PRP induced by low-dose collagen (RIA). $PGI_2$ formation |

| | | | | |
|---|---|---|---|---|
| | | | | from AA by bovine coronary-artery slices was inhibited less than 10% at 100 $\mu M$.[91] |
| 25. | 3-(1-Imidazolylmethyl)-indole | 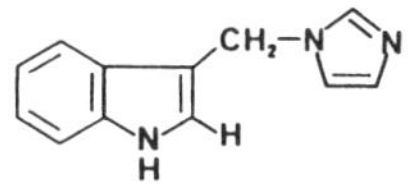 | $C_{12}H_{11}N_3$ (197) | Inhibited the synthesis of $TxA_2$ from $PGH_2$ using human-platelet microsomes, $IC_{50}$ $2 \times 10^{-8}M$ (bioassay). $IC_{50}$ $6.5 \times 10^{-4}M$ for prostacyclin synthetase, $>10^{-3}M$ for $PGH_2$ synthetase.[241]<br>In glucose-fed diabetic rats, weight gain, food consumption, and insulin levels were reduced by 18 or 55 mg/kg p.o. daily.[40] |
| 26. | 2-Cyclopropyl-3-(1-imidazolylmethyl)indole | 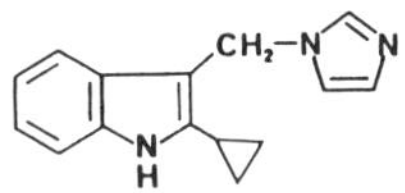 | $C_{15}H_{15}N_3$ (237) | Inhibited the synthesis of $TxA_2$ from $PGH_2$ using human-platelet microsomes, $IC_{50}$ $1 \times 10^{-10}M$ (bioassay). $IC_{50}$ $8.4 \times 10^{-7}M$ for prostacyclin synthetase, $>10^{-4}M$ for $PGH_2$ synthetase.[241] |
| 27. | 2-Isopropyl-3-(1-imidazolylmethyl)indole (UK-34,787) | 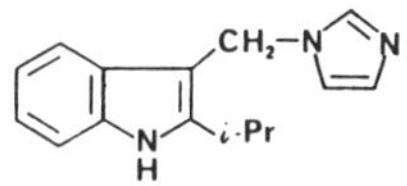 | $C_{15}H_{17}N_3$ (239) | Inhibited the conversion of $PGH_2$ to $TxA_2$ using human-platelet microsomes, $IC_{50}$ $1.7 \times 10^{-8}M$ (bioassay). $IC_{50} > 10^{-4}M$ for prostacyclin synthetase and $PGH_2$ synthetase.[241]<br>The aggregation of human PRP and the release reaction induced by NaAA (1.7 m*M*) was inhibited in samples from some donors by $10^{-4}$—$10^{-8}M$ ("responders") but not in others by $10^{-4}M$ ("nonresponders"). $TxB_2$ and MDA synthesis were inhibited similarly in both groups.[242,243]<br>AA-induced mortality in mice was prevented by pretreatment (2 h) with 25—100 mg/kg, p.o.[20]<br>Prolongs pentobarbitone sleeping time in rats at a dose similar to that needed for complete inhibition of thromboxane synthesis (10 mg/kg p.o.).[79] |
| 28. | 3-(1*H*-Imidazol-1-ylmethyl)-2-methyl-1*H*-indole-1-propionic acid (UK-38,485)[248] Dazmegrel | 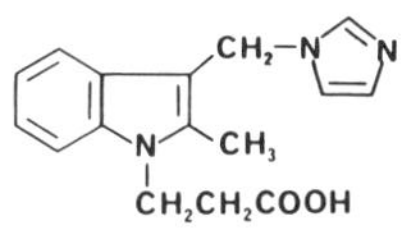 | $C_{16}H_{17}N_3O_2$ (238) | Inhibited human-blood-platelet microsomal $TxA_2$ synthetase, $IC_{50}$ $1.8 \times 10^{-8}M$ (RIA), with negligible effects on PG endoperoxide synthetase (RSV microsomes) and $PGI_2$ synthesis (pig-aortic microsomes) at $10^{-4}M$. Inhibited collagen-induced aggregation of human PRP, $IC_{50}$ $3 \times 10^{-5}M$.[244] In human whole blood stimulated by collagen, $PGD_2$ production was increased (RIA). Inhibition of aggregation due to AA (but not collagen) was more common in whole blood than PRP and was enhanced in both by theophyl- |

**Table 1 (continued)**
**IMIDAZOLES**

| No. | Name of compound | Structure | Formula (mol wt) | Biological activity |
|---|---|---|---|---|
| | | | | line.[245] The aggregation of rabbit PRP due to ADP was inhibited only if pig-aortic microsomes (a source of $PGI_2$ synthetase) were present, in contrast to aspirin where no inhibition was found.[244] Coadministration of forskolin (a stimulator of adenylate cyclase) and dazmegrel to rats potentiated the effects of either drug alone in inhibiting *ex vivo* aggregation of PRP induced by collagen.[246] In clotting blood from rabbits and dogs treated with UK-38,485, serum $TxB_2$ levels were reduced and those of 6-keto-$PGF_{1\alpha}$ increased (RIA).[244] In swine, elevations of 6-keto-$PGF_{1\alpha}$ were less pronounced.[247] In dogs, 1 mg/kg, p.o. reduced serum $TxB_2$ by 90% at 6 h, and by 50% after 15 h, being more potent and longer acting than dazoxiben.[244,248] In horses, serum $TxB_2$ levels were decreased with increased serum 6-keto-$PGF_{1\alpha}$ levels.[249] For a study of the pharmacokinetics in rabbits, see Reference 250. |
| | | | | In healthy volunteers, oral doses (10—100 mg) inhibited serum $TxB_2$ (>99% at 1 h for 40—100 mg) for up to 24 h (0—35% inhibition). Urinary excretion of 2,3-dinor-6-keto-$PGF_{1\alpha}$, and plasma 6-keto-$PGF_{1\alpha}$ were not significantly increased following 50 mg b.i.d. for 7 d. In platelet suspensions stimulated *ex vivo* with AA and in serum of incubated whole blood, $TxB_2$ concentrations were reduced and $PGI_2$, $PGE_2$, and $PGD_2$ increased.[251] In a 2-week, multiple-dose, double-blind trial in man, platelet count and bleeding time were unchanged. A dose of 200 mg, t.i.d. was needed to suppress circadian serum $TxB_2$ by >90% at all times. Elimination was first order with a half life of 0.88 h.[252] |

No protection was afforded against *E. coli* endotoxin infusion in rats by 2 × 15 mg/kg, i.v. even though elevation of plasma $TxB_2$ was prevented.[152] However, in sheep, 2 mg/kg reduced endotoxin-induced pulmonary vasoconstriction and microvascular permeability.[253] In horses, UK-38,485 administered before *E. coli* endotoxin prevented the rise in $TxB_2$ and lactate without altering the clinical response.[254] Pretreatment of neonatal piglets blocked the pulmonary gas exchange and hemodynamic abnormalities induced by i.v. infusion of Group B streptococcal.[255]

In a model of coronary-artery occlusion in conscious rats, pretreatment with a combination of metoprolol (a β-blocker), 2 mg/kg, i.v. and dazmegrel, 5 mg/kg, i.v. reduced mortality at both 20 min and 16 h post occlusion from 60—75% (control or either drug alone) to 25% for the combined-treatment group. The effect was attributed to a decrease in terminal ventricular fibrillation.[256] In dogs with ischemia produced by coronary-artery occlusion, 3 mg/kg i.v., 30 min before occlusion attenuated the reduction of myocardial blood flow and coronary venous $O_2$-saturation, and increased myocardial oxygen uptake.[257] Similar treatment (5 mg/kg, i.v.) of dogs with intermittent (short-term) occlusion reduced the $O_2$-debt, and decreased the release of $K^+$, inorganic phosphate, and lactate.[258]

In a ligation-reperfusion model in anesthetized greyhounds, 3 mg/kg, i.v. 25 min after coronary-artery ligation failed to reduce the incidence of ventricular fibrillation on reperfusion 15 min later.[259]

No benefit in patients with Raynaud's syndrome at doses of 50 mg b.i.d., p.o. for 4 weeks.[260]

Lowers blood pressure in adult SHR with established hypertension at doses of 100 mg/kg daily after 4 d of treatment. Serum $TxB_2$ levels were suppressed (RIA) but urinary excretion of 2,3-nor-6-keto-$PGF_{1\alpha}$ was unchanged (GC/MS).[261] Acute (i.v.) treatment of

**Table 1 (continued)**
**IMIDAZOLES**

| No. | Name of compound | Structure | Formula (mol wt) | Biological activity |
|---|---|---|---|---|
| | | | | young SHR improved glomerular filtration rate and renal plasma flow but the effects were not sustained on chronic (6 weeks, p.o.) treatment.[262]<br>In a model of glomerulopathy in rats induced by i.v. injection of adriamycin (7.5 mg/kg), UK-38,485 [20 mg/kg injected i.p., t.i.d. for 5 d (14 d after adriamycin)] resulted in a significant reduction in proteinuria. Glomerular synthesis and urinary excretion of $TxB_2$ were normalized, but not abolished (RIA).[263] In a rat model of nephrotoxic serum nephritis, induced by infusion of glomerular basement membrane antibody, UK-38,485 completely inhibited platelet and glomerular $TxB_2$ synthesis and prevented the decrease of glomerular filtration rates in isolated glomeruli at 2 h, and 3 h (but not 1 h) after administration of nephrotic serum (RIA).[264] However, in the same model, infusion of UK-38,485, 0.33 mg/kg, i.v. 24 h and 14 d after administration of nephrotic serum had no effect on renal plasma flow or glomerular filtration rate.[265] In ablated rats, glomerular filtration rate was increased by UK-38,485, in contrast to the effect of indomethacin.[266] In a model of acute renal failure induced by a low dose of *E. coli* endotoxin in mice, dazmegrel 270 mg/kg i.p. before (30 min) and after (6 h) challenge was ineffective.[267]<br>In healthy volunteers, 14 d dosing with dazmegrel reduced urinary $TxB_2$ (68%) and serum $TxB_2$ (79%) without affecting urinary 6-keto-$PGF_{1\alpha}$ or PAH or inulin clearance (RIA).[268]<br>In insulin-dependent diabetics, albumin-excretion rates (AER) in patients with microalbuminuria were mark- |

edly reduced after 8 and 16 weeks of oral treatment (100 mg b.i.d.). The AER rose to pretreatment levels within 12 weeks of stopping the drug. There was no change in mean blood-glucose levels.[269] In a separate study, no effect was found on the severity of diabetic retinopathy over a 4-month period.[270]

In rats, 1 or 5 mg (but not 25 mg), p.o. 2 h before challenge reduced gastric damage due to acidified taurocholate at 30 min. *Ex vivo* $TxB_2$ synthesis by gastric mucosa was inhibited by oral doses of 5 and 25 mg at 2 h (RIA).[271]

In swine fed on a high-cholesterol, high-fat diet, UK-38,485 (10 mg/kg p.o. q.i.d. for 10 d) restored the elevation in serum $TxB_2$ to that of controls.[272]

In a cerebral-ischemia model in cats, 3 mg/kg, i.v. before or after occlusion of the right middle cerebral artery (4 h) and reperfusion (2 h) was of no benefit in modifying the evolution of cerebral infarction.[273]

In mice with pentylenetetrazole-induced seizures, 50 mg/kg decreased brain $TxB_2$ production after 2 min of convulsive activity but had no effect on brain 6-keto-$PGF_{1\alpha}$ or the seizure threshold.[274]

Chronic administration in normotensive rats (100 mg/kg/d) for 7 d attenuated the vascular response to periarterial nerve stimulation and angiotensin II but not that due to norepinephrine.[275,276] Similar results were found in spontaneously hypertensive rats, although a lower dose (30 mg/kg/d for 7 d) was inactive.[276]

UK-38,485 did not affect heterotopic heart-graft survival in rats.[277]

For a study of 8 analogues, see Reference 79. For structure-activity relationships in the series, see Reference 248.

29. 5-[(1*H*-Imidazol-1-yl)-methyl]benzofuran-2-carboxylic acid[278]

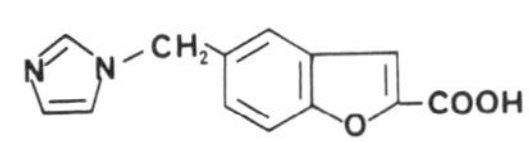

$C_{13}H_{10}N_2O_3$ (242)

Inhibited the conversion of $PGH_2$ to $TxB_2$ by human-platelet microsomes, $IC_{50}$ $3.4 \times 10^{-8} M$ (RIA).[79,278]

For a study of structure-activity relationships in this series of compounds, see Reference 278.

**Table 1 (continued)**
**IMIDAZOLES**

| No. | Name of compound | Structure | Formula (mol wt) | Biological activity |
|---|---|---|---|---|
| 30. | 5-[(1*H*-Imidazol-1-yl)-methyl]benzo[b]thiophene-2-carboxylic acid[278] | 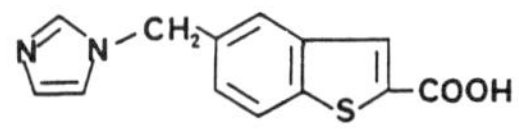 | $C_{13}H_{10}N_2O_2S$ (258) | Inhibited the conversion of $PGH_2$ to $TxB_2$ by human-platelet microsomes, $IC_{50}$ 2.1 × $10^{-8}$*M* (RIA).[79,278] |
| 31. | 5-[(1*H*-Imidazol-1-yl)-methyl]indole-2-carboxylic acid[278] | 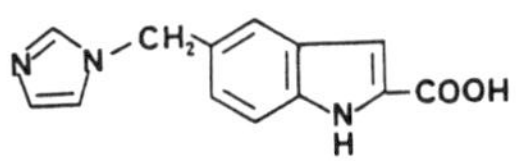 | $C_{13}H_{11}N_3O_2$ (241) | Inhibited the conversion of $PGH_2$ to $TxB_2$ by human-platelet microsomes, $IC_{50}$ 5.0 × $10^{-9}$*M* (RIA).[79,278] |
| 32. | 6-[(1*H*-Imidazol-1-yl)-methyl]benzofuran-2-carboxylic acid[278] | 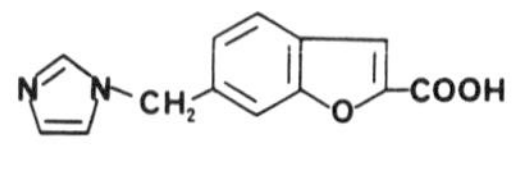 | $C_{13}H_{10}N_2O_3$ (242) | Inhibited the conversion of $PGH_2$ to $TxB_2$ by human-platelet microsomes, $IC_{50}$ 2.0 × $10^{-8}$*M* (RIA).[79,278] |
| 33. | 6-[(1*H*-Imidazol-1-yl)methyl]benzo[b]thiophene-2-carboxylic acid[278] | 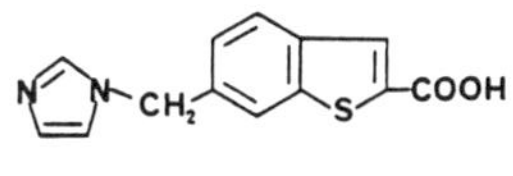 | $C_{13}H_{10}N_2O_2S$ (258) | Inhibited the conversion of $PGH_2$ to $TxB_2$ by human-platelet microsomes, $IC_{50}$ 1.8 × $10^{-8}$*M* (RIA).[79,278] |
| 34. | 6-[(1*H*-Imidazol-1-yl)methyl]indole-2-carboxylic acid[278] | 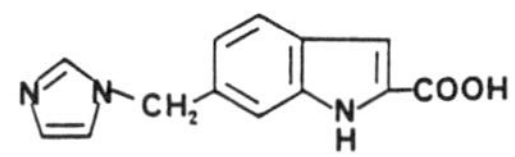 | $C_{13}H_{11}N_3O_2$ (241) | Inhibited the conversion of $PGH_2$ to $TxB_2$ by human-platelet microsomes, $IC_{50}$ 3.3 × $10^{-8}$*M* (RIA).[79,278] |
| 35. | 3-Methyl-6-[(1*H*-imidazol-1-yl)methyl]-benzo[b]thiophene-2-carboxylic acid[278] [UK-45,651] | 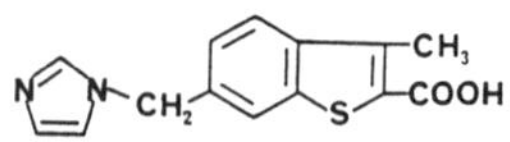 | $C_{14}H_{12}N_2O_2S$ (272) | Inhibited the conversion of $PGH_2$ to $TxB_2$ by human-platelet microsomes, $IC_{50}$ 5.2 × $10^{-9}$. Inhibited serum $TxB_2$ production in dogs following 1 mg/kg p.o. (RIA).[79,278] |
| 36. | 3-Methyl-2-[(1*H*-imidazol-1-yl)-methyl]benzo[b]thiophene-5-carboxylic acid[279] [UK-47,852] | 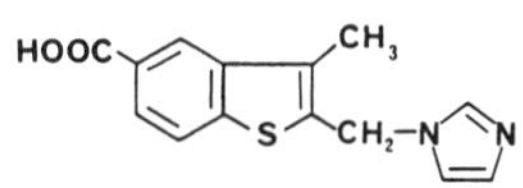 | $C_{14}H_{12}N_2O_2S$ (272) | Inhibited the conversion of $PGH_2$ to $TxB_2$ by human-platelet microsomes, $IC_{50}$ 1.7 × $10^{-8}$*M* (RIA). In rabbits, 0.1 mg/kg i.v. produced complete inhibition of $TxB_2$ production 75 min after dosing. In dogs, 0.5 mg/kg p.o. produced complete inhibition of |

| | | | | |
|---|---|---|---|---|
| | | | | serum $TxB_2$ production for $\geqslant$ 6 h (RIA).[79,279]<br>For a similar study of analogues, see References 79,279. |
| 37. | 6-[(5-Methylimidazol-1-yl)methyl]-2-naphthoic acid hydrochloride | 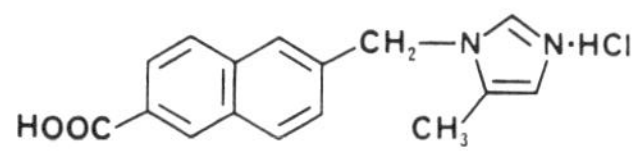 | $C_{16}H_{15}ClN_2O_2$ (302) | Inhibits the $TxB_2$ production in washed human platelets induced with thrombin, $IC_{50}$ 3.6 × $10^{-8}M$, and in rat PRP by 76%, 5 h following a 10 mg/kg, p.o. dose (RIA). In a thrombus model in dogs, 0.1 mg/kg, i.v. prevented cyclical-flow variations induced by stenosis of the coronary artery.[280] |
| 38. | 6-[(Imidazol-1-yl)methyl]-5,6,7,8-tetrahydronaphthalene-2-carboxylic acid, hydrochloride [DP-1904] | 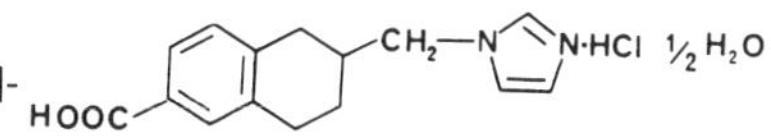 | $C_{15}H_{17}ClN_2O_2$ (292) | Inhibited serum $TxB_2$ production in the rat after oral doses of 0.1—10 mg/kg. Infarct size in rats following 1 h coronary-artery ligation and 48 h reperfusion was reduced by 10 mg/kg × 3, i.p. and p.o. given after ligation (based on CPK activities). The duration of early ventricular tachycardia following 15-min ventricular ligation in rats was shortened by 10 mg/kg, i.v.<br>Blood pressure in SHR was reduced, and development of hypertension in young SHR delayed by chronic treatment with 10 mg/kg/d, p.o.[281] |
| 39. | 1-(3-Benzyloxy-1[*E*]-octenyl)imidazole (CBS-645) (Midazogrel) | 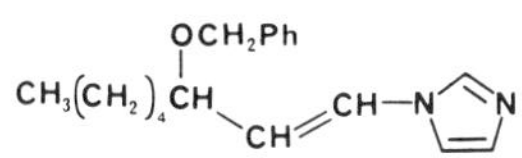 | $C_{18}H_{24}N_2O$ (284) | Inhibited the production of $TxB_2$ from NaAA by resuspended human or rabbit platelets, $IC_{50}$ 6μ*M*, or rat platelets, $IC_{50}$ 10μ*M* (RTLC).<br>$TxB_2$ formation in clotting blood was inhibited up to 4 h following doses of 12.5—50 mg/kg, i.g. (rabbit) and 50—400 mg/kg, p.o. (human) (RIA). Bleeding time in the rat was doubled 4 h following an oral dose of 25 mg/kg.[282] |
| 40. | 1-[3-(4-Methoxybenzyloxy)-2-(4-carboxybenzyloxy)-propyl]imidazole[283] | 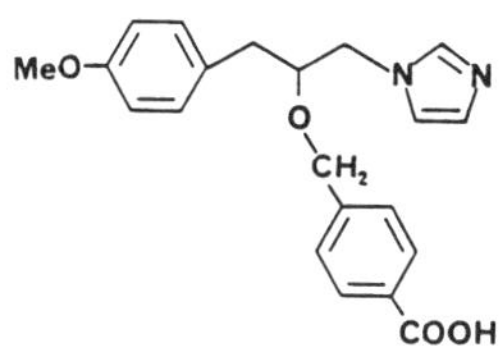 | $C_{22}H_{24}N_2O_5$ (396) | Inhibited thromboxane synthesis in human PRP induced by collagen, $IC_{50}$ 6.7 μ*M* (RIA), and from $PGH_2$ by human-platelet microsomes, $IC_{50}$ 1.1 μ*M*.[283] |

## Table 1 (continued)
## IMIDAZOLES

| No. | Name of compound | Structure | Formula (mol wt) | Biological activity |
|---|---|---|---|---|
| 41. | 1-[3-(4-Methoxybenzyloxy)-2-(4-propoxycarbonylbenzyloxy)propyl]-imidazole[283] | 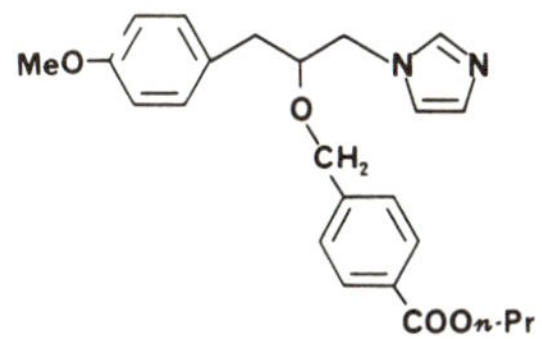 | $C_{25}H_{30}N_2O_5$ (438) | Inhibited thromboxane synthesis in human PRP stimulated by collagen, $IC_{50}$ 0.18 $\mu M$ (RIA).[283] |
| 42. | 2,2-Dimethyl-6-[2-(1*H*-imidazol-1-yl)-1-[[(4-methoxyphenyl)methoxy]methyl]ethoxy]hexanoic acid (SC 41156) | 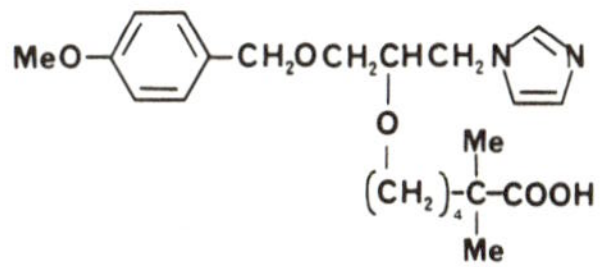 | $C_{22}H_{32}N_2O_5$ (404) | Inhibited collagen-induced $TxA_2$ formation in human platelets, $IC_{50}$ 0.13 $\mu M$ (10-fold more potent than dazoxiben), with no effects on $PGI_2$ formation by guinea-pig-aorta microsomes at $10^{-4}M$. 6-Keto-$PGF_{1\alpha}$ formation was potentiated in collagen-stimulated human whole blood. $TxB_2$ formation induced by collagen *ex vivo* was inhibited in whole blood from guinea pigs, $ED_{50}$ 3.4 mg/kg, p.o. (1 h); dogs, $ED_{50}$ 0.7 mg/kg, p.o. (1 h); and rhesus monkeys, $ED_{50}$ 0.08 mg/kg, p.o. (1 h). Duration of action in rhesus monkeys exceeded 24 h at doses of 1—10 mg/kg, p.o.[284,284a] |
| 43. | RO-22-4679 (a 1-substituted imidazole) | | | Ventricular fibrillation induced by circumflex coronary-artery occlusion in conscious mongrel dogs was reduced by 0.3 mg/kg/h i.v. Platelet deposition into the infarcted myocardium was significantly reduced.[285,286] Platelet deposition in the oxygenator and endo- and epicardium during cardiopulmonary bypass in dogs was reduced, though not significantly.[287] |
| 44. | Ketoconazole | 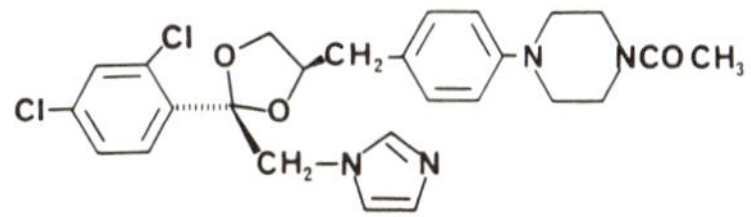 | $C_{26}H_{28}Cl_2N_4O_4$ (531) | Inhibited the synthesis of $TxB_2$ from AA by a guinea-pig-lung preparation, $IC_{50}$ 1—2 × $10^{-4}M$ (increased $PGE_2$, $PGD_2$), and in human platelets, $IC_{50}$ ~ 3 × $10^{-5}M$ (with increase in $PGE_2$) (RTLC).[288] |

| | | | | |
|---|---|---|---|---|
| | | | | In humans, 400 mg p.o., reduced $TxB_2$ elevation induced by arm ischemia (cuff). In nonstressed volunteers, 400 mg p.o. reduced plasma $TxB_2$ levels at 6, 8 h to 5 pg/ml from an initial value of 170 pg/ml.[289] In volunteers with cold-induced vasoconstriction of the forearm, the same dose also reduced $TxB_2$ levels but did not influence skin temperature or blood flow.[290] In a limb-ischemia model in dogs (thigh tourniquet), ketoconazole (2 × 400 mg) decreased baseline plasma $TxB_2$ levels but had no effect on tissue Tx synthesis or permeability.[291]<br>Infusion, (2.5 mg/kg bolus followed by 10 mg/kg/h for 2 h), 1 h after challenge prevented white-blood-cell sequestration in the inflammatory response in dogs following acid aspiration, reversed plasma-mediated negative inotropism, and restored cardiac output.[292] |
| 45. | Clotrimazole (2-Chlorophenyldiphenyl methylimidazole) | 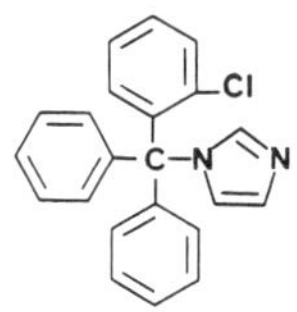 | $C_{22}H_{17}ClN_2$ (345) | Inhibited $TxA_2$ synthesis by rabbit PRP induced by $TxB_2$ collagen, $IC_{50}$ 10 $\mu M$ (bioassay).[3] Decreased production from AA (RTLC) in cell-free guinea-pig-lung preparation ($IC_{50}$ 3 × $10^{-6}M$) and in suspended human platelets ($IC_{50}$ 3.7 × $10^{-7}M$) with increased production of $PGE_2$ (and $PGD_2$ in the lung preparation).[288]<br>Inhibited synthesis of $TxB_2$ in human leukocytes from endogenous AA, $IC_{50}$ 0.07 μg/ml, with only a small increase in $PGE_2$ (RIA). Decreased $PGE_2$ output at 30 μg/ml. At 3—30 μg/ml, inhibited the response of lymphocytes to PHA.[44]<br>Clotrimazole is a topical antifungal. |
| 46. | Miconazole (1-[2-(2,4-Dichlorophenyl)-2-(2,4-dichlorobenzyloxy)-ethyl]imidazole) | 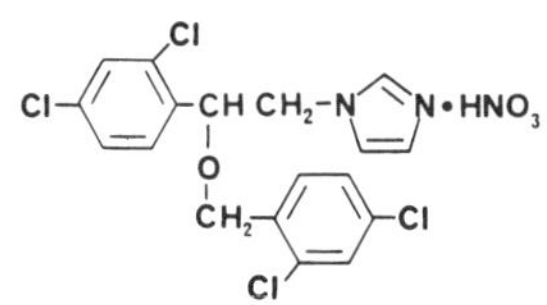 | $C_{18}H_{14}Cl_4N_2O$ (416) | Inhibited $TxB_2$ synthesis from AA by a guinea-pig-lung preparation, $IC_{50}$ 1—2 × $10^{-4}M$ (increased $PGE_2$, $PGD_2$) and in human platelets, $IC_{50}$ ~ 3 × $10^{-6}M$ (increased $PGE_2$) (RTLC).[288] |

**Table 1 (continued)**
**IMIDAZOLES**

| No. | Name of compound | Structure | Formula (mol wt) | Biological activity |
|---|---|---|---|---|
| 47. | Imidazo[1,5-a]pyridine-5-hexanoic acid (CGS-13080) (Pirmagrel) | 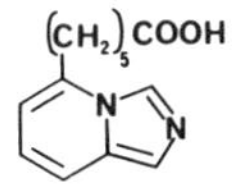 | $C_{13}H_{16}N_2O_2$ (232) | Inhibited $TxB_2$ synthesis from $PGH_2$ in a cell-free preparation from human platelets, $IC_{50}$ 3 n*M* (RTLC). $IC_{50}$s for $PGH_2$ synthetase 3.6 m*M*, prostacyclin synthetase 530 μ*M*, lipoxygenase >1 m*M*. Blocked $TxB_2$ synthetase in washed human platelets stimulated with A-23187 with increased $PGE_2$ production.[293] In human blood incubated with CGS-13080 *in vitro*, serum $TxB_2$ was completely inhibited and $PGI_2$ generation stimulated.[294]<br>In rats, ≤1 mg/kg, p.o. suppressed elevations in plasma $TxB_2$ induced by ionophore A-23187 with increases in $PGE_2$ and 6-keto-$PGF_{1\alpha}$.[293] In rabbits dosed with 5 or 10 mg, s.c., serum levels of $TxB_2$ were inhibited 81% at 2 h and 56% at 24 h. Collagen-induced platelet aggregation was inhibited 2 h after administration of 5 mg, s.c. Serum levels of 6-keto-$PGF_{1\alpha}$ were increased 587% at 2 h relative to control. In human blood, serum $TxB_2$ was inhibited by 100 ng/ml with increased 6-keto-$PGF_{1\alpha}$ (RIA).[294] Sera from coagulated venous blood of beagles following 3 mg/kg, p.o. dosing showed marked inhibition of $TxA_2$ production and increased $PGI_2$ and $PGE_2$ (RIA). $PGI_2$ and $PGE_2$ remained elevated at 18 h.[295]<br>In rats, 3 mg/kg, p.o. inhibited platelet $TxB_2$ production stimulated by i.v. collagen (100 μg/kg) (RIA) with increases in 6-keto-$PGF_{1\alpha}$, and partially inhibited thrombocytopenia.[73]<br>In a thrombotic model of sudden death in mice, 1—10 mg/kg, i.v. protected against AA-induced sudden death but not that due to the thromboxane agonist U-46619.[296] PAF-induced sudden death in |

rabbits was prevented (83%) by 2.5 mg/kg, i.v., with minimal increases in mean arterial blood pressure and no increase in plasma $TxB_2$. (RIA)[160]

In a thrombus model in dogs, induced by electrical stimulation of the circumflex coronary-artery wall, i.v. infusion of 1 mg/kg/h starting 30 min before challenge reduced $TxB_2$ generation, thrombus mass, and coronary-artery occlusion.[297]

$TxB_2$ production from AA, but not aggregation, in cat PRP was inhibited by 1—10 μg/ml (RIA). Cats were protected from acute myocardial ischemia by 1 mg/kg, i.v. followed by 1 mg/kg/h infusion (plasma and tissue CK activities and tissue amino-nitrogen concentrations) with accompanying inhibition of $TxA_2$ synthesis.[298] In anesthetized cats with total occlusion of the anterior descending coronary artery, 3 or 9 mg/kg, i.v. attenuated the decrease in ventricular fibrillation threshold, with a 66% reduction in spontaneous ventricular arrythmia in the first 30 min of occlusion at the high dose.[299]

CGS-13080 attenuated the aggravation of cellular damage caused by infusion of PAF 30 min after coronary ligation in cats.[300]

In human volunteers, maximal reduction of $TxB_2$ occurred after 0.5—1 h (98—99% with 25—100 mg doses). Half-life ~1 h, but 50% of original mean $TxB_2$ concentration was achieved at 4—6 h. $PGE_2$ and 6-keto-$PGF_{1\alpha}$ levels were increased (RIA).[301] Oral doses of 100, 200 mg prolonged bleeding time and inhibited AA-induced aggregation (but not that due to collagen) *ex vivo*. Excretion of 2,3-dinor-6-keto-$PGF_{1\alpha}$, the major urinary metabolite of $PGI_2$, was increased 100% by the high dose (GC-MS), in contrast to aspirin.[100,302]

In patients with severe peripheral vascular disease, long-term administration of CGS-13080, 100 or 200 mg, q.i.d. had no effect on *ex vivo* platelet aggregation, the circulating platelet aggregate ratio or the

**Table 1 (continued)**
**IMIDAZOLES**

| No. | Name of compound | Structure | Formula (mol wt) | Biological activity |
|---|---|---|---|---|
| | | | | bleeding time despite almost maximal inhibition of platelet thromboxane 1 h after dosing.[303] For the synthesis and a study of 21 analogues and derivatives, see Reference 304. For a review, see Reference 305. |
| 48. | Nizofenone 1-[2-(2-Chlorobenzoyl)-4-nitrophenyl]-2-diethylaminomethyl-imidazole | 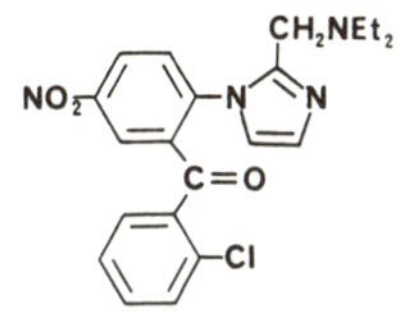 | $C_{21}H_{21}ClN_4O_3$ (413) | Inhibited the production of $TxB_2$ from AA by human-platelet microsomes at 0.3, 1 m*M* with increases in $PGD_2$, $PGE_2$, and $PGF_{2\alpha}$. $PGI_2$ synthesis from AA by rat aorta-wall rings was increased by 0.1, 0.3 m*M* (RTLC).[306] |
| 49. | Sodium 4-[α-hydroxy-5-(1-imidazolyl)-2-methylbenzyl]-3,5-dimethylbenzoate, dihydrate Y-20811 | 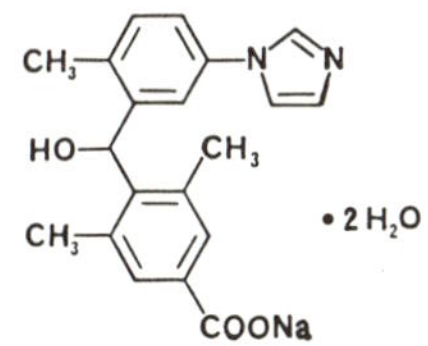 | $C_{20}H_{23}N_2O_5Na$ (394) | Inhibited $TxB_2$ production from AA by human-platelet microsomes, $IC_{50}$ $2.2 \times 10^{-8}$ *M*, without effects on cyclooxygenase or prostacyclin synthetase at $10^{-4}$ *M* (RTLC). Inhibited aggregation of human, rabbit, and guinea-pig PRP induced by AA, but not by ADP unless aortic rings were present.[307] In rabbits, 1 mg/kg, p.o. decreased serum $TxB_2$ with increased 6-keto-$PGF_{1\alpha}$ whereas 3 mg/kg, p.o. inhibited AA-induced platelet aggregation, in both cases for over 48 h. Y-20811 protected rabbits against AA-induced sudden death at 1 mg/kg.[307] |
| 50. | Burimamide | 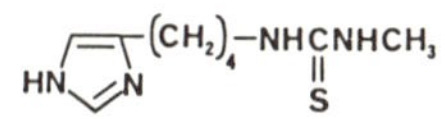 | $C_9H_{16}N_4S$ (212) | Inhibited $TxA_2$ synthesis from $PGH_2$ in indomethacin-treated human-platelet microsomes, $IC_{50}$ 5.6 μg/ml (25 μ*M*) (bioassay). No inhibition of endoperoxide or $PGI_2$ synthetase at 100 μg/ml.[308,309] NaAA-induced aggregation of human PRP was inhibited by 25—120 μ*M*, the degree of inhibition being dependent on the concentration of NaAA used. ADP-induced aggregation was not inhibited at 1.2 m*M*. Most active member of a series of $H_2$-receptor antagonists and histamine analogues tested.[309] |

Protected rabbits from NaAA-induced sudden death at a dose of 1 mg/kg i.v.[308]

## REFERENCES TO TABLE 1


1. **Moncada, S., Bunting, S., Mullane, K., Thorogood, P., Vane, J. R., Raz, A., and Needleman, P.,** Imidazole: a selective inhibitor of thromboxane synthetase, *Prostaglandins,* 13, 611, 1977.
2. **Diczfalusy, U. and Hammarström, S.,** Inhibitors of thromboxane synthetase in human platelets, *FEBS Lett.,* 82, 107, 1977.
3. **Lewis, G. P. and Watts, I. S.,** Prostaglandin endoperoxides, thromboxane $A_2$ and adenosine diphosphate in collagen-induced aggregation of rabbit platelets, *Br. J. Pharmacol.,* 75, 623, 1982.
4. **Chignard, M., Vargaftig, B. B., Sors, H., and Dray, F.,** Synthesis of thromboxane $B_2$ in incubates of dog platelet-rich plasma with arachidonic acid and its inhibition by different drugs, *Biochem. Biophys. Res. Commun.,* 85, 1631, 1978.
5. **Neddleman, P., Bryan, B., Wyche, A., Bronson, S. D., Eakins, K., Ferrendelli, J. A., and Minkes, M.,** Thromboxane synthetase inhibitors as pharmacological tools: differential biochemical and biological effects of platelet suspensions, *Prostaglandins,* 14, 897, 1977.
6. **Needleman, P., Raz, A., Ferrendelli, J. A., and Minkes, M.,** Application of imidazole as a selective inhibitor of thromboxane synthetase in human platelets, *Proc. Natl. Acad. Sci. U.S.A.,* 74, 1716, 1977.
7. **Vincent, J. E., Zijlstra, F. J., and van Vliet, H.,** Effect of an inhibitor of $TXA_2$ synthesis and of $PGE_2$ on the formation of 12-L-hydroxy-5,8,10-heptadecatrienoic acid in human platelets, *Adv. Prostaglandin Thromboxane Res.,* 6, 463, 1980.
8. **Raz, A., Aharony, D., and Kenig-Wakshal R.,** Biosynthesis of thromboxane $B_2$ and 12-L-hydroxy-5,8,10-heptadecatrienoic acid in human platelets: evidence for a common enzymatic pathway, *Eur. J. Biochem.,* 86, 447, 1978.
9. **Fitzpatrick, F. A., and Gorman, R. R.,** A comparison of imidazole and 9,11-azoprosta-5,13-dienoic acid, *Biochim. Biophys. Acta,* 539, 162, 1978.
10. **Fitzpatrick, F. A., and Gorman, R. R.,** Platelet rich plasma transforms exogenous prostaglandin endoperoxide $H_2$ into thromboxane $A_2$, *Prostaglandins,* 14, 881, 1977.
11. **Steinhauer, H. B., Lubrich, L., Guenter, B., and Schollmeyer, P.,** Response of human platelets to inhibition of thromboxane synthesis, *Clin. Hemorheol.,* 3, 1, 1983.
12. **Nijkamp, F. P., Moncada, S., White, H. L., and Vane, J. R.,** Diversion of prostaglandin endoperoxide metabolism by selective inhibition of thromboxane $A_2$ biosynthesis in lung, spleen or platelets, *Eur. J. Pharmacol.,* 44, 179, 1977.
13. **Knope, R., Moe, G. K., Saunders, J., and Tuttle, R.,** Myocardial effects of imidazole, *J. Pharmacol. Exp. Ther.,* 185, 29, 1973.
14. **Anhut, H., Bernauer, W., and Peskar, B. A.,** Pharmacological modification of thromoboxane and prostaglandin release in cardiac anaphylaxis, *Prostaglandins,* 15, 889, 1978.
15. **Smith, E. F., III, Lefer, A. M., and Smith, J. B.,** Influence of thromboxane inhibition on the severity of myocardial ischemia in cats, *Can. J. Physiol. Pharmacol.,* 58, 294, 1980.
16. **Eddy, L. J., Oei, H. H. H., and Glenn, T. M.,** Improved lactate extraction in dogs with coronary artery ligation following administration of a thromboxane synthetase inhibitor, *Res. Commun. Chem. Pathol. Pharmacol.,* 39, 87, 1983.
17. **Kumar, C. and Singh, M.,** Pharmacological interventions and myocardial infarct size in rat, *Eur. J. Pharmacol.,* 109, 117, 1985.
18. **Burke, S. E., Antonaccio, M. J., and Lefer, A. M.,** Lack of thromboxane $A_2$ involvement in the arrhythmias occurring during acute myocardial ischemia in dogs, *Basic Res. Cardiol.,* 77, 411, 1982.
19. **Puig-Parellada, P. and Planas, J. M.,** Action of selective inhibitor of thromboxane synthetase on experimental thrombosis induced by arachidonic acid in rabbits, *Lancet, ii,* 40, 1977.

20. **De Clerck, F., Loots, W., Somers, Y., Van Gorp, L., Verheyen, A., and Wouters, L.,** Thromboxane $A_2$-induced vascular endothelial cell damage and respirator smooth muscle cell contraction: inhibition by flunarizine, a $Ca^{2+}$-overload blocker, *Arch. Int. Pharmacodyn. Ther.*, 274, 4, 1985.
21. **Short, B. L., Gardiner, W. M., Mishik, A. N., Ramwell, P. W., Walker, D., and Fletcher, J. R.,** Thromboxane synthetase inhibitors in septic shock, *Adv. Shock Res.*, 10, 143, 1983.
22. **Cook, J. A., Wise, W. C., and Halushka, P. V.,** Elevated thromboxane levels in the rat during endotoxic shock: protective effects of imidazole, 13-azaprostanoic acid, or essential fatty acid deficiency, *J. Clin. Invest.*, 65, 227, 1980.
23. **Smith, E. F., III, Tabas, J. H., and Lefer, A. M.,** Beneficial effects of imidazole in endotoxic shock, *Prostaglandins Med.*, 4, 215, 1980.
24. **Littleton, M., Prancan, A., Simon, D.,** Thromboxane $A_2$ in the development of shock in the rabbit, *Pharmacologist*, 27, 242, 1985.
25. **Marita, O., Bekemeier, H., and Hirschelmann, R.,** Effect of antirheumatics and inhibitors of cyclooxygenase, lipoxygenases and thromboxane synthetase on cobra venom factor rat paw edema, *Biomed. Biochim. Acta*, 43, S 291, 1984.
26. **Papanicolaou, N., Gkika, E. L., Gkikas, G., Bariety, J.,** Selective inhibition of renal thromboxane biosynthesis increased sodium excretion rate in normal and saline-loaded rats, *Clin. Sci.*, 68, 79, 1985.
27. **Herceg, R., Braunlich, H., and Bartha, J.,** Influence of an inhibition of thromboxane synthetase by imidazole on kidney function in rats during postnatal development, *Arch. Int. Pharmacodyn. Ther.*, 275, 151, 1985.
28. **Papanicolaou, N., Hatziantoniou, C., and Bariety, J.,** Selective inhibition of thromboxane synthesis partially protected while inhibition of angiotesin II formation did not protect rats against acute renal failure induced with glycerol, *Prostaglandins Leukotrienes Med.*, 21, 29, 1986.
29. **Burch, R. M., Knapp, D. R., Knapp and Halushka, P. V.,** Vasopressin stimulates thromboxane synthesis in the toad urinary bladder: effects of thromboxane synthesis inhibition, *Adv. Prostaglandin Thromboxane Res.*, 6, 505, 1980.
30. **Heersche, J. N. M. and Jez, D. H.,** The effect of imidazole and imidazole-analogues on bone resorption *in vitro:* a suggested role for thromboxane $A_2$, *Prostaglandins*, 21, 401, 1981.
31. **Cowan, D. H.,** Platelet adherence to collagen: role of prostaglandin-thromboxane synthesis, *Br. J. Haemetol.*, 49, 425, 1981.
32. **Spagnuolo, P. J., Ellner, J. L., Hassid, A., and Dunn, M. J.,** Thromboxane $A_2$ mediates augmented polymorphonuclear leukocyte adhesiveness, *J. Clin. Invest.*, 66, 406, 1980.
33. **Dorsch, W., Hintschich, C., Neuhauser, J., and Weber, J.,** Sequential histamine inhalations cause increased reactivity in guinea pigs: role of platelets, thromboxanes and prostacyclin, *Arch. Pharmacol.*, 327, 148, 1984.
34. **Yanni, J. M. and Smith, W. L.,** Intravenous SRS-induced increases in tracheal mucous gel layer thickness: evidence for thromboxane involvement, *Prostaglandins*, 31, 19, 1986.
35. **Seeger, W., Wolf, H., Stähler, G., Neuhof, H., and Roka, L.,** Increased pulmonary vascular resistence and permeability due to arachidonate metabolism in isolated rabbit lungs, *Prostaglandins*, 23, 157, 1982.
36. **Patterson, G. A., Rock, P., Mitzner, W. A., Adkinson, N. F., Jr., and Sylvester, J. T.,** Effects of imidazole and indomethacin on fluid balance in isolated sheep lungs, *J. Appl. Physiol.*, 58, 892, 1985.
37. **Jakubowski, A., and Pick, E.,** The mechanism of action of lymphokines VII. Modulation of the action of macrophage migration inhibitory factor by antioxidants and drugs affecting thromboxane synthesis, *Immunopharmacology*, 6, 215, 1983.
38. **Kelly, J. P., Johnson, M. C., and Parker, C. W.,** Effect of inhibitors of arachidonic acid metabolism on mitogenesis in human lymphocytes: possible role of thromboxanes and products of the lipoxygenase pathway, *J. Immunol.*, 122, 1563, 1979.
39. **Parker, C. W., Stenson, W. F., Huber, M. G., and Kelly, J. P.,** Formation of thromboxane $B_2$ and hydroxyarachidonic acids in purified human lymphocytes in the presence and absence of PHA, *J. Immunol.*, 122, 1572, 1979.
40. **Lands, W. E. M., Sullivan, A. C., Tobias, L. D., and Triscari, J.,** European Patent, 028, 410.
41. **Fantozzi, R.,** Imidazole 2-hydroxybenzoate: a new antiinflammatory drug. Interaction with the arachidonic acid cascade, *Drugs Exp. Clin. Res.*, 10, 853, 1984.
42. **Pagella, P. G., Bellavite, O., Agozzino, S., Donà, G. C., Cremonesi, P., and De Santis, F.,** Pharmacological studies of imidazole 2-hydroxybenzoate (ITF 182), an antiinflammatory compound with an action on thromboxane $A_2$ production, *Arzneim.-Forsch.*, 33, 716, 1983.

42a. **Fumiagalli, M., Cunietti, E., Vaiani, G., Monti, M., Ferrari, F., and Gandini, R.,** Controlled clinical trial of imidazole 2-hydroxybenzoate (ITF 182) versus sulindac in patients with rheumatoid arthritis, *Clin. Ther.*, 8, 292, 1986.

43. **Pagella, P. G., Agozzino, S., Bellavite, O., Donà, G. C., and Mendola, N.,** Different sensitivity of basilar and saphenous arteries to thromboxane $A_2$-induced contractions: effect of imidazole 2-hydroxybenzoate (ITF 182), *Arzneim.-Forsch.*, 34, 1514, 1984.

44. **Gordon, D., Nouri, A. M. E., and Thomas, R. U.,** Selective inhibition of thromboxane biosynthesis in human blood mononuclear cells and the effects on mitogen-stimulated lymphocyte proliferation, *Br. J. Pharmacol.*, 74, 469, 1981.
45. **Tai, H.-H. and Yuan, B.,** On the inhibitory potency of imidazole and its derivatives on thromboxane synthetase, *Biochem. Biophys. Res. Commun.*, 80, 236, 1978.
46. **Yoshimoto, T., Yamamoto, S., and Hayaishi, O.,** Selective inhibition of prostaglandin endoperoxide thromboxane isomerase by 1-carboxyalkylimidazoles, *Prostaglandins*, 16, 529, 1978.
47. **Blackwell, G. J., Flower, R. J., Russel-Smith, N., Salmon, J. A., Thorogood, P. B., and Vane, J. R.,** 1-n-Butylimidazole: a potent and selective inhibitor of "thromboxane synthetase". *Br. J. Pharmacol.*, 64, 435P, 1978.
48. **Blackwell, G. J., Flower, R. J., Russel-Smith, N., Salmon, J. A., Thorogood, P. B., and Vane, J. R.,** Prostacyclin is produced in whole blood, *Br. J. Pharmacol.*, 64, 436P, 1978.
49. **Best, L. C., Holland, T. K., Jones, P. B. B., and Russell, R. G. G.,** The interrelationship between thromboxane biosynthesis, aggregation and 5-hydroxytryptamine secretion in human platelets *in vitro, Thromb. Haemostasis*, 43, 38, 1980.
50. **Lewis, G. P., Smith, J. R., and Williamson, I. H. M.,** Prostaglandin endoperoxides are more important than thromboxane $A_2$ in thrombus formation *in vivo, Thromb. Haemostasis*, 50, 241, 1983.
51. **Fitzpatrick, F. A. and Stringfellow, D.,** Influence of thromboxane synthetase inhibitors on virus replication in human lung fibroblasts *in vitro, Biochem. Biophys. Res. Commun.*, 116, 264, 1983.
52. **Wong, P. Y.-K., Lee, W. H., Chao, H.-W., and Cheung. W.-Y.,** The role of calmodulin in prostaglandin metabolism, *Ann. N.Y. Acad. Sci.*, 356, 179, 1980.
53. **Wong, P. Y.-K. and Cheung, W. Y.,** Calmodulin stimulates thromboxane synthesis in human platelets: studies with thromboxane synthetase inhibitors, *Prog. Lipid Res.*, 20, 447, 1981.
54. **Prancan, A. V., Lefort, J., Chignard, M., Gerozissis, K., Dray, F., and Vargaftig, B. B.,** L8027 and 1-nonylimidazole as non-selective inhibitors of thromboxane synthesis, *Eur. J. Pharmacol.*, 60, 287, 1979.
55. **Bunting, S., Castro, S., Salmon, J. A., and Moncada, S.,** The effect of cyclo-oxygenase and thromboxane synthetase inhibitors on shock induced by injection of heterologous blood in cats, *Thromb. Res.*, 30, 609, 1983.
56. **Harris, R. H., Fitzpatrick, T., Schmeling, J., Ryan, R., Klot, P., and Ramwell, P. W.,** Inhibition of dog platelet reactivity following 1-benzylimidazole administration, *Adv. Prostaglandin Thromboxane Res.*, 6, 457, 1980.
57. **Hall, E. R., Chen, Y.-C., Ho, T., and Wu, K. K.,** The reduction of platelet thrombi on damaged vessel wall by a thromboxane synthetase inhibitor in platelets, *Thromb. Res.*, 27, 501, 1982.
58. **Flower, R. J., Russell-Smith, N. C., Salmon, J. A., and Thorogood, P.,** 1-Benzylimidazole: a potent and selective inhibitor of "thromboxane synthetase" *Ex Vivo, Br. J. Pharmacol.*, 74, 791P, 1981.
59. **Tuttle, R. S., Garcia-Minor, C., and Simon, M.,** Cardiovascular effects of 1-benzylimidazole, *J. Pharmacol. Exp. Ther.*, 194, 624, 1975.
60. **Whittle, B. J. R., Kauffman, G. L., and Moncada, S.,** Vasoconstriction with thromboxane $A_2$ induces ulceration of the gastric musosa, *Nature (London)*, 292, 472, 1981.
61. **Saito, H., Idevra, T., and Takeuchi, J.** Effects of a selective thromboxane $A_2$ synthetase inhibitor on immune complex glomerulonephritis, *Nephron*, 36, 38, 1984.
62. **Stenson, W. F., Nickells, M. W., and Atkinson, J. P.,** Metabolism of exogenous arachidonic acid by murine macrophage-like tumor cell lines, *Prostaglandins*, 21, 675, 1981.
63. **Harris, D. N.,Greenberg, R., Phillips, M. B., Osman, G. H., Jr., and Antonaccio, M. J.,** Effect of SQ 80,338 (1-(3-phenyl-2-propenyl)-1-H-imidazole) on thromboxane synthetase activity and arachidonic acid-induced platelet aggregation and bronchoconstriction, *Adv. Prostaglandin Thromboxane Res.*, 6, 437, 1980.
64. **Greenberg, R., Antonaccio, M. J., and Steinbacher, T.,** Thromboxane $A_2$ mediated bronchoconstriction in the anesthetized guinea pig, *Eur. J. Pharmacol.*, 80, 19, 1982.
65. **Watkins, W. D., Hüttemeier, P. C., Kong, D., and Peterson, M. B.,** Thromboxane and pulmonary hypertension following *E. coli* endotoxin infusion in sheep: effect of an imidazole derivative, *Prostaglandins*, 23, 273, 1982.
66. **Uderman, H. D., Workman, R. J., and Jackson, E. K.,** Attenuation of the development of hypertension in spontaneously hypertensive rats by the thromboxane synthetase inhibitor; 4′-(Imidazol-1-yl)acetophenone, *Prostaglandins*, 24, 237, 1982.

67. **Grimm, L. J., Knapp, D. R., Senator, D., and Halushka, P. V.,** Inhibition of platelet thromboxane synthesis by 7-(l-Imidazolyl)heptanoic acid: dissociation from inhibition of aggregation, *Thromb. Res.*, 24, 307, 1981.
68. **Kayama, N., Sakaguchi, K., Kaneko, S., Kubota, T., Fukuzawa, T., Kawamura, S., Yoshimoto, T., and Yamamoto, S.,** Inhibition of platelet aggregation by 1-alkylimidazole derivatives, thromboxane $A_2$ synthetase inhibitors, *Prostaglandins,* 21, 543, 1981.
69. **Wise, W. C., Cook, J. A., Halushka, P. V., and Knapp, D. R.,** Protective effects of thromboxane synthetase inhibitors in rats in endotoxic shock, *Circ. Res.*, 46, 854, 1980.
70. **Burch, R. M., Knapp, D. R., and Halushka, P. V.,** Vasopressin-stimulated water flow is decreased by thromboxane synthetase inhibition or antagonism, *Am. J. Physiol.*, 239, F160, 1980.
71. **Emms, H. and Lewis, G. P.,** The roles of prostaglandin endoperoxides, thromboxane $A_2$ and adenosine diphosphate in collagen-induced aggregation in man and the rat, *Br. J. Pharmacol.*, 87, 109, 1986.
72. **Butler, K. D., Maguire, E. D., Smith, J. R., Turnbull, A. A., Wallis, R. B., and White, A. M.,** Prolongation of rat tail bleeding time caused by oral doses of a thromboxane synthetase inhibitor which have little effect on platelet aggregation. *Thromb. Haemostasis,* 47, 46, 1982.
73. **Maguire, E. D., and Wallis, R. B.,** *In vivo* redirection of prostaglandin endoperoxides into 6-keto $PGF_{1\alpha}$ formation by thromboxane synthetase inhibitors in the rat, *Thromb. Res.*, 32, 15, 1983.
74. **Maguire, E. D. and Wallis, R. B.,** Redirection of platelet derived prostaglandin endoperoxides into 6-keto $PGE_{1\alpha}$ formation caused by thromboxane synthetase inhibitors in the rat, *Thromb. Haemostasis,* 50, 279, 1983.
75. **Honn, K. V.** Inhibition of tumor cell metastasis by modulation of the vascular prostacyclin/thromboxane $A_2$ system, *Clin. Exp. Metastasis,* 1, 103, 1983.
76. **Wright, W. B., Jr., Press, J. B., Chan, P. S., Marsico, J. W., Haug, M. F., Lucas, J., Tauber, J., and Tomcufcik, A. S.,** Thromboxane synthetase inhibitors and antihypertensive agents 1. N-[1*H*-Imidazol-1-y1)alkyl]aryl amides and N-[(1*H*-1,2,4-Triazol-1-yl)alkyl]aryl amides, *J. Med. Chem.*, 29, 523, 1986.
77. **Press, J. B., Wright, W. B., Jr., Chan, P. S., Marsico, J. W., Haug, M. F., Tauber, J., and Tomcufcik, A. S.,** Thromboxane synthetase inhibitors and antihypertensive agents 2. N-[(1*H*-Imidazol-1-yl)alkyl]-1*H*-isoindole-1,3(2*H*)-diones and N-[(1*H*-1,2,4-Triazol-1-yl)alkyl]isoindole-1,3(2*H*)-diones as unique antihypertensive agents, *J. Med. Chem.*, 29, 816, 1986.
78. **Iizuka, K., Akahane, K., Momose, D., Nakazawa, M., Tanouchi, T., Kawamura, M., Ohyama, I., Kajiwara, I., Iguchi, Y., Okada, T., Taniguchi, K., Miyamoto, T., and Hayashi, M.,** Highly selective inhibitors of thromboxane synthetase. I. Imidazole derivatives, *J. Med. Chem.*, 24, 1139, 1981.
79. **Cross, P. E., and Dickinson, R. P.,** The design of thromboxane synthetase inhibitors, *Spec. Publ. R. Soc. Chem.*, (50), 268, 1984.
80. **Cross, P. E., Dickinson, R. P., Parry, M. J., and Randall, M. J.,** Selective thromboxane synthetase inhibitors. 1. 1-[(aryloxy)alkyl]-1*H*-imidazoles, *J. Med. Chem.*, 28, 1427, 1985.
81. **Sneddon, J.,** UK-37,248-01, *Drugs Future,* 6, 693, 1981.
82. **Randall, M. J., Parry, M., Hawkeswood, E., Cross, P. E., and Dickinson, R. P.,** UK-37,248, A novel, selective thromboxane synthetase inhibitor with platelet anti-aggregatory and anti-thrombotic activity, *Thromb. Res.*, 23, 145, 1982.
83. **Randall, M. J., Parry, M., Hawkeswood, E., Cross, P. E., and Dickinson, R. P.,** UK-37,248, A novel, selective thromboxane synthetase inhibitor with platelet anti-aggregatory and anti-thrombotic activity, *Thromb. Haemostasis,* 46, 278, 1981.
84. **Bertelé, V., Falanga, A., Tomasiak, M., Chiabrando, C., Cerletti, C., and de Gaetano, G.,** Pharmacologic inhibition of thromboxane synthetase and platelet aggregation: modulatory role of cyclooxygenase products, *Blood,* 63, 1460, 1984.
85. **Parry, M. J.,** Effects of thromboxane synthetase inhibition on arachidonate metabolism and platelet behaviour, *Br. J. Clin. Pharmacol.*, 15, 23S, 1983.
86. **Rajtar, G., Cerletti, C., Castagnoli, M. N., Bertelé, V., and de Gaetano, G.,** Prostaglandins and human platelet aggregation: implications for the anti-aggregating activity of thromboxane-synthetase inhibitors, *Biochem. Pharmacol.*, 34, 307, 1985.
87. **Menys, V. C. and Davies, J. A.,** Thromboxane-mediated activation of platelet and enhancement of platelet uptake onto collagen-coated glass or deendothelialized rabbit aorta. Comparative effects of a thromboxane synthetase inhibitor (dazoxiben), *Lab. Invest.*, 50, 184, 1984.
88. **Defreyn, G., Deckmyn, H., and Vermylen, J.,** A thromboxane synthetase inhibitor reorients endoperoxide metabolism in whole blood towards prostacyclin and prostaglandin $E_2$, *Thromb. Res.*, 26, 389, 1982.

89. **Orchard, M. A., Waddell, K. A., Lewis, P. J., and Blair, I. A.,** Thromboxane synthase inhibition causes redirection of prostaglandin endoperoxides to prostaglandin $D_2$ during collagen stimulated aggregation of human platelet rich plasma, *Thromb. Res.,* 39, 701, 1985.
90. **Patrignani, P., Filabozzi, P., Catella, F., Pugliese, F., and Patrono, C.,** Differential effects of dazoxiben, a selective thromboxane synthase inhibitor, on platelet and renal prostaglandin endoperoxide metabolism, *J. Pharmacol. Exp. Ther.,* 228, 472, 1984.
91. **Smith, E. F., III, Darius, H., Ferber, H., and Schrör, K.,** Inhibition of thromboxane and 12-HPETE formation by dazoxiben and its two thiophenic acid-substituted derivatives, *Eur. J. Pharmacol.,* 112, 161, 1985.
92. **Tahamont, M. V., Gee, M. H., Perkowski, S. Z., and Flynn, J. T.,** Effects of thromboxane on the function of complement stimulated leukocytes, *Fed. Proc. Fed. Am. Soc. Exp. Biol.,* 44, 1906, 1985.
93. **O'Keefe, E. H., Liu, E. C. K., Greenberg, R., and Ogletree, M. L.,** Effects of a thromboxane synthetase inhibitor and a thromboxane antagonist on release and activity of thromboxane $A_2$ and prostacyclin *in vitro, Prostaglandins,* 29, 785, 1985.
94. **Tyler, H. M.,** Dazoxiben: a pharmacological tool or clinical candidate? *Br. J. Clin. Pharmacol.,* 15, 13S, 1983.
95. **Irisarri, E., Kessedjian, M. J., Charuel, C., Faccini, J. M., Greaves, P., Monro, A. M., Nachbaur, J., and Rabemampianina, Y.,** Dazoxiben, a prototype inhibitor of thromboxane synthesis, has little toxicity in laboratory animals, *Hum. Toxicol.,* 4, 311, 1985.
96. **Tyler, H. M., Saxton, C. A. P. D., and Parry, M. J.,** Administration to man of UK-37,248-01, a selective inhibitor of thromboxane synthetase, *Lancet,* i, 629, 1981.
97. **Vermylen, J., Defreyn, G., Carreras, L. O., Machin, S. J., van Schaeren, J., and Verstraete, M.,** *Lancet,* i, 1073, 1981.
98. **Fitzgerald, G. A., Brash, A. R., and Pedersen, A. K.,** Endogenous prostacyclin biosynthesis and platelet function during selective inhibition of thromboxane synthase in man, *Thromb. Haemostasis,* 50, 280, 1983.
99. **Fitzgerald, G. A., Brash, A. R., Oates, J. A., and Pedersen, A. K.,** Endogenous prostacyclin biosynthesis and platelet function during selective inhibition of thromboxane synthase in man, *J. Clin. Invest.,* 71, 1336, 1983.
100. **Oates, J. A., Brash, A., and Fitzgerald, G.,** Comparison of the effects of selective inhibition of thromboxane synthase with those of inhibition of the cyclooxygenase enzyme in man, *Trans. Am. Clin. Climatol. Assoc.,* 95, 157, 1983.
101. **Knudsen, J. B., Juhl, A., and Gormsen, J.,** Thromboxane synthase inhibition in patients with atherosclerotic heart disease, *Lancet,* ii, 198, 1981.
102. **Dale, J., Thaulow, E., Myhre, E., and Parry, J.,** The effect of a thromboxane synthetase inhibitor, dazoxiben, and acetylsalicylic acid on platelet function and prostaglandin metabolism, *Thromb. Haemostasis,* 50, 703, 1983.
103. **Carter, A. J. and Heptinstall, S.,** Platelet aggregation in whole blood: the role of thromboxane $A_2$ and adenosine diphosphate, *Thromb. Haemostasis,* 54, 612, 1985.
104. **Jones, E. W., Cockbill, S. R., Cowley, A. J., Hanley, S. P., and Heptinstall, S.,** Effects of dazoxiben and low-dose aspirin on platelet behaviour in man, *Br. J. Clin. Pharmacol.,* 15, 39S, 1983.
104a. **Sills, T., Cowley, A. J., and Heptinstall, S.,** Aspirin and dazoxiben as inhibitors of platelet behavior: modification of their effects by agents that alter cAMP production, *Thromb. Res.,* 42, 91, 1986.
104b. **Sills, T., and Heptinstall, S.,** Effects of a thromboxane synthetase inhibitor and a cAMP phosphodiesterase inhibitor, singly and in combination, on platelet behavior, *Thromb. Haemostasis,* 55, 305, 1986.
105. **Bertelé, V., Falanga, A., Tomasiak, M., Cerletti, C., and de Gaetano, G.,** SQ 22536, An adenylate-cyclase inhibitor, prevents the antiplatelet effect of dazoxiben, a thromboxane-synthetase inhibitor, *Thromb. Haemostasis,* 51, 125, 1984.
106. **Heptinstall, S., Bientz, N., Cockbill, S. R., Hanley, S. P., and Peacock, I.,** Different effects of thromboxane synthetase inhibitors on platelets from different individuals, *Lancet,* ii, 1156, 1982.
107. **Gresele, P., Deckmyn, H., and Vermylen, J.,** Reorientation of cyclic endoperoxide metabolism and efficacy of thromboxane synthetase inhibitors, *Thromb. Haemostasis,* 50, 284, 1983.
108. **Gresele, P., Deckmyn, H., Huybrechts, E., and Vermylen, J.,** Serum albumin enhances the impairment of platelet aggregation with thromboxane synthase inhibition by increasing the formation of prostaglandin $D_2$, *Biochem. Pharmacol.,* 33, 2083, 1984.
109. **Patscheke, H.,** Thromboxane synthase inhibition potentiates washed platelet activation by endogenous and exogenous arachidonic acid, *Biochem. Pharmacol.,* 34, 1151, 1985.
110. **Bertelé. V., Falanga, A., Roncaglioni, M. C., Cerletti, C., and de Gaetano, G.,** Thromboxane synthetase inhibition results in increased platelet sensitivity to prostacyclin, *Thromb. Haemostasis,* 47, 294, 1982.

111. **Cerletti, C., Rajtar, G., Bertelé, V., and de Gaetano, G.,** Inhibition of arachidonate-induced human platelet aggregation by a single low oral dose of aspirin in combination with a thromboxane synthase inhibitor, *Thromb. Haemostasis,* 52, 215, 1984.
112. **Bertelé, V. and de Gaetano, G.,** Potentiation by dazoxiben, a thromboxane synthetase inhibitor, of platelet and aggregation inhibitory activity of a thromboxane receptor antagonist and of prostacyclin, *Eur. J. Pharmacol.,* 85, 331, 1982.
113. **Gresele, P., Van Houtte, E., Arnout, J., Deckmyn, H., and Vermylen, J.,** Thromboxane synthase inhibition combined with thromboxane receptor blockade: a step forward in antithrombotic strategy? *Thromb. Haemostasis,* 52, 364, 1984.
114. **Latta, G., Schrör, K., and Verheggen, R.,** Different roles for platelet-derived thromboxane $A_2$ ($TxA_2$) in platelet activation and coronary arterial vasoconstriction, *Br. J. Pharmacol.,* 84, 41P, 1985.
115. **Smith, J. B.,** Effect of thromboxane synthetase inhibitors on platelet function: enhancement by inhibition of phosphodiesterase, *Throm. Res.,* 28, 477, 1982.
116. **Gresele, P., Deckmyn, H., Arnout, J., Zoja, C., and Vermylen, J.,** Lack of synergism between dazoxiben and dipyridamole following administration to man, *Thromb. Res.,* 37, 231, 1985.
117. **Smith, E. F., III, Lefer, A. M., Smith, J. B., and Nicolaou, K. C.,** Thromboxane synthetase inhibitors differentially antagonize thromboxane receptors in vascular smooth muscle, *Arch. Pharmacol.,* 318, 130, 1981.
118. **Carter, A. J., Bevan, J. A., Hanley, S. P., Morgan, W. E., and Turner, D. R.,** A comparison of human pulmonary arterial and venous prostacyclin and thromboxane synthesis — effect of a thromboxane synthase inhibitor, *Thromb. Haemostasis,* 51, 257, 1984.
119. **Menys, V. C. and Davies, J. A.,** Selective inhibition of thromboxane synthetase with dazoxiben — basis of its inhibitory effect on platelet adhesion, *Thromb. Haemostasis,* 49, 96, 1983.
120. **Gryglewski, R.,** Prostacyclin-Experimental and clinical approach. *Adv. Prostaglandin, Thromboxane, Leukotriene Res.,* 11, 457, 1983.
121. **Deckmyn, H., Van Houtte, E., Verstraete, M., and Vermylen, J.,** Manipulation of the local thromboxane and prostacyclin balance *in vivo* by the antithrombotic compounds dazoxiben, acetylsalicylic acid and nafazatrom, *Biochem. Pharmacol.,* 32, 2757, 1983.
122. **Heiss, M., Haas, S., and Blümel, G.,** The antithrombotic effect of a new thromboxane-synthetase inhibitor (UK-37,248) in comparison with acetylsalicyclic acid (ASA) in experimental thrombosis, *Haemostasis,* 12, 102, 1982.
123. **Randall, M. J. and Wilding, R. I. R.,** Acute arterial thrombosis in rabbits: reduced platelet accumulation after treatment with thromboxane synthetase inhibitor dazoxiben hydrochloride, (UK-37,248-01), *Thromb. Res.,* 28, 607, 1982.
124. **Zimmermann, R., Peter, J., Jung, G., Horsch, A., Mörl, H., and Harenberg, J.,** Antithrombotic and opposite effects of drugs influencing the prostaglandin system, *Thromb. Haemostasis,* 46, 179, 1981.
125. **Bergqvist, D., Björck, C.-G., Dougan, P., Esquivel, C. O., Lannerstad, O., Nilsson, B., Saldeen, P., and Saldeen, T.,** The effect of inhibition of thromboxane synthesis in experimental thrombosis and hemostasis, *Thromb. Res.,* 37, 435, 1985.
126. **Schumacher, W. A. and Lucchesi, B. R.,** Effect of the thromboxane synthetase inhibitor UK-37,248 (dazoxiben) upon platelet aggregation, coronary artery thrombosis and vascular reactivity, *J. Pharmacol. Exp. Ther.,* 227, 790, 1983.
127. **Lee, E. C., Schumacher, W. A., and Lucchesi, B. R.,** Effect of a thromboxane synthetase inhibitor UK-37,248 (dazoxiben) on coronary vascular reactivity, *Clin. Res.,* 31, 814A, 1983.
128. **Bush, L. R., Campbell, W. B., Tilton, G. D., Buja, L. M., and Willerson, J. T.,** Effects of the selective thromboxane synthetase inhibitor, dazoxiben, on cyclic flow variations in stenosed canine coronary arteries, *Trans. Assoc. Amer. Phys.,* 96, 103, 1983.
129. **Bush, L. R., Campbell, W. B., Buja, L. M., Tilton, G. D., and Willerson, J. T.,** Effects of the selective thromboxane synthetase dazoxiben inhibitor on variations in cyclic blood flow in stenosed canine cornonary arteries, *Circulation,* 69, 1161, 1984.
130. **Burke, S. E., Lefer, A. M., Smith, G. M., and Smith, J. B.,** Prevention of extension of ischaemic damage following acute myocardial ischemia by dazoxiben, a new thromboxane synthetase inhibitor, *Br. J. Clin. Pharmacol.,* 15, 97S, 1983.
131. **Thiemermann, C. and Schrör, K.,** Comparison of the thromboxane synthetase inhibitor dazoxiben and the prostacyclin mimetic iloprost in an animal model of acute ischemia and reperfusion, *Biomed. Biochim. Acta,* 43, S151, 1984.
132. **Thiemermann, C.,** Different roles for thromboxane synthetase inhibitors and prostacyclin mimetics in myocardial reperfusion damage, Abstracts 2nd Int. Symp. Prostaglandins, Nürnberg-Fürth, May 9 to 11, 1984.
133. **Chan, P. S., Quirk, G. J., Bielen, S. J., Saunders, T. K., Ronsberg, M. A., Lucas, J., and Cervoni, P.,** Studies on the antiarrythmic activity of thromboxane synthetase inhibitors, dazoxiben and OKY-1581 in various animal models, *Fed. Proc. Fed. Am. Soc. Exp. Biol.,* 44, 712, 1985.

134. **Coker, S. J., Parratt, J. R., Ledingham, I. McA., and Zeitlin, I. J.,** Evidence that thromboxane contributes to ventricular fibrillation induced by reperfusion of the ischaemic myocardium, *J. Mol. Cell. Cardiol.*, 14, 483, 1982.
135. **Coker, S. J., Ledingham, I. McA., Parratt, J. R., and Zeitlin, I. J.,** Inhibition of thromboxane synthesis with UK-37,248 prevents fibrillation following reperfusion of the ischaemic myocardium, *Br. J. Pharmacol.*, 76, 221P, 1982.
136. **Kiff, P. S., Bergman, G. W., Westwick, J., Atkinson, L., Kakkar, V. V., and Jewitt, D. E.,** The release of thromboxane during atrial pacing and the haemodynamic and metabolic effects of its inhibition by dazoxiben, *Am. J. Cardiol.*, 49, 902, 1982.
137. **Kakkar, V. V., Westwick, J., Kiff, P. S., Bergman, G., Atkinson, L., and Jewitt, D. E.,** Haemodynamic and metabolic effects of dazoxiben at rest and during atrial pacing, *Thromb. Haemostasis*, 50, 220, 1983.
138. **Kiff, P. S., Bergman, G., Atkinson, L., Jewitt, D. E., Westwick, J., and Kakkar, V. V.,** Haemodynamic and metabolic effects of dazoxiben at rest and during arterial pacing, *Br. J. Clin. Pharmacol.*, 15, 73S, 1983.
139. **Reuben, S. R., Kuan, P., Cairns, J., and Gyde, O. H.,** Effects of dazoxiben on exercise performance in chronic stable angina, *Br. J. Clin. Pharmacol.*, 15, 83S, 1983.
140. **Hendra, T., Collins, P., Penny, W. J., and Sheridan, D. J.,** Failure of thromboxane synthetase inhibition to improve exercise capacity in angina, *Clin. Science*, 65, 36P, 1983.
141. **Hendra, T., Collins, P., Penny, W., and Sheridan, D.,** Dazoxiben in stable angina, *Lancet, i*, 1041, 1983.
142. **Hendra, T., Collins, P., Penny, W., and Sheridan, D. J.,** Failure of thromboxane synthetase inhibition to improve exercise tolerance in patients with stable angina, *Int. J. Cardiol.*, 5, 382, 1984.
143. **Hutton, I., Tweddel, A. C., Rankin, A. C., Walker, I. D., and Davidson, J. F.,** Evaluation of selective thromboxane synthetase inhibitor in patients with coronary heart disease, *Circulation*, 64 (Supp. IV, Abstr. 10) 1981.
144. **Thaulow, E., Dale, J., and Myhre, E.,** Effects of a selective thromboxane synthetase inhibitor, dazoxiben, and of acetylsalicylic acid on myocardial ischemia in patients with coronary artery disease, *Am. J. Cardiol.*, 53, 1255, 1984.
145. **Hutton, I., Tweddel, A. C., Rankin, A. C., Walker, I. D., and Davidson, J. F.,** Effects of dazoxiben on transcardiac thromboxane levels and haemodynamics in coronary heart disease, *Br. J. Clin. Pharmacol.*, 15, 79S, 1983.
146. **McGibney, D., Menys, V. C., Nelson, G. I. C., Kumar, E. B., Taylor, S. H., and Davies, J. A.,** Effects of UK 37248, a thromboxane synthetase inhibitor, on platelet behavior in patients with coronary heart disease (CHD) undergoing exercise to angina, *Clin. Science*, 62, 12P, 1982.
147. **Mogensen, F., Knudsen, J. B., Rasmussen, V., Kjoller, E., and Gormsen, J.,** Effect of specific thromboxane-synthetase inhibition on thromboxane and prostaglandin synthesis in stable angina induced by exercise test, *Thromb. Res.*, 37, 259, 1985.
148. **Parry, M. J., Randall, M. J., Tyler, H. M., Myhre, E., Dale, J., and Thaulow, E.,** Selective inhibition of thromboxane synthetase by dazoxiben increases prostacyclin production by leucocytes in angina patients and healthy volunteers, *Lancet*, ii, 164, 1982.
149. **Oei, H. H. H., Zoganas, H. C., Sakane, Y., Robson, R. D., and Glenn, T. M.,** Inhibition of thromboxane biosynthesis in splanchnic ischemia shock, *Circ. Shock*, 18, 95, 1986.
150. **Halushka, P. V., Cook, J. A., and Wise, W. C.,** Beneficial effects of UK 37248, a thromboxane synthetase inhibitor, in experimental endotoxic shock in the rat, *Br. J. Clin. Pharmacol.*, 15, 133S, 1983.
151. **Cook, J. A., Haluskha, P. V., and Wise, W. C.,** Effect of the thromboxane (Tx) $A_2$ synthetase inhibitor, UK37,248, in endotoxin (LPS) shock: prevention of splanchnic infarction and improved functional parameters, *Physiologist*, 24, 116, 1981.
152. **Furman, B. L., McKechnie, K., and Parratt, J. R.,** Failure of drugs that selectively inhibit thromboxane synthesis to modify endotoxin shock in conscious rats, *Br. J. Pharmacol.*, 82, 289, 1984.
153. **Ball, H. A., Parratt, J. R., and Zeitlin, I. J.,** Effect of dazoxiben, a specific inhibitor of thromboxane synthetase, on acute pulmonary responses to *E. coli* endotoxin in anaesthetized cats, *Br. J. Clin. Pharmacol.*, 15, 127S, 1983.
154. **Webb, P. J., Westwick, J., Scully, M. F., Zahavi, J., and Kakkar, V. V.,** Do prostacyclin and thromboxane play a role in endotoxic shock? *Br. J. Surg.*, 68, 720, 1981.
155. **Winn, R., Harlan, J., Nadir, B., Harker, L., and Hildebrandt, J.,** Thromboxane $A_2$ mediates lung vasoconstriction but not permeability after endotoxin, *J. Clin. Invest.*, 72, 911, 1983.

156. **Harlan, J., Winn, R., Weaver, J., Hildebrandt, J., and Harker, L.,** Selective blockade of thromboxane $A_2$ synthesis during experimental *E. coli* bacteremia in the goat: effects on hemodynamics and lung water, *Chest.* 83, 75S, 1983.
157. **Sandler, H., Gerdin, B., and Saldeen, T.,** Studies on the role of thromboxane in thrombin-induced pulmonary insufficiency in the rat, *Thromb. Res.*, 42, 165, 1986.
158. **Lefer, A. M., Okamatsu, S., Smith, E. F., III, and Smith, J. B.,** Beneficial effects of a new thromboxane synthetase inhibitor in arachidonate-induced sudden death, *Thromb. Res.*, 23, 265, 1981.
159. **Lefer, A. M., Burke, S. E., and Smith, J. B.,** Role of thromboxanes and prostaglandin endoperoxides in the pathogenesis of eicosanoid-induced sudden death, *Thromb. Res.*, 32, 311, 1983.
160. **Lefer, A. M., Müller, H. F., and Smith, J. B.,** Pathophysiological mechanisms of sudden death induced by platelet activating factor, *Br. J. Pharmacol.*, 83, 125, 1984.
160a. **Honey, A. C., Lad, N., and Tuffin, D. P.,** Effect of indomethacin and dazoxiben on intravascular platelet aggregation in the anesthetized rabbit, *Thromb. Haemostasis*, 56, 80, 1986.
161. **Farrukh, I. S., Michael, J. R., Summer, W. R., Adkinson, N. F., Jr., and Gurtner, G. H.,** Thromboxane-Induced pulmonary vasoconstriction: involvement of calcium, *J. Appl. Physiol.*, 58, 34, 1985.
162. **Wasserman, M. A. and Malo, P. E.,** SK&F 88046: Inhibition of thromboxane-induced bronchoconstriction in anesthetized dogs, *Prostaglandins, Leukotrienes Med.*, 17, 213, 1985.
163. **Oyarzun, M. J., Donoso, P., Arias, M., and Quijada, D.,** Thromboxane mediates the increase in alveolar surfactant pool induced by free fatty acid infusion in the rabbit, *Respiration*, 46, 231, 1984.
164. **Garcia-Szabo, R. R., Peterson, M. B., Watkins, W. D., Bizios, R., Kong, D. L., and Malik, A. B.,** Thromboxane generation after thrombin: protective effect of thromboxane synthetase inhibition on lung fluid balance, *Circ. Res.*, 53, 214, 1983.
165. **Garcia-Szabo, R. R., Minnear, F. L., Bizios, R., Johnson, A., and Malik, A. B.,** Role of thromboxane in the pulmonary response to pulmonary microembolization, *Chest*, 83, 77S, 1983.
166. **Noonan, T. C. and Malik, A. B.,** Pulmonary vascular response to leukotriene $D_4$ in unanesthetized sheep: role of thromboxane, *J. Appl. Physiol.* 60, 765, 1986.
167. **Gee, M. H., Perkowski, S. Z., Tahamont, M. V., Flynn, J. T., and Wasserman, M. A.,** Thromboxane as a mediator of pulmonary dysfunction during intravascular complement activation in sheep, *Am. Rev. Respir. Dis.*, 133, 269, 1986.
168. **Leeman, M., Boeynaems, J. M., Degaute, J. P., Vincent, J. L., Kahn, R. J.,** Administration of dazoxiben, a selective thromboxane synthetase inhibitor in the adult respiratory distress syndrome, *Chest*, 87, 726, 1985.
169. **Muccitelli, R. M., Osborn, R. R., and Weichman, B. M.,** Effect of inhibition of thromboxane production on the leukotriene $D_4$-mediated bronchoconstriction in the guinea pig, *Prostaglandins*, 26, 197, 1983.
170. **Van Assche, F. A., Spitz, B., Vermylen, J., and Deckmijn, H.,** Preliminary observations on treatment of pregnancy-induced hypertension with a thromboxane synthetase inhibitor, *Am. J. Obstet. Gynecol.*, 148, 216, 1984.
171. **Zipser, R. D., Kronborg, I., Rector, W., Reynolds, T., and Daskalopoulos, G.,** Therapeutic trial of thromboxane synthesis inhibition in the hepatorenal syndrome, *Gastroenterology*, 87, 1228, 1984.
172. **Cowley, A. J., Jones, E. W., and Hanley, S. P.,** Effects of dazoxiben, an inhibitor of thromboxane synthetase, on forearm vasoconstriction in response to cold stimulation, and on human blood vessel prostacyclin production, *Br. J. Clin. Pharmacol.*, 15, 107S, 1983.
173. **Cowley, A. J., Jones, E. W., Carter, A. J., Hanley, S. P., and Heptinstall, S.,** The effects of dazoxiben, an inhibitor of thromboxane synthetase, on cold-induced forearm vasoconstriction and platelet behaviour in different individuals, *Br. J. Clin. Pharmacol.*, 19, 1, 1985.
174. **Tindall, H., Tooke, J. E., Martin, M. F. R., and Davies, J. A.,** Effect of dazoxiben, a thromboxane synthetase inhibitor on skin blood flow following cold challenge in patients with Raynaud's phenomenon, *Thromb. Haemostasis*, 50, 281, 1983.
175. **Tindall, H., Tooke, J. E., Menys, V. C., Martin, M. F. R., and Davies, J. A.,** Effect of dazoxiben, a thromboxane synthetase inhibitor on skin blood flow following cold challenge in patients with Raynaud's phenomenon, *Eur. J. Clin. Invest.*, 15, 20, 1985.
176. **Gresele, P., Bounameaux, H., Arnout, J., Perez-Requejo, J. L., Deckmyn, H., and Vermylen, J.,** Thromboxane $A_2$ and prostacyclin do not modulate the systemic hemodynamic response to cold in humans, *J. Lab. Clin. Med.*, 106, 534, 1985.

177. **Coffman, J. D. and Rasmussen, H. M.,** Effect of thromboxane synthetase inhibition in Raynaud's phenomenon, *Clin. Pharmacol. Ther.*, 36, 369, 1984.
178. **Jones, E. W. and Hawkey, C. J.,** A thromboxane synthetase inhibitor in Raynaud's phenomenon, *Prostaglandins Leukotrienes Med.*, 12, 67, 1983.
179. **Ettinger, W. H., Wise, R. A., Schaffhauser, D., and Wigley, F. M.,** Controlled double-blind trial of dazoxiben and nifedipine in the treatment of Raynaud's phenomenon, *Am. J. Med.*, 77, 451, 1984.
180. **Malamet, R., Wise, R. A., Ettinger, W. H., and Wigley, F. M.,** Nifedipine in the treatment of Raynaud's phenomenon. Evidence for inhibition of platelet activation, *Am. J. Med.*, 78, 602, 1985.
181. **Belch, J. J. F., Cormie, J., Newman, P., McLaren, M., Barbenel, J., Capell, H., Lieberman, P., Forbes, C. D., and Prentice, C. R. M.,** Dazoxiben, a thromboxane synthetase inhibitor, in the treatment of Raynaud's syndrome: a double-blind trial, *Br. J. Clin. Pharmacol.*, 15, 113S, 1983.
182. **Bounameaux, H., Gresele, P., Hanss, M., DeCock, F., Vermylen, J., and Collen, D.,** Aspirin, indomethacin and dazoxiben do not affect the fibrinolytic activation induced by venous occlusion, *Thromb. Res.*, 40, 161, 1985.
183. **Lee, R., Bevan, D., Flute, P. T., and Dormandy, J. A.,** The effects of dazoxiben on platelet behavior in patients with severe peripheral vascular disease, *Thromb. Haemostasis*, 50, 220, 1983.
184. **Raftery, A. T., Livesey, S., and Forty, J.,** Initial impressions of dazoxiben in the treatment of the ischaemic limb, *Br. J. Clin. Pharmacol.*, 15, 119S, 1983.
185. **Vermylen, J. and Deckmyn, H.,** Reorientation of prostaglandin endoperoxide metabolism by a thromboxane synthetase inhibitor: *in vitro* and clinical observations, *Br. J. Clin. Pharmacol.*, 15, 17S, 1983.
186. **Ehrly, A. M.,** Influence of a thromboxane synthesis inhibitor on the muscle tissue microcirculation of patients with intermittent claudication, *Br. J. Clin. Pharmacol.*, 15, 117S, 1983.
187. **Li, D. M. F., De Garis, R. M., and Dusting, G. J.,** Inhibition of vasoconstrictor mechanisms by dazoxiben in the rat mesenteric vasculature, *Eur. J. Pharmacol.*, 110, 351, 1985.
188. **Ceuppens, J. L., Vertessen, S., Deckmyn, H., and Vermylen, J.,** Effects of thromboxane $A_2$ on lymphocyte proliferation, *Cell. Immunol.*, 90, 458, 1985.
189. **Rola-Pleszczynski, M., Gagnon, L., Bolduc, D., and LeBreton, G.,** Evidence for the involvement of the thromboxane synthase pathway in human natural cytotoxic cell activity, *J. Immunol.*, 135, 4114, 1985.
190. **Dorsch, W., Ring, J., and Melzer, H.,** A selective inhibitor of thromboxane biosynthesis enhances immediate and inhibits late cutaneous allergic reactions in man, *J. Allerg. Clin. Immunol.*, 72, 168, 1983.
191. **Joseph, R., Steiner, J. T., Poole, C. J. M., Littlewood, J., and Rose, F. C.,** Thromboxane synthetase inhibition: potential therapy in migraine, *Headache*, 25, 204, 1985.
192. **Goldman, M., Hall, C., Hawker, R. J., and McCollum, C. N.,** The influence of thromboxane synthetase inhibition in platelet deposition in vascular grafts, *Thromb. Haemostasis*, 50, 222, 1983.
193. **Hanson, S. R. and Harker, L. A.,** Effect of dazoxiben on arterial graft thrombosis in the baboon, *Br. J. Clin. Pharmacol.*, 15, 57S, 1983.
194. **Hanson, S. R., Harker, L. A., and Bjornsson, T. D.,** Effect of platelet-modifying drugs on arterial thromboembolism in baboons, *J. Clin. Invest.*, 75, 1591, 1985.
195. **Jorgensen, K. A., Kemp, E., Barfort, P., Starklint, H., Larsen, S., Petersen, P. H., and Knudsen, J. B.,** The survival of pig to rabbit renal xenografts during inhibition of thromboxane synthesis, *Thromb. Res.*, 32, 585, 1983.
196. **Coffman, T. M., Yarger, W. E., and Klotman, P. E.,** Functional role of thromboxane production by acutely rejecting renal allografts in rats, *J. Clin. Invest.*, 75, 1242, 1985.
197. **Klotman, P. E., Smith, S. R., Volpp, B. D., Coffman, T. M., and Yarger, W. E.,** Thromboxane synthetase inhibition improves function of hydronephrotic rat kidneys, *Am. J. Physiol.*, 250, F282, 1986.
198. **Partridge, N. C., Hillyard, C. J., Nolan, R. D., and Martin, T. J.,** Regulation of prostaglandin production by osteoblast-rich calvarial cells, *Prostaglandins*, 30 527, 1985.
199. **Dodd, N. J., Gordge, M. P., and Weston, M. J.,** Use of a thromboxane synthetase inhibitor, dazoxiben, during haemodialysis, *Br. J. Clin. Pharmacol.*, 15, 67S, 1983.
199a. **Hiraku, S., Taniguchi, K., Wakitani, K., Omawari, N., Kira, H., Miyamoto, T., Okegawa, T., Kawasaki, A., and Ujiie, A.,** Pharmacological studies on the $TxA_2$ synthetase inhibitor *(E)*-3-[*p*-(1*H*-imidazol-1-ylmethyl)phenyl]-2-propenoic acid (OKY-046), *Jpn. J. Pharmacol.*, 41, 393, 1986.
200. **Naito, J., Komatsu, H., Ujiie, A., Hamano, S., Kubota, T., and Tsuboshima, M.,** Effects of thromboxane synthetase inhibitors on aggregation of rabbit platelets, *Eur. J. Pharmacol.*, 91, 41, 1983.

201. **Naito, J., Hiraku, S., and Kuga, T.,** Thromboxane $A_2$ ($TXA_2$) synthetase inhibition by (E)-3-[4-(1-imidazolylmethyl)phenyl]-2-propenoic acid hydrochloride (OKY-046) and sodium (E)-3-[4-(3-pyridylmethyl)phenyl]-2-methylpropenoate (OKY-1581), and their medical usefulness, *Oyo Yakuri,* 27, 267, 1984; *Chem. Abstr.,* 100, 203371c, 1984.
202. **Kitamura, S., Ishihara, Y., and Takaku, F.,** Effect of thromboxane synthetase inhibitors (OKY-046, OKY-1580) on the action of bronchoactive agents in guinea pig tracheal strips and on arachidonate metabolism in guinea pig lung lobes, *Prostaglandins Leukotrienes Med.,* 14, 341, 1984.
203. **Hayashi, T. and Sumiyoshi, A.,** Influence of thromboxane $A_2$ synthetase inhibitors (OKY-046, OKY-1580) on the aortic intimal thickening after mechanical injury, *Ketsueki to Myakkan,* 13, 444, 1982; *Chem. Abstr.,* 99, 16278b, 1983.
204. **Sakai, K., Ito, T., and Ogawa, K.,** Roles of endogenous prostacyclin and thromboxane $A_2$ in the ischemic canine heart, *J. Cardiovasc. Pharmacol.,* 4, 129, 1982.
205. **Ogawa, K., Sakai, K., Ito, T., Watanabe, J., and Satake, T.,** Effects of selective thromboxane synthetase inhibitor and indomethacin on prostacyclin and thromboxane $A_2$ from ischemic canine heart, *Adv. Prostaglandin Thromboxane Leukotriene Res.,* 11, 371, 1983.
206. **Moriuchi, M.,** The efficacy of prostacyclin ($PGI_2$) and/or OKY-046, a specific thromboxane synthetase inhibitor, in acute myocardial infarction. Experimental study, *Kokyu to Junkan,* 32, 955, 1984; *Chem. Abstr.,* 102, 1111y, 1985.
207. **Ogura, T.,** Effect of OKY-046, a selective thromboxane $A_2$ synthase inhibitor, on ventricular arrythmias and prostaglandins during coronary artery ligation and reperfusion in anesthetized dogs, *Nichidai Igaku Zasshi,* 45, 467, 1986; *Chem. Abstr.,* 106, 27555d, 1987.
208. **Ujiie, A., Hiraku, S., and Naito, J.,** Pharmacological action of OKY-046, a specific inhibitor of thromboxane synthetase with special reference to inhibition of thromboxane $A_2$ production and acceleration of prostacyclin production, *Oyo Yakuri,* 29, 659, 1985; *Chem. Abstr.,* 103, 98495h, 1985.
209. **Tsuji, M., Saito, S., Tamura, Y., Moriuchi, M., Kaseda, N., Ozawa, Y., and Hatano, M.,** Efficacy of OKY-046 (a specific $TXA_2$ synthetase inhibitor) in patients with effort angina, Abst. Kyoto Conf. Prostaglandins, Kyoto, Japan, Nov. 25 to 28, 1984, 233.
210. **Yui, Y., Hattori, R., Takatsu, Y., and Kawai, C.,** Selective thromboxane $A_2$ synthetase inhibition in vasospastic angina pectoris, *J. Am. Coll. Cardiol.,* 7, 25, 1986.
211. **Uchida, Y. and Murao, S.,** Effects of thromboxane synthetase inhibitors on cyclical reduction of coronary blood flow in dogs, *Jpn. Heart J.,* 22, 971, 1981.
212. **Lelcuk, S., Alexander, F., Valeri, C. R., Shepro, D., and Hechtman, H. B.,** Thromboxane $A_2$ moderates permeability after limb ischemia, *Ann. Surg.,* 202, 642, 1985.
213. **Yamazaki, H., Isohisa, I., and Tanoue, K.,** Sudden death induced by intracoronary platelet aggregation, *Jpn. Circ. J.,* 47, 596, 1983.
214. **Edmonds, L. C. and Lefer, A. M.,** Protective actions of a new thromboxane synthetase inhibitor in arachidonate induced sudden death, *Life Sci.,* 35, 1763, 1984.
215. **Hamano, S., Kusama, H., Komatsu, H., Ujiie, A., Naito, J., and Hiraku, S.,** Effect of OKY-046 on endotoxin shock, *Ketsueki to Myakkan,* 16, 43, 1985; *Chem. Abstr.,* 103, 153687z, 1985.
216. **Goldblum, S. E., Wu, K.-M., and Tai, H.-H.,** *Streptococcus pneumoniae* — induced alterations in levels of circulating thromboxane and prostacyclin: dissociation from granulocytopenia, thrombocytopenia, and pulmonary leukostasis, *J. Infect. Dis.,* 153, 71, 1986.
217. **Ishihara, Y., Uchida, Y., and Kitamura, S.,** Effect of thromboxane synthetase inhibitors (OKY-046, and OKY 1580), on experimentally induced air embolism in anesthetized dogs, *Prostaglandins Leukotrienes Med.,* 21, 197, 1986.
218. **Kitamura, S., Sakashita, I., Hayashi, R., Uchida, Y., and Takaku, F.,** Change of blood level of leukotriene and thromboxane $B_2$ induced by an anaphylactic shock in anesthetized dogs, *Ensho,* 6, 43, 1986; *Chem. Abstr.,* 104, 223354k, 1986.
219. **Garcia-Szabo, R., Kern, D. F., and Malik, A. B.,** Pulmonary vascular response to thrombin: effects of thromboxane synthetase inhibition with OKY-046 and OKY-1581, *Prostaglandins,* 28, 851, 1984.
220. **Kubo, K. and Kobayashi, T.,** Effects of OKY-046, a selective thromboxane synthetase inhibitor, on endotoxin-induced lung injury in unanesthetized sheep, *Am. Rev. Respir. Dis.,* 132, 494, 1985.
221. **Fukushima, M. and Kobayashi, T.,** Effects of thromboxane synthetase inhibition on air emboli lung injury in sheep, *J. Appl. Physiol.,* 60, 1828, 1986.
222. **Kiyomiya, K. and Oh-Ishi, S.,** Involvement of arachidonic acid metabolites in acute inflammation: detection of 6-keto-$PGF_{1\alpha}$, thromboxane $B_2$ and $PGD_2$ in rat pleurisy induced by phorbol myristate acetate, *Jpn. J. Pharmacol.,* 39, 201, 1985.

222a. **Allison, R. C., Marble, K. T., Hernandez, E. M., Townsley, M. I., and Taylor, A. E.,** Attenuation of permeability lung injury after phorbol myristate acetate by verapamil and OKY-046, *Am. Rev. Resp. Dis.*, 134, 93, 1986.

223. **Chung, K. F., Aizawa, H., Leikauf, G. D., Ueki, I. F., Evans, T. W., and Nadel, J. A.,** Airway hyperresponsiveness induced by platelet-activating factor: role of thromboxane generation, *J. Pharmacol. Exp. Ther.*, 236, 580, 1986.

223a. **Chung, K. F., Aizawa, H., Becker, A. B., Frick, O., Gold, W. M., and Nadel, J. A.,** Inhibition of antigen-induced airway hyperresponsiveness by a thromboxane synthetase inhibitor (OKY-046) in allergic dogs, *Am. Rev. Resp. Dis.*, 134, 258, 1986.

224. **O'Byrne, P. M., Leikauf, G. D., Aizawa, H., Bethel, R. A., Ueki, I. F., Holtzman, M. J., and Nadel, J. A.,** Leukotriene $B_4$ induces airway hyperresponsiveness in dogs, *J. Appl. Physiol.*, 59, 1941, 1985.

225. **Aizawa, H., Chung, K. F., Leikauf, G. D., Euki, I., Bethel, R. A., O'Byrne, P. M., Hirose, T., and Nadle, J. A.,** Significance of thromboxane generation in ozone-induced hyperresponsiveness in dogs, *J. Appl. Physiol.*, 59, 1918, 1985.

226. **Kobayashi, H., Adachi, M., Satoh, H., Okada, Y., Takahashi, T., and Yamaguchi, H.,** The effect of thromboxane synthetase inhibitor, OKY-046, on airway hyperresponsiveness induced by ozone exposure in beagles, *Arerugi*, 34, 469, 1985; *Chem. Abstr.*, 103, 194781u, 1985.

227. **Fukumori, T., Tani, E., Maeda, Y., and Sukenaga, A.,** Effect of selective inhibitor of thromboxane $A_2$ synthetase on experimental cerebral vasospasm, *Stroke*, 15, 306, 1984.

228. **Motoki, M.,** Experimental study on pathogenesis and treatment of cerebral vasospasm. I. Effects of the thromboxane $A_2$ synthetase inhibitor (OKY-046) on experimental cerebral vasospasm, *Okayama Igakkai Zasshi*, 96, 149, 1984; *Chem. Abstr.*, 101, 108341e, 1984.

228a. **Komatsu, H., Takehana, Y., Hamano, S., Ujiie, A., and Hiraku, S.,** Beneficial effect of OKY-046, a selective thromboxane $A_2$ synthetase inhibitor, on experimental cerebral vasospasm, *Jpn. J. Pharmacol.*, 41, 381, 1986.

229. **Suzuki, S., Iwabuchi, T., Tanaka, T., Kanayama, S., Ottomo, M., Hatanaka, M., and Aihara, H.,** Prevention of cerebral vasospasm with OKY-046 an imidazole derivative and a thromboxane synthetase inhibitor. A preliminary cooperative clinical study, *Acta Neurochir.*, 77, 133, 1985.

230. **Uyama, O., Nagatsuka, K., Nakabayashi, S., Isaka, Y., Yoneda, S., Kimura, K., and Abe, H.,** The effect of a thromboxane synthetase inhibitor, OKY-046, on urinary excretion of immunoreactive thromboxane $B_2$ and 6-keto-prostaglandin $F_{1\alpha}$ in patients with ischemic cerebrovascular disease, *Stroke*, 16, 241, 1985.

231. **Nagatsuka, K., Uyama, O., Nakabayashi, S., Yoneda, S., Kimura, K., and Kamada, T.,** A new approach to antithrombotic therapy — evaluation of combined therapy of thromboxane synthetase inhibitor and very low dose of aspirin, *Stroke*, 16, 806, 1985.

232. **Hatziantoniou, C. and Papanikolaou, N.,** Renal effect of the inhibitor of thromboxane $A_2$-synthetase OKY-046, *Experientia*, 42, 613, 1986.

233. **Lelcuk, S., Alexander, F., Kobzik, L., Valeri, C. R., Shepro, D., and Hechtman, H. B.,** Prostacyclin and thromboxane $A_2$ moderate postischemic renal failure, *Surgery*, 98, 207, 1985.

234. **Purkerson, M., Martin, K., Yates, J., and Klahr, S.,** Inhibitors of thromboxane synthesis ameliorate the development of hypertension in Wistar rats with spontaneous hypertension (SHR), *Kidney Int.*, 27, 198, 1985.

235. **Stier, C. T., Jr. and Itskovitz, H. D.,** Thromboxane $A_2$ and the development of hypertension in spontaneously hypertensive rats, *Eur. J. Pharmacol.*, 146, 129, 1988.

236. **Chiba, S., Abe, K., Kudo, K., Yasujima, M., Omata, K., Tajima, J., and Yoshinaga, K.,** Effect of Tx synthetase inhibitor, OKY-046, on the blood pressure and renal excretory function in essential hypertension, Abst. Kyoto Conf. Prostaglandins, Kyoto, Japan, Nov. 25 to 28, 1984, 207.

237. **Kitagawa, H., Kurahashi, K., and Fujiwawa, M.,** Gastric mucosal erosion due to a mucosal ischemia produced by a thromboxane $A_2$-like substance in rats under water-immersion stress, *J. Pharmacol. Exp. Ther.*, 237, 300, 1986.

238. **Hamano, S., Kusama, H., Takehana, Y., Komatsu, H., Ujiie, A., and Shibata, K.,** General pharmacological studies of sodium (E)-3-[p-(1H-imidazol-1-ylmethyl)phenyl]-2-propenoate (OKY-046.Na) (1). Its effects on central nervous system and motor nervous system, *Oyo Yakuri*, 31, 527, 1986; *Chem. Abstr.* 105, 35349j, 1986.

239. **Hamano, S., Kusama, H., Tsutsumi, N., Abe, M., Takehana, Y., Komatsu, H., Ujiie, A., and Shibata, K.,** General pharmacological studies of sodium (E)-3-[p-(1H-imidazol-1-ylmethyl)phenyl]-2-propenoate (OKY-046.Na) (2). Its effects on respiratory and circulatory systems, *Oyo Yakuri*, 31, 535, 1986; *Chem. Abstr.* 105, 35350c, 1986.

240. **Shibata, K., Akimoto, A., Kaneko, S., Sakaguchi, N., Yamamoto, R., Nabetani, A., Aoki, M., and Ujiie, A.,** General pharmacological studies of sodium (E)-3-[p-(1H-imidazol-1-ylmethyl)phenyl]-2-propenoate (OKY-046.Na) (4). Its effects on the blood coagulation-fibrinolysis system, urinary excretion, and other parameters, *Oyo Yakuri*, 31, 559, 1986; *Chem. Abstr.*, 105, 35352e, 1986.

241. **Cross, P. E., Dickinson, R. P., Parry, M. J., and Randall, M. J.,** 3-(1-Imidazolylmethyl)indoles: potent and selective inhibitors of human blood platelet thromboxane synthetase, *Agents Actions,* 11, 274, 1981.

242. **Heptinstall, S., Bevan, J., Cockbill, S. R., Hanley, S. P., and Parry, M. J.,** Effects of a selective inhibitor of thromboxane synthetase on human blood platelet behaviour, *Thromb. Res.,* 20, 219, 1980.

243. **Heptinstall, S. and Fox, S. C.,** Human platelet behaviour after inhibition of thromboxane synthetase, *Br. J. Clin. Pharmacol.,* 15, 31S, 1983.

244. **Parry, M. J., Randall, M. J., Hawkeswood, E., Cross, P. E., and Dickinson, R. P.,** Enhanced production of prostacyclin in blood after treatment with selective thromboxane synthetase inhibitor, UK-38,485, *Br. J. Pharmacol.,* 77, 547P, 1982.

245. **Lecrubier, C., Lecompte, T., Kher, A., Dray, F., and Samama, M.,** Antiaggregatory effect *in vitro* of *UK* 38,485 (an inhibitor of thromboxane-synthetase) may depend on formation of $PGD_2$ (PRP) and $PGI_2$ (whole blood), *Thromb. Haemostasis,* 50, 284, 1983.

246. **Agarwal, K. C., Kay, K., Erickson, B. R., and Parks, R. E., Jr.,** Potentiation of forskolin inhibition on platelet aggregation by the inhibitors of cAMP phosphodiesterase and thromboxane synthetase, *Fed. Proc. Fed. Am. Soc. Exp. Biol.,* 44, 1665, 1985.

247. **Fisher, M., Weiner, B., Ockene, S., Hoogasian, S., Natale, A. M., Arsenault, J. R., Johnson, M. H., and Levine, P. H.,** Selective thromboxane inhibition: a new approach to antiplatelet therapy, *Stroke,* 15, 813, 1984.

248. **Cross, P. E., Dickinson, R. P., Parry, M. J., and Randall, M. J.,** Selective thromboxane synthetase inhibitors. 2. 3-(1*H*-imidazol-1-ylmethyl)-2-methyl-1*H*-indole-1-propionic acid and analogues, *J. Med. Chem.,* 29, 342, 1986.

249. **Hardee, M. M. and Moore, J. N.,** Effects of flunixin meglumine, phenylbutazone and a selective thromboxane synthetase inhibitor (UK-38,485) on thromboxane and prostacyclin production in healthy horses, *Res. Vet. Sci.,* 40, 152, 1986.

250. **Rebec, M. V. and Skrimska, V. A.,** Pharmacokinetics of dazmegrel, a specific thromboxane inhibitor, in rabbits utilizing fluorescence high pressure liquid chromatography, *Fed. Proc. Fed. Am. Soc. Exp. Biol.,* 44, 902, 1985.

251. **Fischer, S., Struppler, M., Böhlig, B., Bernutz, C., Wober, W., and Weber, P. C.,** The influence of selective thromboxane synthetase inhibition with a novel imidazole derivative, UK-38,485, on prostanoid formation in man, *Circulation,* 68, 821, 1983.

252. **Lorenz, R. L., Fischer, S., Wober, W., Wagner, H. A., and Weber, P. C.,** Effects of prostanoid formation and pharmacokinetics of dazmegrel (UK-38485), a novel thromboxane synthetase inhibitor in man, *Biochem. Pharmacol.,* 35, 761, 1986.

253. **Henry, C. L., Jr., Ogletree, M. L., Brigham, K. L., and Hammon, J. W., Jr.,** Thromboxane $A_2$ mediates the pulmonary vascular response to endotoxin, *Surg. Forum,* 35, 134, 1984.

254. **Semrad, S. D. and Moore, J. N.,** Effect of specific thromboxane synthetase inhibition in equine endotoxemia, *Vet. Surg.,* 14, 65, 1985.

255. **Truog, W. E., Sorensen, G. K., Standaert, T. A., Redding, G. J.,** Effect of the thromboxane synthetase inhibitor dazmegrel (UK 38,485), on pulmonary gas exchange and hemodynamics on neonatal sepsis, *Pediatr. Res.,* 20, 481, 1986.

256. **Lepran, I., Paratt, J. R., Szekeres, L., and Wainwright, C. L.,** The effects of metoprolol and dazmegrel, alone and in combination, on arrythmias induced by coronary artery occlusion in conscious rats, *Br. J. Pharmacol.,* 86, 229, 1985.

257. **Hoeft, A., Korb, H., Wober, W., Wolpers, H. G., and Hellige, G.,** Hemodynamics under basic conditions and during ischemic stress after inhibition of thromboxane synthetase by UK 38,485, in *Prostaglandins Other Eicosanoids Cardiovasc. Syst., Proc. Int. Symp. Prostaglandins,* Schroer, K., Ed., Karger, Basel, 1985, 235.

258. **Korb, H., Hoeft, A., Wober, W., Wolpers, H. G., and Hellige, G.,** Inhibition of thromboxane synthetase by the imidazole derivative 3-(1H-imidazol-1-ylmethyl)-2-methyl-1H-indole-1-propionic acid as a novel therapeutic approach to experimental myocardial ischemia, *Arzneim.-Forsch.,* 36, 1040, 1986.

259. **Coker, S. J. and Parratt, J. R.,** Relationships between the severity of myocardial ischemia, reperfusion-induced ventricular fibrillation, and the late administration of dazmegrel or nifedipine, *J. Cardiovasc. Pharmacol.,* 7, 327, 1985.

260. **Rustin, M. H. A., Grimes, S. M., Kovacs, I. B., Cooke, E. D., Bowcock, S. A., Sowemimo-Coker, S. O., Turner, P., and Kirby, J. D. T.,** A double blind trial of UK-38,485, an orally active thromboxane synthetase inhibitor, in the treatment of Raynaud's syndrome, *Eur. J. Clin. Pharmacol.,* 27, 61, 1984.

261. **Uderman, H. D., Jackson, E. K., Puett, D., and Workman, R. J.,** Thromboxane synthetase inhibitor UK 38,485 lowers blood pressure in the adult spontaneously hypertensive rat, *J. Cardiovasc. Pharmacol.,* 6, 969, 1984.

262. **Groene, H. J. and Dunn, M. J.,** The role of thromboxane ($TxA_2$) in the control of renal function and blood pressure (BP) in young spontaneously hypertensive rats (SHR), *Clin. Res.,* 31, 749A, 1983.

263. **Remuzzi, G., Imberti, L., Rossini, M., Morelli, C., Carminati, C., Cattaneo, G. M., and Bertani, T.,** Increased glomerular thromboxane synthesis as a possible cause of proteinuria in experimental nephrosis, *J. Clin. Invest.*, 75, 94, 1985.
264. **Lianos, E. A., Andres, G. A., and Dunn, M. J.,** Glomerular prostaglandin and thromboxane synthesis in rat nephrotoxic serum nephritis, *J. Clin. Invest.*, 72, 1439, 1983.
265. **Stork, J. E. and Dunn, M. J.,** Hemodynamic roles of thromboxane $A_2$ and prostaglandin $E_2$ in glomerulonephritis, *J. Pharmacol. Exp. Ther.*, 233, 672, 1985.
266. **Stahl, R. A. K., Kudelka, S., Paravicini, M., and Schollmeyer, P.,** Prostaglandin and thromboxane formation in glomeruli from rats with reduced renal mass, *Nephron,* 42, 252, 1986.
267. **Hirschberg, R., Höfer, W., and Schaefer, K.,** Endotoxin-Induced acute renal failure in mice. Effects of indomethacin and the thromboxane-synthetase antagonist UK-38.485, *Res. Exp. Med.*, 185, 107, 1985.
268. **Zipser, R. D.,** Effects of selective inhibition of thromboxane synthesis on renal function in humans, *Am. J. Physiol.*, 248, F753, 1985.
269. **Barnett, A. H., Leatherdale, B. A., Polak, A., Toop, M., Wakelin, K., Britton, J. R., Bennett, J., Rowe, D., and Dallinger, K.,** Specific thromboxane synthetase inhibition and albumin excretion rate in insulin-dependent diabetes, *Lancet,* i, 1322, 1984.
270. **Barnett, A. H., Armstrong, S., Chisholm, I., Letherdale, B. A., and Wakelin, K.,** Specific thromboxane synthetase inhibition and diabetic retinopathy in insulin dependent diabetics, *Clin. Sci.*, 68, 47P, 1985.
271. **Walt, R. P., Kemp, R. T., Filipowicz, B., Davies, J. G., Bhaskar, N. K., and Hawkey, C. J.,** Gastric mucosal protection with selective inhibition of thromboxane synthesis, *Gut,* 28, 541, 1987.
272. **Weiner, B. H., Ockene, I. S., Fisher, M., Hoogasian, J. J., Arsenault, J. R., Natale, A. M., Love, D. G., and Levine, P. H.,** The effects of thromboxane synthetase inhibition in hyperlipidemia, *Arteriosclerosis,* 3, 496a, 1983.
273. **Moufarrij, N. A., Little, J. R., Skrinska, V., Lucas, F. V., Latchaw, J. P., Slugg, R. M., and Lesser, R. P.,** Thromboxane synthetase inhibition in acute focal cerebral ischemia in cats, *J. Neurosurg.*, 61, 1107, 1984.
274. **McGinley, S., Centra, M., and Lysz, T. W.,** The effect of inhibiting brain thromboxane biosynthesis on pentylenetetrazole-induced seizure threshold, *J. Neurosci. Res.*, 13, 563, 1985.
275. **Jackson, E. K., Uderman, H. D., Herzer, W. A., and Branch, R. A.,** Attenuation of noradrenergic neurotransmission by the thromboxane synthetase inhibitor, UK 38,485, *Life Sci.*, 35, 221, 1984.
276. **Jackson, E. K.,** Effects of thromboxane synthase inhibition on vascular responsiveness in the *in vivo* rat mesentry, *J. Clin. Invest.*, 76, 2286, 1985.
277. **Shaw, J. F. L. and Greatorex, R. A.,** Drugs affecting the prostaglandin synthetic pathway and rat heart allograft survival, *Adv. Prostaglandin Thromboxane Leukotriene Res.*, 13, 219, 1985.
278. **Cross, P. E., Dickinson, R. P., Parry, M. J., and Randall, M. J.,** Selective thromboxane synthetase inhibitors. 3. 1*H*-Imidazol-1-yl-substituted benzo[b]-furan-, benzo[b]thiophene-, and indole-2- and -3-carboxylic acids, *J. Med. Chem.*, 29, 1637, 1986.
279. **Cross, P. E., Dickinson, R. P., Parry, M. J., and Randall, M. J.,** Selective thromboxane synthetase inhibitors. 4. 2-(1*H*-Imidazol-1-ylmethyl) carboxylic acids of benzo[b]furan, benzo[b]thiophene, indole, and naphthalene, *J. Med. Chem.*, 29, 1643, 1986.
280. **Bartmann, W., Beck, G., Lau, H. H., Wess, G., Just, M., Weithmann, U., Seiffge, D., and Schölkens, B. A.,** Synthesis and biological activity of new $TxA_2$-synthetase inhibitors, Abst. 6th Int. Conf. Prostaglandins Related Compounds, Florence, Italy, June 3 to 6, 1986, 364.
281. **Irie, K., Kunitada, S., Masumura, H., Kubo, H., Ashida, S., and Akashi, A.,** Cardiovascular effect of a new thromboxane $A_2$ synthetase inhibitor, 6-(imidazolylmethyl)-5,6,7,8-tetrahydronaphthalene-2-carboxylic acid HCl (DP-1904), Abst. 6th Int. Conf. Prostaglandins Related Compounds, Florence, Italy, 1986, 453.
282. **Sincholle, D., Coquelet, C., and Bonne, C.,** Inhibition of platelet thromboxane synthetase by 1-(3-benzyloxy-1(E)octenyl)imidazole, *Arzneim.-Forsch.*, 36, 117, 1986.
283. **Manley, P. W., Allanson, N. M., Booth, R. F. G., Buckle, P. E., Lai, S. M. F., Lunt, D. O., Kuzniar, E. J., Lad, N., and Tuffin, D. P.,** Structure-activity relationships in an imidazole-based series of thromboxane synthase inhibitors, *J. Med. Chem.*, 30, 1588, 1987.
284. **McCullagh, K. G., Tuffin, D. P., Honey, A., Lad, N., Manley, P., Meyers, P., Porter, R., Wade, P., and Booth, R.,** SC 41156: a novel inhibitor of human thromboxane synthase, Abst. 6th Int. Conf. Prostaglandins, Florence, Italy, June 3 to 6, 1986, 363.
284a. **Manley, P. W., Tuffin, D. P., Allanson, N. M., Buckle, P. E., Lad, N., Lai, S. M. F., Lunt, D. O., Porter, R. A., and Wade, P. J.,** Thromboxane synthase inhibitors. Synthesis and pharmacological activity of (*R*)-, (*S*)-, and (±)-2,2-dimethyl-6-[2-(1H-imidazol-1-yl)-1-[[(4-methoxy-phenyl)methoxy]methyl]ethoxy]-hexanoic acids, *J. Med. Chem.*, 30, 1812, 1987.

285. **Huddleston, C. B., Lupinetti, F. M., Laws, K. H., Collins, J. C., Clanton, J. A., Hawiger, J. J., Oates, J. A., and Hammon, J. W., Jr.,** The effects of RO-22-4679, a thromboxane synthetase inhibitor, on ventricular fibrillation induced by coronary artery occlusion in conscious dogs, *Circ. Res.*, 52, 608, 1983.
286. **Huddleston, C. B., Lupinetti, F. M., Clanton, J., Collins, J., Oates, J. A., and Hammon, J. W., Jr.,** Evaluation of a thromboxane synthetase inhibitor in circumflex coronary artery occlusion and reperfusion, *Curr. Surg.*, 40, 211, 1983.
287. **Huddleston, C. B., Hammon, J. W., Wareing, T. H., Lupinetti, F. M., Clanton, J. A., Collins, J. C., and Bender, H. W.,** Amelioration of the deleterious effects of platelets activated during cardiopulmonary bypass: comparison of a thromboxane synthetase inhibitor and a prostacyclin analog, *J. Thorac. Cardiovasc. Surg.*, 89, 190, 1985.
288. **Tolman, E. L. and Fuller, B. L.,** Inhibition of thromboxane synthesis in guinea pig lung and human platelets by clotrimazole and other imidazole antifungals, *Biochem. Pharmacol.*, 32, 3488, 1983.
289. **Lelcuk, S., Huval, W. V., Valeri, C. R., Shepro, D., and Hechtman, H. B.,** Inhibition of ischemia-induced thromboxane synthesis in man, *J. Trauma*, 24, 393, 1984.
290. **Hechtman, D. H. and Jageneau, A.,** Inhibition of cold-induced vasoconstriction with ketanserin, *Mircovasc. Res.*, 30, 56, 1985.
291. **Lelcuk, S., Alexander, F., Valeri, C. R., Shepro, D., and Hechtman, H. B.,** Ischemia stimulates tissue thromboxane synthesis, *Surg. Forum*, 35, 76, 1984.
292. **Huval, W. V., Dunham, B. M., Lelcuk, S., Valeri, C. R., Shepro, D., and Hechtman, H. B.,** Thromboxane mediation of cardiovascular dysfunction following aspiration, *Surgery*, 94, 259, 1983.
293. **Ku, E. C., McPherson, S. E., Signor, C., Chertock, H., and Cash, W. D.,** Characterization of imidazo[1,5-a]pyridine-5-hexanoic acid (CGS 13080) as a selective thromboxane synthetase inhibitor using *in vitro* and *in vivo* biochemical models, *Biochem. Biophys. Res. Commun.*, 112, 899, 1983.
294. **Mehta, J., Mehta, P., Wilson, D. L., Ostrowski, N., and Brigmon, L.,** Influence of selective thromboxane synthetase blocker CGS-13080 on thromboxane and prostacyclin biosynthesis in whole blood: evidence for synthesis of prostacyclin by leukocytes from platelet-derived endoperoxides, *J. Lab. Clin. Med.*, 106, 246, 1985.
295. **Cohen, D. S., Povalski, H. J., Rinehart, R. K., Tsai, C., Barclay, B. W., Van Orsdell, D., and Sakane, Y.,** Inhibition of thromboxane $A_2$ ($TXA_2$) synthetase causes endoperoxide shunting towards $PGI_2$ and $PGE_2$ synthesis in canine whole blood, *Thromb. Haemostasis*, 50, 285, 1983.
296. **Darius, H. and Lefer, A. M.,** Blockade of thromboxane and the prevention of eicosanoid-induced sudden death in mice, *Proc. Soc. Exp. Biol. Med.*, 180, 364, 1985.
297. **Simpson, P. J., Smith, C. B., Jr., and Lucchesi, B. R.,** Prevention of coronary artery thrombosis by the thromboxane synthetase inhibitor, CGS 13,080, *Pharmacologist*, 27, 268, 1985.
298. **Burke, S. E., DiCola, G., and Lefer, A. M.,** Protection of ischemic cat myocardium by CGS-13080, a selective potent thromboxane $A_2$ synthesis inhibitor, *J. Cardiovasc. Pharmacol.*, 5, 842, 1983.
299. **O'Connor, K. M., Friehling, T. D., Kelliher, G. J., MacNab, M. W., Wetstein, L., and Kowey, P. R.,** Effect of thromboxane synthetase inhibition on vulnerability to ventricular arrythmia following coronary occlusion, *Am. Heart J.*, 111, 683, 1986.
300. **Lepran, I. and Lefer, A. M.,** Ischemia aggravating effects of platelet-activating factor in acute myocardial ischemia, *Basic Res. Cardiol.*, 80, 135, 1985.
301. **MacNab, M. W., Foltz, E. L., Graves, B. S. Rinehart, R. K., Tripp, S. L., Feliciano, N. R., and Sen, S.,** The effects of a new thromboxane synthetase inhibitor, CGS-13080, in man, *J. Clin. Pharmacol.*, 24, 76, 1984.
302. **Fitzgerald, G. A., Feliciano, N., Sen, S. B., and Oates, J. A.,** Selective and non-selective inhibition of thromboxane formation in man, *Circulation*, 68, 103, 1983.
303. **Reilly, I. A. G., Doran, J. B., Smith, B., and FitzGerald, G. A.,** Increased thromboxane biosynthesis in a human preparation of platelet activation: biochemical and functional consequences of selective inhibition of thromboxane synthase, *Circulation*, 73, 1300, 1986.
304. **Ford, N. F., Browne, L. J., Campbell, T., Gemenden, C., Goldstein, R., Gude, C., and Wasley, J. W. F.,** Imidazolo[1,5-a]pyridines: a new class of thromboxane synthetase $A_2$ inhibitors, *J. Med. Chem.*, 28, 164, 1985.
305. **Lefer, A. M.,** Basic properties and indications for CGS-13080, a new selective thromboxane synthetase inhibitor, *Drugs Future*, 9, 437, 1984.
306. **Yasuda, H., Ochi, H., and Tsumagari, T.,** Stimulation of prostacyclin synthesis by nizofenone, *Biochem. Pharmacol.*, 33, 2707, 1984.
307. **Mikashima, H., Ochi, H., Muramoto, Y., Yasuda, H., Tsuruta, M., and Maruyama, Y.,** Effects of Y-20811, a long-lasting thromboxane synthetase inhibitor, on thromboxane production and platelet function, *Thromb. Res.*, 43, 455, 1986.
308. **Allan, G., Kulkarni, P. S., Levi, R., and Eakins, K. E.,** Selective inhibition of thromboxane-$A_2$ ($TxA_2$) biosynthesis by burimamide, *Fed. Proc. Fed. Am. Soc. Exp. Biol.*, 37, 915, 1978.
309. **Allan, G., Eakins, K. E., Kulkarni, P. S., and Levi, R.,** Inhibition of thromboxane $A_2$ biosynthesis in human platelets by burimamide, *Br. J. Pharmacol.*, 71, 157, 1980.

## Table 2
## PYRIDINES

| No. | Name of compound | Structure | Formula (mol wt) | Biological activity |
|---|---|---|---|---|
| 1. | Pyridine | 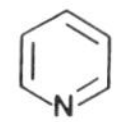 | $C_5H_5N$ (79) | Inhibited the synthesis of $TxB_2$ from $PGH_2$ by human-platelet microsomes, $IC_{50}$ 270 $\mu M$ (RIA), and the aggregation of human PRP induced by AA (0.37 m$M$) or ADP (10 $\mu M$) at 1.5 m$M$. Inhibited $TxB_2$ synthesis from AA by swine-lung microsomes at 10 m$M$ with increased $PGE_2$ and 6-keto-$PGF_{1\alpha}$ production (RTLC).[1,2] Insignificant effects on $PGI_2$ synthetase (swine aorta) or cyclooxygenase (RSV) at 20 m$M$.[2] For a structure-activity study of pyridine derivatives, see Reference 3. |
| 2. | 3-Ethylpyridine | 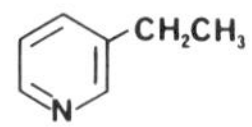 | $C_7H_9N$ (107) | Inhibited the synthesis of $TxB_2$ from $PGH_2$ by human-platelet microsomes, $IC_{50}$ 16 $\mu M$ (RIA), and completely inhibited aggregation of human PRP induced by AA or ADP at 0.25 m$M$. Inhibited $TxB_2$ synthesis from AA by swine-lung microsomes at 1 m$M$ with increased $PGE_2$ and 6-keto-$PGF_{1\alpha}$ production (RTLC). Most active of the three positional isomers.[1,2] |
| 3. | Nicotinic acid | 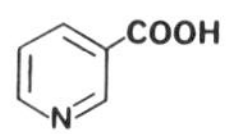 | $C_6H_5NO_2$ (123) | Inhibited the formation of $TxA_2$ induced by phospholipase $A_2$ in rat platelets at 10 m$M$ (bioassay) with increases in $PGF_{2\alpha}$ and $PGE_2$ (RTLC). The aggregation of a rat-platelet suspension induced by collagen was inhibited at 3, 10 m$M$.[4] For the inhibition of $TxB_2$ synthesis from $PGH_2$ by human-platelet microsomes, $IC_{50} > 1000$ $\mu M$.[1,2] |
| 4. | Ethyl nicotinate | 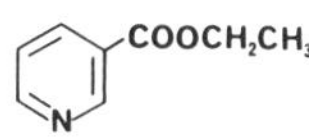 | $C_8H_9NO_2$ (151) | Inhibited the formation of $TxB_2$ from $PGH_2$ by human-platelet microsomes, $IC_{50}$ 33 $\mu M$ (RIA).[1,2] |
| 5. | Butyl nicotinate | 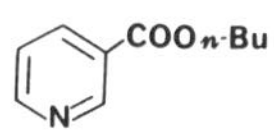 | $C_{10}H_{13}NO_2$ (179) | Inhibited the formation of $TxB_2$ from $PGH_2$ by human-platelet microsomes, $IC_{50}$ 18 $\mu M$ (RIA).[1,2] |

**Table 2 (continued)**
**PYRIDINES**

| No. | Name of compound | Structure | Formula (mol wt) | Biological activity |
|---|---|---|---|---|
| 6. | Hexyl nicotinate | 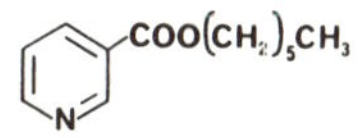 | $C_{12}H_{17}NO_2$ (207) | Inhibited the formation of $TxB_2$ from $PGH_2$ by human-platelet microsomes, $IC_{50}$ 10 μ*M* (RIA).[1,2] Noncompetitive inhibitor: $K_i$ 8.7 μ*M*.[2] |
| 7. | 3-Benzoylpyridine | 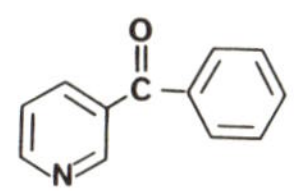 | $C_{12}H_9NO$ (183) | Inhibited the formation of $TxB_2$ from $PGH_2$ by human-platelet microsomes, $IC_{50}$ 18 μ*M* (RIA).[2] |
| 8. | 2-Methyl-1,2-di(3-pyridyl)-1-propanone (Metyrapone) | 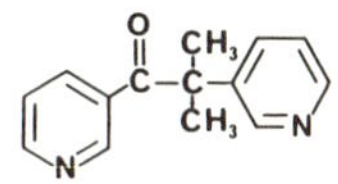 | $C_{14}H_{14}N_2O$ (226) | Inhibited the formation of $TxB_2$ from $PGH_2$ by human-platelet microsomes, $IC_{50}$ 25 μ*M* (RIA),[2] $IC_{50}$ 33 μ*M*;[5] and by bovine-lung microsomes, $IC_{50}$ 70 μ*M*, with increase in $PGE_2$ (but not 6-keto $PGF_{1\alpha}$) (RTLC).[5] Little effect on endoperoxide, $PGE_2$ and $PGI_2$ synthetase activities. Aggregation of human PRP by AA (0.5 m*M*) was completely inhibited by 1.2 m*M*.[5] |
| 9. | 4-Phenylpropylpyridine | 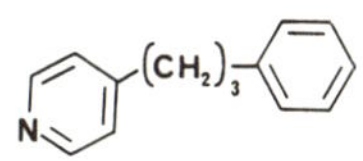 | $C_{14}H_{15}N$ (197) | Inhibited the synthesis of $TxB_2$ from $PGH_2$ by human-platelet microsomes, $IC_{50}$ 2μ*M* (RIA).[2] |
| 10. | 7-(3-Pyridyl)heptanoic acid | 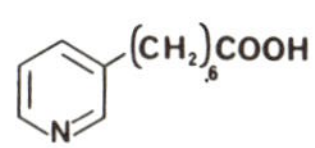 | $C_{12}H_{17}NO_2$ (207) | Inhibited the conversion of $PGH_2$ to thromboxane by a rabbit-platelet enzyme preparation, $IC_{50}$ 68 n*M*. Most potent member of the homologous series.[6] |
| 11. | (*E*)-3-[4-(3-Pyridylmethyl)-phenyl]-2-methylacrylic acid a. Hydrochloride (OKY-1555) | 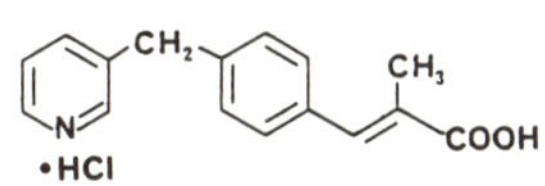 | $C_{16}H_{16}ClNO_2$ (253) | Inhibited the conversion of $PGH_2$ to thromboxane by a rabbit-platelet enzyme preparation ($IC_{50}$ 3 n*M*) (RTLC),[6] by washed rabbit platelets ($IC_{50}$ 2 n*M*), and by washed human platelets ($IC_{50}$ 3 n*M*) (RTLC),[7] with no effect on cyclooxygenase or $PGI_2$ synthetase at $10^{-4}$*M*.[6,7] Blocked AA-induced aggregation of rabbit PRP, $IC_{50}$ 0.3 μ*M* but not that due to ADP or thrombin *in vitro*.[7] |

| | | | |
|---|---|---|---|
| b. Free base (OKY-1580) | 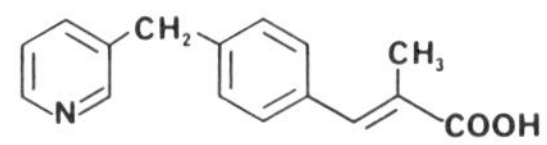 | $C_{16}H_{15}NO_2$ (253) | The $PGH_2$-induced aggregation of human PRP is partially blocked by OKY-1555, this effect being reversed by the adenylate-cyclase inhibitor dideoxyadenosine.[8] Prevented sudden death induced by AA (4 mg/kg) in rabbits at doses of 1 mg/kg i.v. and 30 mg/kg p.o.[7] In beagles with a partially constricted coronary artery, 20 mg/kg i.v. eliminated the cyclical reduction of blood flow in 5/7 animals.[9] Similarly, in mongrels, 12.5 mg/kg, i.v. protected 5/5 animals with enhancement of coronary sinus 6-keto-$PGF_{1\alpha}$ (RIA).[10] Pretreatment with OKY 1580, 100 mg, i.v. attenuated the increase in plasma $TxB_2$ in an experimental air-embolism model in dogs with enhanced $PGI_2$ production (RIA). The increases in tracheal pressure and pulmonary artery pressure were not altered, in contrast to OKY-046.[11] Aortic intimal thickening following mechanical injury in rabbits was not inhibited.[12] Contractile responses induced by histamine, serotonin, acetylcholine, bradykinin, and $PGF_{2\alpha}$ in guinea-pig tracheal strips were attenuated, and induced relaxations by isoproterenol, salbutamol, and $PGE_2$ potentiated. Inhibited biosynthesis of $TxA_2$ and accelerated production of 6-keto $PGF_{1\alpha}$ from AA in isolated perfused guinea-pig-lung lobes.[13] |
| c. Sodium salt (OKY-1581) | 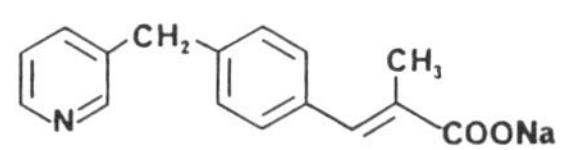 | $C_{16}H_{14}NNaO_2$ (275) | Inhibited rabbit-platelet thromboxane synthetase (enzyme preparation), $IC_{50}$ $3 \times 10^{-9}$ *M* (RTLC), but not cyclooxygenase (from sheep-vesicular microsomes) or $PGI_2$ synthetase (rabbit-aortic microsomes), $IC_{50} > 10^{-4}$ *M*.[14,15] Reduced or prevented the aggregation of rabbit PRP by collagen or AA, but not ADP, thrombin or ionophore A-23187 *in vitro*.[14,16] The concentrations preventing aggregation were much higher than those inhibiting production of $TxA_2$ activity at the same time (e.g., $IC_{50}$ for AA-induced aggregation, $2 \times 10^{-5}$ *M*; $IC_{50}$ for $TxA_2$ synthesis inhibition, $1.1 \times 10^{-7}$ [bioassay].[15,17] The |

**Table 2 (continued)**
**PYRIDINES**

| No. | Name of compound | Structure | Formula (mol wt) | Biological activity |
|---|---|---|---|---|
| | | | | reduction of $TxA_2$ during collagen-induced aggregation was accompanied by increases in PGE, PGF *in vitro* (RIA), (in this study aggregation was not affected).[18] Aggregation of rabbit platelets due to AA, collagen, and ADP was inhibited *in vivo*.[16] |
| | | | | Inhibited $TxA_2$ synthesis in dogs, $ED_{50}$ ~ 100 μg/kg i.v. after 5 min.[19] In rabbits treated with 100 mg p.o. or 5—100 mg s.c., $TxB_2$ production was reduced during collagen-induced aggregation of PRP with elevated PGE and PGF (RIA). Serum $TxB_2$ was reduced for up to 24—48 h, but no effect was seen on aggregation.[18] In a similar study, 1—3 mg/kg i.v. reduced $TxB_2$ (and elevated $PGH_2$) (RTLC) with inhibition of AA and threshold collagen-induced aggregation.[20] ADP-induced aggregation was not inhibited unless aortic rings were present;[20] aortic rings or microsomes enhancing the production of $PGI_2$ when platelet Tx synthetase was inhibited.[21] $PGI_2$ synthesis (as 6-keto-$PGF_{1\alpha}$) in guinea pig aortic rings was stimulated *in vitro* by $10^{-4}$—$10^{-7}$ *M* OKY 1581 in the absence of platelets or other blood elements (RIA).[22] |
| | | | | In monkeys, 0.5 mg/kg p.o. reduced serum $TxB_2$ for 5—7 h (RIA);[14,17] similar results were observed in baboons (with elevated 6-keto-$PGF_{1\alpha}$) although results were not consistent or dose related.[23] Inhibited AA-induced aggregation and $TxB_2$ formation in human PRP ($PGE_2\uparrow$, $PGF_{2\alpha}\uparrow$),[24] and $TxB_2$ formation in resuspended human platelets ($PGD_2\uparrow$, $PGE_2\uparrow$, $PGF_{2\alpha}\uparrow$)[25] with slight increases in 6-keto-$PGF_{1\alpha}$ (RIA). $TxB_2$ synthesis was inhibited during the mechanically induced aggregation of PRP from diseased |

patients ($PGE_2$ ↑) with no correlation between inhibition of $TxB_2$ levels and aggregation (TLC-RIA).[26]

In human volunteers, i.v. injection (83—1667 μg/kg) or oral dosing (10—400 mg) inhibited serum $TxB_2$ production. Similar effects were seen with i.v. infusion (10 μg/kg/min for 3 h). Plasma levels of $TxB_2$ were also shown to be reduced following the i.v. treatment. The major metabolites in plasma are 3-[4-(3-pyridylmethyl)phenyl]-2-methylpropionic acid (OKY-1558) and 4-(3-pyridylmethyl)benzoic acid (OKY-1565), both being active, with the latter persisting over 24 h. In clotting whole blood, serum 6-keto-$PGF_{1\alpha}$ was increased following the 10—50 mg oral or 1667 μg/kg i.v. doses (RIA). The aggregation response due to collagen or AA (but not ADP) was reduced but bleeding time was not altered.[27,28]

Oral administration for 5 days (200 mg. t.i.d.) inhibited serum $TxA_2$ production by 32-72% (RIA), markedly depressed collagen- or AA-induced aggregation and caused slight increases in bleeding time. In all studies hemodynamics were not affected and no side effects were noted.[27]

The combination of OKY-1581 and anagrelide or other phosphodiesterase inhibitors showed synergy in the inhibition of collagen-induced aggregation of human PRP, but not that due to ADP, 9,11-azo $PGH_2$ or 1-alkyl-2-acetyl-GPC.[29]

Decreased the formation of $TxB_2$ from AA by non-stimulated rat-alveolar macrophages with increases in $PGE_2$ and $PGD_2$ (but not HHT or lipoxygenase products) (RTLC),[30] and the formation of $TxB_2$ (and 6-keto-$PGF_{1\alpha}$ at higher concentrations) in rat-peritoneal macrophages stimulated with *E. coli* lipopolysaccharide.[31] OKY-1581 reversibly inhibited the activity of human natural cytotoxic cells, the effect being enhanced by the addition of $PGH_2$.[32]

In rabbits, 30 and 300 mg/kg p.o. reduced the thrombus weight and % obliteration induced by perivasal application of $AgNO_3$ to the carotid artery.[16,17]

## Table 2 (continued)
## PYRIDINES

| No. | Name of compound | Structure | Formula (mol wt) | Biological activity |
|---|---|---|---|---|
| | | | | In dogs, 1 mg/kg i.v. every 4 h for 24 h reduced the thrombus size, left ventricular infarction, and ventricular arrythmias in a coronary-artery thrombosis model (electrical stimulation of the circumflex artery). |
| | | | | Platelet aggregation of PRP due to AA and ADP was inhibited at 4 and 24 h, and that due to collagen at 24 h.[33] |
| | | | | In dogs with a partially obstructed coronary artery, 1 mg/kg i.v. prevented blockage independently of the degree of partial obstruction (in contrast to cyclooxygenase inhibitors). The antiaggregatory effects of OKY-1581 were actually reversed by cyclooxygenase inhibitors in severely obstructed arteries.[34] The synthesis of thromboxane (from $PGH_2$) in reperfused infarcted canine myocardium was inhibited by 100 μg/kg/min infusion for 15 min immediately before sacrifice.[35] |
| | | | | In dogs, OKY-1581 prevented the increase in $TxB_2$ levels and the secondary increase in coronary resistance during long-term preservation perfusion of the heart. The increase in 6-keto $PGF_{1\alpha}$ was not changed.[36] |
| | | | | In cats, an infusion of 1.5 mg/kg/h inhibited the increase in circulating $TxB_2$ due to coronary-artery occlusion (RIA), and prevented the rise in plasma creatine-kinase activity (but not S-T segment changes). The loss of myocardial creatine-kinase activity in the ischemic region of treated cats was efficiently prevented (biopsy) indicating significant cardioprotection.[37] In isolated cat hearts, OKY-1581 prevented $TxB_2$ release during ischemia induced by |

reduced perfusion at $5 \times 10^{-6}$ *M*. After reperfusion, contractile force was more fully restored with lowered coronary vascular resistance. Myocardial creatine-kinase activity (biopsy) was increased in treated hearts and that in the perfusate lowered.[38]

In patients with acute myocardial infarction, infusion of 2—3 μg/kg/min reduced elevated $TxB_2$ levels and markedly reduced the release of CK.[39] In a second study, 600 mg/d orally of either OKY-1581 or OKY-046 prevented the progressive increase in plasma $TxB_2$, but did not affect 6-keto-$PGF_{1\alpha}$ levels (RIA). In patients with angina pectoris, improvement was claimed in 19/26 cases following treatment with 300—800 mg of either compound.[40]

Prevented sudden death in rabbits induced by AA[14,16,41] and prevented the increase in $TxB_2$ with enhanced 6-keto-$PGF_{1\alpha}$ production.[41] Inhibition of AA-induced vascular contraction was also observed following 0.01 mg/kg.[14] Sudden death induced by the thromboxane agonist U-46619 in mice was not prevented.[42]

Prevented the increase in vascular permeability in the contralateral, nonembolized lung in dogs following unilateral experimental pulmonary microembolism. The increase in platelet aggregation following microembolism was also prevented.[43,44]

In cats, 2 mg/kg i.v. reduced the pulmonary lobar arterial pressure increase in response to AA (but not the thromboxane agonist U-46619).[45] Similarly, in sheep, 1.5 mg/kg prevented the increased arterial $TxB_2$ *and* 6-keto-$PGF_{1\alpha}$ generation due to thrombin-induced intravascular coagulation (RIA). The initial increases in pulmonary artery pressure and pulmonary vascular resistance were attenuated, and increases in lymph flow were delayed.[46] The increases in pulmonary vascular resistance in perinatal lambs due to AA infusion was diminished by 50 mg OKY-1581 injected into the pulmonary arterial circuit.[47]

**Table 2 (continued)**
**PYRIDINES**

| No. | Name of compound | Structure | Formula (mol wt) | Biological activity |
|---|---|---|---|---|
| | | | | The pulmonary hypertension in swine induced by cuprophan-activated plasma infusion was abolished by infusion of OKY-1581.[48] |
| | | | | In endotoxin-induced shock in rats, 50 mg/kg i.v. prevented the decrease of platelets, and prevented increases in plasma glutamic oxaloacetic transaminase, glutamic pyruvic transaminase and lactate dehydrogenase activities.[49] Similarly, pretreatment of rats with 5 mg/kg, i.v. attenuated the decrease in cardiac output, and improved gastrointestinal and renal perfusion, and liver blood flow following *Salmonella enteritidis* endotoxin injection.[50] In baboons, 2 mg/kg i.v. prevented the development of pulmonary hypertension and the increase in plasma $TxB_2$ after i.v. *E. coli* endotoxin. Plasma 6-keto-$PGF_{1\alpha}$ was increased 26×, (RIA); however, there was no increase in survival.[51,52] |
| | | | | The incidence of cerebral infarction in rabbits due to AA injection in the internal carotid artery was significantly reduced by 100 mg/kg p.o.[17] In an experimentally induced cerebral-vasospasm model in rabbits (intracisternal injection of autologous blood), 30 mg/kg, i.v. then 150 mg/kg, s.c. once daily post subarachnoid hemorrhage (SAH) prevented radiographic vertibrobasilar arterial spasm on the 3rd day post-SAH, and increased blood flow on the 4th day post SAH, in contrast to prostacyclin- or carbacyclin-treated animals.[53] In a similar model in dogs, 160 mg i.v. followed by 4 g/24 h infusion for 4 d, immediately after subarachnoid blood injection almost completely abolished the late spasm and prevented the early spasm.[54] In a second study, an |

infusion of 50 μg/kg/min for 2 h, 5 d after intracisternal blood injection, did not reverse the angiographic cerebral vasospasm although platelet aggregation due to collagen was inhibited.[55] Little benefit was found in a similar model in cats using regional cerebral blood flow as an index.[56] In rats, 30 mg/kg, i.v. 15 min before infusion of NaAA into the internal carotid artery prevented elimination of sensory-evoked responses and maintained normal levels of labile phosphates.[57]

Inhibition (>90%) of brain $TxB_2$ production by OKY-1581 (20 mg/kg, i.v. 1 h before challenge) had no effect on the tonic-seizure threshold induced by pentylenetetrazole in mice.[58]

In pregnant dogs, i.v. OKY-1581 decreased blood pressure and increased cardiac output and renal blood flow with little effect on uterine blood flow.[59]

At doses of 200 mg/kg p.o. for 2 d, only slight lowering of blood pressure was observed in spontaneously hypertensive rats, in contrast to 1-benzylimidazole. Blood pressure increases due to epinephrine were not reversed.[60]

In a model of glomerulonephritis in rats induced by injection of rabbit antibodies for rat glomerular protein, OKY-1581 prevented decreases in renal plasma flow and glomerular-filtration rate at 1—3 h,[61] but did not improve renal function or lessen proteinuria at 24 h.[62] Chronic oral administration of OKY-1581 ameliorated the progressive kidney disease in rats following removal of >70% of the kidney. Acute i.v. administration increased renal plasma flow and GFR in rats with a remnant kidney, but not in normal animals.[63]

In perfused hydronephrotic rabbit kidneys, OKY-1581 inhibited Tx production without altering $PGE_2$ or $PGI_2$ release (bioassay), and reversed the renal vasoconstriction induced by bradykinin and angiotensin.[64] Leukotriene-induced increases in total vascular resistance in perfused rat kidneys were not affected.[65]

**Table 2 (continued)**
**PYRIDINES**

| No. | Name of compound | Structure | Formula (mol wt) | Biological activity |
|---|---|---|---|---|
| | | | | Taurocholate-induced gastric-mucosal lesions in rats were reduced dose dependently by 5—20 mg/kg, i.g. with decreased mucosal $TxB_2$ (RIA) and enhanced $PGI_2$ and $PGE_2$ production.[66] The survival of cardiac allografts in rats was increased by a combination of azathioprine and OKY-1581, but not by either drug alone.[67] The basal tone of the fetal or prenatal lamb ductus venosus was not affected by $10^{-8}$ or $10^{-7}M$.[68] The production of $TxB_2$ by human umbilical veins, untreated or stimulated with AA, was inhibited by 0.1 m*M* with increases in 6-keto-$PGF_{1\alpha}$ synthesis (RIA).[69] Vasopressin-induced water flow in the toad bladder was suppressed at $1 \times 10^{-6}M$, but enhanced at $1 \times 10^{-4}$ *M*.[70] |
| 12. | 4-[(3-pyridylmethyl)-amino]-benzoic acid | 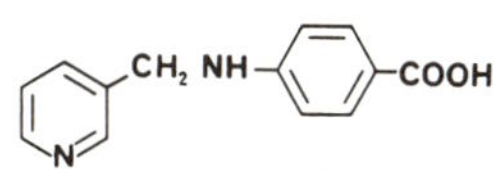 | $C_{13}H_{12}N_2O_2$ (228) | Attenuated the elevation in plasma $TxB_2$ in rats treated with i.v. *Salmonella enteritidis* endotoxin (15 mg/kg) at doses of 30 mg/kg i.p., enhanced survival, and prevented splanchnic infarction. Plasma PGE and 6-keto-$PGF_{1\alpha}$ were not significantly altered over controls (RIA).[71] |
| 13. | Sodium 5-(3-pyridinylmethyl)-2-benzofurancarboxylate<br>Sodium furegrelate (U-63557A) | 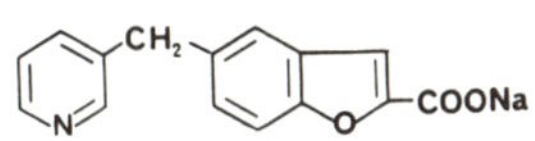 | $C_{15}H_8NNaO_3$ (273) | Inhibited the synthesis of $TxB_2$ from $PGH_2$ by human-platelet microsomes, $IC_{50}$ 15 n*M* (RIA), and by human PRP. Aggregation of human PRP induced by AA was suppressed at 54 or 108 μ*M* with elevation of $PGE_2$.[72] In combination with nimodipine (a calcium channel blocker), synergistically inhibited ADP- and thrombin-induced aggregation of human PRP. Alone, U-63557A inhibited biosynthesis of $TxB_2$ by platelets in response to ADP or thrombin, but not aggregation (RIA).[73] No effects were found |

on thrombin-stimulated or basal synthesis of 6-keto-$PGF_{1\alpha}$ by human endothelial cells at 108 $\mu M$, or on leukotriene synthesis in human PMN cells at $10^{-4} M$.[72] Leukocyte adhesion to a nylon mesh was inhibited *ex vivo* 24 h (but not 2—8 h) after i.v. administration to dogs.[74]

In rhesus monkeys, 3 mg/kg p.o. inhibited platelet Tx synthetase (≥80%) for at least 12 h; 14 d dosing (10 mg/kg b.i.d.) inhibited AA or collagen-induced $TxB_2$ synthesis for ≥4 d after dosing (RIA).[72]

In dogs, 0.1—5 mg/kg i.v. or 1—5 mg/kg p.o. prevented the blockage of stenosed coronary arteries caused by platelet aggregation.[72] However, in a coronary-artery-thrombus model induced by electrical stimulation of the intimal surface of the vessel in open-chest dogs, thrombus mass was not reduced by 10 mg/kg i.v. bolus + 5 mg/kg/h i.v. infusion, despite inhibition of platelet aggregation and $TxB_2$ production. The 6-keto-$PGF_{1\alpha}$ concentration was unchanged (RIA).[75] For a discussion of the pharmacokinetics of U-63557A in dogs, see References 76, 77.

In a model of acute myocardial infarction in rats (ligation of the left coronary artery), 8 mg/kg i.v., 2 min post-ischemia, followed by 8 mg/kg i.p. either 4 or 24 h later limited the extension of infarct size when analyzed after 48 h. Indices of infarct size were losses of CK activity and amino-nitrogen concentrations, and the % left ventricular wall spared.[78]

Survival of heart allograft transplants in rats was enhanced by subtherapeutic doses of cyclosporine in combination with U-63557A, but not by the latter alone.[79] In an autogenous-vein-graft model in dogs, early (1 wk) femoral-vein-graft patency was improved, but platelet deposition on carotid-vein grafts was not decreased.[80]

The survival time in rats following traumatic shock was improved by 4 mg/kg with reduction in plasma

## Table 2 (continued)
## PYRIDINES

| No. | Name of compound | Structure | Formula (mol wt) | Biological activity |
|---|---|---|---|---|
| | | | | and peritoneal fluid $TxB_2$ and the toxic peptide MDF.[81]<br>Mesenteric vascular responses to nerve stimulation, angiotensin II and (in contrast to UK-38,485 or OKY-1581) norepinephrine in spontaneously hypertensive rats were attenuated by chronic oral treatment with a high dose (100 mg/kg/d for 7 d), but not a low dose (30 mg/kg/d for 7 d) of U-63557A.[82]<br>The early pulmonary-artery hypertension in sheep following administration of *E. coli* endotoxin was significantly reduced by 30 mg/kg i.v. followed by 18 mg/kg/h. However, no improvement in microvascular response was found in the permeability phase.[83]<br>Infusion into the main pulmonary artery of fetal lambs did not change pulmonary blood flow, pulmonary mean arterial pressure, or pulmonary vascular resistance in spite of >90% reduction in arterial plasma $TxB_2$.[84]<br>The protective effect of eicosapentaenoic acid on impaired cerebral blood flow in ischemic gerbils was potentiated by U-63557A.[85]<br>For a structure-activity study of 15 analogues, see Reference 86. For a review, see Reference 87. |
| 14. | 2-(3-Pyridylmethyl)benzofuran-5-carboxylic acid | 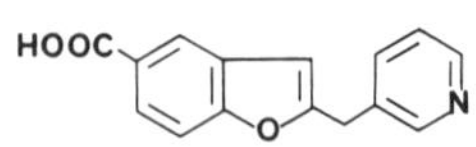 | $C_{15}H_{11}NO_3$ (253) | Inhibited the conversion of $PGH_2$ to $TxB_2$ by human-platelet microsomes, $IC_{50}$ $3.2 \times 10^{-8} M$ (RIA).[88] |
| 15. | 3-Methyl-2-(3-pyridylmethyl)benzo[b]thiophene-5-carboxylic acid [UK-49,883] | 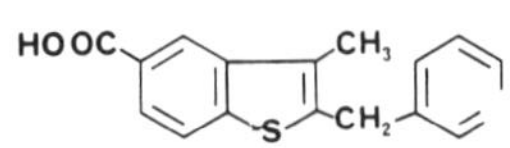 | $C_{16}H_{13}NO_2S$ (283) | Inhibited the conversion of $PGH_2$ to $TxB_2$ by human-platelet microsomes, $IC_{50}$ $2.6 \times 10^{-8} M$ (RIA). In dogs, 0.5 mg/kg p.o. produced inhibition of serum $TxB_2$ production for $\geq$6 h.[88] |

| | | | | |
|---|---|---|---|---|
| 16. | Nictindole, 2-Isopropyl-3-nicotinylindole [(3-(2-isopropylindolyl)-3-pyridyl ketone] (L-8027) | 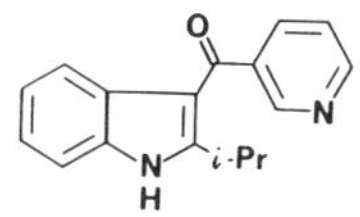 | $C_{17}H_{16}N_2O$ (264) | Inhibited $TxA_2$ synthesis from PG endoperoxides by horse-platelet microsomes,[89,90] $IC_{50}$ 0.25—0.8 $\mu M$ (bioassay),[89] guinea-pig-lung microsomes, $IC_{50}$ 900 $\mu M$ (RTLC), and human-platelet microsomes, $IC_{50}$ 2 $\mu M$ (RTLC);[91] and inhibited PG synthesis (cyclooxygenase) by BSVM $IC_{50}$ 5.9 $\mu M$, RSVM, $IC_{50}$ 17 $\mu M$ (bioassay),[89] and SSVM, $IC_{50}$ 2 $\mu M$(RTLC).[91] Did not inhibit $PGI_2$ formation by rabbit mesenteric arteries at 1 $\mu M$[89] but did inhibit $PGI_2$ formation from $PGH_2$ by bovine-aortic microsomes, $IC_{50}$ 0.1—1 m$M$,[91] and synthesis from $PGH_2$ in human-platelet microsomes, $IC_{50}$ ~10 $\mu M$ (RTLC).[92] Abolished aggregation of rabbit [89] and guinea pig.[93] PRP induced by AA with suppression of the release of $TxA_2$ (and $PGE_2$ in guinea pigs). In dog PRP, $TxB_2$ synthesis ($IC_{50}$ 1.6 $\mu M$) and $PGE_2$ synthesis ($IC_{50}$ 1.8 $\mu M$) from AA were inhibited at similar levels.[94] Inhibited aggregation of rabbit PRP due to collagen,[95] and inhibited AA-, collagen-, and the second wave of ADP-induced aggregation and $TxA_2$ synthesis (bioassay) in cat PRP.[96] In human PRP, both aggregation and $TxA_2$ formation due to AA,[97] adrenaline and ADP (second wave) were inhibited, whereas only $TxA_2$ formation was inhibited using low-dose collagen, or thrombin (bioassay). Collagen-induced aggregation was inhibited at higher concentrations.[98]<br>Inhibited AA-induced bronchoconstriction, thrombocytopenia, and hypotension in guinea pigs at doses of 1—10 $\mu$g/kg i.v.[93,99] Selectively inhibited the release of $TxA_2$ activity (bioassay) from antigen-challenged perfused lungs of sensitized guinea pigs at 0.1—1 $\mu M$,[90] and reduced basal tension and enhanced the antigen- and histamine-induced contractions of tracheal spirals from sensitized guinea pigs.[100]<br>In cats, 2 mg/kg i.v. antagonized the hyperthermic responses due to intracerebronventricular injection of *Salmonella typhosa* endotoxin or NaAA (but not $PGE_1$).[101] |

## Table 2 (continued)
## PYRIDINES

| No. | Name of compound | Structure | Formula (mol wt) | Biological activity |
|---|---|---|---|---|
| | | | | Inhibited PHA-induced mitogenesis ($IC_{50}$ 14 μ*M*) and $TxB_2$ synthesis (at 20 μ*M*) in human lymphocytes (RIA).[102] |
| 17. | 3-Methyl-2-(3-pyridyl)-1-indoleoctanoic acid CGS-12970 | 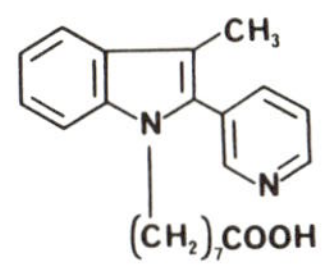 | $C_{22}H_{26}N_2O_2$ (350) | Inhibited the synthesis of $TxA_2$ by human-platelet microsomes, $IC_{50}$ 12 n*M* (RTLC), with minimal effects on cyclooxygenase, prostacyclin synthetase, or 15-lipoxygenase. In human PRP, $TxB_2$ formation in response to collagen was reduced without effects on aggregation (RIA). Similar results were seen in rats *ex vivo*. Aggregation of human PRP induced by ADP, AA, PAF, 5-HT, thrombin, or U-46619 (a thromboxane mimetic) was also not prevented.<br>In rabbits, 1 or 3 mg/kg, p.o. inhibited *ex vivo* $TxB_2$ formation by 94 or 98% at 1 h, with the effects lasting 24 h at the high dose.<br>Thrombocytopenia in guinea pigs induced by Forssman antiserum (or ADP) was inhibited 1 h following 30—100 mg/kg p.o. (100 mg/kg p.o.) of CGS-12970 in contrast to other thromboxane-synthetase inhibitors or indomethacin.<br>No inhibition was found in thrombocytopenia induced by the Arthus reaction (guinea pigs) or i.v. collagen (rats), or in thrombus formation on a cotton thread in an arteriovenous shunt (rats).[103]<br>In a myocardial-infarct model in rats, CGS-12970 (8 mg/kg i.v. total dose) administered 1—2 min and 4 h after coronary-artery ligation significantly reduced myocardial CK and amino-nitrogen loss from the left ventricular free wall at 48 h post-ligation, indicating a reduction in ischemic damage.[104] |
| 18. | 5-Chloro-1-methyl-2-(3-pyridyl)-3-indolehexanoic acid (CGS-15435A) | 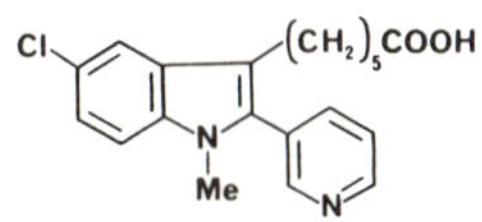 | $C_{20}H_{21}ClN_2O_2$ (356.8) | Inhibited human-platelet Tx synthetase ($IC_{50}$ 1n*M*) with minimal effects on cyclooxygenase ($IC_{50}$ 1.2 m*M*), $PGI_2$ synthetase ($IC_{50}$ 90μ*M*) or lipoxygenase ($IC_{50}$ 60μ*M*). |

| | | | | |
|---|---|---|---|---|
| | | | | In dogs, 3 mg/kg, p.o. inhibited serum Tx by 95% with increases in 6-keto-$PGF_{1\alpha}$ and $PGE_2$.<br>In rabbits, pretreatment with CGS-15435A (8.6 $\mu M$/kg, i.v.) prevented sudden death and thrombocytopenia due to AA injection at 15 min or 24 h after dosing, in contrast to dazoxiben (15 min but not 2 h).[105] |
| 19. | E-7-Phenyl-7-(3-pyridyl)-6-heptenoic acid CV-4151 | 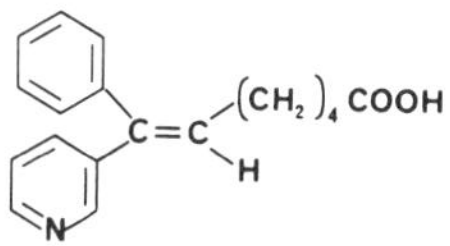 | $C_{18}H_{19}NO_2$ (281) | Inhibited the production of $TxB_2$ from $PGH_2$ by horse-platelet microsomes, $IC_{50}$ 2.6 × $10^{-8}$ *M* (RIA), with little or no effects on cyclooxygenase, $PGI_2$ synthetase, and 15- and 5-lipoxygenase at $10^{-4}$ *M*. In the rat, serum $TxB_2$ levels were reduced by 53 or 90% at 24 h following 1 or 10 mg/kg p.o. with increased 6-keto-$PGF_{1\alpha}$. *Ex vivo* aggregation of PRP induced by AA was reduced by 57, 72 and 23% at 2, 8 and 24 h following 1 mg/kg, p.o.[106,107] Administration of 10 mg/kg, p.o. to rats once daily for 14 d produced a constant lowering of serum $TxB_2$. 6-Keto-$PGF_{1\alpha}$ was concomitantly raised, and remained elevated 48 h after final dosing. Serum $TxB_2$ was reduced following oral administration to dogs (2 h $ID_{50}$ 0.17 mg/kg) with effects lasting over 24 h at doses of 1 and 10 mg/kg (RIA).[108]<br>In rabbits, doses of 1, 10 mg/kg, p.o. 2 h before challenge protected 60, 100% of animals from sudden death induced by AA (1.5 mg/kg, i.v.).[106,107]<br>In rats, 10 mg/kg, p.o. 2 h before challenge decreased the ECG changes induced by i.v. collagen.[109]<br>In dogs, CV-4151 (1 mg/kg infusion before challenge) did not prevent mortality following coronary-artery ligation. However on reperfusion after 1 h, ventricular arrhythmias were suppressed, and mortality prevented. Myocardial infarct size 1 h after reperfusion was reduced, and release of $TxB_2$ from the ischemic area abolished.[110]<br>In anginal patients, oral doses of up to 50 mg, b.i.d. reduced the mean frequency of anginal attacks from |

**Table 2 (continued)**
**PYRIDINES**

| No. | Name of compound | Structure | Formula (mol wt) | Biological activity |
|---|---|---|---|---|
| | | | | 6.3 to 3/wk and nitroglycerine consumption from 2.1 to 1.1 mg/wk. No side effects were noted in healthy volunteers administered 100 mg, b.i.d. orally for 3.6 d.[111]<br>In 4-week-old spontaneously hypertensive rats, 3 or 10 mg/kg, p.o. for 3 weeks delayed the development of hypertension for 1 week. Urinary excretion of water, sodium creatinine, and 6-keto-$PGF_{1\alpha}$ were increased, and that of $TxB_2$ decreased (RIA). CV-4151 inhibited medullary and cortical microsomal $TxA_2$-synthetase activity more effectively in 5-week SHR than in age-matched normotensive rats.[112]<br>For a structure-activity study of 74 analogues, see Reference 106. |
| 20. | *Z*-2,2-Dimethyl-7-(3-pyridyl)-7-(2-thienyl)-6-heptenoic acid | 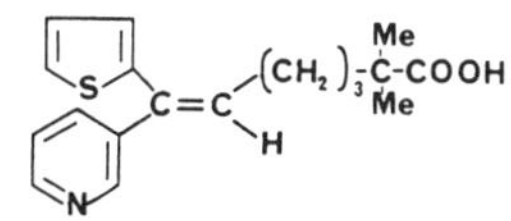 | $C_{18}H_{21}NO_2S$ (315) | Inhibited $TxB_2$ synthesis from $PGH_2$ by horse-platelet microsomes, $IC_{50}$ 1.8 × $10^{-8}$*M* (RIA).<br>In the rat, 1 mg/kg p.o. inhibited serum $TxB_2$ by 17% at 24 h.[106] |
| 21. | *E*-7-(2-Naphthyl)-7-(3-pyridyl)-6-heptenoic acid | 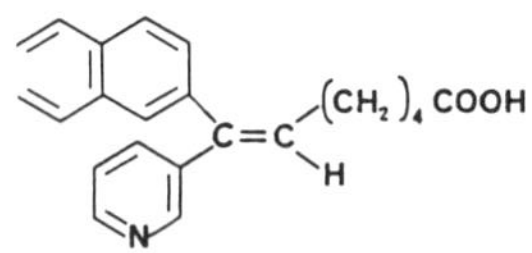 | $C_{22}H_{21}NO_2$ (331) | Inhibited $TxB_2$ synthesis from $PGH_2$ by horse-platelet microsomes, $IC_{50}$ 1.9 × $10^{-8}$ *M* (RIA).[106] |
| 22. | 7-[4-(3-Hydroxyoct-1(*E*)-enyl)pyrid-3-yl]hept-5(*Z*)-enoic acid | 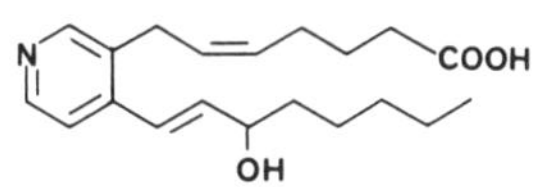 | $C_{20}H_{29}NO_3$ (331) | Inhibited the synthesis of $TxA_2$ from AA by a human-platelet suspension, $IC_{50}$ 3 μ*M*, with increased production of $PGE_2$, $PGD_2$ and $PGF_{2\alpha}$. Inhibited AA-induced platelet aggregation at higher concentrations.[113] |

| | | | | |
|---|---|---|---|---|
| 23. | 7-[4-(3-Hydroxy-octyl)pyrid-3-yl]heptanoic acid | 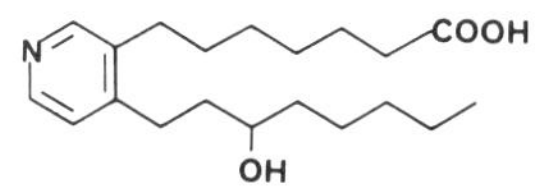 | $C_{20}H_{33}NO_3$ (335) | Inhibited the synthesis of $TxA_2$ from AA by a human-platelet suspension, $IC_{50}$ 1 $\mu M$.[113] |

## REFERENCES TO TABLE 2


1. **Tai, H.-H., Lee, N., and Tai, C. L.,** Inhibition of thromboxane synthesis and platelet aggregation by pyridine and its derivatives, *Adv. Prostaglandin Thromboxane Res.*, 6, 447, 1980.
2. **Tai, H.-H., Tai, C. L., and Lee, N.,** Selective inhibition of thromboxane synthetase by pyridine and its derivatives, *Arch. Biochem. Biophys.*, 203, 758, 1980.
3. **Akahane, K., Momose, D., Iizuka, K., Miyamoto, T., Hayashi, M., Iwase, K., and Moriguchi, I.,** Structure-activity study of pyridine derivatives inhibiting thromboxane synthetase, *Eur. J. Med. Chim. Ther.*, 19, 85, 1984.
4. **Vincent, J. E. and Zijlstra, F. J.,** Nicotinic acid inhibits thromboxane synthesis in platelets, *Prostaglandins*, 15, 629, 1978.
5. **Tai, H.-H., Tai, C. L., and Lee, N.,** Metyrapone, an inhibitor of thromboxane synthetase and platelet aggregation, *Fed. Proc. Fed. Am. Soc. Exp. Biol.*, 38, 407, 1979.
6. **Tanouchi, T., Kawamura, M., Ohyama, I., Kajiwara, I., Iguchi, Y., Okada, T., Miyamoto, T., Taniguchi, K., Hayashi, M., Iizuka, K., and Nakazawa, M.,** Highly selective inhibitors of thromboxane synthetase. 2. Pyridine derivatives, *J. Med. Chem.*, 24, 1149, 1981.
7. **Miyamoto, T., Taniguchi, K., Tanouchi, T., and Hirata, F.,** Selective inhibitor of thromboxane synthetase: pyridine and its derivatives, *Adv. Prostaglandin Thromboxane Res.*, 6, 443, 1980.
8. **Gorman, R. R.,** Biology and biochemistry of thromboxane synthetase inhibitors, *Adv. Prostaglandin Thromboxane Res.*, 11, 235, 1983.
9. **Uchida, Y. and Murao, S.,** Effects of thromboxane synthetase inhibitors on cyclical reduction of coronary blood flow in dogs, *Jpn. Heart J.*, 22, 971, 1981.
10. **Tada, M., Esumi, K., Yamagishi, M., Kuzuya, T., Matsuda, H., Abe, H., Uchida, Y., and Murao, S.,** Reduction of prostacyclin synthesis as a possible cause of transient flow reduction in a partially constricted canine coronary artery, *J. Mol. Cell. Cardiol.*, 16, 1137, 1984.
11. **Ishihara, Y., Uchida, Y., and Kitamura, S.,** Effect of thromboxane synthetase inhibitors (OKY-046, OKY-1580) on experimentally induced air embolism in anesthetized dogs, *Prostaglandins Leukotrienes Med.*, 21, 197, 1986.
12. **Hayashi, T. and Sumiyoshi, A.,** Influence of thromboxane $A_2$ synthetase inhibitors (OKY-046, OKY-1580) on the aortic intimal thickening after mechanical injury, *Ketsueki to Myakkan*, 13, 444, 1982; *Chem. Abstr.*, 99, 16278b, 1983.
13. **Kitamura, S., Iishihara, Y., and Takaku, F.,** Effect of thromboxane synthetase inhibitors (OKY-046, OKY-1580) on the action of bronchoactive agents in guinea pig tracheal strips and on arachidonate metabolism in guinea pig lung lobes, *Prostaglandins Leukotrienes Med.*, 14, 341, 1984.
14. **Hiraku, S., Katsube, N., Wakitani, K., Sakaguchi, K., Inagawa, T., Kawasaki, A., Tsuboshima, M., Naito, J., and Ujiie, A.,** Pharmacological effects of OKY-1581, a thromboxane $A_2$ synthetase inhibitor, *Rinsho Kagaku Shimpojumu*, 21, 68, 1981; *Chem. Abstr.*, 98, 191519g, 1983.
15. **Naito, J., Komatsu, H., Ujiie, A., Hamano, S., Kubota, T., and Tsuboshima, M.,** Effects of thromboxane synthetase inhibitors on aggregation of rabbit platelets, *Eur. J. Pharmacol.*, 91, 41, 1983.
16. **Naito, J., Hiraku, S., and Kuga, T.,** Thromboxane $A_2$ ($TXA_2$) synthetase inhibition by (E)-3-[4-(1-imidazolylmethyl)phenyl]-2-propenoic acid hydrochloride (OKY-046) and sodium (E)-3-[4-(3-pyridylmethyl)phenyl]-2-methylpropenoate (OKY-1581), and their medical usefulness, *Oyo Yakuri*, 27, 267, 1984; *Chem. Abstr.*, 100, 203371c, 1984.
17. **Hiraku, S., Wakitani, K., Katsube, N., Kawasaki, A., Tsuboshima, M., Naito, J., Ujiie, A., Komatsu, H., and Iizuka, K.,** Pharmacological studies on OKY-1581: a selective thromboxane synthetase inhibitor, *Adv. Prostaglandin Thromboxane Leukotriene Res.*, 11, 241, 1983.
18. **Smith, J. B. and Jubiz, W.,** OKY-1581: a selective inhibitor of thromboxane synthesis *in vivo* and *in vitro*, *Prostaglandins*, 22, 353, 1981.

19. **Oshima, T., McCluskey, E. R., Honda, A., and Needleman, P.,** Pharmacological manipulation of canine cyclooxygenase and thromboxane synthetase *in vivo*: differential renal and platelet recovery rates, *J. Pharmacol. Exp. Ther.*, 229, 598, 1984.
20. **Okuma, M., Takayama, H., Uchino, H., and Kondo, N.,** Effects of intravenous injection of thromboxane synthetase inhibitor on aggregation and arachidonate metabolism of rabbit platelets, *Thromb. Haemostasis,* 50, 284, 1983.
21. **Nakagawa, M., Tsuji, H., Ijichi, H., and Kuga, M.,** Utilization of platelet endoperoxides as the substrate for prostacyclin generation of vessel wall, *Thromb. Haemostasis,* 50, 478, 1983.
22. **Bielen, S. J., Lucas, J., Chan, P. S., and Cervoni, P.,** Thromboxane synthetase inhibitors induce prostacyclin synthesis in guinea pig aorta *in vitro, IRCS Med. Sci.*, 13, 334, 1985.
23. **Roy, A. C., Adaikan, P. G., and Karim, S. M. M.,** Effect of intravenous infusion of OKY-1581 (sodium-(E)-3-[4-(3-pyridylmethyl)phenyl]-2-methylacrylate) on circulatory thromboxane $A_2$ and prostacyclin levels in anaesthetized baboon, *Prostaglandins Med.*, 7, 253, 1981.
24. **Uotila, P., Matintalo, M., and Dahl, M. L.,** Arachidonic acid-induced platelet aggregation and thromboxane formation is inhibited by OKY-1581, *Prostaglandins Leukotrienes Med.*, 12, 299, 1983.
25. **Uotila, P. and Matintalo, M.,** Inhibition of thromboxane synthetase by OKY-1581 stimulates the formation of $PGE_2$, $PGF_{2\alpha}$, $PGD_2$ and 6-keto-$PGF_{1\alpha}$ in human platelets, *Prostaglandins Leukotrienes Med.*, 14, 41, 1984.
26. **Steinhauer, H. B., Lubrich, I., Guenter, B., and Schollmeyer, P.,** Response of human platelets to inhibition of thromboxane synthesis, *Clin. Hemorheol,* 3, 1, 1983.
27. **Ito, T., Ogawa, K., Sakai, K., Watanabe, J., Satake, T., Kayama, N., Hiraku, S., and Naito, J.,** Effects of a selective inhibitor of thromboxane synthetase (OKY-1581) in humans, *Adv. Prostaglandin Thromboxane Leukotriene Res.*, 11, 245, 1983.
28. **Yui, Y., Hattori, R., Takatsu, Y., Nakajima, H., Wakabayashi, A., Kawai, C., Kayama, N., Hiraku, S., Inagawa, T., Tsubojima, M., and Naito, J.,** Intravenous infusion of a selective inhibitor of thromboxane $A_2$ synthetase in man: influence on thromboxane $B_2$ and 6-keto-prostaglandin $F_{1\alpha}$ levels and platelet aggregation, *Circulation,* 70, 599, 1984.
29. **Smith, J. B.,** Effect of thromboxane synthetase inhibitors on platelet function: enchancement by inhibition of phosphodiesterase, *Thromb. Res.*, 28, 477, 1982.
30. **Punnonen, K., Uotila, P., and Mäntylä, E.,** The effects of aspirin and OKY-1581 on the metabolism of exogenous arachidonic acid in rat alveolar macrophages, *Res. Commun. Chem. Pathol. Pharmacol.*, 44, 367, 1984.
31. **Feuerstein, N. and Ramwell, P. W.,** OKY-1581, a potential selective thromboxane synthetase inhibitor, *Eur. J. Pharmacol.*, 69, 533, 1981.
32. **Rola-Pleszczynski, M., Gagnon, L., Bolduc, D., and LeBreton, G.,** Evidence for the involvement of the thromboxane synthetase pathway in human natural cytotoxic cell activity, *J. Immunol.*, 135, 4114, 1985.
33. **Shea, M. J., Driscoll, E. M., Romson, J. L., Pitt, B., and Lucchesi, B. R.,** Effect of OKY-1581, a thromboxane synthetase inhibitor, on coronary thrombosis in the conscious dog, *Eur. J. Pharmacol.*, 105, 285, 1984.
34. **Aiken, J. W., Shebuski, R. J., Miller, O. V., and Gorman, R. R.,** Endogenous prostacyclin contributes to the efficacy of a thromboxane synthetase inhibitor for preventing coronary artery thrombosis, *J. Pharmacol. Exp. Ther.*, 219, 299, 1981.
35. **McCluskey, E. R., Kramer, J. B., Corr, P. B., and Needleman, P.,** *In vivo* inhibition of thromboxane synthetase in infarcted canine myocardium, *Biochem. Biophys. Res. Commun.*, 121, 552, 1984.
36. **Van Rijk, G. L., Foegh, M., Ramwell, P. W., Goldman, M., and Lower, R. R.,** Long-Term myocardial preservation: thromboxane production and coronary resistance, *J. Surg. Res.*, 35, 417, 1983.
37. **Burke, S. E., Lefer, D. J., and Lefer, A. M.,** Cardioprotective actions of a selective thromboxane synthetase inhibitor in acute myocardial ischemia, *Arch. Int. Pharmacodyn.*, 265, 76, 1983.
38. **Lefer, A. M., Messenger, M., and Okamatsu, S.,** Salutary actions of thromboxane synthetase inhibition during global myocardial ischemia, *Arch. Pharmacol.*, 321, 130, 1982.
39. **Tada, M., Hoshida, S., Kuzuya, T., Inoue, M., Abe, H., Minamino, T., and Abe, H.,** Augmented thromboxane-$A_2$ generation and efficacy of its blockade in acute myocardial-infarction, *Int. J. Cardiol.*, 8, 301, 1985.
40. **Ito, T., Ogawa, K., Watanabe, J., Chen, L. S., Shikano, M., Imaizumi, M., Shibata, T., Ito, Y., Miyazaki, Y., and Satake, T.,** Selective thromboxane synthetase inhibitor and ischemic heart disease, *Biomed. Biochim. Acta,* 43, S125, 1984.
41. **Yamazaki, H., Isohisa, I., and Tanoue, K.,** Sudden death induced by intracoronary platelet aggregation, *Jpn. Circ. J.*, 47, 596, 1983.

42. **Myers, A., Penhos, J., Ramey, E., and Ramwell, P.,** Thromboxane agonism and antagonism in a mouse sudden death model, *J. Pharmacol. Exp. Ther.*, 224, 369, 1983.
43. **Hirose, T., Aoki, E., Aizawa, H., Ishibashi, M., Domae, M., Ikeda, T., and Tanaka, K.,** The potential beneficial effect of a thromboxane synthetasc inhibitor, OKY-1581, on increased lung vascular permeability in experimental pulmonary microembolization in dogs, *Jpn. J. Med.*, 21, 180, 1982; *Chem. Abstr.*, 99, 343h, 1983.
44. **Hirose, T., Aoki, E., Domae, M., Ishibashi, M., Ikeda, T., and Tanaka, K.,** Protective effect of a thromboxane synthetase inhibitor, (OKY-1581), on increased lung vascular permeability in pulmonary microembolization in dogs, *Prostaglandins Leukotrienes Med.*, 10, 187, 1983.
45. **Kadowitz, P. J., Nandiwada, P. A., Spannhake, E. W., Rosenson, R. S., McNamara, D. B., and Hyman, A. L.,** Pulmonary vascular responses to thromboxane $A_2$ as unmasked by OKY-1581: a novel inhibitor of thromboxane synthesis, *Chest*, 5, 72S, 1983.
46. **Garcia-Szabo, R., Kern, D. F., and Malik, A. B.,** Pulmonary vascular response to thrombin: effects of thromboxane synthetase inhibition with OKY-046 and OKY-1581, *Prostaglandins*, 28, 851, 1984.
47. **Tod, M. L. and Cassin, S.,** Thromboxane synthase inhibition and perinatal pulmonary response to arachidonic acid, *J. Appl. Physiol.*, 58, 710, 1985.
48. **Cheung, A. K., Baranowski, R., and Wayman, A. L.,** The role of thromboxane in cuprophan-induced pulmonary hypertension, *Kidney Int.*, 31, 1072, 1987.
49. **Goto, F., Sato, H., and Fujita, T.,** Antishock activity of thromboxane-synthesis inhibitors, *Rinsho Yakuri*, 13, 639, 1982; *Chem. Abstr.*, 98, 119391s, 1983.


49. **Goto, F., Sato, H., and Fujita, T.,** Antishock activity of thromboxane-synthesis inhibitors, *Rinsho Yakuri*, 13, 639, 1982; *Chem. Abstr.*, 98, 119391s, 1983.


50. **Tempel, G. E., Cook, J. A., Wise, W. C., Halushka, P. V., and Corral, D.,** Improvement in organ blood flow by inhibition of thromboxane synthetase during experimental endotoxic shock in the rat, *J. Cardiovasc. Pharmacol.*, 8, 514, 1986.
51. **Casey, L. C., Fletcher, J. R., Zmudka, M. I., and Ramwell, P. W.** Prevention of endotoxin-induced pulmonary hypertension in primates by the use of a selective thromboxane synthetase inhibitor, OKY 1581, *J. Pharmcol. Exp. Ther.*, 222, 441, 1982.
52. **Casey, L. C., Fletcher, J. R., Zmudka, M. I., and Ramwell, P. W.,** The role of thromboxane in primate endotoxin shock, *J. Surg. Res.*, 39, 140, 1985.
53. **Chan, R. C., Durity, F. A., Thompson, G. B., Nugent, R. A., and Kendall, M.,** The role of the prostaglandin-thromboxane system in cerebral vasospasm following induced subarachnoid hemorrhage, *J. Neurosurg.*, 61, 1120, 1984.
54. **Sasaki, T., Wakai, S., Asano, T., Takakura, K., and Sano, K.,** Prevention of cerebral vasospasm after SAH with a thromboxane synthetase inhibitor, OKY-1581, *J. Neurosurg.*, 57, 74, 1982.
55. **Fukumori, T., Tani, E., Maeda, Y., and Sukenaga, A.,** Effect of selective inhibitor of thromboxane $A_2$ synthetase on experimental cerebral vasospasm, *Stroke*, 15, 306, 1984.
56. **Yabuno, N.,** Prostacyclin and thromboxane in cerebral vasospasm. II. Effects of thromboxane synthetase inhibitor (OKY-1581) on experimentally-induced cerebral vasospasm, *Acta Med. Okayama*, 38, 239, 1984; *Chem. Abstr.*, 101, 144111p, 1984.
57. **Fredriksson, K., Rosen, I., Johansson, B. B., and Wieloch, T.,** Cerebral platelet thromboembolism and thromboxane synthetase inhibition, *Stroke*, 16, 800, 1985.
58. **McGinley, S., Centra, M., and Lysz, T. W.,** The effect of inhibiting brain thromboxane biosynthesis on pentylenetetrazole-induced seizure threshold, *J. Neurosci. Res.*, 13, 563, 1985.
59. **Murayama, K., Kasai, H., Adachi, T., Utsunomiya, O., and Ouchi, H.,** Comparative study of prostaglandin $I_2$: (PG) and thromboxane $A_2$: ($TXA_2$) synthetase inhibitor (OKY-1581) on hemodynamics in pregnant dogs, *Nippon Sanka Fujinka Gakkai Zasshi*, 35, 344, 1983; *Chem. Abstr.*, 98, 210596y, 1983.
60. **Lucas, J., Chan, P. S., Meteja, N., Cervoni, P., Ronsberg, M. A., and Lipchuck, L. M.,** 1-Benzylimidazole, a thromboxane synthetase inhibitor acutely lower blood pressure mainly by alpha-adrenoceptor blockade in spontaneously hypotensive rats (SHR), *Prostaglandins Leukotrienes Med.*, 12, 409, 1983.
61. **Lianos, E. A., Andres, G. A., and Dunn, M. J.,** Glomerular prostaglandin and thromboxane synthesis in rat nephrotoxic serum nephritis, *J. Clin. Invest.*, 72, 1439, 1983.
62. **Stork, J. E. and Dunn, M. J.,** Hemodynamic roles of thromboxane $A_2$ and prostaglandin $E_2$ in glomerulonephritis, *J. Pharmacol. Exp. Ther.*, 233, 672, 1985.
63. **Purkerson, M. L., Joist, J. H., Yates, J., Valdes, A., Morrison, A., and Klahr, S.,** Inhibition of thromboxane synthesis ameliorates the progressive kidney disease of rats with subtotal renal ablation, *Proc. Natl. Acad. Sci. U.S.A.*, 82, 193, 1985.

64. **Kawasaki, A. and Needleman, P.,** Contribution of thromboxane to renal resistance changes in the isolated perfused hydronephrotic rabbit kidney, *Circ. Res.*, 50, 486, 1982.
65. **Yoshizawa, M.,** Renal effects of leukotrienes and their metabolic aspects in isolated perfused rat kidney, *Keio Igaku,* 62, 269, 1985; *Chem. Abstr.*, 103, 99442a, 1985.
66. **Konturek, S. J., Brzozowski, T., Radecki, R., and Dobrzanska, M.,** Generation of endogenous prostaglandins and thromboxanes in taurocholate-induced gastric mucosal lesions, *Scand. J. Gastroenterol.*, 19 (Suppl. 92), 91, 1984.
67. **Foegh, M. L., Khirabadi, B., and Ramwell, P. W.,** Prolongation of experimental cardiac allograft survival with thromboxane-related drugs, *Transplantation,* 40, 124, 1985.
68. **Adeagbo, A. S. O., Coceani, F., and Olley, P. M.,** The response of the lamb ductus venosus to prostaglandins and inhibitors of prostaglandin and thromboxane synthesis, *Circ. Res.*, 51, 580, 1982.
69. **Mehta, J., Mehta, P., and Ostrowski, N.,** Stimulation of vessel wall prostacyclin by selective thromboxane synthetase inhibitor OKY 1581, *Prostaglandins Leukotrienes Med.*, 12, 49, 1983.
70. **Marumo, F.,** Effects of ONO-3122 (an enhancer of $PGH_2$ production) and OKY-1581 (an inhibitor of $TxA_2$ production) on the vasopressin-induced water flow in the toad bladder, *Pharmacol.*, 31, 34, 1985.
71. **Anderegg, K., Anzeveno, P., Cook, J. A., Halushka, P. V., McCarthy J., Wagner, E., and Wise, W. C.,** Effects of a pyridine derivative thromboxane synthetase inhibitor and its inactive isomers in endotoxic shock in the rat, *Br. J. Pharmacol.*, 78, 725, 1983.
72. **Gorman, R. R., Johnson, R. A., Spilman, C. H., and Aiken, J. W.,** Inhibition of platelet thromboxane $A_2$ synthase activity by sodium 5-(3′-pyridinylmethyl)benzofuran-2-carboxylate, *Prostaglandins,* 26, 325, 1983.
73. **Onoda, J. M., Sloane, B. F., and Honn, K. V.,** Antithrombogenic effects of calcium channel blockers: synergism with prostacyclin and thromboxane synthase inhibitors, *Thromb. Res.*, 34, 367, 1984.
74. **Hansen, J. P. and VanderLugt, J. T.,** The effects of cyclooxygenase and thromboxane synthetase inhibition of *ex vivo* canine leukocyte adhesion, *Fed. Proc. Fed. Am. Soc. Exp. Biol.*, 44, (Abstr. 3688), 1041, 1985.
75. **Hook, B. G., Schumacher, W. A., Lee, D. L., Jolly, S. R., and Lucchesi, B. R.,** Experimental coronary artery thrombosis in the absence of thromboxane $A_2$ synthesis: evidence for alternate pathways for coronary thrombosis, *J. Cardiovasc. Pharmacol.*, 7, 174, 1985.
76. **Wynalda, M. A., Liggett, W. F., and Fitzpatrick, F. A.,** Sodium 5-(3′-pyridinylmethyl)benzofuran-2-carboxylate (U-63557A), a new selective thromboxane synthase inhibitor: intravenous and oral pharmacokinetics in dogs and correlations with *ex situ* thromboxane $B_2$ production, *Prostaglandins,* 26, 311, 1983.
77. **Lakings, D. B. and Friis, J. M.,** Liquid chromatographic-ultraviolet methods for furegrelate in serum and urine: preliminary pharmacokinetic evaluation in the dog, *J. Pharm. Sci.*, 74, 455, 1985.
78. **Hock, C. E., Phillips, G. R., III, and Lefer, A. M.,** Protective action of a thromboxane synthetase inhibitor in preventing extension of infarct size in acute myocardial infarction, *Prostaglandins Leukotrienes Med.*, 17, 339, 1985.
79. **Aziz, S. and Jamieson, S. W.,** Improved efficacy of cyclosporine in combination with platelet-active agents, *Surg. Forum,* 36, 343, 1985.
80. **Endean, E. D., Boorstein, J. M., Hees, P. L., and Cronenwett, J. L.,** Effect of thromboxane synthetase inhibition on canine autogenous vein grafts, *J. Surg. Res.*, 40, 297, 1986.
81. **Hock, C. E. and Lefer, A. M.,** Beneficial effect of a thromboxane synthetase inhibitor in traumatic shock, *Circ. Shock,* 14, 159, 1984.
82. **Jackson, E. K.,** Effects of thromboxane synthetase inhibition of vascular responsiveness in the *in vivo* rat mesentery, *J. Clin. Invest.*, 76, 2286, 1985.
83. **Gunther, R. A., Smith, G. J., and Holcroft, J. W.,** Pulmonary response to selective inhibition of thromboxane $A_2$ synthesis during endotoxemia utilizing a unique inhibitor, *Surg. Forum,* 35, 42, 1984.
84. **Clozel, M. and Clyman, R. I., Soifer, S. J., and Heymann, M. A.,** Thromboxane is not responsible for the high pulmonary vascular resistance in fetal lambs, *Pediatr. Res.*, 19, 1254, 1985.
85. **Black, K. L., Hsu, S., Radin, N. S., and Hoff, J. T.,** Sodium 5-(3′-pyridinylmethyl)benzofuran-2-carboxylate (U-63557A) potentiates the protective effect of intravenous eicosapentaenoic acid on impaired cerebral blood flow in ischemic gerbils, in *Prostaglandins Other Eicosanoids Cardiovasc. Syst., Proc. Int. Symp. Prostaglandins,* Schroer, K., Ed., Karger, Basel, 1985, 213.
86. **Johnson, R. A., Nidy, E. G., Aiken, J. W., Crittenden, N. J., and Gorman, R. R.,** Thromboxane $A_2$ synthase inhibitors. 5-(3-Pyridylmethyl)-benzofuran-2-carboxylic acids, *J. Med. Chem.*, 29, 1461, 1986.
87. **Lefer, A. M.,** Pharmacology and therapeutic action of the thromboxane synthetase inhibitor furegrelate, *Drugs Future,* 11, 197, 1986.
88. **Cross, P. E. and Dickinson, R. P.,** The design of selective thromboxane synthetase inhibitors, *Spec. Publ. R. Soc. Chem.*, 50, 268, 1984.

89. **Gryglewski, R. J., Zmuda, A., Korbut, R., Krecioch, E., and Bieron, K.,** Selective inhibition of thromboxane $A_2$ biosynthesis in blood platelets, *Nature (London)*, 267, 627, 1977.
90. **Gryglewski, R. J.,** Prostaglandin and thromboxane biosynthesis inhibitors, *Arch. Pharmacol.*, 297, S85, 1977.
91. **Tobias, L. D. and Hamilton, J. G.,** Inhibition of arachidonate metabolism by selected compounds *in vitro* with particular emphasis on the thromboxane $A_2$ synthase pathway, *Adv. Prostacyclin Thromboxane Res.*, 6, 453, 1980.
92. **Dicfalusy, U. and Hammarström, S.,** Inhibitors of thromboxane synthase in human platelets, *FEBS Lett.*, 82, 107, 1977.
93. **Prancan, A. V., Lefort, J., Chignard, M., Gerozissis, K., Dray, F., and Vargaftig, B. B.,** L8027 And 1-nonyl-imidazole as non-selective inhibitors of thromboxane synthesis, *Eur. J. Pharmacol.*, 60, 287, 1979.
94. **Chignard, M., Vargaftig, B. B., Sors, H., and Dray, F.,** Synthesis of thromboxane $B_2$ in incubates of dog platelet-rich plasma with arachidonic acid and its inhibition by different drugs, *Biochem. Biophys. Res. Commun.*, 85, 1631, 1978.
95. **Wallis, R. B. and Zelaschi, D.,** Differential effects of cyclo-oxygenase inhibitors and thromboxane synthase inhibitors on rabbit platelet aggregation: evidence for the importance of prostaglandin endoperoxides as mediators in arachidonate-induced aggregation but not in collagen-induced aggregation, *Biochem. Soc. Trans.*, 8, 726, 1980.
96. **Marcinkiewicz, E., Grodzinska, L., and Gryglewski, R. J.,** Platelet aggregation and thromboxane $A_2$ formation in cat platelet rich plasma, *Pharmacol. Res. Commun.*, 10, 1, 1978.
97. **Gryglewski, R. J., Zmuda, A., Dembinska-Kiec, A., and Krecioch, E.,** A potent inhibitor of thromboxane $A_2$ biosynthesis in aggregating human blood platelets, *Pharmacol. Res. Commun.*, 9, 109, 1977.
98. **Grodzinska, L. and Marcinkiewicz, E.,** The generation of $TxA_2$ in human platelet rich plasma and its inhibition by nictindole and prostacyclin, *Pharmacol. Res. Commun.*, 11, 133, 1979.
99. **Chignard, M., Prancan, A., Lefort, J., Dray, F., and Vargaftig, B. B.,** Arachidonate-Mediated bronchoconstriction and platelet activation are inhibited by microgram doses of compound L8027 which are not selective for thromboxane synthetase, *Agents Actions,* (Suppl. AAS4), 184, 1979.
100. **Hitchcock, M.,** Stimulation of the antigen-induced contraction of guinea-pig trachea and immunological release of histamine and SRS-A from sensitized guinea-pig lung by (2-isopropyl-3-indolyl)-3-pyridyl ketone (L8027) and indomethacin, *Br. J. Pharmacol.*, 71, 65, 1980.
101. **Clark, W. G. and Lipton, J. M.,** Antagonism of hyperthermogenic agents by L 8027, an inhibitor of prostaglandin and thromboxane synthetase (40473), *Proc. Soc. Exp. Biol. Med.*, 160, 473, 1979.
102. **Kelly, J. P., Johnson, M. C., and Parker, C. W.,** Effect of inhibitors of arachidonic acid metabolism on mitogenesis in human lymphocytes: possible role of thromboxanes and products of the lipoxygenase pathway, *J. Immunol.*, 122, 1563, 1979.
103. **Ambler, J., Butler, K. D., Ku, E. C., Maguire, E. D., Smith, J. R., and Wallis, R. B.,** CGS 12970: a novel, long acting thromboxane synthetase inhibitor, *Br. J. Pharmacol.*, 86, 497, 1985.
104. **Hock, C. E. and Lefer, A. M.,** CGS-12970, A thromboxane synthetase inhibitor, limits ischemic damage following coronary artery occlusion, *Res. Commum. Chem. Pathol. Pharmacol.*, 52, 285, 1986.
105. **Olson, R. W., Cohen, D. S., Ku, E. C., Kimble, E. F., Renfroe, H. B., and Smith, E. F., III,** CGS 15435A, a thromboxane synthetase inhibitor with an extended duration of action: a comparison with dazoxiben, *Eur. J. Pharmacol.*, 133, 265, 1987.
106. **Kato, K., Ohkawa, S., Terao, S., Terashita, Z., and Nishikawa, K.,** Thromboxane synthetase inhibitors (TXSI). Design, synthesis, and evaluation of a novel series of ω-pyridylalkenoic acids, *J. Med. Chem.*, 28, 287, 1985.
107. **Nishikawa, K., Terashita, Z., Imamoto, T., Imura, Y., Hirata, M., and Terao, S.,** *(E)*-7-Phenyl-7-(3-pyridyl)-6-heptenoic acid (CV-4151): a potent, specific thromboxane $A_2$ synthetase inhibitor, *Adv. Prostaglandin Thromboxane Leukotriene Res.*, 15, 523, 1985.
108. **Terashita, Z., Imura, Y., Tanabe, M., Kawazoe, K., Nishikawa, K., Kato, K., and Terao, S.,** CV-4151 — A potent, selective thromboxane $A_2$ synthetase inhibitor, *Thromb. Res.*, 41, 223, 1986.
109. **Matsumura, H., Terashita, Z., Nishikawa, K., and Imai, Y.,** Antagonism of collagen-induced ECG changes in rats by a thromboxane synthetase inhibitor, CV-4151, *Nippon Yakurigaku Zasshi,* 87, 397, 1986; *Chem. Abstr.*, 104, 218806e, 1986.
110. **Imamoto, T., Terashita, Z., Tanabe, M., Nishikawa, K., and Hirata, M.,** Protective effect of a novel thromboxane synthetase inhibitor, CV-4151, on myocardial damage due to coronary occlusion and reperfusion in the hearts of anesthetized dogs, *J. Cardiovasc. Pharmacol.*, 8, 832, 1986.
111. **Anon.,** Takeda's new antithrombotic in angina, *SCRIP,* No. 1057, 24, 1985.
112. **Shibouta, Y., Terashita, Z., Inada, Y., and Nishikawa, K.,** Delay of the initiation of hypertension in spontaneously hypertensive rats by CV-4151, a specific thromboxane $A_2$ synthetase inhibitor, *Eur. J. Pharmacol.*, 109, 135, 1985.
113. **Corey, E. J., Pyne, S. G., and Schafer, A. I.,** Synthesis of a new series of potent inhibitors of thromboxane $A_2$ biosynthesis, *Tetrahedron Lett.*, 24, 3291, 1983.

## Table 3
## ENDOPEROXIDE AND THROMBOXANE ANALOGUES

| No. | Name of compound | Structure | Formula (mol wt) | Biological activity |
|---|---|---|---|---|
| 1. | 9α,11α-Azoprost-*(Z)*5-enoic acid | 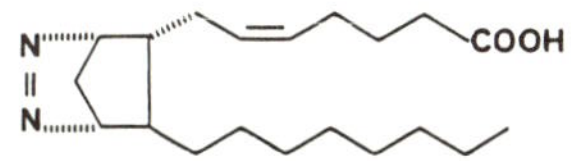 | $C_{20}H_{34}N_2O_2$ (334) | Inhibited the conversion of $PGH_2$ to $TxB_2$ by human-platelet microsomes, $IC_{50}$ 5.0 μ*M* (RIA), and AA-induced aggregation of human PRP at 28 μ*M*. Contracted rat-aortal strip, $EC_{50}$ 64 ng/ml.[1] |
| 2. | 9α,11α-Azoprost-*(E)*13-enoic acid | 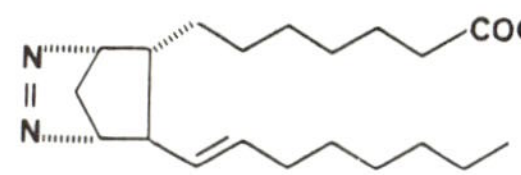 | $C_{20}H_{34}N_2O_2$ (334) | Inhibited the conversion of $PGH_2$ to $TxB_2$ by human-platelet microsomes, $IC_{50}$ 5.0 μ*M* (RIA), and AA-induced aggregation of human PRP at 28 μ*M*. Contracted rat-aortal strip, $EC_{50}$ 250 ng/ml.[1] |
| 3. | 9α,11α-Azoprost-*(Z)*5,*(E)*13-dienoic acid[2] (U-51605) (Azo Analogue 1) | 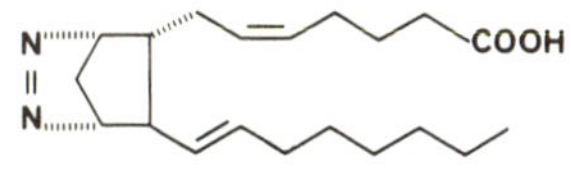 | $C_{20}H_{32}N_2O_2$ (332) | Inhibited the conversion of $PGH_2$ to $TxB_2$ by human-platelet microsomes, $IC_{50}$ 0.2 μ*M* (RIA), with increased production of $PGE_2$,[1,2] and the conversion of $PGH_2$ to $TxA_2$ by microsomes from guinea-pig lung, dog lung and human platelets, $IC_{50}$ 150—250 ng/ml (bioassay and RIA).[3] $TxB_2$ production by monkey-spleen microsomes or rabbit-lung microsomes was completely inhibited by $2 \times 10^{-5}$ *M*; however the synthesis of prostacyclin from $PGH_2$ in a bovine corpus-luteum preparation was also inhibited, $IC_{50}$ $2.7 \times 10^{-7}$ *M*.[4]<br>Inhibited the aggregation of human PRP induced by AA, $PGH_2$,[5] and collagen, and inhibited the second wave of ADP- and epinephrine-induced aggregation.[2] The inhibition of $TxB_2$ synthesis was associated with increased $PGE_2$ production (RIA, RTLC).[2] Activity 200 × imidazole in suppressing $TxB_2$ formation in human PRP or washed-platelet suspensions aggregated with AA or $PGH_2$ (RIA); with the aggregation of washed-platelet suspensions being inhibited by U-51605, in contrast to imidazole.[6,7]<br>Inhibited aggregation of human ($IC_{50}$ 6 μ*M*) and rabbit ($IC_{50}$ 55 μ*M*) PRP induced by U-46619 (see |

| | | | | |
|---|---|---|---|---|
| | | | | compound 9).[8] The c-AMP-lowering activity of $PGH_2$ as well as the aggregation of human PRP was blocked by 5.6 $\mu M$.[9] However, only the second wave of aggregation induced by platelet-activating factor or lysophosphatidic acid was inhibited.[10] The adherence of human polymorphonuclear leukocytes to nylon stimulated by *E. coli* lipopolysaccharide was inhibited (66%) by 10 μg/ml.[11] Contracted rat aorta, $EC_{50}$ 270 ng/ml.[1] Inhibited proliferation of B16a melanoma cells at 5 μg/ml[12] and B16a cell-DNA synthesis at 1—25 μg/ml.[12,13] Reduced the yield of viruses hosted by human-lung fibroblasts, coincidentally with inhibition of $TxB_2$, at 1 μg/ml.[14] Inhibited the AA- or U-46619-induced retraction of clots (formed in human PRP using batroxobin) at 9—18 $\mu M$, in contrast to the thromboxane-synthetase inhibitor dazoxiben.[15] |
| 4. | 9α,11α-Azo-15α-hydroxyprost-(*E*)13-enoic acid | 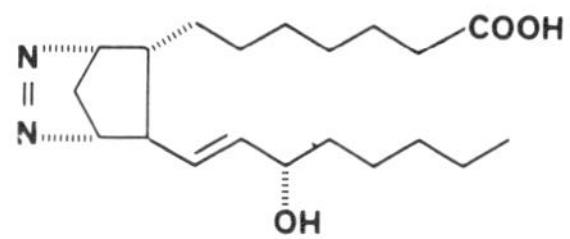 | $C_{20}H_{34}N_2O_3$ (350) | Inhibited the conversion of $PGH_2$ to $TxB_2$ by human-platelet microsomes, $IC_{50}$ 6.0 $\mu M$. Weak agonist towards aggregation of human PRP; contracted rat aorta, $EC_{50}$ 26 ng/ml.[1] |
| 5. | 9α,11α-Azo-15α-hydroxyprosta-(*Z*)5,(*E*)13-dienoic acid[16,17] | 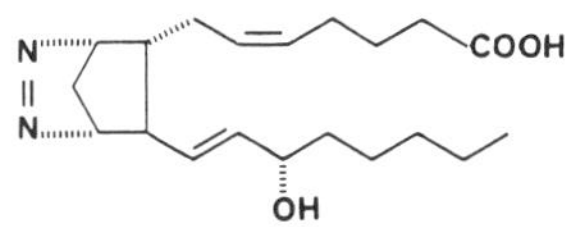 | $C_{20}H_{32}N_2O_3$ (348) | Inhibited the conversion of $PGH_2$ to $TxB_2$ by human-platelet microsomes, $IC_{50}$ 0.4 $\mu M$ (RIA),[1] 2 $\mu M$ (RTLC).[18] Caused rapid irreversible aggregation of human PRP (8 × $PGG_2$), and contracted rabbit aorta (7 × $PGH_2$)[16] and rat aorta ($EC_{50}$ 2.5 ng/ml).[1] |
| 6. | 9α,11α-Azo-13-oxa-15-hydroxyprostanoic acid[19] | 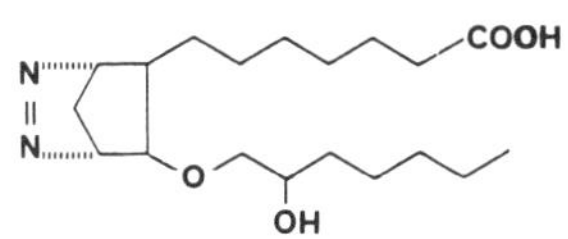 | $C_{19}H_{34}N_2O_4$ (354) | Inhibited the formation of $TxB_2$ from AA by washed human platelets at $10^{-4}$ $M$ (GC-MS or RTLC) with increased $PGE_2$ and $PGF_{2\alpha}$, and from $PGH_2$ by human-platelet microsomes, $IC_{50}$ ~$10^{-6}$ $M$, with increased $PGF_{2\alpha}$, $PGE_2$ and $PGD_2$ (RTLC). Inhibited AA- but not ADP-induced aggregation of human |

## Table 3 (continued)
## ENDOPEROXIDE AND THROMBOXANE ANALOGUES

| No. | Name of compound | Structure | Formula (mol wt) | Biological activity |
|---|---|---|---|---|
| | | | | PRP, $IC_{50}$ 3 × $10^{-5}$ *M*; and antagonized aggregation induced by $PGH_2$, $TxA_2$, and the endoperoxide analogue U-44609 in the micromolar range.[19,20] |
| 7. | 9,11-Epoxymethanoprostanoic acid | 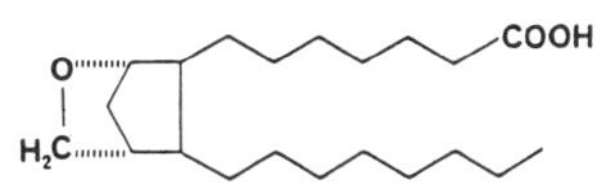 | $C_{21}H_{38}O_3$ (338) | Inhibited the conversion of $PGH_2$ to $TxB_2$ by human-platelet microsomes, $IC_{50}$ 7 μ*M* (RTLC).[21] |
| 8. | 9α,11α-Epoxymethano-15α-hydroxyprosta-(*Z*)5,(*E*)13-dienoic acid[22] (U-44069) | 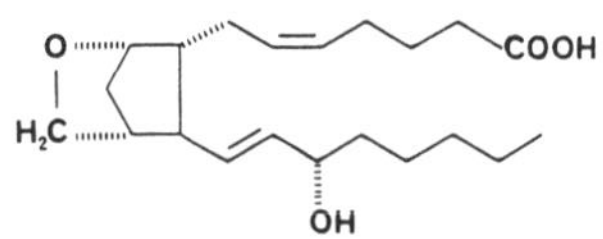 | $C_{21}H_{34}O_4$ (350) | Inhibited the conversion of $PGH_2$ to $TxB_2$ by human-platelet microsomes, $IC_{50}$ 2 × $10^{-5}$ *M* (RTLC),[18] 32 μ*M* (RTLC);[21] and the conversion of AA to $TxB_2$ by sheep-lung microsomes at 15 μ*M*.[23] Caused aggregation of human PRP (0.6 × $PGG_2$), and contraction of rabbit-aortic strips (3.6 × $PGH_2$).[24] |
| 9. | 9α,11α-Methanoepoxy-15α-hydroxyprosta-(*Z*)5,(*E*)13-dienoic acid)[22] (U-46619) | 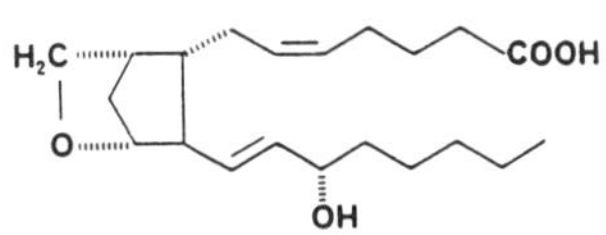 | $C_{21}H_{34}O_4$ (350) | Inhibited the conversion of $PGH_2$ to $TxB_2$ by human-platelet microsomes, $IC_{50}$ 600 μ*M* (RTLC).[21] Caused aggregation of human PRP (3.7 × $PGG_2$), and contraction of rabbit-aortic strips (6.2 × $PGH_2$).[24] |
| 10. | 9α,11α-Iminoepoxy-prosta-(*Z*)5,(*E*)13-dienoic acid[25] (U-54701) | 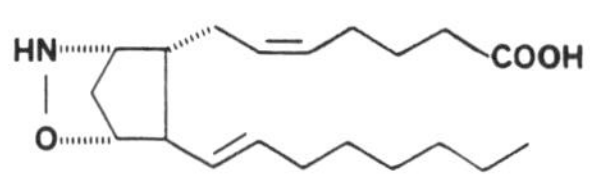 | $C_{20}H_{33}NO_3$ (335) | Inhibited human-platelet and rabbit-lung microsomal enzyme preparations ($10^{-6}$—$10^{-5}$ *M*) (RTLC and GC), and AA-induced aggregation of human PRP. Augmented $PGI_2$ production in rabbit-lung microsomes.[26]<br>Inhibited the proliferation of B16a melanoma cells at 25 μg/ml and B16a cell-DNA synthesis at 10—25 μg/ml.[12]<br>Reduced the yield of viruses cultured in human-lung fibroblasts at 5 μg/ml.[14] |
| 11. | 9α,11α-Iminomethano-15α-hydroxyprosta-(*Z*)5,(*E*)13-dienoic acid[27] | 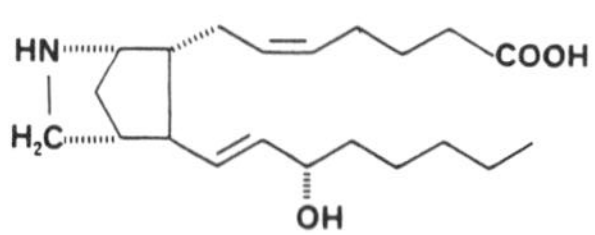 | $C_{21}H_{35}NO_3$ (349) | Inhibited the production of $TxB_2$ from AA by resuspended human platelets, $IC_{50}$ 830 × imidazole (RTLC).[27] |

| | | | | |
|---|---|---|---|---|
| 12. | 15-Deoxy-15,16-dehydro-11a-carbathromboxane $A_2$[28] | 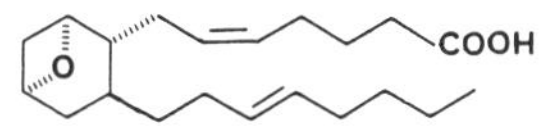 | $C_{21}H_{32}O_3$ (332) | Inhibited $PGH_2$- or AA-induced aggregation of human platelets and $TxB_2$ synthesis. No rat-aorta agonist or $TxA_2$-antagonist activity.[28,29] |
| 13. | 11a-Carbathromboxane $A_2$ (9α,11α-epoxy-(15S)-hydroxy-11a-carbathromba-5*Z*,13*E*-dienoic acid)[28] | 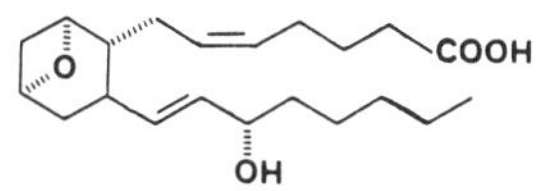 | $C_{21}H_{34}O_4$ (350) | Inhibited $PGH_2$- or AA-induced aggregation and $TxB_2$ synthesis in human platelets, and inhibited aggregation due to 9,11-methanoepoxyprosta-5,13-dienoic acid. No rat-aorta agonist or $TxA_2$-antagonist activity.[29] |
| 14. | (±)-Carbocyclic thromboxane $A_2$ ($CTA_2$) 9α,11α-Carba-15α-hydroxy-11a-carbathromba-*(Z)*5,*(E)*13-dienoic acid[30,31] | 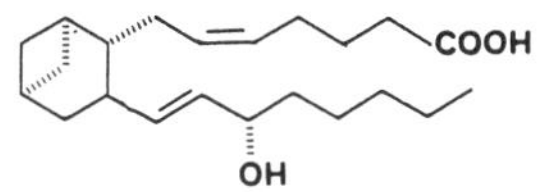 | $C_{22}H_{36}O_3$ (348) | Potent coronary vasoconstrictor (cat); stimulated coronary vascular smooth muscle at 29 p*M*. Inhibited AA- and $PGH_2$-induced aggregation of human PRP at 1—5 μ*M* and inhibited Tx synthesis from AA in washed rabbit platelets at 100 μ*M* (RTLC).[30,32]<br>Caused MI and sudden death in rabbits *in vivo*.[32]<br>The racemic compound contracted isolated rat aorta (threshold dose $10^{-13}$ g/ml) and induced reversible aggregation of human PRP at 36 μg/ml.[31] |
| 15. | Pinane-thromboxane $A_2$ ($PTA_2$) 9α,11α-Dimethylcarba-15α-hydroxy-11a-carbathromba-*(Z)*5,*(E)*13-dienoic acid[33-36] | 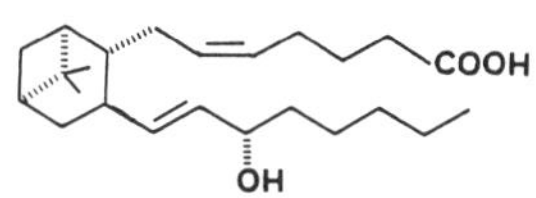 | $C_{24}H_{40}O_3$ (376) | Inhibited thromboxane synthesis from AA in human PRP, $IC_{50}$ 50 μ*M* (RIA); and in washed rabbit platelets at 100 μ*M* with increased formation of $PGE_2$, $PGD_2$, and $PGF_2$ (RTLC). No effect on $PGI_2$ synthetase at 100 μ*M*. Inhibited aggregation of human PRP induced by AA, PG endoperoxide analogues ($IC_{50}$ 2 μ*M*), and (partially) collagen, but not the primary wave of ADP- or epinephrine-induced aggregation.[33,37] AA-induced aggregation of cat and rabbit platelets was also prevented.[38]<br>Inhibited cat coronary-artery contraction induced by 9,11-azo $PGH_2$, $IC_{50}$ 0.1 μ*M*,[33] and antagonized $CTA_2$-induced constriction of rabbit pulmonary and cat coronary arteries at 1 μ*M* but not the response to KCl or angiotensin II.[38]<br>In a myocardial-ischemia model in cats (ligation of the coronary artery), an infusion of 0.5 μmol/kg/h 30 min post occlusion prevented the increase in plasma $TxB_2$ levels at 2—5 h and prevented the |

## Table 3 (continued)
## ENDOPEROXIDE AND THROMBOXANE ANALOGUES

| No. | Name of compound | Structure | Formula (mol wt) | Biological activity |
|---|---|---|---|---|
| | | | | large increase in plasma-CK activities at 4 and 5 h. The differences in myocardial-CK activities between ischemic and nonischemic regions were abolished and the decrease in percent-bound cathepsin D was prevented.[39] |
| | | | | Survival following traumatic shock in rats was prolonged by an infusion of 1 μmol/kg/h starting 15 min after trauma. The accumulation of $TxB_2$, the lysosomal protease cathepsin D, and the cardiotoxic peptide MDF in circulating blood was prevented, and mean arterial pressure changes were reduced.[40,41] |
| 16. | 12-*epi*-10β,11aβ-Dimethylcarba-15α-hydroxy-11a-carbathromba-*(Z)*5,*(E)*13-dienoic acid [(+)-*(Z)*-7-[(1*S*,2*R*,3*S*,5*S*)-2-[(I*E*,3*S*)-3-Hydroxy-1-octenyl]-10-norpinan-3-yl]-5-heptanoic acid][42] | 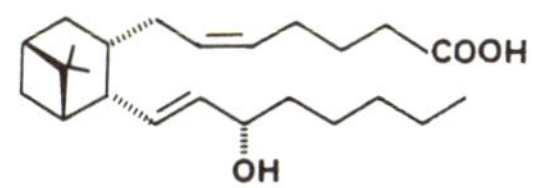 | $C_{24}H_{40}O_3$ (376) | Inhibited the conversion of $PGH_2$ to $TxB_2$ by human-platelet microsomes (57% at 100 μ*M*) (RTLC), and the aggregation of human PRP induced by collagen ($IC_{50}$ 41 μ*M*) and adrenaline/NaAA ($IC_{50}$ 14 μ*M*), but not that due to ADP, thrombin, or PAF at 300 μ*M*. Most active compound of 12 stereoisomers. $LTE_4$-induced bronchoconstriction in guinea pigs was inhibited (17%) by 10 mg/kg i.v.[42] |
| 17. | 9α,11α-Ethano-10-oxa-15β-hydroxyprosta-5*(Z)*,13*(E)*-dienoic acid[43] (SQ 26,329) | 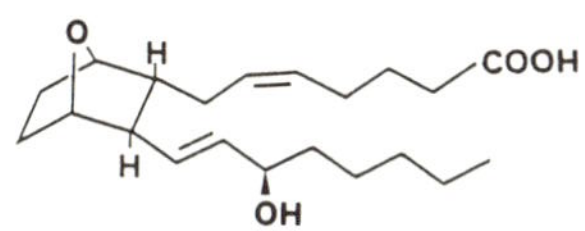 | $C_{21}H_{34}O_4$ (350) | Inhibits $TxA_2$ synthetase, $IC_{50}$ 470 μ*M*. Study of stereoisomers.[43] |
| 18. | 8-*epi*-9β,11β-Ethano-10-oxa-15α-hydroxy-ω-pentanor-15-cyclohexyl-prosta-5*(Z)*,13*(E)*-dienoic acid (SQ 27,427) | 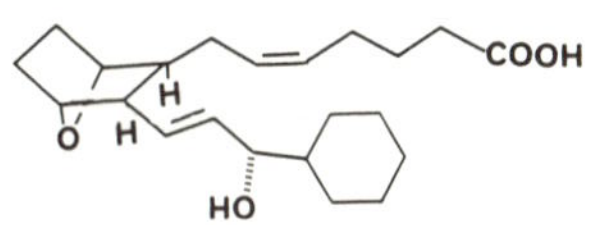 | $C_{22}H_{34}O_4$ (362) | Weak inhibitor of $TxB_2$ formation from AA by lysed human platelets, $IC_{50}$ 340 μ*M*, but not of $PGE_2$ (BSVM) or $PGH_2$ (bovine aorta). Potent inhibitor of aggregation induced by AA, ADP, epinephrine, collagen, and the $TxA_2$ agonists 9,11-azo $PGH_2$ and SQ 26655 at concentrations that did not alter $TxB_2$ levels. Specific $TxA_2$-receptor antagonist.[44] |

| | | | | |
|---|---|---|---|---|
| 19. | (±)-8-*epi*-9α,11α-Ethano-15α-and 15β-hydroxyprosta-5(*E*)-en-13-ynoic acid | 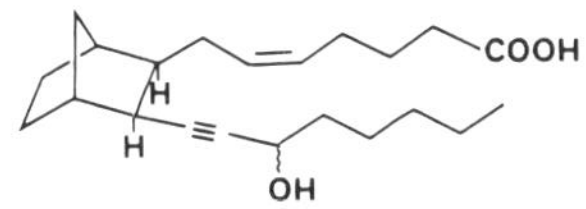 | $C_{22}H_{34}O_3$ (346) | Claimed to be a specific inhibitor of thromboxane synthetase. Inhibits platelet aggregation, ~0.5 × $PGE_1$.[45] |
| 20. | (±)-8-*epi*-9α,11α-Ethano-15α-hydroxyprosta-5(*Z*),13(*E*)-dienoic acid | 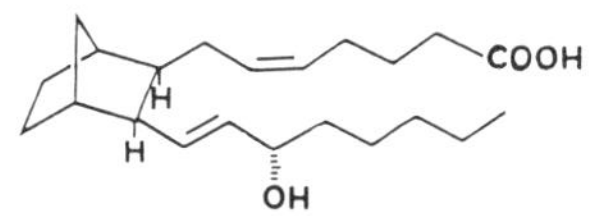 | $C_{22}H_{36}O_3$ (348) | Weak inhibitor of thromboxane synthetase and ADP-induced platelet aggregation. Potent hypotensive effects in anaesthetized rats.[46] |
| 21. | (±)-5-*endo*-(2*Z*),6-*exo*(1*E*,3*S*)-3-diazo-5-(7-hydroxy-2-heptenyl)-6-(3-hydroxy-1-octenyl)bicyclo[2.2.1]-heptan-2-one[47] | 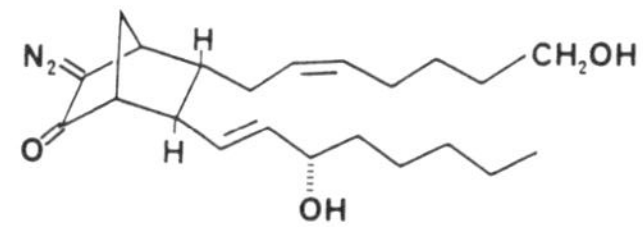 | $C_{22}H_{34}N_2O_2$ (358) | Inhibited thromboxane synthetase, $IC_{50}$ 20 μ*M*.[47] |
| 22. | (±)-5-*endo*-(2*Z*),6-*exo*(1*E*,3*S*)-3-oximino-5-(7-hydroxy-2-heptenyl)-6-(3-hydroxy-1-octenyl)bicyclo[2.2.1]-heptan-2-one[47] | 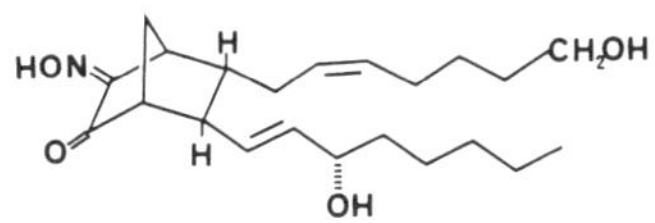 | $C_{22}H_{35}NO_3$ (361) | Inhibited thromboxane synthetase, $IC_{50}$ 20 μ*M*.[47] |
| 23. | 9β,11β-Dimethylcarba-13-oxa-11a-carbathromba-5(*Z*)-enoic acid | 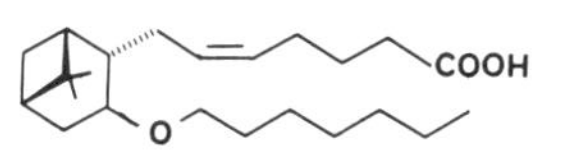 | $C_{23}H_{40}O_3$ (364) | Caused a 75% inhibition of thromboxane synthesis from $PGH_2$ in washed rabbit platelets at 100 μg (RTLC); inhibited AA- and collagen-induced aggregation of washed human platelets at 20 μg.[48] |
| 24. | 8-[2,2-Dimethyl-6-[4(*S*)-hydroxynon-2-ynyl]-1,3-dioxan-4-yl]oct-5(*Z*)-enoic acid | 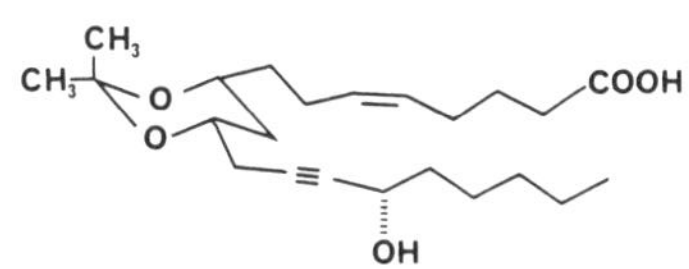 | $C_{23}H_{38}O_5$ (394) | Inhibited thromboxane synthesis (65%) from $PGH_2$ in washed rabbit platelets at 100 μg (RTLC).[48] |
| 25. | 8-[2,2-Dimethyl-6-[4(*S*)-*t*-butoxynon-2-ynyl]-1,3-dioxan-4-yl]oct-5(*Z*)-enoic acid | 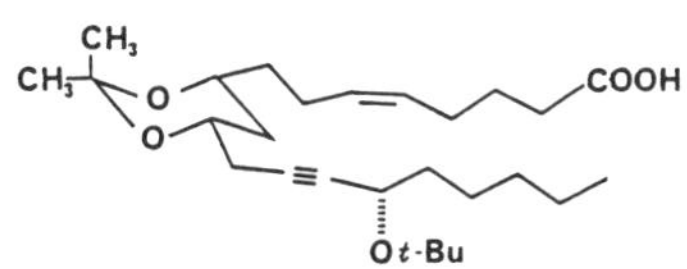 | $C_{27}H_{46}O_5$ (450) | Inhibited thromboxane synthesis (80%) from $PGH_2$ in washed rabbit platelets and $PGI_2$ production (60%) in bovine-aortic microsomes at 100 μg (RTLC).[48] |

## REFERENCES TO TABLE 3


1. **Gorman, R. R., Shebuski, R. J., Aiken, J. W., and Bundy, G. L.,** Analysis of the biological activity of azoprostanoids in human platelets, *Fed. Proc. Fed. Am. Soc. Exp. Biol.,* 40, 1997, 1981.
2. **Gorman, R. R., Bundy, G. L., Peterson, D. C., Sun, F. F., Miller, O. V., and Fitzpatrick, F. A.,** Inhibition of human platelet thromboxane synthetase by 9,11-azoprosta-5,13-dienoic acid, *Proc. Natl. Acad. Sci. U.S.A.,* 74, 4007, 1977.
3. **Aiken, J. W.,** Pharmacology of thromboxane synthetase inhibitors, *Adv. Prostaglandin Thromboxane Leukotriene Res.,* 11, 253, 1983.
4. **Sun, F. F., Chapman, J. P., and McGuire, J. C.,** Metabolism of prostaglandin endoperoxide in animal tissues, *Prostaglandins,* 14, 1055, 1977.
5. **Fitzpatrick, F. A. and Gorman, R. R.,** Platelet rich plasma transforms exogenous prostaglandin endoperoxide $H_2$ into thromboxane $A_2$, *Prostaglandins,* 14, 881, 1977.
6. **Fitzpatrick, F. A. and Gorman, R. R.,** A comparison of imidazole and 9,11-azoprosta-5,13-dienoic acid: two selective thromboxane synthetase inhibitors, *Biochem. Biophys. Acta,* 539, 162, 1978.
7. **Needleman, P., Bryan, B., Wyche, A., Bronson, S. D., Eakins, K., Ferrendelli, J. A., and Minkes, M.,** Thromboxane synthetase inhibitors as pharmacological tools: differential biochemical and biological effects on platelet suspensions, *Prostaglandins,* 14, 897, 1977.
8. **Anderson, L. and MacIntyre, D. E.,** Differences between the thromboxane $A_2$ receptors on rabbit and human platelets, *Br. J. Pharmacol.,* 77, 546P, 1982.
9. **Gorman, R. R., Fitzpatrick, F. A., and Miller, O. V.,** A selective thromboxane synthetase inhibitor blocks the cAMP lowering activity of $PGH_2$, *Biochem. Biophys. Res. Commun.,* 79, 305, 1977.
10. **MacIntyre, D. E., Shaw, A. M., Pollock, W. K., Marks, G., and Westwick, J.,** Role of endogenous arachidonate metabolites in phospholipid-induced human platelet activation, *Adv. Prostaglandin Thromboxane Leukotriene Res.,* 11, 423, 1983.
11. **Spagnuolo, P. J., Ellner, J. J., Hassid, A., and Dunn, M. J.,** Thromboxane $A_2$ mediates augmented polymorphonuclear leukocyte adhesiveness, *J. Clin. Invest.,* 66, 406, 1980.
12. **Honn, K. V. and Meyer, J.,** Thromboxanes and prostacyclin: positive and negative modulators of tumor growth, *Biochem. Biophys. Res. Commun.,* 102, 1122, 1981.
13. **Dunn, J. R., II, Romine, M., Skoff, A., and Honn, K. V.,** Arachidonic acid metabolites regulation of tumor cell proliferation, *J. Cell Biol.,* 87, CC 11a, 1980.
14. **Fitzpatrick, F. A. and Stringfellow, D.,** Influence of thromboxane synthetase inhibitors on virus replication in human lung fibroblasts *in vitro, Biochem. Biophys. Res. Commun.,* 116, 264, 1983.
15. **Di Minno, G., Bertelé, V., Cerletti, C., DeGaetano, G., and Silver, M. J.,** Arachidonic acid induces human platelet-fibrin retraction: the role of platelet cyclic endoperoxides, *Thromb. Res.,* 25, 299, 1982.
16. **Corey, E. J., Nicolaou, K. C., Machida, Y., Malmsten, C. L., and Samuelsson, B.,** Synthesis and biological properties of a 9,11-azo-prostanoid: highly active biochemical mimic of prostaglandin endoperoxides, *Proc. Natl. Acad. Sci. U.S.A.,* 72, 3355, 1975.
17. **Corey, E. J., Narasaka, K., and Shibasaki, M.,** A direct, stereocontrolled total synthesis of the 9,11-azo analogue of the prostaglandin endoperoxide, $PGH_2$, *J. Am. Chem. Soc.,* 98, 6417, 1976.
18. **Diczfalusy, U. and Hammarström, S.,** Inhibitors of thromboxane synthetase in human platelets, *FEBS Lett.,* 82, 107, 1977.
19. **Kam, P. S.-T., Portoghese, P. S., Gerrard, J. M., and Dunham, E. W.,** Synthesis and biological evaluation of 9,11-azo-13-oxa-15-hydroxyprostanoic acid, a potent inhibitor of platelet aggregation, *J. Med. Chem.,* 22, 1402, 1979.
20. **Kam, S.-T., Portoghese, P. S., Dunham, E. W., and Gerrard, J. M.,** 9,11-azo-13-oxa-15-hydroxyprostanoic acid: a potent thromboxane synthetase inhibitor and a $PGH_2/TXA_2$ receptor antagonist, *Prostaglandins Med.,* 3, 279, 1979.
21. **Sun, F. F.,** Biosynthesis of thromboxanes in human platelets. I. Characterization and assay of thromboxane synthetase, *Biochem. Biophys. Res. Commun.,* 74, 1432, 1977.
22. **Bundy, G. L.,** The synthesis of prostaglandin endoperoxide analogs, *Tetrahedron Lett.,* 1957, 1975.
23. **Tai, H.-H. and Yuan, B.,** Biosynthesis of thromboxanes in sheep lung: characterization, solubilization and resolution of the microsomal thromboxane synthetase complex, *Fed. Proc. Fed. Am. Soc. Exp. Biol.,* 36, 309, 1977.
24. **Malmsten, C.,** Some biological effects of prostaglandin endoperoxide analogs, *Life Sci.,* 18, 169, 1976.

25. **Bundy, G. L., and Peterson, D. C.,** The synthesis of 15-deoxy-9,11-(epoxyimino)prostaglandins-potent thromboxane synthetase inhibitors, *Tetrahedron Lett.*, 41, 1978.
26. **Fitzpatrick, F., Gorman, R., Bundy, G., Honohan, T., McGuire, J., and Sun, F.,** 9,11-Iminoepoxyprosta-5,13-dienoic acid is a selective thromboxane $A_2$ synthetase inhibitor, *Biochim. Biophys. Acta*, 573, 238, 1979.
27. **Corey, E. J., Niwa, H., Bloom, M., and Ramwell, P. W.,** Synthesis of a new prostaglandin endoperoxide ($PGH_2$) analog and its function as an inhibitor of the biosynthesis of thromboxane $A_2$ ($TXBA_2$), *Tetrahedron Lett.*, 671, 1979.
28. **Maxey, K. M., and Bundy, G. L.,** The synthesis of 11a-carbathromboxane $A_2$, *Tetrahedron Lett.*, 21, 445, 1980.
29. **Gorman, R. R., Maxey, K. M., and Bundy, G. L.,** Inhibition of human platelet thromboxane synthetase by 11a-carbathromboxane $A_2$ analogs, *Biochem. Biophys. Res. Commun.*, 100, 184, 1981.
30. **Nicolaou, K. C., Magolda, R. L., and Claremon, D. A.,** Carbocyclic thromboxane $A_2$, *J. Am. Chem. Soc.*, 102, 1404, 1980.
31. **Ohuchida, S., Hamanaka, N., and Hayashi, M.,** Synthesis of thromboxane $A_2$ analog DL-(9,11),(11,12)-dideoxa-(9,11),(11,12)-dimethylene thromboxane $A_2$, *Tetrahedron Lett.*, 3661, 1979.
32. **Lefer, A. M., Smith, E. F., III, Araki, H., Smith, J. B., Aharony, D., Claremon, D. A., Magolda, R. L., and Nicolaou, K. C.,** Dissociation of vasoconstrictor and platelet aggregatory activities of thromboxane by carbocyclic thromboxane $A_2$, a stable analog of thromboxane $A_2$, *Proc. Natl. Acad. Sci. U.S.A.*, 77, 1706, 1980.
33. **Nicolaou, K. C., Magolda, R. L., Smith, J. B., Aharony, D., Smith, E. F., and Lefer, A. M.,** Synthesis and biological properties of pinane-thromboxane $A_2$, a selective inhibitor of coronary artery constriction, platelet aggregation, and thromboxane formation, *Proc. Natl. Acad. Sci. U.S.A.*, 76, 2566, 1979.
34. **Nicolaou, K. C., Magolda, R. L., and Claremon, D. A.,** Synthesis of thromboxane $A_2$ analogs, *Adv. Prostaglandin Thromboxane Res.*, 6, 481, 1980.
35. **Ansell, M. F., Caton, M. P. L., and Stuttle, K. A. J.,** Two syntheses of pinane thromboxane $A_2$, *J. Chem. Soc. Perkin Trans. I*, 1069, 1984.
36. **Ansell, M. F., Caton, M. P. L., Palfreyman, M. N., and Stuttle, K. A. J.,** Synthesis of structural analogs of thromboxane $A_2$, *Tetrahedron Lett.*, 4497, 1979.
37. **Aharony, D., Smith, J. B., Smith, E. F., Lefer, A. M., Magolda, R. L., and Nicolaou, K. C.,** Pinane thromboxane $A_2$: a $TXA_2$ antagonist with antithrombotic properties, *Adv. Prostaglandin Thromboxane Res.*, 6, 489, 1980.
38. **Smith, E. F., III, Lefer, A. M., Smith, J. B., and Nicolaou, K. C.,** Thromboxane synthetase inhibitors differentially antagonize thromboxane receptors in vascular smooth muscle, *Arch. Pharmacol.*, 318, 130, 1981.
39. **Schrör, K., Smith, E. F., III, Bickerton, M., Smith, J. B., Nicolaou, K. C., Magolda, R., and Lefer, A. M.,** Preservation of ischemic myocardium by pinane thromboxane $A_2$, *Am. J. Physiol.*, 238, H87, 1980.
40. **Lefer, A. M., Araki, H., Smith, J. B., Nicolaou, K. C., and Magolda, R. L.,** Protective effects of a novel thromboxane analog in lethal traumatic shock, *Prostaglandins Med.*, 3, 139, 1979.
41. **Araki, H., Lefer, A. M., Smith, J. B., Nicolaou, K. C., and Magolda, R.,** Beneficial actions of a new thromboxane analog in traumatic shock, *Adv. Prostaglandin Thromboxane Res.*, 7, 835, 1980.
42. **Bounameaux, von Y., Coffey, J. W., O'Donnell, M., Kling, K., Quinn, R. J., Schönholzer, P., Szente, A., Tobias, L. D., Tschopp, T., Welton, A. F., and Fischli, A.,** Synthese Stereoisomerer Pinanthromboxane und Evaluation der Verbindungen als Plättchenaggregationsinhibitoren, *Helv. Chim. Acta*, 66, 989, 1983.
43. **Sprague, P. W., Heikes, J. E., Gougoutas, J. Z., Malley, M. F., Harris, D. N., and Greenberg, R.,** Synthesis and *in vitro* pharmacology of 7-oxabicyclo[2.2.1]heptane analogs of thromboxane $A_2/PGH_2$, *J. Med. Chem.*, 28, 1580, 1985.
44. **Harris, D. N., Greenberg, R., Phillips, M. B., Michel, I. M., Goldenberg, H. J., Haslanger, M. F., and Steinbacher, T. E.,** Effects of SQ 27,427, a thromboxane $A_2$ receptor antagonist in the human platelet and isolated smooth muscle, *Eur. J. Pharmacol.*, 103, 9, 1984.
45. **Larock, R. C., Burkhart, J. P., and Oertle, K.,** Organopalladium approaches to prostaglandins. 2. Synthesis of prostaglandin endoperoxide analogs via $\pi$-allylpalladium additions to bicyclic olefins, *Tetrahedron Lett.*, 23, 1071, 1982.
46. **Barraclough, P.,** A simple synthesis of a stable thromboxane $A_2$ analogue, *Tetrahedron Lett.*, 21, 1897, 1980.
47. **Adams, J. L. and Metcalf, B. W.,** The synthesis of a 3-diazobicyclo[2.2.1]heptan-2-one inhibitor of thromboxane $A_2$ synthetase, *Tetrahedron Lett.*, 25, 919, 1984.
48. **Fried, J., Barton, J., Kittisopikul, S., Needleman, P., and Wyche, A.,** Synthesis and biological properties of selective inhibitors of the prostaglandin cascade, *Adv. Prostaglandin Thromboxane Res.*, 6, 427, 1980.

## Table 4
## MISCELLANEOUS COMPOUNDS

| No. | Name of compound | Structure | Formula (mol wt) | Biological activity |
|---|---|---|---|---|
| 1. | L-1Tosylamido-2-phenylethyl chloromethyl ketone (TPCK) | 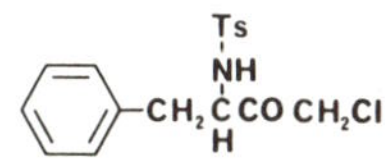 | $C_{17}H_{18}ClNO_3S$ (352) | Inhibited $TxB_2$ synthesis from endogenous (thrombin or trypsin stimulated) or exogenous AA in human platelets at 0.2—0.5 m*M*. The metabolism of $PGH_2$ by intact or sonicated platelets was also inhibited at 0.1—0.5 m*M* with increased production of $PGF_{2\alpha}$ and $PGD_2$ (RTLC). TPCK is also a protease inhibitor specific for chymotrypsin but not trypsin or thrombin, and inhibits collagen-, carageenan-, and thrombin-induced aggregation (0.05—0.2 m*M*) as well as platelet phospholipase $A_2$ (1 m*M*).[1] |
| 2. | *N*-Acetyl-L-phenylalanyl-L-phenylalanyl-L-histidine methyl ester Ac-Phe-Phe-His-OMe (ZAMI-420) | 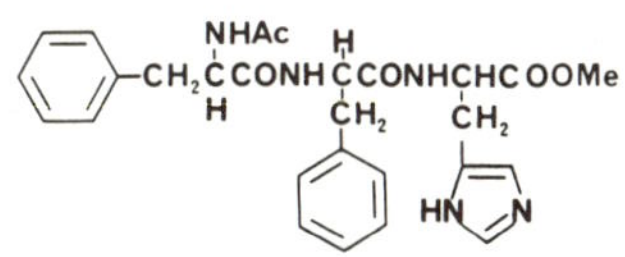 | $C_{27}H_{31}N_5O_5$ (505) | Inhibited aggregation of guinea-pig PRP by AA with reduction of $TxA_2$ (bioassay) or $TxB_2$ formation (RTLC or RIA) at 0.5—4 m*M*. The synthesis of PGs was slightly augmented. Cyclooxygenase activity was not affected.[2] Oral administration to rats prevented gastric mucosal damage by ethanol ($ED_{50}$ 84 mg/kg), serotonin ($ED_{50}$ 55 mg/kg) and aspirin ($ED_{50}$ 170 mg/kg), the compound being almost as potent as carbenoxolone ($ED_{50}$s 47.2, 55, and 150 mg/kg, respectively) and more potent than cimetidine against ethanol- and serotonin-induced damage.[2] |
| 3. | 5-Amino-3,4′-bipyridin-6(1*H*)-one Amrinone | 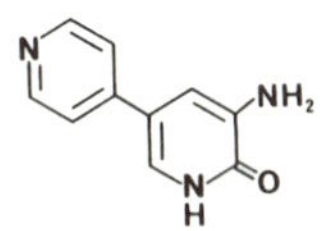 | $C_{10}H_9N_3O$ (187) | Doses of 1 and 2 mg/kg i.v. decreased the plasma $TxB_2$ concentration and increased 6-keto-$PGF_{1\alpha}$ levels in rabbits. The generation of $TxB_2$ from AA by washed human platelets was significantly inhibited by both $10^{-6}$ and $10^{-3}$ M (RIA).[3] Aggregation of human PRP induced by ADP, collagen, $PGH_2$, and U-46619 (a thromboxane agonist) was inhibited at higher concentrations than those required to inhibit AA-induced aggregation. Amrinone alone did not alter c-AMP or cGMP levels in human PRP.[4] In hu- |

| | | | | |
|---|---|---|---|---|
| | | | | man whole blood *in vitro*, amrinone inhibited $TxB_2$ production at pharmacological levels without effects on 6-keto-$PGF_{1\alpha}$.[4a] Amrinone is a positive inotropic agent and vasodilator. |
| 4. | Sodium benzyl 4-[1-oxo-2-(4-chlorobenzyl)-3-phenylpropyl]m phenyl phosphonate [N-0164] | 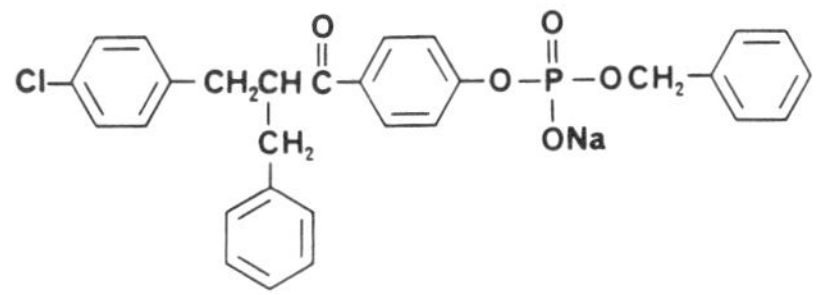 | $C_{29}H_{25}ClNaO_4P$ (527) | Inhibited the conversion of $PGH_2$ to $TxA_2$ by human-platelet microsomes, $IC_{50}$ 11.6—12.5 µg/ml (2.2—2.4 × $10^{-5}$ m*M*) (bioassay); with no inhibition of endoperoxide synthesis or antagonism of $TxA_2$ at 25 µg/ml, or inhibition of PG synthesis at 50 µg/ml.[5,6] <br> The aggregation of washed human platelets induced by AA or thrombin was inhibited at concentrations (3.75 µg/ml) that had no measurable effect on $TxB_2$ synthesis; higher concentrations (37.5—75 µg/ml) inhibited both thromboxane synthetase and cyclooxygenase (no increase in $PGD_2$, $PGE_2$ or $PGF_{2\alpha}$) (RTLC). Similar results were found in human platelets using $PGH_2$ as the aggregation inducer; however in lysed platelets, $TxB_2$ synthesis was inhibited at the concentration inhibiting aggregation. No effect on basal platelet adenyl cyclase at 60 µg/ml.[7] <br> N-0164 is an antagonist of platelet $PGD_2$ and $TxA_2$ receptors,[8] and antagonizes contractile responses due to $PGE_2$ and $PGF_{2\alpha}$ in several smooth-muscle preparations.[9] |
| 5. | (±)-α-Benzyl-α-p-chlorobenzyl-4-hydroxyacetophenone phenyl hydrogen phosphonate (as sodium salt)[N-0096] | 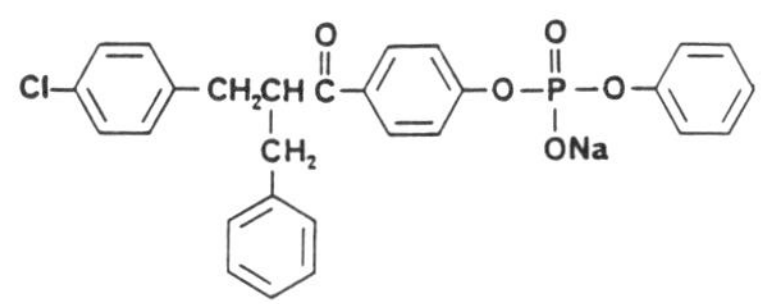 | $C_{28}H_{23}ClNaO_4P$ (513) | "Inhibits thromboxane synthesis at 10 µ*M*, cyclooxygenase at 20—50 µ*M*." Potentiated the bronchodilator effect of $PGE_2$ in cats with bronchoconstriction induced by 5-HT at 2—17 mg/kg i.v., presumably by inhibiting Tx synthesis. Bronchoconstriction elicited by AA was also inhibited.[10] |
| 6. | Sulfasalazine 2-Hydroxy-5-[[4-pyridylamino)sulfonylphenyl]-azo]benzoic acid | 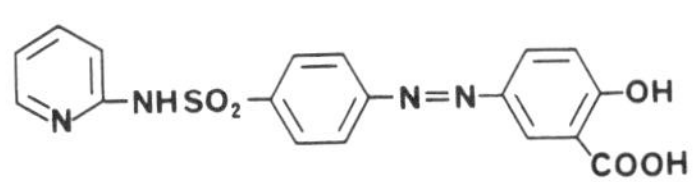 | $C_{18}H_{14}N_4O_5S$ (398) | Inhibited Tx synthesis from AA in human platelets, $IC_{50}$ 0.9 m*M*, and partially inhibited cyclooxygenase (but not platelet lipoxygenase).[11] In a *Salmonella enteritidis* endotoxic shock model in rats, 500 mg/kg p.o. at 48, 24, 6 h before challenge inhibited $TxB_2$ |

## Table 4 (continued)
## MISCELLANEOUS COMPOUNDS

| No. | Name of compound | Structure | Formula (mol wt) | Biological activity |
|---|---|---|---|---|
| | | | | formation without affecting 6-keto-$PGF_{1\alpha}$ production at 2 h (RIA).[12] Sulfasalazine is an antiinflammatory drug used in ulcerative colitis. |
| 7. | Methylsulfasalazine 2-Hydroxy-5-[[4-(3-methyl-2-pyridylamino)sulfonyl-phenyl]azo]benzoic acid | 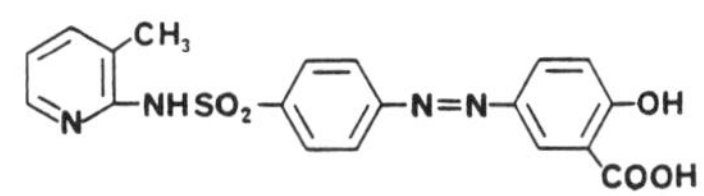 | $C_{19}H_{16}N_4O_5S$ (412) | Inhibited Tx synthesis from AA in human platelets, $IC_{50}$ 0.3 m*M*, and partially inhibited cyclooxygenase.[11] |
| 8. | 1-[(5-Hydroxy-1-methyl-2-indole)carbonyl]-2-isopropylhydrazine | 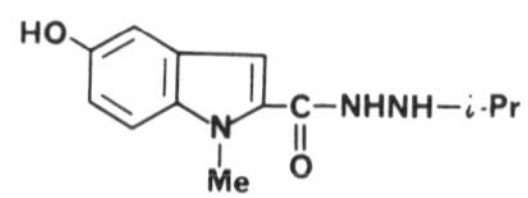 | $C_{13}H_{17}N_3O_2$ (247) | Caused 100% inhibition of aggregation induced by AA (at 1 μ*M*), ADP (second wave) (at 10 μ*M*), or $PGH_2$ (at 10 μ*M*) in human PRP. $TxB_2$ production was inhibited during aggregation induced by AA (RIA).[13] |
| 9. | 1-[(5-Hydroxy-1-methyl-2-indole)carbonyl]-2-(2-phenylethyl)hydrazine | 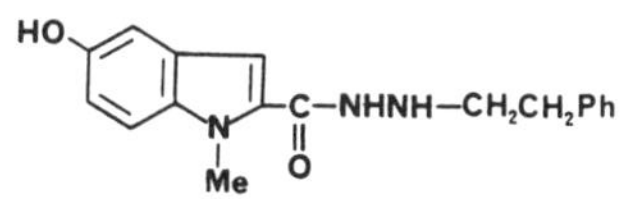 | $C_{18}H_{19}N_3O_2$ (309) | Caused 100% inhibition of aggregation induced by AA or ADP (second wave) (but not $PGH_2$) in human PRP at $10^{-5}$ *M*.[13] |
| 10. | 1-[(5-Benzoyloxy-1-methyl-2-indole)carbonyl]-2-cyclopentylhydrazine | 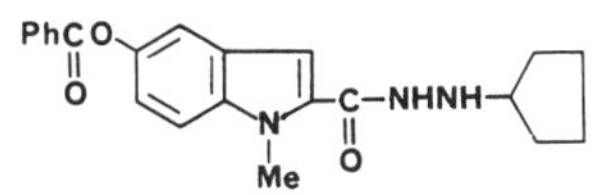 | $C_{22}H_{23}N_3O_3$ (377) | Caused 100% inhibition of aggregation induced by AA, ADP (second wave), or $PGH_2$ in human PRP at $10^{-5}$ *M*.[13] |
| 11. | 1,4-Bis(*N*-morpholino)-5*H*-pyridazino[4,5-*b*]indole | 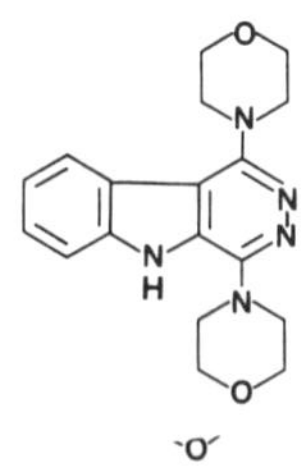 | $C_{18}H_{21}N_5O_2$ (349) | Selective inhibitor of thromboxane synthetase. Study of 36 analogues.[14] |

| | | | | |
|---|---|---|---|---|
| 12. | 3,4-Dihydro-4-oxo-5*H*-pyridazino-[4,5-*b*]indole | 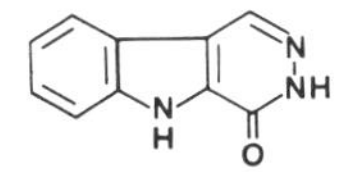 | $C_{10}H_7N_3O$ (185) | Inhibited ADP-, AA- and $PGH_2$-induced platelet aggregation. Study of 7 analogues.[15] |
| 13. | 1,2,3,4-Tetrahydro-1-oxo-3-acetyl-4-nonyl-5*H*-pyridazino-[4,5-*b*]indole | 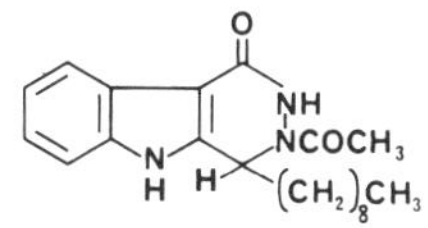 | $C_{21}H_{29}N_3O$ (339) | Inhibited thromboxane synthetase *in vitro*, and *ex vivo* using guinea-pig platelets. Most active of 11 analogues.[16] |
| 14. | Anisodamine | 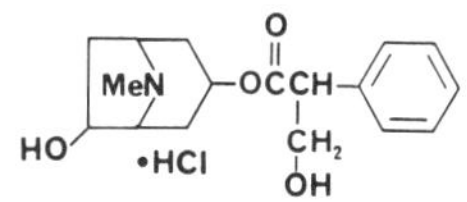 | $C_{17}H_{24}ClNO_4$ (342) | At 0.25 mg/ml, inhibited the secondary wave of aggregation induced by ADP and abolished AA- and epinephrine-induced aggregation of human PRP; inhibited $TxB_2$ production induced by AA or ADP at 0.5 mg/ml (RIA). Granulocyte aggregation induced by ZAP or FMLP was inhibited (50%) by 1 mg/ml. The possibility of a mechanism involving cyclooxygenase inhibition was not ruled out.[17]<br>The elevation of the ST segment of the ECG in dogs with experimental acute myocardial ischemia was markedly decreased by 10 mg/kg, i.v.[18]<br>In dogs, the hypotension and elevation in 6-keto-$PGF_{1\alpha}$ due to injection of *E. coli* endotoxin was attenuated by i.v. anisodamine.[19]<br>Anisodamine is used in China to treat meningococcemia. |
| 15. | Sodium 7-[3-(4-acetyl-3-hydroxy-2-propylphenoxy)-2-hydroxypropoxy]-4-oxo-8-propyl-4*H*-1-benzopyran-2-carboxylate (FPL 55712) | 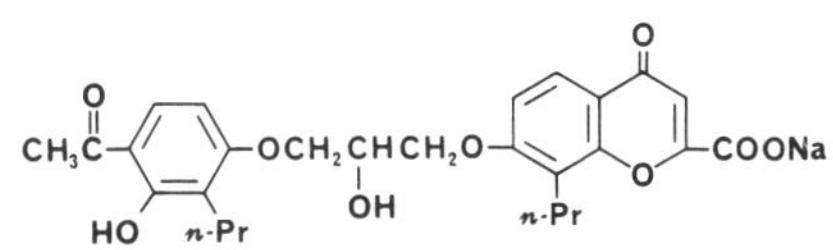 | $C_{27}H_{29}NaO_9$ (520) | Inhibited conversion of $PGH_2$ to $TxB_2$ by human-platelet microsomes, $IC_{50}$ 6.5 $\mu M$ based on unconverted $PGH_2$.[20] FPL 55712 is a selective antagonist of SRS-A at concentrations of $10^{-8}$—$10^{-6}$ *M*, but also inhibits cyclic nucleotide phosphodiesterase and antagonizes $PGF_{2\alpha}$ and $PGE_1$ at higher concentrations. |
| 16. | Picotamide<br>4-Methoxy-*N*,N[1]-bis(3-pyridylmethyl)-isophthalamide<br>(G 137) | 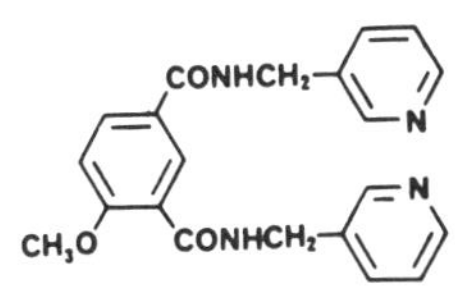 | $C_{21}H_{20}N_4O_3$ (376) | Inhibited $TxB_2$ production in human whole blood stimulated with collagen at $5 \times 10^{-5}$ *M* with increased generation of 6-keto $PGF_{1\alpha}$ (RIA). In PRP from subjects treated previously with aspirin, platelet aggregation induced by the endoperoxide analogue |

**Table 4 (continued)**
**MISCELLANEOUS COMPOUNDS**

| No. | Name of compound | Structure | Formula (mol wt) | Biological activity |
|---|---|---|---|---|
| | | | | U-46619 was also inhibited. Picotamide is therefore a thromboxane-synthetase inhibitor and endoperoxide/thromboxane-receptor antagonist.[21]<br>Oral administration to human volunteers (1000 mg) caused inhibition of collagen-, AA-, and U-46619-induced aggregation and reduction of serum $TxB_2$ levels with no changes in other hemostatic parameters.[21]<br>In patients with vascular disease and enhanced plasma β-thromboglobulin, 300 mg q.i.d. for 1 month returned β-thromboglubulin levels to normal from 1 week of treatment with no side effects.[21] |
| 17. | Benzydamine (*N,N*-Dimethyl-3-[[1-phenylmethyl)-1*H*-indazol-3-yl]oxy]-1-propanamine) | 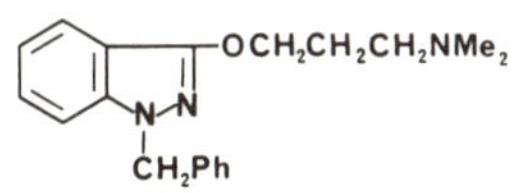 | $C_{19}H_{23}N_3O$ (309) | Inhibited the conversion of $PGG_2$ to $TxA_2$ by horse-platelet microsomes, $IC_{50}$ 100 μg/ml (bioassay), and inhibited ram seminal vessel, cyclooxygenase, $IC_{50}$ 250 μg/ml.[22] |
| 18. | Hydralazine (1-Hydrazinophthalazine) | 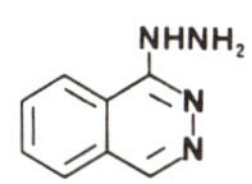 | $C_8H_8N_4$ (160) | Inhibited aggregation of human PRP induced by AA at $10^{-4}$ *M* and the conversion of AA to $TxB_2$ by human-platelet microsomes, with increased $PGF_{2\alpha}$ production at $10^{-4}$—$10^{-3}$ *M* (RTLC).[23] The conversion of AA to $TxB_2$ by washed human platelets was inhibited by $\geq 10^{-3}$ *M* with increased $PGF_{2\alpha}$ and $PGE_2$ production (HPLC) in one study,[24] whereas $PGE_2$, $PGD_2$, $PGF_{2\alpha}$, (and HETE and MDA) production were simultaneously decreased in another at 0.75 m*M* (RTLC).[25]<br>In rabbits, 3.2 mg/kg i.m. every 8 h for 3 d decreased platelet $TxB_2$ production from the 4th dose onwards.[26]<br>Incubation of rabbit aortic rings with AA in the presence of 0.25 m*M* hydralazine stimulated $PGI_2$ pro- |

| | | | | |
|---|---|---|---|---|
| | | | | duction (as 6-keto-$PGF_{1\alpha}$ by RTLC).[26] In the isolated rat aorta, $PGI_2$ synthesis was enhanced by 0.75 m*M*, and that of $TxB_2$ and $PGD_2$ reduced (RTLC).[27]<br>The smooth-muscle tone of SHR and normotensive rat portal vein was inhibited *in vivo*.[28]<br>Hydralazine is a smooth-muscle dilator and antihypertensive agent. |
| 19. | Trapidil<br>7-Diethylamino-5-methyl-*s*-triazolo[1,5-*a*]pyridine | 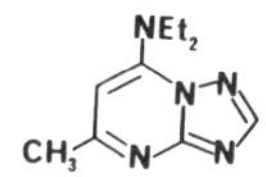 | $C_{10}H_{15}N_5$ (205) | Inhibited the aggregation of rat PRP and contraction of rabbit-aortic strip induced by $PGG_2$/$TxA_2$, and inhibited $TxA_2$ biosynthesis in suspended rabbit platelets at 30—100 μg/ml (MS).[29] However the inhibition of $TxA_2$ biosynthesis requires intact platelets, and this effect is therefore unlikely to involve inhibition of thromboxane synthetase.[30] $PGI_2$ generation by rat aorta was stimulated both *in vitro* and *ex vivo* (bioassay).[31]<br>In a model of ischemic heart injury induced by injection of $TxA_2$ into the rabbit coronary artery, trapidil reduced ischemic changes in the ECG, the incidence of myocardial infarction, depression of serum HDL cholesterol, and histopathological changes, and inhibited the increase in plasma $TXB_2$ with increased plasma 6-keto-$PGF_{1\alpha}$ production (MS).[29]<br>Appeared to be of benefit in preventing cerebral vasospasm and cerebral ischemia in patients following aneurysmal rupture at doses of 100—150 mg t.i.d.[32] |
| 20. | 3-Dimethylamino-5-(3′-trifluoromethylbenzylidene)-6-methyl-(4*H*)-pyridazine (PC 88) | 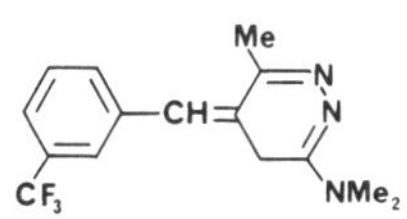 | $C_{15}H_{16}F_3N_3$ (295) | Inhibited the synthesis of $TxA_2$ from AA by horse-platelet microsomes, $IC_{50}$ 553 μ*M* (RIA).[33] |
| 21. | 3-Dimethylamino-5-(2′,6′-dichlorobenzylidene)-6-methyl-(4*H*)-pyridazine (PC 89) | 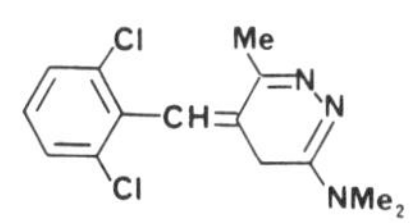 | $C_{15}H_{16}F_3N_3$ (295) | Inhibited the synthesis of $TxA_2$ from AA by horse-platelet microsomes noncompetitively, $IC_{50}$ 3.3 m*M* and stimulated production of $PGI_2$ by horse-aorta microsomes, $IC_{50}$ 6.8 μ*M* (RIA).[34] |

**Table 4 (continued)**
**MISCELLANEOUS COMPOUNDS**

| No. | Name of compound | Structure | Formula (mol wt) | Biological activity |
|---|---|---|---|---|
| 22. | Pinacidil | 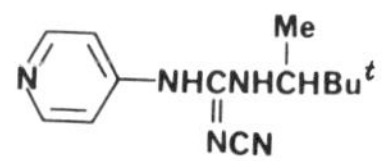 | $C_{13}H_{19}N_5$ (245) | Inhibited $TxB_2$ production from AA by washed human platelets (63% at 0.01 *M*) with increases in $PGE_2$ and $PGF_{2\alpha}$. ADP-induced aggregation of human PRP was inhibited by 94% at 5 m*M*.[35]<br>Pinacidil is an antihypertensive. |
| 23. | Dipyridamole | 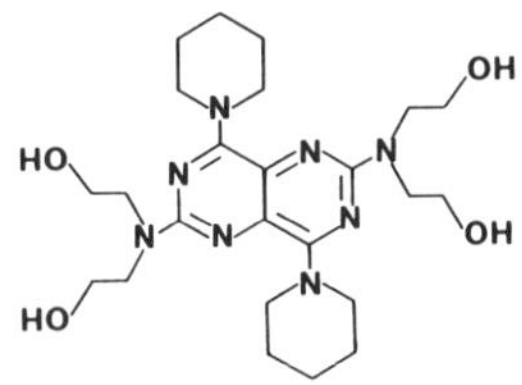 | $C_{24}H_{40}N_8O_4$ (504) | Dipyridamole has been shown to inhibit the conversion of AA to $TxB_2$ (~30%) by human-platelet microsomes at $10^{-3}$ *M* (RTLC)[23] and $PGH_2$ to $TxA_2$ by horse-platelet microsomes at 0.3—1.0 m*M* (bioassay).[36] Collagen-induced platelet aggregation in rabbits,[37] AA-induced aggregation of human platelets (at $1.75 \times 10^{-4}$ *M*)[23] and AA-induced $TxA_2$ generation in human platelets (at 5—50 μg/ml) were also inhibited.[38] In human-platelet suspensions, the reduction of $TxB_2$ synthesis from exogenous AA is accompanied by increased $PGE_2$, $PGD_2$, $PGF_{2\alpha}$, and decreased HHT, HETE, and MDA production at 0.2 m*M* (RTLC).[25] Inhibition of thromboxane-synthetase activity was also proposed based on the similarity of the behavior of dipyridamole and imidazole in a vascular smooth-muscle model.[39] However other workers have shown the absence of effects on thromboxane synthesis at lower concentrations.[40-42] $PGI_2$ formation in isolated rat aorta and lung is significantly increased.[27] In post-myocardial-infarction patients, 200 mg orally, b.i.d. for 3 weeks lowered serum $TxB_2$ levels significantly at 14 and 21 d (but not at 7 d) (RIA).[43]<br>Although the precise mechanism of action of dipyridamole is controversial,[44] it seems unlikely to involve inhibition of thromboxane synthetase at therapeutic doses. |

| | | | | |
|---|---|---|---|---|
| | | | | Dipyridamole is used clinically as a coronary vasodilator and antiplatelet compound (usually with aspirin). |
| 24. | Benzimidazole | 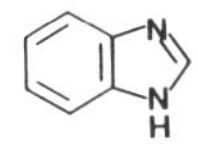 | $C_7H_6N_2$ (118) | Inhibited the synthesis of $TxA_2$ from AA by dog PRP, $IC_{50}$ 1.2 m*M* (bioassay).[45] Inhibited the synthesis of $TxB_2$ by human blood mononuclear cells at 300 μg/ml with minimal increases in $PGE_2$ (RIA), and inhibited mitogen-stimulated transformation.[46] |
| 25. | Benzimidazolamine | 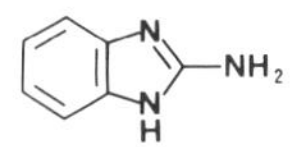 | $C_7H_7N_3$ (133) | Inhibited the synthesis of $TxA_2$ from AA by dog PRP, $IC_{50}$ 0.3 m*M*,[45] 0.4 m*M*,[47] and from $PGH_2$ by washed dog platelets at 2 m*M* (bioassay).[45] $PGE_2$ synthesis from AA by dog PRP was also inhibited, $IC_{50}$ 0.8 m*M*.[47] |
| 26. | Propanolol | 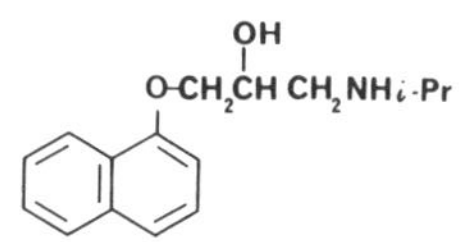 | $C_{16}H_{21}NO_2$ (259) | DL-Propanolol and its pharmacologically inactive D-isomer have been postulated to inhibit thromboxane synthetase based on the inhibition of thrombin- and AA-induced aggregation of PRP from patients receiving 640 mg/d, and inhibition of platelet aggregation and Tx synthesis *in vitro*.[48,49] However, in human-platelet suspensions, the decreased synthesis of $TxB_2$ from exogenous AA is accompanied by decreases in $PGE_2$, $PGD_2$, $PGF_{2\alpha}$, and HHT at 1.0 m*M* (RTLC),[25] and various mechanisms not involving thromboxane synthetase have been proposed to account for the effects of β-blockers on platelets.[50-54] |
| 27. | Timolol | 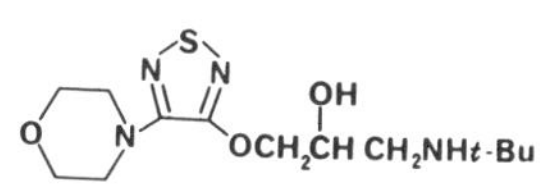 | $C_{13}H_{24}N_4O_3S$ (316) | In patients treated 1 week following myocardial infarction, timolol reduced serum $TxB_2$ after 4 weeks (but not 12 weeks) of treatment (RIA). Whether this resulted from direct inhibition of thromboxane synthetase or not was not established.[55] |
| 28. | Verapamil | 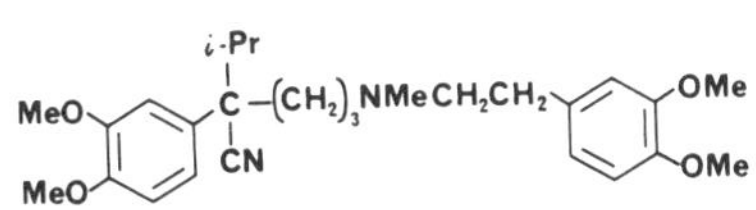 | $C_{27}H_{38}N_2O_4$ (454) | Verapamil (0.5 μg/ml) inhibited aggregation of human PRP induced by threshold ADP, AA, and epinephrine, and inhibited generation of $TxA_2$ at concentrations below those required for aggregation (RIA).[56] The inhibition of $TxB_2$ synthesis from AA in human-platelet suspensions by 1.0 m*M* was accompanied by increased $PGE_2$, $PGD_2$, $PGF_{2\alpha}$, and HETE, and decreased HHT and MDA (RTLC).[25,57] |

## Table 4 (continued)
## MISCELLANEOUS COMPOUNDS

| No. | Name of compound | Structure | Formula (mol wt) | Biological activity |
|---|---|---|---|---|
| | | | | However, at lower concentrations (10 and 100 μ*M*) verapamil had no effect on the metabolism of AA, suggesting that the antiplatelet effects do not involve thromboxane-synthetase inhibition at therapeutic concentrations.[57] |
| | | | | In a rat-lung homogenate, $PGI_2$ formation was increased and $TxB_2$ formation decreased by 1.0 m*M* (RTLC).[27] |
| 29. | Nifedipine | 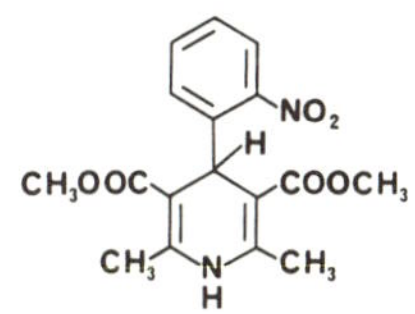 | $C_{17}H_{18}N_2O_6$ (346) | Inhibited the synthesis of $TxB_2$ from AA by human-platelet suspensions at 0.2 m*M* with increased $PGF_{2\alpha}$, $PGE_2$, $PGD_2$, and decreased HHT, HETE, and MDA production (RTLC). ADP-induced aggregation of human PRP was inhibited at the same concentration.[25] |
| 30. | Vincristine | 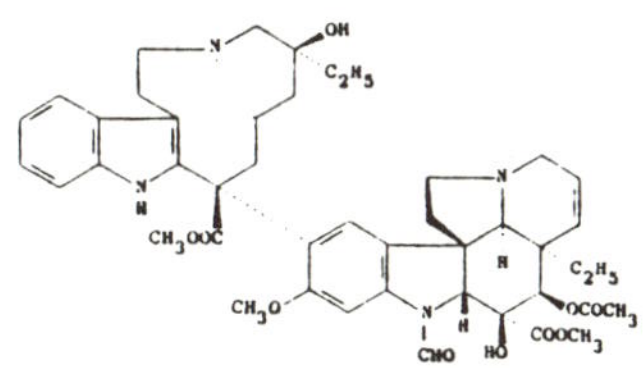 | $C_{46}H_{56}N_4O_{10}$ (825) | Inhibited aggregation of human PRP induced by AA, epinephrine (2nd phase), collagen, and, less effectively, ADP, and thrombin at 300 μ*M*. In washed platelets, the inhibition of $TxB_2$ formation from AA was accompanied by increased $PGD_2$ and $PGE_2$ production (RTLC).[58] |
| 31. | Nitroglycerine | $CH_2-ONO_2$<br>$CH-ONO_2$<br>$CH_2-ONO_2$ | $C_3H_5N_3O_9$ (227) | Stated to be an inhibitor of rabbit platelet Tx synthetase, and inhibited thrombin-, ADP-, and AA-induced aggregation of rat and human platelets.[59] However, other workers concluded that nitroglycerine had no effect on $TxB_2$ formation in human subjects.[60] |

## REFERENCES TO TABLE 4


1. **Yahn, D. M. and Feinstein, M. B.,** Inhibition of platelet thromboxane synthetase by L-1-tosylamido-2-phenylethyl chloromethyl ketone, *Prostaglandins,* 21, 243, 1981.
2. **Gervasi, G. B., Fossati, A., Caliari, S., Rapalli, L., and Bergamaschi, M.,** Prevention of experimentally induced gastric damage with the tripeptide ZAMI-420, a new thromboxane synthesis inhibitor, *Int. J. Tissue React.,* 5, 253, 1983.
3. **Kinney, E. L., Draganis, T., Luderer, J. R., and Demers, L. M.,** Mechanism of action of amrinone: role of thromboxane synthetase inhibition, *Prostaglandins Leukotrienes Med.,* 11, 213, 1983.
4. **Lippton, H. L., Horwitz, P. M., McNamara, D. B., Ignarro, L. J., Landry, A. Z., Hyman, A. L., and Kadowitz, P. J.,** The effects of amrinone on human platelet aggregation: evidence that amrinone does not act through a cyclic nucleotide mechanism in platelet rich plasma, *Prostaglandins Leukotrienes Med.,* 18, 193, 1985.

4a. **Pattison, A., Eason, C. T., and Bonner, F. W.,** The *in vitro* effect of amrinone on thromboxane $B_2$ synthesis in human whole blood, *Thromb. Res.,* 42, 817, 1986.

5. **Kulkarni, P. S. and Eakins, K. E.,** N-0164 inhibits generation of thromboxane-$A_2$-like activity from prostaglandin endoperoxides by human platelet microsomes, *Prostaglandins,* 12, 465, 1976.
6. **Eakins, K. E. and Kulkarni, P. S.,** Selective inhibitory actions of sodium-p-benzyl-4-[1-oxo-2-(4-chlorobenzyl)-3-phenylpropyl]phenyl phosphonate (N-0164) and indomethacin on the biosynthesis of prostaglandins and thromboxanes from arachidonic acid, *Br. J. Pharmacol.,* 60, 135, 1977.
7. **Needleman, P., Bryan, B., Wyche, A., Bronson, S. D., Eakins, K., Ferrendelli, J. A., and Minkes, M.,** Thromboxane synthetase inhibitors as pharmacological tools: differential biochemical and biological effects on platelet suspensions, *Prostaglandins,* 14, 897, 1977.
8. **Hamid-Bloomfield, S. and Whittle, B. J. R.,** Prostaglandin $D_2$ interacts at thromboxane receptor-sites on guinea pig platelets, *Br. J. Pharmacol.,* 88, 931, 1986.
9. **Eakins, K. E., Rajadhyaksha, V., and Schroer, R.,** Prostaglandin antagonism by sodium-p-benzyl-4-[1-oxo-2-(4-chlorobenzyl)-3-phenylpropyl]phenylphosphonate (N-0164), *Br. J. Pharmacol.,* 58, 333, 1976.
10. **Frey, H.-H. and Dengjel, C.,** Effects of inhibitors of thromboxane synthesis on reactions of the cat bronchus *in situ* to prostaglandins, *Prostaglandins,* 20, 87, 1980.
11. **Stenson, W. F. and Lobos, E.,** Inhibition of platelet thromboxane synthetase by sulfasalazine, *Biochem. Pharmacol.,* 32, 2205, 1983.
12. **Saija, A., Matera, G., Trimarchi, G. R., Altavilla, D., Foca, A., Costa, G., Mastroeni, P., and Caputi, A. P.,** Sulphasalazine reduces thromboxane $B_2$ synthesis induced by experimental endotoxic shock in the rat, *IRCS Med. Sci.,* 13, 26, 1985.
13. **Monge, A., Erro, A., Parrado, P., Font, M., Aldana, I., Rocha, E., and Fernandez-Alvarez, E.,** Effects of 2-indolecarbohydrazides on thromboxane synthetase activity and on *in vitro* and *ex vivo* blood platelet aggregation, *Arzneim-Forsch.,* 36, 1184, 1986.
14. **Monge, A., Aldana, I., Erro, A., Parrado, P., Font, M., Rocha, E., Prieto, I., Fremont-Smith, M., and Fernandez-Alvarez, E.,** New synthetic thromboxane $A_2$ inhibitors with the pyridazine [4,5-b]indole and pyridazine[4,5-a]indole structures as platelet antiaggregants, *An. R. Acad. Farm.,* 50, 365, 1984; *Chem Abstr.,* 102, 214821s, 1985.
15. **Monge, A., Aldana, I., Erro, A., Parrado, P., Font, M., Rocha, E., Prieto, I., Fremont-Smith, M., and Fernandez-Alvarez, E.,** Effect of pyridazino[4,5-b]indoles on thromboxane synthetase. New selective inhibitors. Platelet aggregation inhibitors, *Acta Farm. Boraerense,* 3, 21, 1984; *Chem. Abstr.,* 103, 16630m, 1985.
16. **Monge, A., Aldana, I., Erro, A., Parrado, P., Font, M., Rocha, E., Prieto, I., Quiroga, J., and Fernandez-Alvarez, E.,** Selective inhibitors of thromboxane synthetase. New platelet aggregation inhibitors; *Rev. Farmacol. Clin. Exp.,* 1, 131, 1984; *Chem. Abstr.,* 103, 189196c, 1985.
17. **Xiu Rui-Juan, Hammerschmidt, D. E., Coppo, P. A., and Jacob, H. S.,** Anisodamine inhibits thromboxane synthesis, granulocyte aggregation, and platelet aggregation: a possible mechanism for its efficacy in bacteremic shock, *JAMA,* 247, 1458, 1982.
18. **Shi, J., Miao, Z., Zhang, S., Zhou, X., and Yu, Z.,** The protective effect of anisodamine (654-2) on the acute ischemic myocardium in anesthetized dogs, *Tianjin Yiyao,* 12, 551, 1984; *Chem. Abstr.,* 102, 142927f, 1985.
19. **Xiao, D., Wang, X., and Chen H.,** Changes of plasma 6-keto-prostaglandin $F_{1\alpha}$ levels during canine endotoxic shock, *Zhongguo Yixve Kexueyuan Xuebao,* 7, 50, 1985; *Chem. Abstr.,* 103, 154789w, 1985.
20. **Welton, A. F., Hope, W. C., Tobias, L. D., and Hamilton, J. G.,** Inhibition of antigen-induced histamine release and thromboxane synthase by FPL 55712, a specific SRA-A antagonist? *Biochem. Pharmacol.,* 30, 1378, 1981.

21. **Berrettini, M., De Cunto, M., Parise, P., Grasselli, S., and Nenci, G. G.,** Picotamide, a derivative of 4-methoxy-isophthalic acid, inhibits thromboxane synthetase and receptors *in vitro* and *in vivo*, *Thromb. Haemostasis*, 50, 127, 1983.
22. **Moncada, S., Needleman, P., Bunting, S., and Vane, J. R.,** Prostaglandin endoperoxide and thromboxane generating systems and their selective inhibition, *Prostaglandins*, 12, 323, 1976.
23. **Greenwald, J. E., Wong, L. K., Rao, M., Bianchine, J. R., and Panganamala, R. V.,** A study of three vasodilating agents as selective inhibitors of thromboxane $A_2$ biosynthesis, *Biochem. Biophys. Res. Commun.*, 84, 1112, 1978.
24. **Luderer, J. R., Demers, L. M., Janson, R. W., Nomides, C. T., and Hayes, A. H., Jr.,** The effect of hydralazine on arachidonic acid metabolism in isolated, washed human platelets, *Res. Commun. Chem. Path. Pharmacol.*, 28, 43, 1980.
25. **Srivastava, K. C. and Awasthi, K. K.,** Effect of some vasodilating and antihypertensive drugs on the *in vitro* biosynthesis of prostaglandins from (1-$^{14}$C) arachidonic acid in washed human blood platelets, *Prostaglandins Leukotrienes Med.*, 8, 317, 1982.
26. **Greenwald, J. E., Wong, L. K., Alexander, M., and Bianchine, J. R.,** *In vivo* inhibition of thromboxane biosynthesis by hydralazine, *Adv. Prostaglandin Thromboxane Res.*, 6, 293, 1980.
27. **Srivastava, K. C. and Awasthi, K. K.,** Arachidonic acid metabolism in isolated rat aorta and lung of the rat: effects of dipyridamole, nifedipine, propanolol, hydralazine and verapamil, *Prostaglandins Leukotrienes Med.*, 10, 411, 1983.
28. **Greenberg, S., Glenn, T. M., and Gaines, K.,** Effect of hydralazine on spontaneous activity of portal veins from spontaneously hypertensive rats, in *Chemical Biological Hydroxamic Acids*, Proc. 1st Int. Symp., 1981, Kehl, H., Ed., S. Karger, Basel, 1982, 174.
29. **Ohnishi, H., Kosuzume, H., Hayashi, Y., Yamaguchi, K., Suzuki, Y., and Itoh, R.,** Effects of trapidil on thromboxane $A_2$-induced aggregation of platelets, ischemic changes in heart and biosynthesis of thromboxane $A_2$, *Prostaglandins Med.*, 6, 269, 1981.
30. **Block, H.-U., Heinroth, I., Giessler, Ch., Pönicke, K., Mentz, P., Zehl, U., Rettkowski, W., Dunemann, A., and Förster, W.,** Zur Beeinflussung der Biosynthese und Wirkung von Thromboxan $A_2$ and Prostazyklin durch Trapidil (Rocornal), *Biomed. Biochem. Acta*, 42, 283, 1983.
31. **Kawamura, T., Kitani, T., Okajima, Y., Okuda, S., Urano, S., Watada, M., Nakagawa, M., and Ijichi, H.,** Effect of trapidil on prostaglandin generation of arterial wall, *Prostaglandins Med.*, 5, 113, 1980.
32. **Suzuki, S., Sobata, E., and Iwabuchi, T.,** Prevention of cerebral ischemic symptoms in cerebral vasospasm with trapidil, an antagonist and selective synthesis inhibitor of thromboxane $A_2$, *Neurosurgery*, 9, 679, 1981.
33. **Pham, H. C., Lasserre, B., Pham, H. C. A., Dossou-Gbete, V., Palhares de Miranda, A. L., Kaiser, R., Tronche, P., and Couguelet, J.,** Inhibition of thromboxane biosynthesis by 3-dimethylamino-5-(3′-trifluoromethylbenzylidene)-6-methyl-(4*H*)-pyridazine, *IRCS Med. Sci.*, 13, 690, 1985.
34. **Pham Huu Chanh, Lasserre, B., Tronche, P., Couquelet, J., Dossou-Gbete, V., and Palhares de Miranda, A. L.,** Enhanced prostacyclin biosynthesis and decreased thromboxane formation by 3-dimethylamino-5-(2′,6′-dichlorobenzylidene)-6-methyl-(4*H*)-pyridazine (PC 89), *Prostaglandins Leukotrienes Med.*, 37, 1985.
35. **Goodman, R. P., Little, D. M., and Wright, J. T., Jr.,** Inhibition of platelet aggregation and thromboxane production by pinacidil, *Prostaglandins Leukotrienes Med.*, 19, 115, 1985.
36. **Katano, Y. and Imai, S.,** The effects of dipyridamole on $TxA_2$ formation by horse platelet microsomes, *Prostaglandins Leukotrienes Med.*, 10, 179, 1983.
37. **Suehiro, A., Uomoto, M., Nakajima, T., Kimura, N., Kakishita, E., and Nagai, K.,** Effect of antithrombotic agents in hyperlipidemic animals, *Ketsueki to Myakkan*, 12, 271, 1981; *Chem. Abstr.*, 96, 115680w, 1982.
38. **Mehta, J., Mehta, P., and Hay, D.,** Effect of dipyridamole on prostaglandin generation by human platelets and vessel walls, *Prostaglandins*, 24, 751, 1982.
39. **Ally, A. I., Manku, M. S., Horrobin, D. F., Morgan, R. O., Karmazin, M., and Karmali, R. A.,** Dipyridamole: a possible potent inhibitor of thromboxane $A_2$ synthetase in vascular smooth muscle, *Prostaglandins*, 14, 607, 1977.
40. **Mentz, P., Poenicke, K., Block, H. U., Giessler, C., Blass, K. E., Bayer, B. L., and Foerster, W.,** Stimulation of prostacyclin biosynthesis as a possible mechanism of action of dipyridamole, *Arzneim. Forsch.*, 31, 2075, 1981.
41. **Moncada, S., Flower, R. J., and Russel-Smith, N.,** Dipyridamole and platelet function, *Lancet*, ii, 1257, 1978.
42. **Uotila, P., Dahl, M.-L., Matintalo, M., and Puustinen, T.,** The effects of aspirin and dipyridamole on the metabolism of arachidonic acid in human platelets, *Prostaglandins Leukotrienes Med.*, 11, 73, 1983.
43. **Safai-Kutti, S., Kutti, J., Vedin, A., and Wilhelmsson, C.,** Plasma concentrations of platelet-specific proteins and serum thromboxane $B_2$ production in response to treatment with dipyridamole. A pilot study of 27 post-myocardial infarction patients, *Eur. Heart J.*, 6, 468, 1985.

44. **Moncada, S., and Korbut, R.,** Dipyridamole and other phosphodiesterase inhibitors act as antithrombotic agents by potentiating endogenous prostacyclin, *Lancet,* i, 1286, 1978.
45. **Chignard, M. and Vargaftig, B. B.,** Synthesis of thromboxane $A_2$ by non-aggregating dog platelets challenged with arachidonic acid or with prostaglandin $H_2$, *Prostaglandins,* 14, 222, 1977.
46. **Gordon, D., Nouri, A. M. E., and Thomas, R. U.,** Selective inhibition of thromboxane biosynthesis in human blood mononuclear cells and the effects on mitogen-stimulated lymphocyte proliferation, *Br. J. Pharmacol.,* 74, 469, 1981.
47. **Chignard, M., Vargaftig, B. B., Sors, H., and Dray, F.,** Synthesis of thromboxane $B_2$ in incubates of dog platelet-rich plasma with arachidonic acid and its inhibition by different drugs, *Biochem. Biophys. Res. Commun.,* 85, 1631, 1978.
48. **Johnson, A. R. and Campbell, W. B.,** Antiplatelet activity of propranolol: inhibition of thromboxane synthetase, *Fed. Proc. Fed. Am. Soc. Exp. Biol.,* 39, 392, 1980.
49. **Campbell, W. B., Johnson, A. R., Callahan, K. S., and Graham, R. M.,** Anti-platelet activity of beta-adrenergic antagonists: inhibition of thromboxane synthesis and platelet aggregation in patients receiving long-term propranolol treatment, *Lancet,* ii, 1382, 1981.
50. **Heinroth, I., Block, H. U., Poenicke, K., and Foerster, W.,** Influence of propranolol, pindolol, practolol and talinolol on arachidonic acid (AA)- and U-46619-induced aggregation and on AA-induced thromboxane $A_2$ formation in platelets, *Prostaglandins Leukotrienes Med.,* 12, 189, 1983.
51. **Mehta, J., Mehta, P., and Ostrowski, N.,** Influence of propranolol and 4-hydroxypropranolol on platelet aggregation and thromboxane $A_2$ generation, *Clin. Pharmacol. Ther.,* 34, 559, 1983.
52. **Luderer, J. R., Demers, L., Schnaars, R., Miller, K., and Hayes, A. H., Jr.,** The effect of propanolol on platelet arachidonic acid metabolism and platelet aggregation in man, *Clin. Pharmacol. Ther.,* 29, 263, 1981.
53. **Siess, W., Lorenz, R., Roth, P., and Weber, P. C.,** Effects of propranolol *in vitro* and *in vivo* on platelet function and thromboxane formation in normal volunteers, *Agents Actions,* 13, 29, 1983.
54. **Greer, I. A., Walker, J. J., McLaren, M., Calder, A. A., and Forbes, C. D.,** Inhibition of thromboxane and prostacyclin production in whole blood by adrenoceptor antagonists, *Prostaglandins Leukotrienes Med.,* 19, 209, 1985.
55. **Maidment, C. G. H., Dawson, C. M., Jones, S. P., and Lea, E. J. A.,** Platelet thromboxane production after myocardial infarction: the effect of timolol, *Eur. Heart J.,* 4(Suppl. E), 28, 1983.
56. **Mehta, J., Mehta, P., Ostrowski, N., and Crews, F.,** Effects of verapamil on platelet aggregation, ATP release and thromboxane generation, *Thromb. Res.,* 30, 469, 1983.
57. **Dahl, M.-L. and Uotila, P.,** Verapamil decreases the formation of thromboxane from exogenous $^{14}C$-arachidonic acid in human platelets *in vitro, Prostaglandins Leukotrienes Med.,* 17, 191, 1985.
58. **Shah, N. T. Karpen, C. W., and Panganamala, R. V.,** *In vitro* effects of vincristine on arachidonic acid metabolism in human platelets and rat arterial tissue, *Thromb. Res.,* 23, 225, 1981.
59. **Förster, W.,** Effect of various agents on prostaglandin biosynthesis and the anti-aggregatory effect, *Acta Med. Scand. (Suppl.),* 642, 35, 1980.
60. **Fitzgerald, D. J., Roy, L., Robertson, R. M., and Fitzgerald, G. A.,** The effects of organic nitrates on prostacyclin biosynthesis and platelet function in humans, *Circulation,* 70, 297, 1984.

# *Modulators of Eicosanoid Actions*

# CLASSIFICATION OF PROSTANOID RECEPTORS

**R. M. Eglen and R. L. Whiting**

## INTRODUCTION

Neurohormones are considered to exert their physiological effects by interacting with specific receptors on the effector organ,[1] and for over 10 years it has been considered that this is also the case for prostaglandins.[2] However, it is only within the last 6 years that significant advances have been made with regard to the pharmacological classification of prostaglandin-receptor subtypes.[2-4] It has been argued that the development of therapeutic agents of a prostaglandin nature has been hampered by a lack of a definitive prostaglandin-receptor system[4] and only recently have potent selective antagonists or agonists been developed. The actions of eicosanoid antagonists are discussed in more detail in the accompanying chapters by Sanner and by Musser et al. The purpose in this chapter is to assess the evidence for classification of prostaglandin receptors from a classical pharmacological standpoint.

It would therefore be instructive to briefly review the development of prostaglandin receptors as a concept. This subject has also been detailed in recent reviews.[2-5] The bias of the present authors is towards a functional classification of prostaglandin receptors using isolated-tissue data.

## HISTORICAL PERSPECTIVE

Andersen and Ramwell attempted in 1974 to classify the actions of prostaglandins into four classes on the basis of rank orders of agonist potencies.[6] The information was derived from both *in vitro* and *in vivo* experiments and four orders of activity were noted, using $PGE_2$, $PGF_{2\alpha}$, and $PGA_2$. However, these classes were not formally denoted as receptors. Jones[7] proposed the existence of different receptors for $PGD_2$ and $PGE_2$ in the sheep cardiovascular system and Welburn and Jones[8] for $PGE_2$ and $PGF_{2\alpha}$ in the rabbit jejunum.[8] Later, in 1980, Coleman[9] and co-workers proposed the existence of three receptors, for $PGE_2$, $PGF_{2\alpha}$, and $TxA_2$, by comparing agonist potencies on a wide range of isolated-tissue responses.

Gardiner and Collier[10] proposed an alternative scheme in 1980 in which prostaglandin receptors were classified into two classes: those which elicited excitatory or contractile actions were denoted as Class I ($\chi$) while those which elicited inhibitory or relaxant responses were denoted as Class II ($\psi$).

In 1981, Andersen and colleagues[11] expanded their classification of 1974, by analyzing structure-activity relationships of prostaglandins using both agonist potencies and ligand-binding affinities. They concluded that there were different structural requirements for $PGE_2$-, $PGF_{2\alpha}$-, and $PGI_2$-like compounds, and postulated the existence of three different receptors.

In 1982, the first general classification of prostaglandin receptors was proposed by the Glaxo group of Kennedy, Coleman, and co-workers,[2] although it was emphasized that this was a working hypothesis only and probably not definitive. This classification had considerable advantages over previous schemes and is more fully discussed below.

## GENERAL CLASSIFICATION OF PROSTAGLANDIN RECEPTORS

In recent years a general classification of prostaglandin receptors has emerged from the Glaxo group.[2,3,4] They proposed that different prostaglandin receptors exist for each of the naturally occurring prostaglandins. Thus, it was proposed that five receptors exist, denoted as DP, EP, FP, IP, and TP which are selectively stimulated by $PGD_2$, PGE series prostaglandins, $PGF_{2\alpha}$, $PGI_2$, and $TxA_2$, respectively.[2] Recently, it has been suggested that the EP receptors can be subdivided into a further two subtypes, $EP_1$ and $EP_2$ mediating contractile and relaxant effects of PGE-series prostaglandins, respectively.[4] Evidence for subdivisions of the EP, TP, and IP receptors have been proposed[4,12] and these are discussed below.

The Glaxo scheme possessed a number of advantages over previous nomenclatures, including the fact that other products of cyclooxygenase metabolism such as $PGI_2$ and $TxA_2$ were included. In addition, the classification, although defined primarily on the basis of selective agonists, was also substantiated by two antagonists for the putative EP and TP class. A third advantage was that the classification was derived from *in vitro* preparations alone, using tissues which exhibited a single response to the prostaglandin, thus providing circumstantial evidence for the presence of one particular receptor subtype.

It is generally appreciated that receptor analysis should theoretically be undertaken *in vitro*, since under such conditions the concentration at the receptor can be reasonably assessed,[13] and consequently affinity constants can be calculated. Using such affinity constants, one can postulate receptor subtypes. Analysis from *in vivo* data, because of pharmacokinetic problems, is problematical because equilibrium conditions cannot be established and such data should, therefore, only be used to corroborate *in vitro* classifications. The precise estimation of affinity constants in receptor classification, is critical, and such data in terms of $pA_2$ estimations from isolated tissues are shown in Tables 1 to 9. The Glaxo scheme[2] is described in more detail below.

The Glaxo scheme[2] was based upon the selective agonism of the naturally occurring prostaglandins and consequently, these compounds are among the most potent agonists for the particular receptor class. However, a number of synthetic agonists have been shown to exert greater selectivity for putative prostanoid subtypes. In addition, the development of selective antagonists for the $EP_1$ subtype have also enabled further characterizations to be made. The scheme is illustrated in Table 10.

## EP RECEPTORS

### Agonists

The rank order of prostaglandins at this subtype has been shown to be $PGE_1 = PGE_2 > PGI_2 = PGF_{2\alpha} > PGD_2 =$ U46619 at EP receptors in the guinea-pig ileum, and this profile is seen in other tissues such as the guinea-pig fundus,[3] trachea,[14] oesophageal muscularis mucosa,[36] and dog fundus.[3]

The most potent agonists at the subtype mediating contraction are 16,16-dimethyl $PGE_2$, ICI 80205, and sulprostone.[2] These agonists are weak or inactive at preparations containing FP or TP receptors.[2] $PGE_1$ and $PGE_2$ can also exert relaxant activities in the cat and guinea-pig trachea, provided that the resting tone of the tissue is high.[4] In contrast, none of the other agonists above exhibit relaxant effects.[15] It has been proposed, therefore, that EP receptors can be subdivided into two types: $EP_1$ and $EP_2$. The former are selectively stimulated by agonists such as 16,16-dimethyl $PGE_2$ (although it should be noted that this compound exhibits significant TP-agonist activity[16]), and elicit primarily contractile actions,[15] while $EP_2$ receptors may be selectively stimulated by AY 23626 and elicit mainly relaxant actions.[15]

### Antagonists

Two $EP_1$ antagonists have been described, SC-19220[2,17] and AH 6809.[18] The former, although exhibiting a relatively low affinity ($pA_2$ values = 5.2, Table 1), was shown to selectively inhibit the actions of PGE-series compounds with regard to contractile effects on tissues such as the guinea-pig ileum.[2]

**Table 1**
**AH 6809**

| Preparation | Agonist | $pA_2$ | Slope | Receptor | Ref. |
|---|---|---|---|---|---|
| Guinea-Pig ileum | $PGE_1$ | 7.3 | 0.81 | $EP_1$ | 36 |
| | 16,16-dimethyl $PGE_2$ | 7.4 | 0.84 | $EP_1$ | 36 |
| | $PGE_2$ | 6.8 | 1.02 | $EP_1$ | 18 |
| | $PGF_{2\alpha}$ | 6.9 | 0.66 | $EP_1$ | 18 |
| | $PGI_2$ | 7.3 | 0.81 | $EP_1$ | 18 |
| | Ach | <5.0 | | — | 18 |
| Guinea-Pig fundus | $PGE_2$ | 6.6 | 0.86 | $EP_1$ | 18 |
| | $PGF_{2\alpha}$ | 6.6 | 0.78 | $EP_1$ | 18 |
| | Ach | <5.0 | — | — | |
| Guinea-Pig trachea (contraction) | 16,16-dimethyl $PGE_2$ | 7.1 | 0.88 | $EP_1$ | 36 |
| Guinea-Pig OMM | $PGE_2$ | 7.2 | 0.79 | $EP_1$ | 36 |
| Dog fundus | $PGE_2$ | 6.6 | 1.0. | $EP_1$ | 18 |
| | $PGF_{2\alpha}$ | 6.2 | 0.99 | $EP_1$ | 18 |
| | Ach | <5.0 | — | — | 18 |
| Cat trachea | $PGE_2$ | <5.0 | — | $EP_2$ | 18 |
| Guinea-Pig trachea (relaxation) | $PGE_2$ | <5.0 | — | $EP_2$ | 36 |
| Chick ileum | $PGE_2$ | <5.0 | — | $EP_2$ | 18 |
| Dog iris | $PGF_{2\alpha}$ | <5.0 | — | FP | 18 |
| Guinea-Pig lung | U46619 | <5.0 | — | TP | 18 |
| Guinea-Pig aorta | U46619 | <5.0 | — | TP | 36 |
| Human platelet (whole blood) | $PGD_2$ | 5.7 | 0.72 | DP | 18 |
| | $PGI_2$ | <3.5 | — | IP | 18 |
| | U46619 | 4.4 | 1.28 | TP | 18 |
| | ADP | <3.5 | — | — | 18 |
| Human platelet (resuspended) | $PGD_2$ | 6.3 | 0.83 | DP | 18 |
| | $PGI_2$ | <4.5 | — | IP | 18 |
| | U46619 | 5.7 | 1.07 | TP | 18 |
| | ADP | <5.0 | — | — | 18 |

*Note*: OMM, oesophageal muscularis mucosae; — , denotes Schild slope unavailable; Ach, acetylcholine.

AH 6809 exhibits similar properties, but possesses a higher affinity ($pA_2$ values $\simeq$ 7.0, Table 2). To date, none of the relaxant effects of PGE-series prostaglandins in the guinea-pig and cat trachea are antagonized by these antagonists[2,18] and it has been proposed that this provides further evidence for the existence of two subtypes of the EP receptor, denoted as $EP_1$ and $EP_2$.[18] It should be noted that there are problems associated with each of these $EP_1$ antagonists: SC-19220 is insoluble in water and possesses weak antagonist activity (Table 1). AH 6809, while possessing a higher affinity and better water solubility, also possesses DP-receptor antagonist activity at higher concentrations, emphasizing the need to use preparations containing one receptor of a particular type. In addition, AH 6809 has limited use in *in vivo* applications because of extensive protein binding.[19]

## DP RECEPTORS

### Agonists

The DP receptor is perhaps the most poorly defined in the receptor classification of Coleman et al.[2] The order of potency has been shown[2] to be $PGD_2$ > ($PGE_2$, $PGF_{2\alpha}$, $PGI_2$, U46619). However, there has yet to be a preparation described which contains DP receptors alone.[2,20-22] The inhibition of guinea-pig platelet aggregation has been shown to be mediated

## Table 2
## SC-19920

| Preparation | Agonist | $pA_2$ | Slope | Receptor | Ref. |
|---|---|---|---|---|---|
| Guinea-Pig ileum | $PGE_2$ | 5.4 | 1.24 | $EP_1$ | 3 |
| | $PGF_{2\alpha}$ | 5.3 | 0.80 | $EP_1$ | 3 |
| | Ach | <4.0 | — | — | 3 |
| Guinea-Pig fundus | $PGE_2$ | 5.6 | 1.12 | $EP_1$ | 3 |
| | $PGF_{2\alpha}$ | 5.2 | 0.93 | $EP_1$ | 3 |
| | Ach | <4.0 | — | — | |
| | U46619 | 5.7 | 0.7 | $EP_1$ | |
| | WY 17186 | 5.0 | — | $EP_1$ | |
| Dog fundus | $PGE_2$ | 5.6 | 0.94 | $EP_1$ | 3 |
| | $PGF_{2\alpha}$ | 5.4 | 1.35 | $EP_1$ | 3 |
| | Ach | <4.0 | — | — | 3 |
| Guinea-Pig trachea | $PGF_2$ | 5.5 | | $EP_1$ | 2 |
| | $PGF_{2\alpha}$ | 5.7 | 0.6 | $EP_1$ | 2 |
| | U46619 | <3.6 | — | TP | 2 |
| | WY17186 | <3.6 | — | TP | 2 |
| Cat trachea | $PGE_2$ | <4.0 | — | $EP_2$ | 4 |
| Chick ileum | $PGD_2$ | <4.0 | — | $EP_2$ | 4 |
| Dog iris | $PGF_{2\alpha}$ | <3.5 | — | FP | 4 |
| Cat iris | $PGF_{2\alpha}$ | <3.5 | — | | 4 |
| Guinea-Pig lung | U46619 | <4.0 | — | TP | 4 |
| Dog saphenous vein | U46619 | 3.9 | — | TP | 4 |
| Human platelets | U46619 | <3.0 | — | TP | 4 |
| Rabbit aorta | U46619 | <3.5 | — | TP | 4 |
| Human platelet | $PGI_2$ | <3.5 | — | IP | 4 |

*Note*: — , data not available; Ach, acetylcholine.

## Table 3
## AH-19437

| Preparation | Agonist | $pA_2$ | Slope | Receptor | Ref. |
|---|---|---|---|---|---|
| Guinea-Pig ileum | $PGE_2$ | <4.6 | — | $EP_1$ | 4 |
| Guinea-Pig fundus | $PGE_2$ | <4.6 | — | $EP_1$ | 4 |
| | U46619 | — | — | — | |
| Guinea-Pig trachea | U46619 | 6.5 | 1.0 | TP | 3 |
| | WY17186 | 6.6 | 1.0 | TP | 3 |
| Dog iris | U46619 | <4.6 | — | TP | 4 |
| | $PGF_{2\alpha}$ | <5.0 | — | FP | 4 |
| Cat iris | $PGF_{2\alpha}$ | <5.0 | — | FP | 4 |
| Cat trachea | $PGE_2$ | <4.6 | — | $EP_2$ | 4 |
| Chick ileum | $PGE_2$ | <4.6 | — | $EP_2$ | 4 |
| | | — | — | | |
| Guinea-Pig lung | U46619 | 6.6 | 1.6 | TP | 4 |
| | $PGF_{2\alpha}$ | 5.9 | 0.9 | TP | 3 |
| | WY17186 | 6.4 | 1.2 | TP | 3 |
| Dog saphenous vein | U46619 | 6.0 | 1.2 | TP | 3 |
| Rat aorta | U46619 | 5.9 | 1.0 | TP | 3 |
| Human platelet (whole blood) | U46619 | 6.0 | 1.0 | TP | 3 |

*Note*: — , data not available.

**Table 4**
**AH-23848**

| Preparation | Agonist | $pA_2$ | Slope | Receptor |
|---|---|---|---|---|
| Guinea-Pig fundus | $PGE_2$ | <5.0 | — | $EP_1$ |
| | U46619 | <6.0 | — | $EP_1$ |
| Dog iris | $PGF_{2\alpha}$ | <5.0 | — | FP |
| | U46619 | <5.0 | — | FP |
| Cat trachea | $PGE_2$ | <5.0 | — | $EP_2$ |
| Chick ileum | $PGE_2$ | <5.0 | — | $EP_2$ |
| | U46619 | <5.0 | — | $EP_2$ |
| Guinea-Pig lung | U46619 | 8.2 | 1.0 | TP |
| Dog saphenous vein | U46619 | 8.3 | 0.9 | TP |
| Rat aorta | U46619 | 7.9 | 1.0 | TP |
| | SQ 26655 | 8.3 | 1.0 | TP |
| | $PGD_2$ | 8.1 | 1.1 | TP |
| | $PGF_{2\alpha}$ | 8.0 | 1.1 | TP |
| Human platelet | U46619 | 7.8 | 1.4 | TP |
| (whole blood) | SQ 26655 | 7.9 | 1.5 | TP |
| Human platelet (resuspended) | U46619 | 8.3 | 1.2 | TP |

*Note*: — , data not available.

This table based upon unpublished observations of R. A. Coleman.[37]

**Table 5**
**EP 045**

| Preparation | Agonist | $pA_2$ | Slope | Receptor | Ref. |
|---|---|---|---|---|---|
| Rabbit aorta | U46619 | 6.3 | 0.98 | TP | 2 |
| Dog saphenous vein | U46619 | 7.2 | 0.97 | TP | 2 |
| Guinea-Pig trachea | U46619 | 7.5 | 0.97 | TP | 2 |
| Human platelet (resuspended) | | 7.0 | 1.0 | TP | 2 |

**Table 6**
**BM 13177**

| Preparation | Agonist | $pA_2$ | Slope | Receptor | Ref. |
|---|---|---|---|---|---|
| Rabbit aorta | U46619 | 6.3 | 1.1 | TP | 2 |
| Guinea-Pig ileum | $PGE_2$ | >4.0 | — | $EP_1$ | 36 |

*Note*: — , data not available.

by both $PGD_2$ and $PGI_2$, although a nonspecific action of $PGD_2$ in this preparation has been reported.[21] In addition, a biphasic concentration-response curve for $PGD_2$ has been shown to occur in this preparation, since at higher concentrations, the proaggregant actions of $PGD_2$ at TP receptors become apparent.[22] In the presence of a TP antagonist such as BM 13,177 only an inhibition of aggregation is seen.[22] BW 245C has been proposed as a selective agonist,[21] although the compound also possesses IP-agonist activity.

**Antagonists**

The problems of defining this receptor class are increased by the lack of a selective

**Table 7**
**SQ 29548**

| Preparation | Agonist | $pA_2$ | Slope | Receptor | Ref. |
|---|---|---|---|---|---|
| Guinea-Pig ileum | $PGE_2$ | >4.0 | — | $EP_1$ | 36 |
| Guinea-Pig trachea (contract) | 16,16-dimethyl $PGE_2$ | 5.2 | 0.8 | $EP_1$ | 36 |
| Guinea-Pig trachea (relaxation) | $PGE_2$ | >5.0 | — | $EP_2$ | 36 |
| Guinea-Pig OMM | $PGE_2$ | >5.0 | — | $EP_1$ | 36 |
| | U46619 | 9.3 | 0.8 | TP | 36 |
| | $PGD_2$ | 9.4 | 0.8 | TP | 36 |
| Guinea-Pig aorta | U46619 | 9.3 | 1.0 | TP | 36 |
| Rat aorta | U46619 | 9.0 | 1.0 | TP | 12 |

*Note*: OMM, oesophageal muscularis mucosae: — , data not available.

**Table 8**
**EP 092**

| Preparation | Agonist | $pA_2$ | Slope | Receptor |
|---|---|---|---|---|
| Human platelets (resuspended) | U46619 | 6.0 | 1.0 | TP |

**Table 9**
**N-0164**

| Preparation | Agonist | $pA_2$ | Slope | Receptor |
|---|---|---|---|---|
| Guinea-Pig platelet | $PGD_2$ | 3.6 | NA | DP |
| | U46619 | 4.7 | 1.1 | TP |

**Table 10**
**CLASSIFICATION OF RECEPTORS ACCORDING TO COLEMAN ET AL.[2]**

| Receptor | Agonist | Antagonist | Preparation | Response |
|---|---|---|---|---|
| DP | $PGD_2$ | — | Guinea-Pig platelet | Anti-Aggregation |
| $EP_1$ | $PGE_2$ | AH 6809 | Guinea-Pig ileum | Contraction |
| $EP_2$ | $PGE_2$ | — | Cat trachea | Relaxation |
| FP | $PGF_{2\alpha}$ | — | Cat iris | Contraction |
| IP | $PGI_2$ Iloprost | — | Rat platelet | Anti-Aggregation |
| TP | $TxA_2$ U46619 | AH 23848 | Rat aorta | Contraction |

antagonist.[2] N-0164 has been suggested[22] as a potential antagonist but it is extremely weak, ($pA_2 \simeq 3.6$, Table 9) possesses TP-antagonist action and may also possess thromboxane-synthetase-inhibitory activity (see chapters in this volume by Sanner and by Walker).

## FP RECEPTORS

### Agonists

The cat and dog iris muscle,[23] in contrast to the bovine iris muscle,[24] are highly sensitive to the actions of $PGF_{2\alpha}$ alone, and it has been proposed that the receptors in these two tissues represent a distinct receptor.[2] The rank order of agonist potency has been reported to be $PGF_{2\alpha} > PGD_2 >$ U-46619 $> PGE_2 > PGI_2$ (Reference 2). In addition, two $PGF_{2\alpha}$ analogues, fluoprostenol (ICI 81008) and cloprostenol (ICI 80996), have been shown to be very potent FP agonists, and exhibit little or no action at EP or TP receptors.[2] The luteolytic activity of these compounds has been suggested to be due to their FP-agonist properties.

**Antagonists**

A specific agonist for this receptor class is unavailable and so definitive characterization is still limited.

## IP RECEPTORS

**Agonists**

The order of potency of agonists at putative IP receptors inhibiting aggregation of rat platelets is as follows: (Iloprost) $PGI_2 > PGE_2 \gg PGF_{2\alpha} > PGD_2 \geqslant$ U46619 (Reference 2). Iloprost resembles $PGI_2$ in that it is both an inhibitor of platelet aggregation and a vasodilator[25] but it is chemically more stable.[25] It is a weak agonist at receptors producing contraction in the trachea and is inactive at $EP_2$ and TP receptors.[2] It is, however, more potent at IP receptors on platelets than on vascular smooth muscle[2] and, while this may indicate IP-receptor heterogeneity, differences in effective receptor reserve may also provide an explanation.[13]

**Antagonists**

There are to date no selective IP-receptor antagonists, and consequently no definitive characterization of the putative subtype can be undertaken. FCE 2217 has been proposed as an IP antagonist,[26] since it antagonizes contractile responses to $PGI_2$ in the isolated guinea-pig atria and trachea.[26] However, this compound also acts as a full agonist at inhibiting aggregation of human platelets.[27] The use of FCE 22176 as an IP antagonist is therefore in doubt, particularly since it has been shown that contractile responses of $PGI_2$ in the guinea-pig trachea have been shown to be mediated through $EP_1$ receptors.[28]

## TP RECEPTORS

**Agonists**

The order of potency of agonists at this subtype in the rat aortic has been shown to be U46619 $\gg PGD_2 > PGI_2 = PGF_{2\alpha} > PGE_2$ (Reference 2). The existence of this subtype was first postulated on the basis of selective agonism by U46619, a stable potent thromboxane mimetic.[29] Other agonists include $TxA_2$, pinane $TxA_2$ (which has partial agonist activity) and 16,16-dimethyl $PGE_2$.[16]

**Antagonists**

There are now a number of selective, potent TP antagonists available, including SQ 29548, EP 045, AH 23848, AH 19437, BM 13177, and 13-azaprostanoic acid (see Tables 3 to 8). All these antagonists act in a competitive manner. Two antagonists, EP 035 and EP 157, act as TP antagonists, and also partial IP agonists.[29] Some antagonists exhibit differing affinities at TP receptors on the vasculature and platelets.[12] However, the difference is small and is not convincing evidence for subtypes of the TP receptor as has been postulated to be the case.

## PROBLEMS OF PROSTAGLANDIN-RECEPTOR CLASSIFICATION

The postulation of receptor subtypes is subject to a number of strict criteria, and these have been fully described in reviews by Furchgott[31] and Kenakin.[13] The criteria originally outlined by Furchgott are briefly paraphrased below. Criteria for receptor classification include:

1. The response of the tissue preparations to an agonist should be solely due to the direct action of the agonist on one type of receptor. It should not be due to an action on more than one type of receptor, or due to an indirect action.
2. The altered sensitivity to an agonist in the presence of competitive antagonist should be due solely to competition between the antagonist and agonist for the receptor.
3. The response to the addition of an agonist should be measured once a plateau had been attained.
4. The agonist or antagonist concentration in the external solution should be maintained at a steady level until the response is measured.
5. The concentration of agonist or antagonist at the receptor should be in equilibrium with the external solution. Thus, processes of uptake, degradation, nonspecific binding, and transport into cells should be minimal.
6. The experimental design should include correction for sensitivity changes.

It is important therefore to discuss prostaglandin-receptor classification in the light of such criteria.

It is generally accepted that the most definitive evidence of differences in receptors is a large difference (at least threefold, although tenfold is more convincing) in the affinity of competitive antagonists, determined using functional isolated-tissue analysis. It is a feature of the putative prostaglandin-receptor schemes that only two classes of such antagonists are available (for the $EP_1$ and TP receptors). There are as yet no specific antagonists available for the DP, FP, or TP receptors.

It should be noted that even where such antagonists exist, the range of affinities, as estimated by the $pA_2$ values is large (see Tables 1 to 8). Theoretically, if two antagonists act on the same receptor, then the antagonist $pA_2$ value should be independent of the agonist used.[13] It is unlikely that the range of $pA_2$ observed with antagonists are indicative of multiple subtypes of the $EP_1$ or TP receptor for example, but probably illustrate the difficulties encountered in determining $pA_2$ values under the ideal experimental conditions described above. This emphasizes the need for antagonists exhibiting large (i.e., >100-fold) selectivities.

In lieu of such compounds, receptors have been proposed on the basis of rank orders of agonist potencies. While such orders of potency may be indicative of potential subtypes, the evidence is not definitive. The potencies of agonists should be defined under ideal, i.e., equilibrium conditions, and processes such as agonist uptake or degradation should be eliminated, since these processes can vary from tissue to tissue, greatly influencing the potency.[13] This consideration is particularly relevant to prostaglandins, where conversion to active metabolites is common. This also raises the question of classifying prostaglandin receptors *in vivo* where such problems are even more pronounced, and consequently equilibrium conditions cannot be established. A further consideration is that theoretically the relative potency of a full agonist in general and a partial agonist in particular, can vary between tissues because of differences in efficacy (i.e., the effective receptor reserve).[13] Therefore, two tissues with identical receptors, but different effective receptor reserves can influence greatly the rank order of potency.

Studies using the available specific antagonists have shown that, depending upon the concentration, prostaglandins of one type can act as partial agonists at receptors of another type (e.g., $PGI_2$ compounds act as partial agonists at $EP_1$ receptors;[28] $PGD_2$ can act as a partial agonist at TP receptors),[22] and this further underlines the difficulty of using agonists in the standard receptor classification.

To date, the existence of some prostanoid receptors are proposed on the basis of a selective response to a given agonist (e.g., FP, DP, and IP receptors). However, it should be noticed that there may be other reasons for the lack of a response to a low partial agonist, apart from an absence of a particular receptor type, e.g., the effective receptor reserve. In the guinea-pig portal vein, for example, no contractile response is observed to $PGD_2$. However, $PGD_2$ does appear to bind to TP receptors in this tissue, since it can antagonize the responses to the TP-agonist U46619.[36] In contrast, in the guinea-pig aorta, both U46619 and $PGD_2$ act as full agonists at the TP receptor.[36] It is likely that in the portal vein the effective receptor reserve is lower than in the aorta, and not that the receptors are different. A similar problem is observed with pinane $TxA_2$. This compound antagonizes the responses to $TxA_2$ in some tissues such as the guinea-pig trachea and yet acts as a partial agonist at TP receptors inhibiting the aggregation of human platelets. Again it is likely that $TxA_2$ possesses a low efficacy and that in the trachea it can elicit a partial response because of lower effective receptor reserve whereas in the platelet the effective receptor reserve is greater and a response is observed. It is unlikely that the receptors differ. Similar observations have been made in other receptor systems, e.g., prenalterol at $\beta_1$-adrenoceptors[32] and McN-A-343 at muscarinic receptors.[33]

## LIGAND-BINDING STUDIES

Ligand-binding data, in which the affinity of a compound which inhibits the binding of a radioligand is characterized, has been extensively used to characterize receptor schemes. In general, the evidence that the binding site represents a functional receptor arises from a comparison of affinity constants, estimated from isolated tissue responses and direct radioligand binding. In many receptor classifications, including dopamine, β-adrenergic,[34] α-adrenergic, and muscarinic the degree of corroboration is good. However, this is not the case with other schemes such as subdivisions of the 5-$HT_1$ receptor subtype.

Comparison of affinity constants from radioligand-binding studies and isolated-tissue studies is still in its infancy with regard to prostanoid receptors. There are several reasons for this, although the lack of competitive, selective antagonists of high affinity (i.e., $K_D \simeq$ 1 n*M*) is perhaps the main problem. Radioligand binding has therefore employed agonists and this is subject to a number of disadvantages. Such agonists do not generally exhibit a high enough affinity and can bind to two states of the receptor in the presence of GTP. Attempts have been made to compare the affinities of a series of agonists (determined by radioligand binding) with potencies estimated using iolated tissues. Since the potency of an agonist is dependent on factors apart from affinity (i.e., its efficacy), such comparisons may be invalid.

However, comparisons between rank orders of affinity and potency have been made and recently reviewed.[2] It has been seen that binding sites identified with agonists are characterized by a high affinity for one of the natural prostaglandins above all others. This has been considered to be consistent with the Glaxo classification.[2] These comparisons will not be discussed in detail here, since recent reviews have appeared on this subject.[2,6]

## ALTERNATIVE CLASSIFICATIONS

Although the Glaxo scheme[2] has gained some acceptance, and also provides a good working tool, it suffers from the disadvantage of a lack of selective antagonists for four of the putative subtypes (DP, $EP_2$, FP and IP). An alternative scheme is proposed by Gardiner et al.,[10,35] and this is discussed below.

**Table 11**
**CLASSIFICATION OF RECEPTORS ACCORDING TO GARDINER AND COLLIER[10]**

| Receptor | Agonist | Antagonist | Preparation | Response |
|---|---|---|---|---|
| CLASS I ($\chi$) | | | | |
| $\chi_1$ | $TxA_2$ | EP045 | Guinea-Pig lung | Contraction |
| $\chi_2$ | $PGF_{2\alpha}$ $PGD_2$ | — | Rat uterus | Contraction |
| $\chi_3$ | $PGE_2$ | SC19920 | Guinea-Pig ileum | Contraction |
| CLASS II ($\Psi$) | | | | |
| | TR 4979 | — | Guinea-Pig trachea | Relaxation |

Putative receptor classes were identified according to the action of the prostaglandin. Two classes were proposed.[10] Class I ($\chi$) for stimulatory/contractile effects and Class II $\Psi$ for inhibitory/relaxant effects. This was initially designed to encompass the actions of prostaglandins on the airways, although modifications of the scheme were made to encompass actions of $TxA_2$ and so on. The Class I receptor is now subdivided into $\chi_1$, $\chi_2$, and $\chi_3$. This is shown in Table 11.

There are many similarities between the Glaxo scheme[2] and Gardiner et al.[10,35] For example, the TP receptor corresponds to $\chi_1$ receptor; the FP receptor to the $\chi_2$ receptor, and the $EP_1$ receptor to the $\chi_3$. In addition, the $\Psi$ class may correspond to the $EP_2$ class, although there is one important exception; Coleman et al.[2] propose that the $EP_2$ receptor mediates contraction of the chick ileum, and is insensitive to the action of $EP_1$ antagonists. However, TR 4979 was inactive on the chick ileum[35] but relaxed the cat trachea, a preparation also considered to possess $EP_2$ receptors. The discrepancy may involve further subtypes, but the problem of differing effective receptor reserves may also be relevant here. Until a selective $EP_2$ antagonist is developed, no definitive answer can be made.

Gardiner[35] considers that the selective action of TR 4979 for relaxant responses strengthens the postulate that there are only two major classes of prostanoid receptors (i.e., excitatory and inhibitory). An alternate explanation is the TR 4979 is the first selective $EP_2$ agonist.

While the advantage of the Gardiner scheme is its simplicity, it does bear many resemblances to the Glaxo scheme. It is likely that the actions of the prostaglandins are mediated through different receptors, which would require the presence of at least five subtypes. As with the Coleman scheme, its definitive answer will only arise through the development of selective antagonists.

## CONCLUSION

Prostaglandin receptors, if indeed they do exist, are currently the subject of much intensive research. The most comprehensive classification available, is that of the Coleman et al. at Glaxo, and this bears a number of similarities to that proposed by Gardiner. Both schemes possess the advantage that the classifications are based upon *in vitro* data, although the major criticism is a lack of selective antagonists. The development of such compounds is of critical importance, both in terms of definitively defining the receptor subtypes, and also to develop novel therapeutic agents.

## ADDENDUM

Since the original time of writing, two important advances have been made in terms of defining prostanoid receptor subtypes. The Glaxo[38] group has postulated that EP receptors are composed of a third subtype which is denoted as $EP_3$. This subtype mediates inhibition of electrically evoked twitch contractions of the guinea pig vas deferens (a preparation which therefore acts as a sensitive $Ep_3$ bioassay) and also inhibition of gastric acid secretion in the isolated rat gastric mucosa.[39] Although the identification of the $EP_3$ receptor in other tissues is hampered by a lack of selective agonists and antagonists, the concept may have utility in the development of novel anti-secretory agents.

Secondly, Giles et al.[40] have reported the development of a potent, selective, and competitive DP receptor antagonist, BW868C. This antagonist therefore provides further evidence of the DP receptor subtype and is a useful tool in its pharmacological identification.

## REFERENCES


1. **Snyder, S. H. and Gooman, R. R.,** Multiple neurotransmitter receptors. *J. Neurochem.,* 35, 5, 1980.
2. **Coleman, R. A., Humphrey, P. P. A., and Kennedy, L.,** Prostanoid receptors in smooth muscle: further evidence for a proposed classification, in *Trends in Autonomic Pharmacology,* Vol. 3, Kalsner, S., Ed., Taylor and Francis, London, chap. 3, 1985.
3. **Kennedy, L., Coleman, R. A., Humphrey, P. P. A., Levy, G. P., and Lumley, P.,** Studies on the characterisation of prostanoid receptors: a proposed classification, *Prostaglandins,* 24, 667, 1982.
4. **Coleman, R. A., Humphrey, P. P. A., Kennedy, F., and Lumley, P.,** Prostanoid receptors — the development of a working classification, *Trends Pharm. Sci.,* 5, 303, 1984.
5. **Robertson, R. P.,** Characterisation and regulation of prostaglandin and leukotriene receptors: an overview, *Prostaglandins,* 31, 395, 1986.
6. **Andersen, N. H. and Ramwell, P. W.,** Biological aspects of prostaglandins *Arch. Int. Med.,* 133, 30, 1974.
7. **Jones, R. L.,** Cardiovascular actions of prostaglandins D and E in the sheep: evidence for two distinct receptors, *Adv. Prostaglandin Thromboxane Res.,* 1, 221, 1976.
8. **Welburn, P. J. and Jones, R. L.,** A comparison of prostaglandin $F_{2\alpha}$ and three 16-aryloxy analogues on the isolated rabbit jejunum, *Prostaglandins,* 15, 287, 1977.
9. **Coleman, R. A., Humphrey, P. P. A., Kennedy, I., Leug, G. P., and Lumley, P.,** Preliminary characterisation of three types of prostanoid receptor mediating smooth muscle contraction, *Br. J. Pharmacol.,* 69, 265P, 1980.
10. **Gardiner, P. J. and Collier, H. O. J.,** Specific receptors for prostaglandins in airways, *Prostaglandins,* 19, 819, 1980.
11. **Andersen, N. M., Imamoto, S., Subramanian, N., Picker, D. M., Ladner, D. W., Biswanath de, B., Tynan, S. S., Eggerman, T. H., Harker, L. A., Robertson, R. P., Oien, H. G., and Rao, Ch. V.,** Molecular basis for prostaglandin potency. 111 Tests of the significance of the "hairpin conformation" in biorecognition phenomena, *Prostaglandins,* 22, 841, 1981.
12. **Ogletree, M. L., Allen, G. T., O'Keefe, E. M., Liu, E. C.-K., and Hedberg, A.,** Activities of various prostanoids at thromboxane receptors revealed by selective antagonists: studies in human platelets and rat and guinea-pig smooth muscles, Proc. 6th Int. Meet. Prostaglandins, Florence, Italy, 1986, 30.
13. **Kenakin, T. P.,** The classification of drugs and drug receptors in isolated tissues, *Pharmacol. Rev.,* 36, 165, 1984.
14. **Coleman, R. A. and Kennedy, I.,** Characterisation of the prostanoid receptors mediating contractions of guinea-pig isolated trachea, *Prostaglandins,* 29, 363, 1985.
15. **Coleman, R. A., Kennedy, I., and Sheldrick, R. L. G.,** New evidence with selective agonists and antagonists for the subclassification of $PGE_2$-sensitive (EP-) receptors. Proc. 6th Int. Meet. Prostaglandins, Florence, Italy, 1986, 164.
16. **Jones, R. L., Peesapati, V., and Wilson, N. H.,** Antagonism of the thromboxane-sensitive contractile systems of the rabbit aorta, dog saphenous vein and guinea-pig trachea, *Br. J. Pharmacol.,* 76, 423, 1982.
17. **Bennett, A. and Posner, J.,** Studies on prostaglandin antagonists, *Br. J. Pharmacol.,* 42, 584, 1971.
18. **Coleman, R. A., Kennedy, I., and Sheldrick, R. A.,** AH 6809, A prostanoid $EP_1$-receptor blocking drug, *Br. J. Pharmacol.,* 85, 273P, 1985.
19. **Coleman, R. A. and Denyer, L. H.,** The influence of protein binding on the potency of the prostanoid $EP_1$-receptor blocking drug AH 6809, *Br. J. Pharmacol.,* 86, 803P, 1985.

20. **Narumiya, S. and Toda, N.,** Different responsiveness of prostaglandin $D_2$-sensitive systems to prostaglandin $D_2$ and its analogues, *Br. J. Pharmacol.*, 85, 367, 1985.
21. **Hamid, S. and Whittle, B. J. R.,** Interaction of prostaglandin $D_2$ with prostacyclin, carbacyclin and the hydantoin prostaglandin, BW 245C in guinea-pig platelets, *Br. J. Pharmacol.*, 85, 285, 1985.
22. **Hamid-Bloomfield, S. and Whittle, B. J. R.,** Prostaglandin $D_2$ interacts at thromboxane receptor-sites on guinea-pig platelets, *Br. J. Pharmacol.*, 88, 931, 1986.
23. **Alphen, G. W. M. M. and Angel, M. A.,** Activity of prostaglandin E, F, A and B on sphincter, dialator and ciliary muscle preparations of the cat eye, *Prostaglandins*, 9, 157, 1975.
24. **Dong, Y. J. and Jones, R. L.,** Effects of prostaglandins and thromboxane analogues on bullock and dog iris sphincter preparations, *Br. J. Pharmacol.*, 76, 149, 1982.
25. **Schrör, K., Darius, M., Marzky, R., and Ohlendorf, R.,** The antiplatelet and cardiovascular actions of a new carbacyclin derivative (ZK 36374) — equipotent to $PGI_2$ *in vitro*, *Naunyn-Schmeideberg's Arch. Pharmacol.*, 316, 252, 1981.
26. **Fassina, G., Froldi, G., and Caparrolta, L.,** A stable, isosterically modified prostacyclin analogue, FCE-22176, acting as a competitive antagonist to prostacyclin in guinea-pig trachea and atria, *Eur. J. Pharmacol.*, 113, 459, 1985.
27. **Wilkins, A. J. and MacDermot, J.,** The putative procyclin receptor antagonist (FCE-22176) is a full agonist on human platelets and NCB-20 cells, *Eur. J. Pharmacol.*, 127, 117, 1986.
28. **Dong, Y. J., Jones, R. L., and Wilson, N. H.,** Prostaglandin E receptor subtypes in smooth muscle: agonist activities of stable prostacyclin analogues, *Br. J. Pharmacol.*, 87, 97, 1986.
29. **Coleman, R. A., Humphrey, P. P. A., Kennedy, I., Levy, G. P., and Lumley, P.,** Comparison of the actions of U46619, a prostacyclin $H_2$ analogue with those of prostaglandin $H_2$ and thromboxane $A_2$ on some isolated smooth muscle preparations, *Br. J. Pharmacol.*, 73, 773, 1981.
30. **Armstrong, R. A., Jones, R. L., MacDermot, J., and Wilson, N. H.,** Prostaglandin endoperoxide analogues which are both thromboxane receptor antagonists and prostacyclin mimetics, *Br. J. Pharmacol.*, 87, 543, 1986.
31. **Furchgott, R. F.,** The classification of adrenoceptors (adrenergic receptors). An evaluation from the standpoint of receptor theory, in *Handbook of Experimental Pharmacology, Catecholamines*, 33 ed., Blashko, H. and Muscholl, E., Eds., Springer-Verlag, New York, 1972, 283.
32. **Kenakin, T. P. and Beek, D.,** Is prenalterol (M133/80) really a selective beta-1 adrenoceptor agonist? Tissue selectivity resulting from differences in stimulus-response relationships, *J. Pharmacol. Exp. Ther.*, 213, 406, 1980.
33. **Eglen, R. M., Michel, A. D., and Whiting, R. L.,** $M_1$ muscarinic receptor selectivity of McN-A-343 may not be due to receptor heterogeneity, *Br. J. Pharmacol.*, 86, 610P, 1985.
34. **Nahorski, S. R.,** Identification and significance of beta-adrenoceptor subtypes, *Trends Pharm. Sci.*, 2, 95, 1981.
35. **Gardiner, P. J.,** Characterization of prostanoid relaxant/inhibitory receptors (Ψ) using a highly selective agonist, TR 4979, *Br. J. Pharmacol.*, 87, 45, 1986.
36. **Eglen, R. M. and Whiting, R. L.,** The action of prostanoid receptor agonists and antagonists on smooth muscle and platelets, *Br. J. Pharmacol.*, 94, 1988.
37. **Coleman, R. A.,** Unpublished observations.

## ADDITIONAL REFERENCES

38. **Coleman, R. A., Kennedy, I., Sheldrick, R. L. G., and Tolowinska, I. Y.,** Further evidence for the existence of three subtypes of $PGE_2$-sensitive (EP) receptors, *Br. J. Pharmacol.*, 95, 407, 1988.
39. **Reeves, J. J., Bunce, K. T., Sheldrick, R. L. G., and Stabels, R.,** Evidence for the PGE receptor subtype mediating inhibition of acid secretion in the rat, *Br. J. Pharmacol.*, 95, 805, 1988.
40. **Giles, H., Leff, P., Bolofo, M. L., Kelly, M. G., and Robertson, A. D.,** BW A868C: a novel, highly potent and selective DP-receptor antagonist, *Br. J. Pharmacol.*, 95, 522, 1988.

# EICOSANOID RECEPTOR ANTAGONISTS

**John H. Sanner**

## INTRODUCTION

### Eicosanoid Receptors

Prostaglandins and related lipids produce most of their varied biological effects by reacting with specific cellular elements, or receptors. Subtypes of receptors for several other types of biologically active substances, such as cholinergic and adrenergic agents, histamine, and serotonin, have been classified largely on the basis of specific or selective blockade of certain functions with receptor-oriented antagonists. Such classification of eicosanoid receptors has been hindered by the large number of agonistic agents involved, the multiplicity of biological events they initiate, and the lack of clearly defined, specific antagonists, but the task is now being undertaken by several groups. Progress in the classification of eicosanoid receptors is covered in the previous chapter by Eglen and Whiting.

In this chapter, we describe the inhibitory activities of several chemical compounds that have characteristics of receptor-oriented antagonism. This information may be useful in the future classification of eicosanoid receptors and the subsequent development of more useful agonistic and antagonistic agents directed at these receptors.

### Criteria for Inclusion

For the purpose of this chapter we have categorized eicosanoid inhibitors as apparent receptor-oriented antagonists based on the following criteria:

1. Selective inhibition — This is defined as inhibition of one or more eicosanoids to a greater extent or at a lower dose or concentration than noneicosanoids that have the same type of activity. Theoretically, absolute specificity might be expected from a receptor-oriented antagonist, but this ideal is nearly impossible in practice.
2. Competitive antagonism — Substances that compete with a natural agonist at its receptor site should show characteristics of competitive antagonism against the biological response of the agonist. This is characterized by a shift of the agonist dose-response curve to the right without a reduction in the maximum response, a linear Schild plot with a slope near unity, or a characteristically competitive Lineweaver-Burke plot. Although receptor-oriented noncompetitive antagonism is quite possible, the characteristic of competitive antagonism is a good indication of an action directed at the receptor.
3. Receptor binding — Receptor binding is the most direct indication of receptor-oriented, competitive activity, but it does not indicate whether the agent is agonistic or antagonistic, or if it is a partial agonist having both agonistic and antagonistic activities. Failure of a putative antagonist to bind to a receptor may result from several factors: the compound is not truly a receptor-oriented antagonist; the binding substance is not a true eicosanoid receptor; or the wrong receptor is being studied.

### Historical

Patulin was the first substance used as a prostaglandin antagonist in an attempt to determine the composition of irin, a substance released from injured eyes.[1,2] Irin was later shown to be a mixture of prostaglandins,[3,4] but patulin proved to be quite nonspecific in its inhibitory activities,[5] and it is not included in our classification of receptor-oriented antagonists.

In 1969 and 1970, three different types of substances were independently reported to be selective, competitive prostaglandin antagonists in intestinal smooth-muscle preparations. These antagonists were 7-oxa-prostaglandin analogues, especially 7-oxa-13-prostynoic acid (7-OPA),[6] the dibenzoxazepine compound SC-19220,[7] and polyphloretin phosphate (PPP).[8] These agents have been tested in a number of laboratories, and there is considerable information available on their activities, much of which was included in past reviews.[9-12]

In 1973, the compound FPL-55712 was reported to selectively inhibit the actions of slow reacting-substance (SRS) in anaphylaxis,[13] which was subsequently identified as a mixture of leukotrienes.[14,15] FPL-55712 is commonly accepted as a selective antagonist of SRS or leukotrienes, and it has been the subject of past reviews.[16-18] The development of leukotriene antagonists has been actively pursued recently, and several new antagonists have been reported. These include FPL 57231,[16] FPL 59257,[16] desamino-2-nor-leukotriene analogues,[19] ICI-19350,[20] certain imidodisulfamides,[21,22] KC-404,[23] $LTB_4$ diacetate,[24] $LTB_4$ dimethylamide,[25] LY163443,[26] LY171883,[27] 4R,5S,6Z-2-nor-$LTD_1$,[28] REV 5901,[29] SK&F 102922,[30] SKF 101132,[31,32] and Wy-44,329.[33] The subjects of leukotriene receptors and antagonists have been covered in recent reviews.[34-37]

Some nonsteroidal anti-inflammatory agents (especially the fenamates, and to some extent indomethacin) have been found to selectively inhibit some prostaglandin actions as well as their synthesis. A detailed review of this activity by the fenamates has been published by McLean and Gluckman.[38]

Thromboxane antagonists are among the most recent eicosanoid antagonists. Compounds with antithromboxane activity include AH 19437,[39] 13-azaprostanoic acid (13-APA),[40] 9,11-azo-13-oxa-15-hydroxy-prostanoic acid (AOHP),[41] BM 13.177,[42,43] EP045,[44] EP092,[45] 9-11,epoxy-imino-prosta-5,13-dienoic acid (9,11-EIP),[46] ONO-11105, ONO-11119, ONO-11120,[47] pinane thromboxane $A_2$ and analogues,[48,49] SKII-144,[50] SQ 27,427,[51] SQ 29,548,[52] and trimethoquinol and its isomers and analogues.[53-55]

## ACTIVITIES CATEGORIZED BY AGENT

Table 1 shows published *in vitro* activities and Table 2 shows published *in vivo* activities of putative eicosanoid-receptor antagonists. Abstracts and oral reports are generally not included unless the information was not otherwise available at the time of this writing. For purposes of receptor classification, it may be as important to know where an agent is not active as it is to know where it is active, so negative results are listed insofar as they have been published. In these cases the type of antagonism is indicated as "none".

Figures 1, 2, and 3 show representative chemical structures of prostaglandin antagonists, leukotriene antagonists, and thromboxane antagonists, respectively.

## ACTIVITIES CATEGORIZED BY BIOLOGICAL SYSTEM

The following text describes some of the activities of putative eicosanoid antagonists on specific biological systems. This information was selected to show interrelationships among the various antagonists that may be useful for defining eicosanoid receptors, developing new agents, or establishing therapeutic uses for the current compounds.

### Gastrointestinal System

Studies comparing isolated preparations of gerbil colon and guinea-pig ileum suggest a difference between prostaglandin-E and -F receptors in these preparations. It was first thought that polyphloretin phosphate antagonizes only F prostaglandins on gerbil colon,[8] but it was soon determined that it is equally potent against E and F prostaglandins.[56] SC-19220, on the other hand, is essentially inactive against F prostaglandins on gerbil colon,[57] although it shows full activity against E prostaglandins, and it appeared to be equally effective against

E and F prostaglandins, on guinea-pig ileum.[58] d,l-11,15-*Bis*-deoxy $PGE_1$, like SC-19220, inhibits only E prostaglandins on gerbil colon,[59] while dimethylamide and dimethylamino $PGF_{2\alpha}$[60] N-0164,[61] and 7-oxa-13-prostynoic acid[6,62,63] inhibit both E and F prostaglandins on this preparation.

Various antagonists also have different activities on rat-stomach strips. Prostaglandin-induced contractions are inhibited on these *in vitro* preparations by 5-(6-carboxyhexyl)-1-octyl-pyrolidine-2,4-dione,[64] indomethacin, meclofenamate,[65] N-0164,[61] and dibenzoxazepine compounds,[65-71] but 7-OPA causes contractions,[66] and PPP has been reported to be either a selective, competitive antagonist[64] or a stimulant[66] on this tissue. Stimulation by the latter two agents may be explained by a partial agonistic activity of 7-OPA as demonstrated on vascular smooth muscle[72] or by inhibition of prostaglandin metabolism by both compounds.[73,74]

Some prostaglandins cause relaxation of certain smooth muscles, and these relaxant effects are usually not inhibited by the present antagonists. For example, neither PPP nor SC-19220 was found to counteract the relaxant effects of $PGE_2$ on circular muscle of guinea-pig ileum or human gastric body and sigmoid colon. On the other hand, $PGF_{2\alpha}$ sometimes relaxed circular muscle of human ascending colon, and this relaxation was prevented by PPP.[75]

Bennett and Posner[66] did not demonstrate selective prostaglandin antagonism with SC-19220 on human gastrointestinal smooth muscle although they confirmed selective activity on guinea-pig and rat tissues. It is also noteworthy that they did not find selective blockade of prostaglandins by 7-OPA on any of the tissues they studied. SC-19220 and PPP block nicotine- and electrically induced contractions of guinea-pig ileum as well as those induced by prostaglandins.[76] This activity appears to be due to inhibition of the release of acetylcholine, suggesting that prostaglandins are involved in this process at ganglia and/or nerve terminals.[77] This does not seem to be the mechanism for the prostaglandin antagonism in the guinea-pig ileum, at least for SC-19220, because it is effective in the presence of atropine.[78]

Using SC-19220 as a prostaglandin antagonist, Kennedy et al.[79] concluded that there are two types of receptors for E prostaglandins. One type (which they classify $EP_1$) is found in guinea-pig fundus, guinea-pig ileum, and dog fundus, and is blocked by SC-19220. The other type ($EP_2$) mediates relaxation of cat trachea and contractions of chick ileum, and is not blocked by SC-19220. On the other hand, AH 19437 selectively antagonized the thromboxane-like actions of U-46619 on all the tissues they studied, so there is no evidence for more than one thromboxane receptor.

*In vivo* activities against prostaglandin-induced diarrhea have been observed with SC-18637 ($ED_{50}$ = 100 mg/kg), SC-19220 ($ED_{50}$ = 17 mg/kg), SC-25038 ($ED_{50}$ = 67 mg/kg), SC-25324 ($ED_{50}$ = 185 mg/kg),[9] PPP (50 to 200 mg/kg),[80] and N-0164 ($ED_{50}$ = 55 mg/kg).[61] The compounds were injected i.p. to mice before i.p. injection of a prostaglandin challenge. The potency of the dibenzoxazepine compounds was enhanced by including polysorbate 80 in the vehicle.[58] I.p. administration of SC-19220 also inhibited the intestinal passage of charcoal in mice.[10] PPP (200 mg/kg i.v. or i.p.) selectively inhibited intestinal activity in cats that was induced by $PGE_2$ or $PGF_{2\alpha}$, but 2 g administered orally to humans did not inhibit prostaglandin-induced diarrhea, and 4 g produced diarrhea.[81]

Administration, i.p. or s.c., of SC-19220 did not reverse $PGE_1$-induced inhibition of gastric-acid secretion in rats,[82,83] but the doses that were employed (which were equal to or only twice the $PGE_1$ dose) were much lower than those generally needed to produce *in vivo* effects with SC-19220.

Guinea-pig isolated ileum is a standard preparation used to assay SRS or leukotrienes, and FPL-55712 shows remarkable selectivity and potency against contractions induced by these substances. It has been reported to produce 50% inhibition of SRS-induced contractions on guinea-pig ileum at a concentration of 0.019 μg/ml.[16] It was initially observed to inhibit

## Table 1
## *IN VITRO* EICOSANOID ANTAGONISM

| Antagonist | Organ or tissue | Species | Substance antagonized | Activity inhibited | Type of antagonism | Ref. |
|---|---|---|---|---|---|---|
| AH 19437 | Aorta | Rat | $TXA_2$,$PGF_{2\alpha}$, U-46619 | Contractions | Competitive | 39,79 |
| | Ileum | Guinea pig | $PGE_2$,$PGF_{2\alpha}$, $PGH_2$ | Contractions | Little or none | 39,79 |
| | | Chick | $PGE_2$ | Contractions | Little or none | 39,79 |
| | Iris sphincter muscle | Dog | $PGF_{2\alpha}$,$PGH_2$ | Contractions | Little or none | 39,79 |
| | | Cat | $PGF_{2\alpha}$ | Contractions | Little or none | 79 |
| | Lung strips | Guinea pig | $PGF_{2\alpha}$, Wy17186, U-46619 | Contractions | Competitive | 79,238 |
| | Platelets | Human | TXA2,U-46619, $PGH_2$ | Aggregation | Selective, competitive | 79,239 |
| | Saphenous vein | Rat | $PGH_2$ | Contractions | Competitive | 39 |
| | | Dog | $PGF_{2\alpha}$, U-46619 | Contractions | Competitive | 79 |
| | Stomach strips | Guinea pig | $PGE_2$, $PGF_{2\alpha}$, Wy17186, U-46619 | Contractions | Little or none | 79,238 |
| | | Dog | $PGE_2$,$PGF_{2\alpha}$ | Contractions | Little or none | 79 |
| | Trachea | Cat | $PGE_2$ | Relaxation | None | 79 |
| | | Guinea pig | $PGE_2$, $PGF_{2\alpha}$ | Contractions | None | 238 |
| | | | U-46619, Wy17186 | Contractions | Competitive | 238 |
| Amide and 1-amino PGF derivatives | Colon | Gerbil | $PGE_2$,$PGF_{2\alpha}$ | Contractions | Selective, competitive | 60 |
| 13-Azaprostanoic acid (13-APA) | Mesenteric arteries | Dog | $PGE_2$, $PGF_{2\alpha}$, U-46619 | Contractions | Selective, competitive | 118 |
| | Platelets | Human | AA,$PGH_2$, U-46619 | Aggregation | Selective | 40,121, 217 |
| | | | $PGF_{2\alpha}$, U-46619 | Receptor binding | Selective competitive | 217 |
| | | | $TXB_2$, 6-Keto-$PGF_{1\alpha}$ | Receptor binding | None | 217 |
| | | Rabbit | AA | Aggregation | Active | 122 |

| | | | | | | |
|---|---|---|---|---|---|---|
| 9,11-Azo-13- oxa-15-hydroxy- prostanoic acid (AOHP) | Platelets | Human | $TXA_2$ | Aggregation | Active | 41 |
| | | | U-44069 | Aggregation | Competitive | 41 |
| p-Biphenyl acetic acid | Colon | Gerbil | $PGE_1$ | Contractions | Fairly selective, reversible | 241 |
| d,1-11,15-Bis-deoxy $PGE_1$ | Adipocytes | Rat | $PGE_1$ | Receptor binding | Competitive | 59 |
| | Colon | Gerbil | $PGE_1$ | Contractions | Selective, competitive | 59 |
| | | | $PGF_{2\alpha}$ | Contractions | None | 59 |
| BM 13.177 | Aorta | Rabbit | U-46619 | Contractions | Competitive | 43 |
| | Platelets | Human | AA,U-44069, U-46619 | Aggregation, shape change, 5-HT release | Selective | 42 |
| 5C-15S $BPTA_2$, 5T-15S $BPTA_2$ | Coronary arteries | Cat | Carbocyclic $TXA_2$ | Vasoconstriction | Active | 49 |
| 5C-15S $BPTA_2$ | Platelets | Human | U-44069, U-46619 | Aggregation | Selective | 49 |
| 5-(6-Carboxyhexyl)-1-octylpyrrolidine-2,4-dione | Colon | Rat | $PGE_1$,$PGE_2$, $PGF_{2\alpha}$ | Contractions | Selective | 64 |
| | Rectum | Chick | $PGE_1$,$PGE_2$, $PGF_{2\alpha}$ | Contractions | Selective | 64 |
| | Stomach strips | Rat | $PGE_1$,$PGE_2$, $PGF_{2\alpha}$ | Contractions | Selective, competitive vs. $PGE_2$ | 64 |
| 11-Deoxy-16, 16-trimethylene prostaglandin $E_1$ | Colon | Gerbil | $PGE_1$,$PGE_2$ | Contractions | Selective competitive | 242 |
| Desacetyl-1-nantradol | Platelets | Human | $PGD_2$ | c-AMP production | Active | 183 |
| | | | | Receptor binding | Active | 183 |
| | | | $PGE_2$ | c-AMP production | Active | 183 |
| | | | | Receptor binding | Active | 183 |
| Desamino-2-nor-leukotriene analogues | Trachea | Guinea pig | $LTD_4$ | Contractions | Competitive | 19 |
| 5,6-(Dibenzyloxy)-1-oxo-2-propyl-2-indan-propionic acid | Ileum | Mouse | $PGF_{2\alpha}$ | Contractions | Selective | 243 |
| Dithiothreitol | Uterus | Rat | $PGE_1$,$PGE_2$, $PGF_{2\alpha}$ | Contractions | Selective, competitive | 93 |

**Table 1 (continued)**
***IN VITRO* EICOSANOID ANTAGONISM**

| Antagonist | Organ or tissue | Species | Substance antagonized | Activity inhibited | Type of antagonism | Ref. |
|---|---|---|---|---|---|---|
| | Platelets | Rat, human | $PGE_1$ | Inhibition of ADP-induced aggregation | Active | 93 |
| | | | $PGE_2$ | Potentiation of ADP-induced aggregation | Active | 93 |
| | Uterus | | $PGE_1$ | Receptor binding | Reversible | 211 |
| Eicosa-5,8,11,14-tetraynoic acid (ETYA) | Umbilical arteries | Human | $PGF_{2\alpha}$ | Contractions | Selective | 94 |
| EP 045 | Aorta | Rabbit | $TXA_2$ | Contractions | Selective | 44 |
| | | | U-46619 | Contractions | Selective, competitive | 44 |
| | Iris sphincter | Bovine | $PGE_2$, 16,16-dimethyl $PGE_2$ | Contractions | None | 244 |
| | Platelets | Human | 9,11-azo $PGH_2$, AA,$TXA_2$,$PGH_2$, U-46619 | Aggregation, shape change | Active | 123,126 |
| | | | AA,$TXA_2$,$PGH_2$, U-44069 | Receptor binding | Active | 126 |
| | Saphenous vein | Dog | $TXA_2$ | Contractions | Selective | 44 |
| | | | U-46619 | Contractions | Selective, competitive | 44 |
| | Trachea | Guinea pig | U-46619 | Contractions | Selective, competitive | 44 |
| | | | 16,16-Dimethyl $PGE_2$, 16-p-chlorophenoxy $PGE_2$ | Contractions | None | 44 |
| | | | 15-Methyl $PGE_2$, $PGE_2$ | Relaxation | None | 44 |
| EP 092 | Vascular smooth-muscle cells | Rat | U 44069, U-46619 | Synthesis of PGI | Active | 45 |

| | | | | | | |
|---|---|---|---|---|---|---|
| 9-11,Epoxy-imino-prosta-5,13-dienoic acid (9,11-EIP) | Platelets | Human | AA,$TXA_2$, Endo-peroxide analogues | Aggregation | Dose-related | 46 |
| Fenbufen | Colon | Gerbil | $PGE_1$ | Contractions | Selective | 241 |
| Flufenamic acid and flufenamates | Astrocytoma cells | Human | $PGE_1$ | c-AMP formation | | 160 |
| | Gastrointestinal lon-gitudinal muscle | Human | $PGF_2$ | Contractions | Potent | 245 |
| | Ovaries | Rat | $PGE_2$ | c-AMP formation | Active | 182 |
| | Tracheal chains | Guinea pig | $PGF_2$ | Contractions | Selective | 156 |
| Fluprofen | Tracheal chains | Guinea pig | $PGF_{2\alpha}$,SRS | Contractions | Active | 158 |
| Flurbiprofen | Coronary arteries | Cat | Carbocyclic $TXA_2$ | Increased perfusion pressure | Dose-related | 246 |
| | Tracheal chains | Guinea pig | $PGF_{2\alpha}$,SRS | Contractions | Partially selective | 158 |
| FPL 55712 | Brain,uterus homogenates | Guinea pig | $LTC_4$ | Receptor binding | Weak | 214 |
| | Bronchi | Guinea pig | $LTC_4$ | Contractions | Variable | 134 |
| | | Human | $LTA_4$,$LTC_4$, $LTD_4$ | Contractions | Selective | 128 |
| | | | SRS | Contractions | Selective | 16,247 |
| | Coronary arteries | Dog | $LTC_4$, $LTD_4$ | Relaxation | None | 248 |
| | Heart | Guinea pig | $LTC_4$, $LTD_4$, | -Inotropism, reduced coronary flow | Competitive | 248 |
| | Ileum | Guinea pig | $LTC_1$ | Contractions | Competitive | 84,249 |
| | | | $LTC_4$ | Receptor binding | Partial | 212 |
| | | | $LTD_4$ | Contractions | Selective, competitive | 16,250 |
| | | | | | More potent than on tra-chea or lung strips | 141 |
| | | | $LTE_4$ | Contractions | Active | 85 |
| | | | SRS | Contractions | Selective, competitive | 13,16, 251-256 |
| | Lung homogenate | Guinea pig | $LTD_4$ | Receptor binding | More effec-tive vs. $LTD_4$ than $LTC_4$ | 214 |

**Table 1 (continued)**
***IN VITRO* EICOSANOID ANTAGONISM**

| Antagonist | Organ or tissue | Species | Substance antagonized | Activity inhibited | Type of antagonism | Ref. |
|---|---|---|---|---|---|---|
| | | | $LTC_4$ | Receptor binding | Weak | 257 |
| | | Rat | $LTC_4$ | Receptor binding | Weak | 213 |
| | Lung strips (superfusion) | Guinea pig | $LTA_4$,$LTC_4$, $LTD_4$,$LTE_4$ | Contractions | Dose-related | 133 |
| | | | $LTB_4$ | Contractions | None | 133 |
| | Lung strips (tissue bath) | Guinea pig | AA | Contractions | Noncompetitive | 131 |
| | | | $LTB_4$ | Contractions | None | 129 |
| | | | $LTC_1$ | Contractions | None | 130,134 |
| | | | $LTD_4$ | Contractions | Selective, competitive | 16,134,137 |
| | | | | | Less potent than on ileum | 141 |
| | | | SRS | Contractions | Selective | 16,129 |
| | | Human | $LTD_4$ | Contractions | Selective | 16 |
| | | | $LTC_4$ | Receptor binding | Weak | 216 |
| | | | SRS | Contractions | Selective | 16,247 |
| | Renal glomeruli | Rat | $LTC_4$ | Receptor binding | Weak, competitive | 258 |
| | Skin | Guinea pig | $LTD_4$ | Vascular permeability | Dose-dependent | 231 |
| | Trachea | Guinea pig | $LTC_1$ | Contractions | Competitive | 84 |
| | | | $LTC_4$ | Contractions | Variable | 134,139 |
| | | | | | Weak | 257 |
| | | | | | Antagonism attenuated by serine borate | 31 |
| | | | $LTD_4$ | Contractions | Competitive | 137 |
| | | | | | Less potent than on ileum | 141 |
| | | | | | Variable | 139,140 |

| | | | | | | |
|---|---|---|---|---|---|---|
| | | | $LTE_4$,$LTF_4$ | Contractions | Competitive | 139,140 |
| | Trachea (with serine borate) | Guinea pig | $LTD_4$,$LTE_4$ | Contractions | Competitive | 142 |
| | | | $LTC_4$ | Contractions | None | 142 |
| | Uterus | Guinea pig | $LTC_4$ | Receptor binding | Binding was inhibited by 10—100 m*M* FPL; stimulated by lower concns. | 259 |
| FPL 57231 | Bronchial strips | Human | SRS | Contractions | Selective | 16 |
| | Ileum | Guinea pig | SRS,$LTD_4$ | Contractions | Selective | 16 |
| | Lung strips | Guinea pig | SRS,$LTD_4$ | Contractions | Selective | 16 |
| | | Human | $LTD_4$ | Contractions | Selective | 16 |
| FPL 59257 | Bronchial strips | Human | SRS | Contractions | Selective | 16 |
| | Ileum | Guinea pig | SRS,$LTD_4$ | Contractions | Selective | 16 |
| | | | | | Noncompetitive | 250 |
| | Lung strips | Guinea pig | SRS,$LTD_4$ | Contractions | Selective | 16 |
| | | Human | SRS | Contractions | Selective | 16 |
| HR-546 | Smooth muscle | | PGE | Contractions | Potent | 16 |
| Hydroxycyclo-hexanyl prostaglandin analogues | Ileum | Guinea pig | $PGF_{2\alpha}$ | Contractions | Selective | 260 |
| 4-Hydroxy-3-nitro-coumarins | Ileum | Guinea pig | SRS | Contractions | Dose-related | 261 |
| 13-Hydroxy-9-oxo-prost-14-ynoic acid | Anterior pituitary | Rat | $PGE_2$ | c-AMP formation | Active | 171 |
| ICI-19350 | Trachea | Guinea pig | $LTE_4$ | Contractions | Active | 20 |
| Imidodisulfamides | Ileum | Guinea pig | SRS-A | Contractions | Selective, moderately potent | 21,22 |
| Indomethacin | Astrocytoma cells | Human | $PGE_1$ | c-AMP formation | Selective competitive | 160 |
| | Colon | Gerbil | $PGE_1$ | Contractions | Competitive, reversible, fairly selective | 241 |
| | Coronary-artery strips | Cat | Carbocyclic $TXA_2$ | Constriction | Dose-related | 246 |
| | Corpus-luteum cell membranes | Bovine | $PGE_1$ | Receptor binding | Competitive | 200 |

**Table 1 (continued)**
***IN VITRO* EICOSANOID ANTAGONISM**

| Antagonist | Organ or tissue | Species | Substance antagonized | Activity inhibited | Type of antagonism | Ref. |
|---|---|---|---|---|---|---|
| | Ileum | Guinea pig | $PGE_2$ | Contractions | Selective | 87 |
| | Stomach strip | Rat | $PGD_2$,$PGI_2$,U-44069, U-46619 | Contractions | Selective | 65 |
| | | | $PGE_2$,$PGF_{2\alpha}$, 6-Keto $PGF_{1\alpha}$ | Contractions | Nonselective | 65 |
| | Uterus | Rat | $PGE_2$ | Contractions | Selective | 87 |
| KC-404 | Trachea | Guinea pig | SRS-A | Contractions | Fairly selective | 23 |
| L-640,035 | Platelets | Human | AA,collagen, U-44069 | Aggregation | Active | 127 |
| | Trachea | Guinea pig | $PGF_{2\alpha}$ | Contractions | Competitive | 262 |
| | | | U-44069, | Contractions | Noncompetitive | 262 |
| | | | $PGD_2$ | Contractions | None | 262 |
| | | | $LTD_4$ | | | |
| $LTB_4$ diacetate | Neutrophils | | $LTB_4$ | Chemotaxis | Competitive | 24 |
| $LTB_4$ dimethylamide | Neutrophils | | $LTB_4$ | Degranulation | Active | 25 |
| $LTB_4$ isomer | Neutrophils | | $LTB_4$ | Degranulation | Active | 263 |
| LY163443 | Ileum, lung strips | Guinea pig | $LTD_4$ | Contractions | Selective | 26 |
| | | | $LTC_4$ | Contractions | Weak | 26 |
| | Trachea | Guinea pig | $LTD_4$,$LTE_4$ | Contractions | Selective | 26 |
| | | | U-46619 | Contractions | Weak | 26 |
| LY171883 | Ileum | Guinea pig | $LTD_4$ | Contractions | Competitive, selective | 27 |
| | | | $LTC_4$ | Contractions | Low activity | 27 |
| | | | $PGF_{2\alpha}$ | Contractions | Low activity | 27 |
| | Lung strips | Guinea pig | $LTD_4$ | Contractions | Competitive, selective, less potent than on ileum | 27 |
| | | | $LTB_4$ | Contractions | None | 27 |

| | | | | | | |
|---|---|---|---|---|---|---|
| | Trachea | Guinea pig | $LTD_4$ | Contractions | Noncompetitive, less potent than on ileum | 27 |
| | | | U-46619 | Contractions | Competitive | 27 |
| Meclofenamic acid and meclofenamates | Astrocytoma cells | Human | $PGE_1$ | c-AMP formation | Selective, possibly competitive | 160 |
| | Bronchial muscle | Human | $PGF_{2\alpha}$ | Contractions | Selective, competitive | 157 |
| | Colon | Guinea pig | $PGE_2$ | Contractions | Selective | 245 |
| | | | $PGD_2$,$PGF_{2\alpha}$ | Contractions | Less inhibited than $PGE_2$ | 245 |
| | Coronary arteries | Cat | Carbocyclic $TXA_2$ | Constriction | Dose-related | 246 |
| | Ileum | Guinea pig | $PGD_2$,$PGE_2$, $PGF_{2\alpha}$ | Contractions | Selective | 245 |
| | Gastrointestinal longitudinal muscle | Human | $PGF_{2\alpha}$ | Contractions | Potent | 245 |
| | | | $PGE_2$ | Contractions | No selective inhibition | 245 |
| | Ovaries | Rat | $PGE_2$ | c-AMP formation | | 182 |
| | Stomach strips | Rat | $PGD_2$,$PGE_2$, $PGF_{2\alpha}$,$PGI_2$, 6-keto-$PGF_{1\alpha}$, U-44069, U-46619 | Contractions | Selective | 65 |
| | | | 6,15-diketo- $PGF_1$, $TXA_2$ | Contractions | Nonselective | 65 |
| | Trachea | Guinea pig | $PGF_{2\alpha}$ | Contractions | Selective | 264 |
| | Uterus | Human | $PGF_{2\alpha}$ | Contractions | Inconsistent | 86 |
| | | | U-46619 | Contractions | Selective | 86 |
| Mefenamic acid and mefenamates | Astrocytoma cells | Human | $PGE_1$ | c-AMP formation | Active | 160 |
| | Colon | Gerbil | $PGE_1$ | Contractions | Selective, competitive | 241 |
| | Gastrointestinal longitudinal muscle | Human | $PGE_2$ | Contractions | Tended to inhibit | 245 |
| | | | $PGF_{2\alpha}$ | Contractions | Often increased contractions | 245 |
| | Ovaries | Rat | $PGE_2$ | c-AMP formation | Active | 182 |
| | Tracheal chains | Guinea pig | $PGF_2$ | Contractions | Selective | 156 |

**Table 1 (continued)**
***IN VITRO* EICOSANOID ANTAGONISM**

| Antagonist | Organ or tissue | Species | Substance antagonized | Activity inhibited | Type of antagonism | Ref. |
|---|---|---|---|---|---|---|
| | Uterus | Human | U-46619 | Contractions | Selective | 86 |
| N-0164 | Colon | Gerbil | $PGE_2$,$PGF_{2\alpha}$ | Contractions | Selective | 61 |
| | Heart | Guinea pig | $PGD_2$,$PGF_{2\alpha}$ | Coronary constriction | Selective | 100 |
| | | | $PGE_2$ | Coronary dilatation | Selective | 100 |
| | | | $PGI_2$ | Coronary dilatation | None | 100 |
| | | | $PGD_2$ | Bradycardia | Active | 100 |
| | | | $PGF_{2\alpha}$ | Tachycardia | Active | 100 |
| | | | $PGE_2$,$PGI_2$ | Potentiation of tachycardia | Active | 100 |
| | Ileum | Guinea pig | $PGE_2$ | Contractions | Selective | 61 |
| | Platelets | Human | 9,11-Azo-$PGH_2$, BW-245C,Cyclo-hexyl-$PGD_2$, 16,16-Dimethyl $PGE_2$,$PGD_2$, U-44069,U-46619, Wy17186, Wy19110 | Aggregation | Selective, competitive | 265-267 |
| | | | Cyclohexyl-$PGI_2$,$PGE_2$, $PGI_2$ | Aggregation | Weak or None | 266,267 |
| | Stomach strips | Rat | $PGE_2$,$PGF_{2\alpha}$ | Contractions | Selective, competitive | 61 |
| | Uterus | Rat | $PGE_2$ | Contractions | Selective | 268 |
| ONO-11105, ONO-11119, ONO-11120 | Platelets | Human | AA,ADP, Collagen, $STA_2$, $TXA_2$,U-46619 | Aggregation | Active | 47 |
| | Aorta | Rat | $STA_2$,$PGF_{2\alpha}$, $TXA_2$,U-46619 | Contractions | Selective | 47 |

| | | | | | | |
|---|---|---|---|---|---|---|
| 7-Oxa-13-prostynoic acid (7-OPA) | Adipocyte homogenates | Rat | $PGE_1$ | Receptor binding | Competitive | 198 |
| | Adipocyte membranes | Rat | $PGE_1$ | Receptor binding | Negligible | 199 |
| | Adrenal glomerulosa cells | Rat | $PGE_2$ | Aldosterone production | | 269 |
| | Aortic strips | Rabbit | $PGE_2$,$PGF_{2\alpha}$ | Contractions | Partial agonism | 72 |
| | Astrocytoma cells | Human | $PGE_1$ | c-AMP production | Selective, competitive | 160 |
| | Cecal tenia | Guinea pig | $PGE_1$,GABA | Contractions | None; sometimes spasmogenic | 91 |
| | Colon | Gerbil | $PGE_1$,$PGE_2$, $PGF_{1\alpha}$,$PGF_{2\alpha}$ | Contractions | Selective | 6,62,63 |
| | Colon, circular muscle | Guinea pig | $PGF_2$ | Contractions | Slightly selective | 66 |
| | Sigmoid colon, circular muscle | Human | $PGF_{2\alpha}$ | Contractions | Nonselective | 66 |
| | Corpus luteum | Bovine | $PGE_1$ | Receptor binding | Weak affinity | 200-202 |
| | Cell membranes | | $PGF_{2\alpha}$ | Receptor binding | Weak affinity | 203,204 |
| | Brain slices | Rat | $PGE_1$ | c-AMP production | None | 168 |
| | Ductus arteriosus | Rabbit | $PGE_1$,$PGF_{2\alpha}$ | Dilatation | None | 270 |
| | Fat cells | Rat | $PGE_1$ | Antilypolytic activity | Partial inhibition; enhanced epinephrine | 271 |
| | Fibroblasts | Mouse | $PGE_1$ | c-AMP production | Nonselective | 166 |
| | Gastric body, longitudinal muscle | Human | $PGE_2$,$PGF_{2\alpha}$ | Contractions | Nonselective | 66 |
| | Gastric body, circular muscle | Human | $PGF_{2\alpha}$ | Contractions | Nonselective | 66 |
| | Granulosa cells | Monkey | $PGE_2$ | Luteinization and progestin secretion | Necrotic changes; nonspecific | 272 |
| | | Pig | $PGE_2$ | c-AMP production | None | 167 |
| | Heart | Rabbit | $PGE_2$ | Inhibition of chronotropic response | None | 273 |

**Table 1 (continued)**
***IN VITRO* EICOSANOID ANTAGONISM**

| Antagonist | Organ or tissue | Species | Substance antagonized | Activity inhibited | Type of antagonism | Ref. |
|---|---|---|---|---|---|---|
| | Ileum, longitudinal muscle | Guinea pig | $PGE_2$,$PGF_{2\alpha}$ | Contractions | Nonselective | 66 |
| | | Human | $PGE_2$,$PGF_{2\alpha}$ | Contractions | Nonselective | 66 |
| | Small intestine, longitudinal muscle | Rabbit | $PGE_2$,$PGF_{2\alpha}$ APCP | Contractions | Selective, competitive | 274 |
| | Intestinal epithelium | Mouse | $PGE_1$ | c-AMP production | Nonspecific | 166 |
| | Neuroblastoma cells | Rat | $PGE_1$ | c-AMP production | Partial; inverse dose relationship | 181 |
| | Ovaries | Rat | $PGE_1$ | Lactic acid production | Agonistic | 275,276 |
| | | | | Amino acid uptake and protein synthesis | Nonselective | 275,276 |
| | | | $PGE_2$ | c-AMP production | None | 277 |
| | | Mouse | $PGE_1$,$PGE_2$, LH | c-AMP production | Competitive | 159 |
| | Ovarian follicles | Rat | $PGE_2$ | Luteinization | None | 278 |
| | Anterior pituitary | Rat | $PGE_1$ | c-AMP production | Complete inhibition by 200 μg/ml | 279 |
| | | | | | Augmentation by 100 mg/ml | 170 |
| | | | | Growth hormone release | Complete inhibition by 200 μg/ml | 279 |
| | | | $PGE_2$ | c-AMP production | Agonistic | 171 |
| | | | | Growth hormone release | Dose-related | 280 |
| | Platelet membranes | Human | $PGE_1$,$PGE_2$ | Receptor binding | Weak competition | 205 |

| | | | | | |
|---|---|---|---|---|---|
| Renal artery strips | Rabbit | $PGE_2$,$PGF_{2\alpha}$ | Contractions | Partial agonism | 72 |
| Skin, smooth ER fraction | Rat | $PGE_2$,$PGF_{2\alpha}$ | Receptor binding | Competitive | 206 |
| Stomach | Dog | $PGE_1$ methyl ester | Antisecretory activity | None | 281 |
| Forestomach | Rat | $PGE_1$ | Receptor binding | Weak competition | 207 |
| Synovial cells | Human | $PGE_1$,CTAP | Hyaluronic acid synthesis and glycolysis | Inhibition | 282 |
| Synovial fibroblasts | Human | $PGE_1$, bradykinin | c-AMP production | Nonselective | 165 |
| Synovial membranes | Human | $PGE_1$,CTAP | c-AMP production, hyaluronic acid synthesis | Selective | 283 |
| Thyroid cells | Bovine | $PGE_1$,$PGE_2$, TSH,LATS | c-AMP production | Dose-related; weakly agonistic alone | 161-163 |
| | | $PGE_1$,TSH | Phagocytosis of latex beads | Selective | 161 |
| | | | Iodide trapping | Selective | 162 |
| Thyroid membranes | Bovine | $PGE_1$ | Receptor binding | Competitive | 208 |
| | | $PGE_1$,$PGE_2$, TSH | c-AMP production | Inhibition | 164 |
| Umbilical arteries | Human | $PGE_2$ | Contractions | Initial contraction, then selective competitive antagonism | 95 |
| Uterus | Guinea pig | $PGE_1$,GABA | Contractions | None; sometimes spasmogenic | 91 |
| | — | $PGE_1$ | Receptor binding | Reversible | 211 |
| | Hamster | PGE1 | Receptor binding | Weak affinity | 209 |
| | Human | $PGE_1$ | Receptor binding | None up to 10 ng/ml | 284 |
| | Rat | $PGE_1$,$PGF_{2\alpha}$ | Contractions | Selective | 172 |
| | | | c-AMP formation | None | 172 |
| Metestrus uterus | Rat | $PGF_{2\alpha}$ | Contractions | Noncompetitive | 92 |

## Table 1 (continued)
## *IN VITRO* EICOSANOID ANTAGONISM

| Antagonist | Organ or tissue | Species | Substance antagonized | Activity inhibited | Type of antagonism | Ref. |
|---|---|---|---|---|---|---|
| | Proestrus uterus | Rat | $PGF_{2\alpha}$, angiotensin II | Contractions | Nonselective | 92 |
| | Vagus nerve | Rabbit | $PGE_1$ | c-AMP formation | None | 169 |
| 7-Oxa-13-prostynoic acid (six-membered ring analogue) | Ileum | Guinea pig | $PGE_1$ | Contractions | Selective | 6 |
| | Colon | Gerbil | $PGE_1$ | Contractions | Selective, noncompetitive | 6,63 |
| | Duodenum | Rabbit | $PGE_1$ | Contractions | Selective | 6 |
| Phenylbutazone | Colon | Gerbil | $PGE_2$ | Contractions | Reversible, fairly selective | 241 |
| Di-4-phloretin phosphate (DPP) | Astrocytoma cells | Human | $PGE_1$ | c-AMP production | Noncompetitive | 177 |
| | Bronchi | Human | $PGF_{2\alpha}$ | Contraction | Selective | 285 |
| | Colon | Gerbil | $PGF_{1\alpha}$ | Contractions | Selective | 286 |
| | Lung | Rabbit | $PGA_1$ | Vasoconstriction | Active | 287 |
| | Neuroblastoma cells | Human | $PGE_1$ | c-AMP production | Competitive | 177 |
| | Platelets | Human | $PGD_2$ | Inhibition of aggregation | Competitive | 288 |
| | | | $PGE_1$,$PGI_2$ | Inhibition of aggregation | None | 288 |
| | | Rabbit | $PGD_2$ | Inhibition of aggregation | None | 288 |
| | | | $PGE_1$,$PGI_2$ | Inhibition of aggregation | Noncompetitive | 288 |
| | Pulmonary vein | Bovine | $PGE_2$ (high concn.), $PGF_{2\alpha}$ | Contractions | Selective | 99 |
| | | | $PGE_2$ (low concn.), $PGE_1$ | Relaxation | Slight | 99 |
| | Stomach strips | Guinea pig | $PGE_1$,$PGF_{2\alpha}$ | Contractions | Selective, competitive | 289 |

| | | | | | | |
|---|---|---|---|---|---|---|
| 4′-Phloretin monophosphate | Colon | Gerbil | $PGF_1$ | Contractions | Selective | 286 |
| Polyphloretin Phosphate (PPP) | Adipocytes | Rat | $PGE_1$ | Receptor binding | None | 198 |
| | Adrenal cortex | Rat | $PGE_1$ | c-AMP formation | Selective | 173 |
| | Astrocytoma cells | Human | $PGE_1$ | c-AMP formation | Selective; complex pattern | 160,177 |
| | Bronchi | Human | $PGF_{2\alpha}$ | Contractions | Selective, competitive | 101,150,285 |
| | | | $PGE_1$,$PGE_2$ | Bronchodilation | None | 150 |
| | | | SRS | Contractions | Selective | 152 |
| | Cerebral artery strips | Dog | $PGE_2$,$PGF_{2\alpha}$ | Contractions | Selective | 96 |
| | | | $PGE_1$ | Relaxation | None | 96 |
| | Colon | Gerbil | $PGE_1$,$PGF_{1\alpha}$, $PGE_2$,$PGF_{2\alpha}$ | Contractions | Selective | 8,56,80, 286,290, 291 |
| | | Rat | $PGE_2$,$PGF_{2\alpha}$ | Contractions | Selective | 292 |
| | Colon, circular muscle | Guinea pig | $PGF_{2\alpha}$ | Contractions | Selective | 66 |
| | Colon, longitudinal muscle | Guinea pig | Electrical stimulation, nicotine | Contractions | Active | 76 |
| | | | $PGE_2$,$PGF_{2\alpha}$ | Contractions | Selective | 66 |
| | Ascending colon, circular muscle | Human | $PGF_{2\alpha}$ | Variable relaxation | Selective | 66 |
| | Sigmoid colon, circular muscle | Human | $PGF_{2\alpha}$ | Contractions | Selective | 66 |
| | Sigmoid colon, longitudinal muscle | Human | $PGE_2$,$PGF_{2\alpha}$ | Contractions | Selective | 66 |
| | Eye; ciliary body | Rabbit | $PGE_1$,$PGE_2$ | Flow conductivity | Active | 293 |
| | Fibroblasts | Mouse | $PGE_1$ | c-AMP production | Nonspecific | 166 |
| | Gastric body, longitudinal muscle | Human | $PGE_2$,$PGF_{2\alpha}$ | Contractions | Selective | 66 |
| | Gastric mucosa | Dog | $PGE_2$,16,16-dimethyl $PGE_2$ | c-AMP production | Selective | 174 |

**Table 1 (continued)**
***IN VITRO* EICOSANOID ANTAGONISM**

| Antagonist | Organ or tissue | Species | Substance antagonized | Activity inhibited | Type of antagonism | Ref. |
|---|---|---|---|---|---|---|
| | Heart | Rabbit | $PGE_2$ | Inhibition of chronotropic response | None | 273 |
| | Ileum | Chicken | $PGE_1$,$PGE_2$, $PGF_{2\alpha}$, antigen | Contractions | Selective | 294 |
| | Ileum, circular muscle | Guinea pig | $PGE_2$ | Inhibition of contractions | None | 75 |
| | Intestine | Human fetus | $PGE_2$,$PGF_{2\alpha}$ | Contractions | Selective | 240 |
| | Intestinal epithelium | Mouse | $PGE_1$ | c-AMP production | Nonspecific | 166 |
| | Jejunum | Rabbit | $PGE_2$,$PGF_{2\alpha}$ | Contractions | Selective | 56 |
| | | | | | None | 89 |
| | Lung strips | Guinea pig | $PGF_{2\alpha}$,$PGI_2$ | Contractions | Competitive | 151 |
| | Mesenteric artery strips | Dog | $PGF_{2\alpha}$ | Contractions | Selective | 96 |
| | Myometrium | Mouse | $PGE_1$ | c-AMP production | None | 176 |
| | Neurohypophysis | Rat | $PGE_2$ | Vasopressin release | Active | 295 |
| | Ovaries | Mouse | $PGE_1$ | c-AMP production | None | 176 |
| | | Rat | $PGE_1$,LH | Lactic acid production | Active | 296 |
| | Ovarian follicles | Rat | $PGE_2$, LH, dibutyryl c-AMP | Luteinization | Active | 297 |
| | Pancreas | | $PGE_1$ | Inhibition of triglyceride lipase | 1 μg/ml inhibited $PGE_1$; >1 μg/ml inhibited lipase | 298 |
| | Pulmonary vein | Bovine | $PGE_2$ (high concn.), $PGF_{2\alpha}$ | Contractions | None | 99 |
| | | | $PGE_2$ (low concn.), $PGE_1$ | Relaxation | None | 99 |

| | | | | | |
|---|---|---|---|---|---|
| Stomach strips | Guinea pig | $PGE_1$ | Contractions | Selective, competitive | 289 |
| | Rat | $PGE_1$,$PGE_2$, $PGF_{2\alpha}$ | Contractions | Selective, competitive | 64 |
| Stomach fundus strips | Rat | $PGE_2$ | Contractions | Variable agonism and antagonism | 66,73 |
| | | 15(S)-methyl-$PGE_2$ methyl ester | Contractions | Inhibition with no potentiation | 73 |
| Forestomach | Rat | $PGE_1$ | Receptor binding | None | 207 |
| Thyroid cells | Bovine | $PGE_2$,TSH, LATS | c-AMP production | Active | 163,175 |
| | | $PGE_2$ | Iodide trapping | Competitive | 175 |
| | | | Phagocytosis of latex beads | Low concn. antagonized; high concn. stimulated | 175 |
| Tracheal chains | Guinea pig | $PGF_{2\alpha}$, 15-oxo $PGF_{2\alpha}$, 13,14-dihydro $PGF_{2\alpha}$, 13,14-dihydro-15-oxo-$PGF_{2\alpha}$ | Contractions | Selective | 149 |
| Umbilical arteries | Human | $PGA_1$,$PGA_2$, $PGB_1$,$PGB_2$, $PGF_{2\alpha}$ | Contractions | 40 μg/ml: selective | 94,97 |
| | | $PGE_2$ | Contractions | 10 μg/ml: selective, competitive; 100 μg/ml: nonselective | 95 |
| Uterus | Cat, dog, guinea pig, rat | $PGF_{2\alpha}$ | Contractions | Competitive | 88 |
| | Rabbit | $PGE_2$,$PGF_{2\alpha}$ | Contractions | Selective | 56 |
| | | $PGE_1$,$PGF_{2\alpha}$ | Contractions | None | 89 |

**Table 1 (continued)**
***IN VITRO* EICOSANOID ANTAGONISM**

| Antagonist | Organ or tissue | Species | Substance antagonized | Activity inhibited | Type of antagonism | Ref. |
|---|---|---|---|---|---|---|
| | Uterus | Rat | $PGE_1$,$PGF_{2\alpha}$ | Contractions | Active | 299 |
| | | | | | 120 and 260 μg/ml: selective | 172 |
| | | | $PGE_1$ | c-AMP production | None | 172 |
| | | | $PGF_{2\alpha}$ | Contractions | Nonselective | 90 |
| | Vagus nerve | Rabbit | $PGA_2$,$PGE_1$, $PGE_2$ | c-AMP production | None | 169,300 |
| | Vascular smooth muscle | Dog | $PGA_2$,$PGE_1$, $PGE_2$ | Stimulation of $Na^+$,$K^+$-ATPase | Active | 300 |
| | Vas deferens | Guinea pig | $PGE_1$ | Inhibition of nerve stimulation | None | 301 |
| $PGD_2$ | Cerebral and mesenteric artery strips | Dog | $PGE_2$,$PGF_{2\alpha}$ | Contractions | Selective, competitive | 98 |
| $PGE_2$ | Platelets | Human | $PGD_2$,$PGE_1$, $PGI_2$ | Inhibition of aggregation | Competitive | 302 |
| Pinane thromboxane $A_2$ ($PTA_2$) | Coronary arteries | Cat | 9,11-Azo-$PGH_2$, U-46619 | Constriction | Active | 48,303 |
| | Platelets | Human | AA, ADP, 9,11-Azo-$PGH_2$, collagen, epinephrine, U-44069, U-46619 | Aggregation | Active | 48,126,303 |
| | | | $PGI_2$,$PGD_2$ | Inhibition of aggregation | None | 48 |
| | | | U-44069 | Receptor binding | Active | 126 |
| | Stomach strips | Rat, human | $PGE_2$, $PGF_{2\alpha}$, $PGI_2$, U-44069, U-46619 | Contractions | Active | 119 |

| | | | | | | |
|---|---|---|---|---|---|---|
| REV 5901 | Lung strips | Guinea pig | $LTC_4$ | Contractions | Active | 29 |
| SC-18637 | Ileum | Guinea pig | $PGE_2$ | Contractions | Selective, competitive | 58 |
| SC-19220 | Adipocytes | Rat | $PGE_1$ | Receptor binding | None | 198 |
| | Aorta | Rat | $PGE_2$,U-46619 | Contractions | Little or none | 79 |
| | Bone cells | Rat | $PGE_2$ | $Ca^{++}$ release | Inhibited only in presence of $PGE_2$ | 178 |
| | | | | c-AMP production | None | 178 |
| | | | | c-AMP formation and release | Formation inhibited more than release | 179 |
| | Bone marrow cultures | Mouse | $PGE_1$,$PGE_2$ | Inhibition of proliferation | Active | 304 |
| | Brain slices | Rat | $PGE_2$ | Norepinephrine overflow | Dose-dependent | 305 |
| | Colon | Gerbil | $PGE_2$ | Contractions | Selective, competitive | 57 |
| | | | $PGF_1$,$PGF_{2\alpha}$ | Contractions | None | 57 |
| | Colon, circular muscle | Guinea pig | 6-keto $PGF_{1\alpha}$, $PGD_2$, $PGF_{2\alpha}$, $PGI_2$,U-46619 | Contractions | Selective | 66,306 |
| | Colon, longitudinal muscle | Guinea pig | Electrical stimulation, nicotine | Contractions | Active | 76 |
| | Colon, proximal ascending | Rat | $PGE_1$ | Contractions | None | 307 |
| | | | $PGE_2$ | Contractions | Slight | 307 |
| | Sigmoid colon, longitudinal muscle | Human | $PGE_2$,$PGF_{2\alpha}$ | Contractions | Nonselective | 66 |
| | Fat cells | Rat | $PGE_2$ | Antilypolytic activity | Complete, enhanced epinephrine | 271 |
| | | | | | Selective | 308,309 |
| | Gastric body, circular or longitudinal muscle | Human | $PGE_2$,$PGF_{2\alpha}$ | Contractions | Nonselective | 66 |

**Table 1 (continued)**
***IN VITRO* EICOSANOID ANTAGONISM**

| Antagonist | Organ or tissue | Species | Substance antagonized | Activity inhibited | Type of antagonism | Ref. |
|---|---|---|---|---|---|---|
| | Heart | Rabbit | $PGE_2$ | Inhibition of chronotropic response | None | 273 |
| | Ileum, circular muscle | Guinea pig | $PGE_2$ | Relaxation | None | 75 |
| | Ileum, longitudinal muscle | Chick | $PGE_2$ | Contractions | None | 79 |
| | | Guinea pig | $PGE_2$,$PGF_{2\alpha}$, $PGE_1$ | Contractions | Selective, usually competitive | 7,66,67, 78,79, 310,311 |
| | | | Electrical stimulation, nicotine | Contractions | Active | 76 |
| | | Human | $PGE_2$, $PGF_{2\alpha}$ | Contractions | Nonselective | 66 |
| | Iris sphincter muscle | Bovine | $PGE_2$ | Contractions | Selective, competitive | 67,307 |
| | | | $PGE_1$,$PGE_2$ | Enhancement of electrical stimulation, spontaneous activity, and tone | Active | 312,313 |
| | | | U-46619 | Contractions | None | 307 |
| | | Dog, cat | $PGE_2$,$PGF_{2\alpha}$ | Contractions | None | 79 |
| | Lung strips | Guinea pig | $PGE_2$, $PGF_{2\alpha}$, Wy-17186, U-46619 | Contractions | None | 238,79 |
| | Neuroblastoma cells | Rat | $PGE_1$ | c-AMP production | None | 181 |
| | $PGB_2$ antiserum | Rabbit | $PGE_2$ | Binding | None | 223 |
| | Saphenous veins | Dog | $PGE_2$,U-46619 | Contractions | Little or none | 79 |

| | | | | | |
|---|---|---|---|---|---|
| Stomach fundic mucosa | Guinea pig | $PGE_1$,$PGA_1$ | c-AMP production | None | 180 |
| Stomach strips | Dog | $PGE_1$,$PGE_2$, $PGF_{2\alpha}$ | Contractions | Selective, competitive | 79 |
| | Guinea pig | $PGE_1$,$PGE_2$, $PGF_{2\alpha}$, Wy17186, U-46619 | Contractions | Selective, competitive | 79,238,314 |
| | Rat | AA,6-15-di-keto-$PGF_{1\alpha}$, 6-keto-$PGF_{1\alpha}$, $PGE_2$,$PGF_{2\alpha}$, $PGI_2$ | Contractions | Selective, competitive | 65-70 |
| | | $TXB_2$,U-44069, U-46619 | Contractions | None | 70 |
| Sympathetic ganglia | Bullfrog | AA,diazepam, $PGE_1$,$PGE_2$ | Inhibition of post-tetanic potentiation of fast excitatory potential | Active | 315 |
| Trachea | Cat | $PGE_2$ | Relaxation | None | 155,79 |
| Trachea | Guinea pig | AA,$PGE_2$, $PGF_{2\alpha}$, 16,16-di-methyl $PGE_2$, iloprost, 6α-Carba-$\Delta^{6,6\alpha}PGI_1$, w-tetra-nor-16-p-fluoro-phenoxy $PGF_{2\alpha}$ | Contractions | Competitive, selective, reversible | 153,154, 238,307 |
| | | U-46619, Wy17186 | Contractions | None | 238 |
| Umbilical arteries and veins | Human | $PGE_2$ | Contractions | Somewhat selective | 110 |

**Table 1 (continued)**
***IN VITRO* EICOSANOID ANTAGONISM**

| Antagonist | Organ or tissue | Species | Substance antagonized | Activity inhibited | Type of antagonism | Ref. |
|---|---|---|---|---|---|---|
| | Vas deferens | Guinea pig | $PGE_2$ | Inhibition of electrically induced contractions | None | 316 |
| | | | $PGE_1$, high concentrations | Potentiation of nerve stimulation | | 301 |
| | | | $PGE_1$, low concentrations | Inhibition of nerve stimulation | None | 301 |
| SC-25038 | Ileum | Guinea pig | $PGE_2$ | Contractions | Selective, competitive | 71 |
| | Stomach strips | Rat | $PGE_2$ | Contractions | Selective | 71 |
| SC-25191 | Ileum | Guinea pig | $PGE_2$ | Contractions | Selective, competitive | 71 |
| | Iris sphincter muscle | Bovine | $PGE_2$ | Contractions | Competitive | 307 |
| | | | 16,16-Di-methyl $PGE_2$, iloprost | Contractions | Active | 307 |
| | Stomach strips | Rat | $PGE_2$ | Contractions | Selective | 71 |
| | Trachea | Guinea pig | 16,16-Di-methyl $PGE_2$, iloprost, 6α-Carba-$\Delta^{6,6\alpha}PGI_1$, w-tetra-nor-16-p-fluoro-phenoxy $PGF_{2\alpha}$ | Contractions | Selective, reversible | 307 |

| | | | | | | |
|---|---|---|---|---|---|---|
| SKII-144 | Mesenteric arteries | Dog | $PGF_{2\alpha}$, U-46619 | Contractions | Selective, competitive | 50 |
| SK&F 88046 | Lung strips | Guinea pig | $LTD_4$ | Contractions | Active | 147 |
| | | | $LTC_4$ | Contractions | None | 147 |
| | | | $CTA_2$,$PGD_2$, $PGF_{2\alpha}$ | Contractions | Selective | 148 |
| | Trachea | Guinea pig | $LTD_4$ | Contractions | None | 148 |
| | | | $CTA_2$,$PGD_2$, $PGF_{2\alpha}$ | Contractions | Selective | 148 |
| SK&F 102922 | Trachea | Guinea pig | $LTC_4$,$LTD_4$ | Contractions | Selective | 30 |
| | | | $PGF_{2\alpha}$,$PGD_2$, $TXA_2$ | Contractions | None | 30 |
| SK&F 101132 | Lung strips, | Guinea pig | $LTC_4$,$LTD_4$, $LTE_4$ | Contractions | Selective | 28,32 |
| | | | $PGF_{2\alpha}$ | Contractions | None | 148 |
| | Pulmonary artery | Guinea pig | $LTD_4$ | Contractions | Selective, competitive | 28 |
| | Trachea | Guinea pig | $LTC_4$, $LTD_4$, $LTE_4$ | Contractions | Selective, competitive | 28,31,32 |
| SQ 26,536 | Platelets | Human | Arachidonic acid, epinephrine, collagen | Aggregation | Selective | 317 |
| SQ 27,427 | Aorta | Rat | 9,11-Azo$PGH_2$, $TXA_2$ | Contractions | Selective, competitive | 51 |
| | Platelets | Human | AA,ADP, epinephrine, collagen, 9,11-azo$PGH_2$ SQ 26,655 | Aggregation | Nonspecific | 51 |
| | Stomach strips | Rat | 9,11-Azo$PGH_2$ | Contractions | Selective | 51 |
| | | | $PGE_2$,$PGF_{2\alpha}$, $PGI_2$ | Contractions | None | 51 |
| | Trachea | Guinea pig | 9,11-Azo$PGH_2$ | Contractions | Selective, competitive | 51 |

**Table 1 (continued)**
***IN VITRO* EICOSANOID ANTAGONISM**

| Antagonist | Organ or tissue | Species | Substance antagonized | Activity inhibited | Type of antagonism | Ref. |
|---|---|---|---|---|---|---|
| | | | $PGF_{2\alpha}$ | Contractions | Moderate | 51 |
| SQ 29,548 | Aorta | Rat | 9,11-Azo$PGH_2$, $PGD_2$,U-46619 | Contractions | Selective, competitive | 52 |
| | Heart | Rat | $LTD_4$ | Coronary constriction | None | 318 |
| | | | U-46619 | Coronary constriction | Selective | 318 |
| | Platelets | Human | AA,collagen, epinephrine, 9,11-azo$PGH_2$, U-46619 | Aggregation | Selective | 52 |
| | | | $PGD_2$ | Inhibition of aggregation | None | 52 |
| | Trachea | Guinea pig | 9,11-Azo$PGH_2$, $PGD_2$,U-46619 | Contractions | Selective, competitive | 52 |
| | | | $PGE_2$ | Contractions | None | 52 |
| | | | $PGF_{2\alpha}$ | Contractions | Partial | 52 |
| Trimethoquinol | Aorta | Rabbit | $PGH_2$ | Contractions | Selective | 53 |
| | | | $TXA_2$ | Contractions | None | 53 |
| | | Rat | $PGE_2$,U-46619 | Contractions | Competitive | 55 |
| | Lung strips | Guinea pig | $LTD_4$ | Contractions | None | 55 |
| | Platelets | Human | AA,9,11-Azo-$PGH_2$,$PGG_2$, $PGH_2$,$TXA_2$, U-44069,U-46619 | Aggregation | Selective | 53,55 |
| | | | | | Stereoselective | 54 |

**Table 1 (continued)**
***IN VITRO* EICOSANOID ANTAGONISM**

| Antagonist | Organ or tissue | Species | Substance antagonized | Activity inhibited | Type of antagonism | Ref. |
|---|---|---|---|---|---|---|
| | Stomach strips | Rat | 6,15-Diketo $PGF_{1\alpha}$,6-keto $PGF_{1\alpha}$, $PGD_2$, $PGF_1$, $PGF_{2\alpha}$, $TXB_2$,U-44069, U-46619 | Contractions | Selective | 65,70 |
| | | | $PGE_2$ | Contractions | Nonselective | 65 |
| | Trachea | Guinea pig | $LTD_4$ | Contractions | None | 55 |
| Wy-44,329 | Ileum | Guinea pig | $LTD_4$ | Contractions | Selective, competitive | 33 |

**Table 2**
***IN VIVO* EICOSANOID ANTAGONISM**

| Antagonist | System studied | Species | Substance antagonized | Activity inhibited | Type of antagonism | Ref. |
|---|---|---|---|---|---|---|
| 13-Azaprostanoic acid | Platelets | Rabbit | Arachidonic acid | Aggregation | Dose-dependent (*ex vivo*) | 122 |
| d,1-11,15-Bis-deoxy $PGE_1$ | Blood pressure | Rat | $PGE_1$ | Vasodepression | Selective, reversible | 116 |
| | | | $PGE_2$,$PGI_2$ | Vasodepression | None | 116 |
| BM 13.177 | Whole animal | Rabbit | Arachidonate | Sudden death | Active | 43 |
| *N*-dimethylamide $PGF_{2\alpha}$ | Lung vasculature | Dog | Arachidonic acid | Increase in lobar artery pressure | None | 113 |
| | | | $PGF_{2\alpha}$ | Increase in lobar artery pressure | Selective, dose-related | 113 |
| *N*-dimethylamino $PGF_{2\alpha}$ | Blood pressure | Rat | Arachidonic acid, U-46619 | Vasoconstriction | None | 114 |
| | | | $PGF_{2\alpha}$ | Vasoconstriction | Competitive | 114 |
| | Lung vasculature | Dog | Arachidonic acid | Increase in lobar artery pressure | None | 113 |
| | | | $PGF_{2\alpha}$ | Increase in lobar artery pressure | Selective | 113 |
| EP-045 | Blood | Guinea pig | U-46619 | Decreased platelet count | Active | 123 |
| | Blood pressure | Dog, guinea pig | U-46619 | Vasodepression | Selective | 117 |
| | Lungs | Dog, guinea pig | U-46619 | Bronchoconstriction | Selective | 117 |
| FPL 55712 | Blood | Rat | $LTC_4$ | Increased hematocrit | Active | 319 |
| | Blood pressure | Rat | $LTC_4$ | Vasopressor effect | Active | 319 |
| | Heart | Pig | $LTD_4$ | Coronary constriction | Active | 320 |
| | Kidney | Rat | $LTC_4$ | Diuresis, saluresis, decreased renal blood flow | Active | 319 |
| | Lungs | Guinea pig | $LTE_4$,SRS | Bronchoconstriction | Short duration | 16,85 |
| | | Human | $LTC_4$ | Bronchoconstriction, cough | Active | 143 |
| | Skin | Guinea pig | $LTD_4$ | Vascular permeability | Active | 231 |

| | | | | | | |
|---|---|---|---|---|---|---|
| | | Rat | $LTE_4$ | Vascular permeability | Short duration | 85 |
| | Whole animal | Mouse | PAF | Lethality | Active | 321 |
| FPL 57231 | Lungs | Guinea pig | SRS | Bronchoconstriction | Short duration | 16 |
| FPL 59257 | Lungs | Guinea pig | SRS | Bronchoconstriction | Long duration | 16 |
| | | Human | $LTC_4$ | Bronchoconstriction, cough | Active | 143 |
| HR-546 | Temperature regulation | Rabbit | $PGE_1$,$PGE_2$ | Hyperthermia | Active | 218,219 |
| | | | Arachidonate, leucocyte pyrogen | Hyperthèrmia | None | 218,219 |
| KC-404 | Lungs | Guinea pig | SRS-A | Bronchoconstriction | Selective | 23 |
| | Skin | Guinea pigs, rats | SRS-A | Vascular permeability | Orally active | 23 |
| LY163443 | Lungs | Guinea pig | Antigen,$LTD_4$ | Bronchoconstriction | Active | 26 |
| | Skin | Guinea pig | $LTD_4$ | Vascular leakage | Active | 26 |
| LY171883 | Lungs | Guinea pig | $LTC_4$ | Bronchoconstriction | Active | 27 |
| Meclofenamic acid and meclofenamates | Blood pressure | Rabbit | $PGF_{2\alpha}$ | Depressor response | Selective | 107 |
| | | Chicken | Antigen, bradykinin, $PGF_{2\alpha}$,SRS | Depressor response | Semiselective | 322 |
| N-0164 | Intestine | Mouse | $PGE_2$ | Diarrhea | Active | 61 |
| 7-Oxa-13-prostynoic acid (7-OPA) | Brain | Rat | $PGE_1$ | ACTH release | Marginal | 323 |
| | | | $PGE_2$ | LH release | Potentiation | 324 |
| | | | $PGF_{1\alpha}$ | ACTH release | None | 323 |
| | | | $PGF_{2\alpha}$ | LH release | None | 324 |
| | Vasculature | Dog | $PGA_1$,$PGE_1$, $PGE_2$ | Vasodilation | None | 108,112 |
| | | | $PGF_{2\alpha}$ | Vasoconstriction | None | 108 |
| Di-4-phloretin phosphate (DPP) | Kidney | Rat | $PGA_2$ | Diuresis | Reversed to antidiuresis | 325 |
| | Skin | Rabbit | Arachidonic acid | Vascular permeability | Active | 230 |
| | Synovial vasculature | Dog | $PGE_1$ | Vasodilation | None | 326 |
| L-640,035 | Lungs | Guinea pig | U-44069, $LTD_4$ | Bronchoconstriction | Relatively selective | 262 |
| | Platelets | Guinea pig | U-44069 | Aggregation | Selective | 127 |

**Table 2 (continued)**
***IN VIVO* EICOSANOID ANTAGONISM**

| Antagonist | System studied | Species | Substance antagonized | Activity inhibited | Type of antagonism | Ref. |
|---|---|---|---|---|---|---|
| | Lungs | Dog | Arachidonic acid, U-44069 | Bronchoconstriction | Selective | 262 |
| ONO-11120 | Platelets | Guinea pig, cat | Arachidonic acid, $STA_2$ | Aggregation (*ex vivo*) | Active | 47 |
| | | | $STA_2$ | Vasopressor response | Active | 47 |
| Polyphloretin phosphate (PPP) | Blood pressure | Bovine | $PGE_1$,$PGE_2$, $PGF_{2\alpha}$ | Depressor response | None | 109 |
| | | Cat | $PGF_{2\alpha}$ | Depressor response | Selective, dose-dependent | 101-103 |
| | | Chicken | $PGE_1$,$PGE_2$, $PGF_{2\alpha}$, antigen | Depressor response | Selective | 106,322 |
| | | Guinea pig | $PGF_{2\alpha}$ | Pressor response | Dose-dependent | 101,102, 104 |
| | | | $PGE_2$ | Depressor response | None | 104 |
| | | Dog | $PGE_2$ | Depressor response | None; (enhanced) | 105 |
| | | | $PGF_2$ | Pressor response | Reversed to depressor response | 105 |
| | | Rabbit | $PGE_1$,$PGE_2$ | Depressor response | None | 56,107 |
| | | | $PGF_{2\alpha}$ | Depressor response | Variable or none | 56,107 |
| | Brain | Rat | $PGE_2$ (i.c.v.) | Hyperthermia and behavioral changes | None | 222 |
| | | | $PGF_2$ (i.c.v.) | Hyperthermia and behavioral changes | Active | 222 |
| | Ear | Rabbit | $PGE_1$ | Enhancement of bradykinin-induced pain | Selective | 229 |
| | Eye | Monkey | $PGE_1$ | Intraocular pressure increase | Active | 235 |

| | | | | | |
|---|---|---|---|---|---|
| | | $PGE_1$,$PGE_2$, $PGF_{2\alpha}$ | Increase in aqueous protein | None | 235 |
| | Rabbit | $PGE_1$,$PGE_2$, $PGF_{2\alpha}$ | Intraocular pressure increase | Active | 232-234, 236 |
| | | $PGE_1$,$PGE_2$ | Vascular permeability | Active | 236 |
| | | $PGE_1$,$PGE_2$, $PGF_1$,$PGF_{2\alpha}$ | Vasodilation | Relatively nonspecific | 237 |
| Heart | Rat | $PGE_2$,$PGF_{2\alpha}$ | Inhibition of aconitine-induced arrhythmias | Active | 327 |
| Intestine | Cat | $PGE_2$,$PGF_{2\alpha}$ | Motility | Selective | 103 |
| | Human | $PGE_2$, $PGF_{2\alpha}$ | Diarrhea | None (high doses produced diarrhea) | 81 |
| | Mouse | $PGE_2$ | Diarrhea | Active | 80 |
| Kidneys | Rat | $PGA_2$ | Diuresis | Reversed to antidiuresis | 325 |
| Lungs | Cat | $PGF_{2\alpha}$ | Bronchoconstriction | Selective | 101-103 |
| | Guinea pig | $PGF_{2\alpha}$,SRS | Bronchoconstriction | Selective | 101,102 |
| Paws | Rat | $PGE_1$ | Edema | Active | 226 |
| Respiration | Guinea pig | $PGE_2$,$PGF_{2\alpha}$ | Increased rate | None | 104 |
| Salivation | Dog | $PGF_{2\alpha}$ | Increase | None | 105 |
| Skin | Human | $PGE_1$ | Erythema | Active intradermally; inactive i.v. | 228 |
| | Rat | $PGE_2$, phospholipase A | Vascular permeability | Active | 227 |
| Temperature regulation | Rat | $PGE_2$ | Hyperthermia | None; PPP induced or prolonged hyperthermia | 221 |
| Uterus and oviduct | Rabbit | $PGE_1$,$PGF_{2\alpha}$ | Motility | None | 107 |
| Vasculature | Dog | $PGA_1$,$PGE_1$, $PGE_2$ | Vasodilation | None | 108 |
| | | $PGF_{2\alpha}$ | Vasoconstriction | None | 108 |

**Table 2 (continued)**
***IN VIVO* EICOSANOID ANTAGONISM**

| Antagonist | System studied | Species | Substance antagonized | Activity inhibited | Type of antagonism | Ref. |
|---|---|---|---|---|---|---|
| $PGF_{2\alpha}$ | Perfused ear | Rabbit | $PGE_1$ | Enhancement of bradykinin-induced pain | Active | 328 |
| | Uterine vasculature | Dog | $PGE_1$ | Vasodilation | Competitive | 115 |
| REV 5901 | Lungs | Guinea pig | SRS-A | Bronchoconstriction | Selective | 146 |
| SC-18637 | Intestine | Mouse | $PGE_2$ | Diarrhea | Active | 58 |
| SC-19220 | Blood pressure | Bovine | $PGE_1$,$PGE_2$, $PGF_{2\alpha}$ | Depressor responses | None | 109 |
| | | Dog | $PGI_2$,6-keto $PGF_{1\alpha}$ | Depressor responses | Active | 111 |
| | | | 15(S)-15-methyl $PGF_{2\alpha}$ | Depressor and pressor responses, respiratory stimulation | Active | 111 |
| | Eye | Rabbit | $PGE_1$,$PGE_2$, $PGF_{1\alpha}$,$PGF_{2\alpha}$ | Effects on ocular blood flow | None | 237 |
| | Intestine | Mouse | $PGE_2$ | Diarrhea | Active | 9,58 |
| | | | | Stimulation of charcoal transport | Active | 10 |
| | Paw | Rat | $PGE_1$ | Potentiation of carrageenan-induced swelling | Active | 224 |
| | Stomach | Rat | $PGE_1$ | Inhibition of gastric acid secretion | None | 82,83 |
| | Synovial vasculature | Dog | $PGE_1$ | Vasodilation | None | 326 |
| | Temperature regulation | Cat | $PGE_1$,leucocyte pyrogen | Hyperthermia | Caused hypothermia and inhibited hyperthermia | 220 |
| | | Rat | $PGE_1$ | Hyperthermia | Active | 219 |
| | | | Sodium arachidonate | Hyperthermia | None | 219 |

| | | | | | | |
|---|---|---|---|---|---|---|
| | | Rabbit | $PGE_2$,leucocyte pyrogen | Hyperthermia | Active | 218 |
| | Vasculature | Dog | $PGA_1$,$PGE_1$, $PGE_2$ | Vasodilation | None | 108 |
| | | | $PGF_{2\alpha}$ | Vasoconstriction | None | 108 |
| SC-25038 | Intestine | Mouse | $PGE_2$ | Diarrhea | Moderate potency | 9 |
| SC-25324 | Intestine | Mouse | $PGE_2$ | Diarrhea | Weak | 9 |
| SK II-144 | Blood pressure | Rat | $PGF_{2\alpha}$ | Hypertensive effect | Selective | 50 |
| | | | $PGI_2$ | Hypertensive effect | None | 50 |
| SK&F 101132 | Lungs | Guinea pig | $LTD_4$ | Broncoconstriction | Active | 32 |
| | Trachea | Guinea pig | $LTD_4$ | Microvascular permeability | Active | 32 |
| SK&F 102922 | Lungs | Guinea pig | $LTC_4$,$LTD_4$ | Bronchoconstriction | Active | 30 |
| SQ 24,775 | Lungs | Guinea pig | Arachidonate | Bronchoconstriction | Selective | 329 |
| SQ 29,548 | Whole animal | Mouse | AA,U-44069 | Sudden death | Dose-dependent | 330 |
| Wy-44,329 | Lungs | Guinea pig | $LTC_4$,$LTD_4$, antigen | Bronchoconstriction | Longer-acting than FPL 55712 | 145 |

contractions produced by $LTC_1$,[84] $LTC_4$,[16] $LTD_4$,[16] and $LTE_4$,[85] but more recent findings indicate that it is active primarily against D and E leukotrienes, especially in airways smooth muscle. The related compounds FPL-57231 and FPL-59257, also selectively inhibit SRS- and $LTD_4$-induced contractions of guinea-pig ileum.[16] FPL 59257 could not be easily washed out of the tissues, and appeared to be noncompetitive.

More recently, LY1673449 and LY171883 were reported to be selective, competitive inhibitors of $LTD_4$-induced contractions on guinea-pig ileum, with low activity against $LTC_4$.[26,27] In contrast, REV 5901 is quite active against $LTC_4$-induced ileal contractions.[29] WY-44,329 also antagonized $LTD_4$ in guinea-pig ileum in a competitive manner, but its activity against $LTC_4$ in this tissue was not determined.[33]

### Uterine Smooth Muscle

Sodium mefenamate and meclofenamate (2 μg/ml) selectively inhibit contractions produced in human myometrium by the endoperoxide analogue, U-46619, but sodium meclofenamate did not consistently inhibit contractions produced by $PGF_{2\alpha}$.[86] Indomethacin (10 to 40 μg/ml) has shown selective inhibition of contractions produced by $PGE_2$ on rat uterus.[87]

The effects of PPP on uterine contractions have not been consistent. Very low concentrations of 0.01 to 0.1 μg/ml were reported to be competitive against $PGF_{2\alpha}$ on cat, dog, guinea-pig, and rat isolated uterus.[88] Selective inhibition of E and F prostaglandins was found with higher concentrations of PPP (2.5 to 30 μg/ml) on rabbit uterus by one group[56] but not by another, using concentrations up to 100 μg/ml.[89] Another group reported that 50 μg/ml was nonselective against $PGF_{2\alpha}$.[90] Diphloretin phosphate (DPP), 5 to 10 μg/ml, partially inhibited contractions produced by $PGE_1$ and gamma amino butyric acid on guinea-pig uterus.[91]

7-OPA (1 to 10 μg/ml) did not inhibit $PGE_1$-induced contractions on guinea-pig uterus, and sometimes it was spasmogenic.[91] The estrogenic state of the uterus might be important. A 7-OPA concentration of $5 \times 10^{-6}$ *M* inhibited contractions induced by $PGF_{2\alpha}$ and angiotensin II on proestrus rat uterus, but not on metestrus uterus. Noncompetitive inhibition of $PGF_{2\alpha}$ was demonstrated by $5 \times 10^{-5}$ *M* 7-OPA on metestrus uterus.[92]

Dithiothreitol (0.1 m*M*) selectively and competitively inhibited contractions produced by $PGE_2$, $PGE_1$, and $PGF_{2\alpha}$ on rat uterus, suggesting the involvement of disulfide groups in prostaglandin-receptor binding.[93]

### Vascular Smooth Muscle

Polyphloretin phosphate, at concentrations between 10 and 100 μg/ml, selectively inhibits contractions produced by prostaglandins on several isolated arterial preparations.[94-98] Contractions elicited by $PGE_2$ or $PGF_{2\alpha}$ in bovine pulmonary vein, however, were not inhibited,[99] nor was the relaxant effect of $PGE_1$ on dog cerebral-artery strips.[96] In contrast to polyphloretin phosphate, diphloretin phosphate in the same concentration range was found to selectively inhibit contractions induced in bovine pulmonary veins by $PGE_1$ and $PGF_{2\alpha}$, and to slightly inhibit $PGE_1$- and $PGE_2$-induced relaxation.[99] N-0164 has shown selective inhibition of coronary vasoconstriction induced in guinea-pig hearts by $PGD_2$ and $PGF_{2\alpha}$. It also inhibited coronary vasodilatation produced by $PGE_2$ but not $PGI_2$.[100]

Antiprostaglandin activity has been demonstrated by PPP on vascular smooth muscle *in vivo*, but the results have not always been positive. It has been found to inhibit $PGF_{2\alpha}$-induced pressor responses in guinea pigs and depressor responses in cats.[101-104] In dogs, it reversed the pressor effect of $PGF_{2\alpha}$ into a prolonged depressor response and enhanced the depressor effect of $PGE_2$.[105] It selectively antagonized depressor responses produced in chickens by $PGE_1$, $PGE_2$ and $PGF_{2\alpha}$.[106] At a dose of 94 mg/kg it did not inhibit $PGF_{2\alpha}$-induced depressor responses in rabbits,[107] but with a dose range of 25 to 200 mg/kg it showed variable antagonism.[56] At low doses of 1 to 3 mg/kg in dogs, PPP did not inhibit local

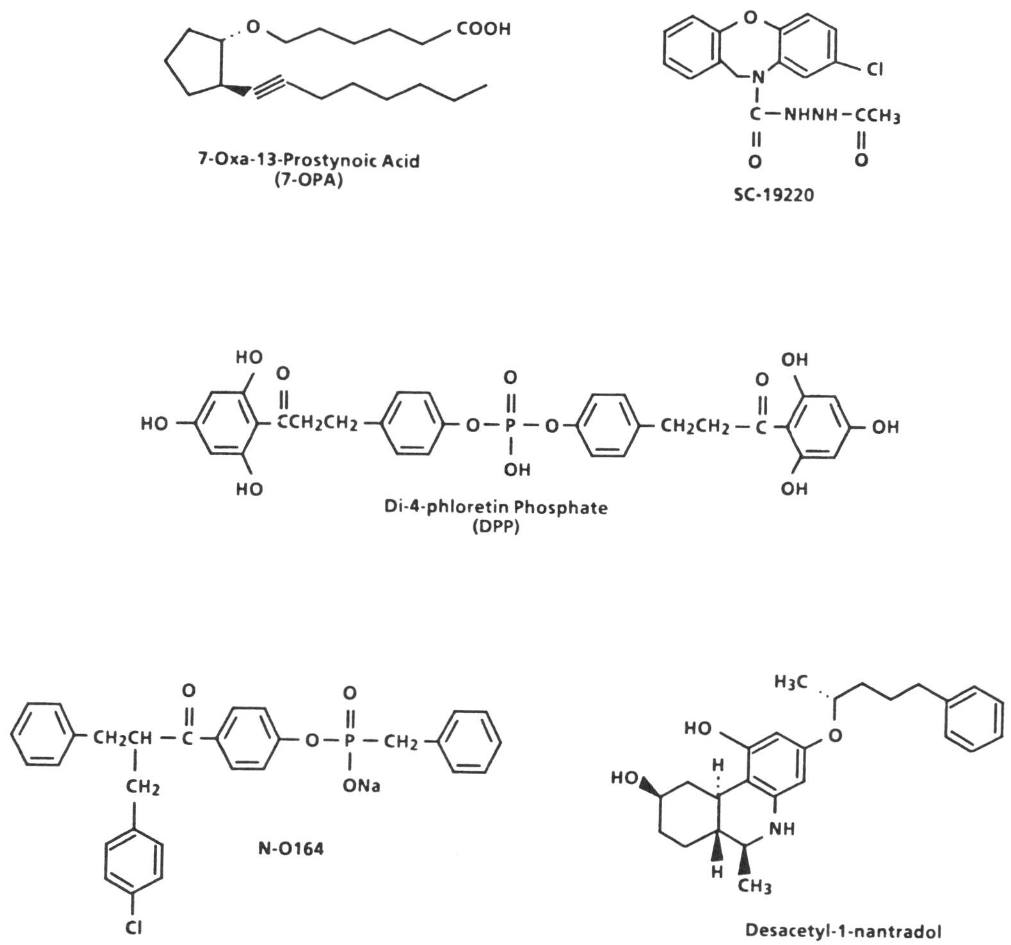


FIGURE 1. Prostaglandin antagonists.

vasodilatation caused by $PGE_1$, $PGE_2$, or $PGA_1$, or local vasoconstriction caused by $PGF_{2\alpha}$.[108] Even at higher doses (40 to 100 mg/kg i.v.), PPP did not inhibit vasodepressor effects of $PGE_2$ in guinea pigs[104] or of $PGE_1$, $PGE_2$, or $PGF_{2\alpha}$ in calves.[109]

In contrast to PPP and its relatives, no definitive prostaglandin antagonism has been demonstrated in vascular smooth muscle by dibenzoxazepine compounds. SC-19220 was judged to be nonspecific on human umbilical arteries and veins although contractions induced by $PGE_2$ were inhibited somewhat more than those induced by 5-HT.[110] It did not inhibit $PGE_2$- or U-46619-induced contractions in rat-aortic strips.[79] No antagonism of prostaglandin-induced vasoconstriction or vasodilatation was seen in dogs with SC-19220 doses of 0.1 to 2.0 mg/kg infused locally,[108] but i.v. doses of 10 mg/kg were reported to inhibit dog blood-pressure responses induced by $PGI_2$, 6-keto-$PGF_{1\alpha}$, $PGF_{2\alpha}$, and 15(S)-15-methyl $PGF_{2\alpha}$.[111]

7-OPA is agonistic in all *in vitro* vascular smooth-muscle preparations that have been studied. This may be due to partial agonism as demonstrated on rabbit-aortic and dog renal-artery strips,[72] and/or inhibition of the inactivation of prostaglandins by 15-hydroxy prostaglandin dehydrogenase.[74] Selective, competitive antagonism against $PGE_2$ was demonstrated, however, after the initial contractions subsided in human umbilical arteries.[95] No antagonism of prostaglandin-induced contraction or relaxation of dog vasculature *in vivo* was seen with local infusion of 7-OPA doses of 0.1 to 0.2 mg/kg.[108,112]

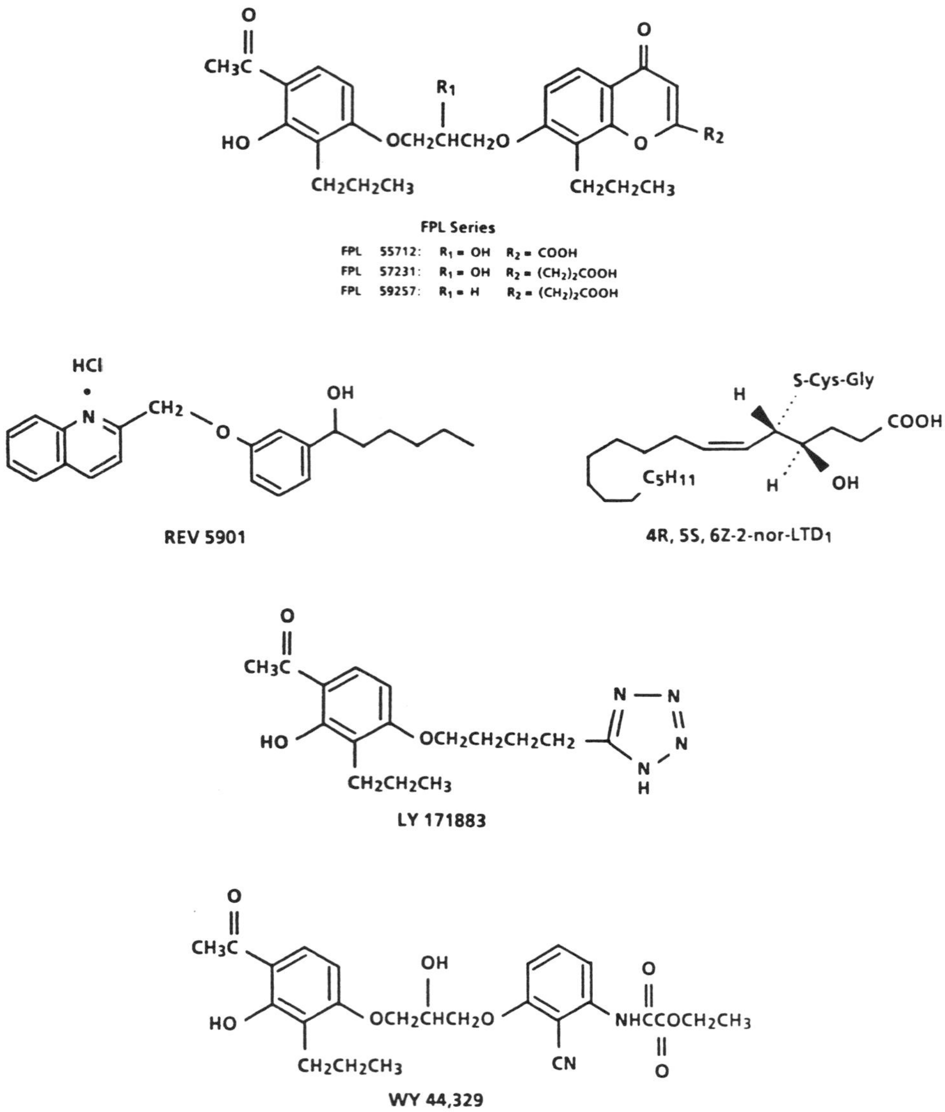


FIGURE 2. Leukotriene antagonists.

*N*-dimethylamine and *N*-dimethylamide analogues of $PGF_{2\alpha}$ inhibit $PGF_{2\alpha}$-induced increases in dog lobar-artery pressure,[113] and the *N*-dimethylamine compound was found to inhibit $PGF_{2\alpha}$-induced vasoconstriction in rats in a competitive manner. It did not inhibit arachidonic acid-induced vasoconstriction, or vasoconstriction induced by the thromboxane mimic, U-46619.[114]

Meclofenamic acid has been observed to selectively inhibit $PGF_{2\alpha}$-induced vasodepression in rabbits,[107] and $PGF_{2\alpha}$ appeared to be competitive against $PGE_1$-induced vasodilatation in dog uterus,[115] suggesting a common receptor for E and F prostaglandins in vascular smooth muscle. Selective antagonism against $PGE_1$ without inhibition of $PGE_2$ or $PGI_2$ has been seen with infusion of d,l-11,15-bisdeoxy $PGE_1$ into the carotid artery of rats.[116]

Thromboxane $A_2$ has potent contracting activity on vascular smooth muscle which might contribute to pathologic vasospasm, so thromboxane antagonists could have important therapeutic applications for the treatment of vasospastic conditions. The search for such antagonists has been aided greatly by the availability of the stable endoperoxide analogues, 9,11-epoxymethano $PGH_2$ (U-44069), 11,9-epoxymethano $PGH_2$ (U-46619), and 9,11-azo $PGH_2$, which mimic the activity of the unstable $TXA_2$. Most of the activities of thromboxane antagonists are based on antagonism of these endoperoxide analogues rather than antagonism of $TXA_2$ itself.

Selective and/or competitive antagonism of $TXA_2$ or the thromboxane-like endoperoxide analogues has been demonstrated on vascular smooth muscle *in vitro* with AH 19437[39] as well as the prostanoid analogues EP 045,[44,117] 13-aza-prostanoic acid,[118] pinane thromboxane $A_2$,[48] and ONO-11120.[47] Pinane thromboxane $A_2$ inhibits contractions induced by $PGE_2$ and $PGF_{1\alpha}$ as well as the endoperoxides in rat-stomach strips,[119] and ONO-11120 also inhibits $PGF_{2\alpha}$-induced vasoconstriction,[47] suggesting a degree of nonspecificity for these compounds.

**Blood Platelets**

The induction of platelet aggregation is a primary activity of thromboxane $A_2$ that might have important pathological implications, so there has been considerable research directed at finding antagonists of this activity. As with the antagonism on vascular smooth muscle, much of this antithromboxane activity has been demonstrated against thromboxane-like endoperoxides rather than thromboxane itself.

Thromboxane antagonism in vascular smooth muscle and in platelets often runs hand-in-hand, but some exceptions have been noted. SQ-27,427 shows selective, competitive antagonism of contractions induced by 9,11-azo $PGH_2$ in vascular, respiratory, and gastrointestinal smooth muscles, but its antiplatelet activity appears to be nonspecific.[51] A difference in the potency of 13-APA as a thromboxane antagonist in platelets and vascular smooth muscle has also been observed.[120]

13-Aza-prostanoic acid (13-APA) specifically inhibits platelet aggregation induced by arachidonic acid, $PGH_2$, and U-44069,[40] and may also disaggregate platelets during the early phase of aggregation induced by these agents.[121] Its specificity is indicated by its ineffectiveness against epinephrine- and ADP-induced aggregation. *In vivo* activity has been shown by the ability of 13-APA, infused into the femoral artery of rabbits, to inhibit deposition of platelets to the de-endothelialized aorta.[122]

EP 045, another prostanoid analogue, blocks platelet shape change and aggregation induced by $TXA_2$, $PGH_2$, U-46619, 9,11-azo $PGH_2$, arachidonic acid, and collagen while only marginally inhibiting the effects of ADP and thrombin.[123] The inhibition of U-46619 appeared to be competitive. EP092, a related compound, also shows properties of a thromboxane antagonist.[124]

The 15-epimers of 9-homo-9,11-epoxy-5,13-prostadienoic acid have opposite activities on platelet aggregation. The 15(S) epimer is an agonist while the 15(R) epimer (SQ 26,536) is an antagonist, with apparent selective activity against thromboxane $A_2$.[125] SQ 27,427, another prostanoid analogue, is a nonspecific, thromboxane inhibitor in platelets, although it shows selective antithromboxane activity in smooth muscle, as described previously.[51]

Pinane thromboxane $A_2$ ($PTA_2$) inhibits human-platelet aggregation induced by 9,11-azo $PGH_2$, U-46619, U-44069, and arachidonic acid, as well as the second wave of aggregation induced by epinephrine and ADP.[48] It also partially inhibits collagen-induced aggregation. The 15(S) epimer is about ten times as potent as the 15(R) epimer. At higher concentrations, $PTA_2$ inhibits the formation of thromboxane as well as its action. Certain analogues of $PTA_2$ also have thromboxane-inhibitory activities. For example, 5(C)-15(S) $BPTA_2$ inhibits platelet aggregation induced by endoperoxide analogues, and is a potent inhibitor of vasoconstriction produced by carbocyclic $TXA_2$.[49] Antithromboxane properties have also been reported for several 3-alkylamino pinane derivatives, especially ONO-11120 which inhibits aggregation induced by $STA_2$, U-46619, arachidonic acid, and collagen.[47] ONO-11120 also selectively

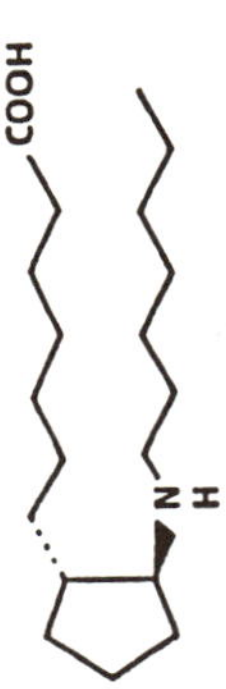

13-Aza-Prostanoic Acid
(13-APA)

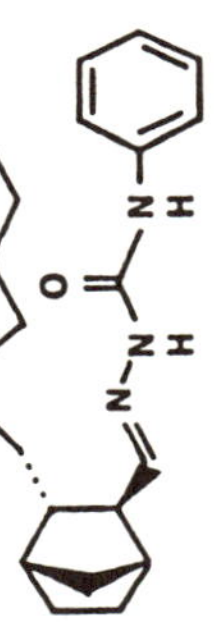

EP 045

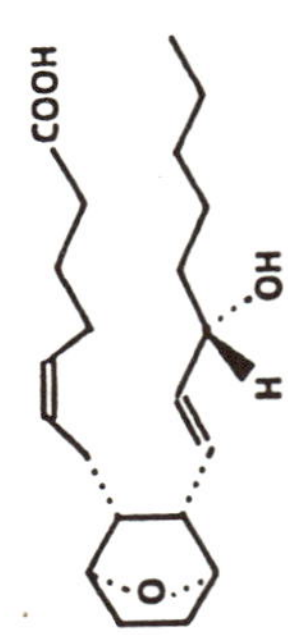

SQ 26,536

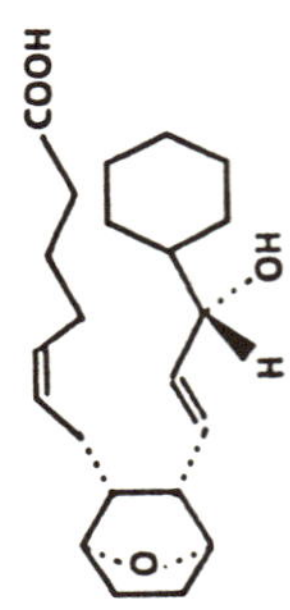

SQ 27,427

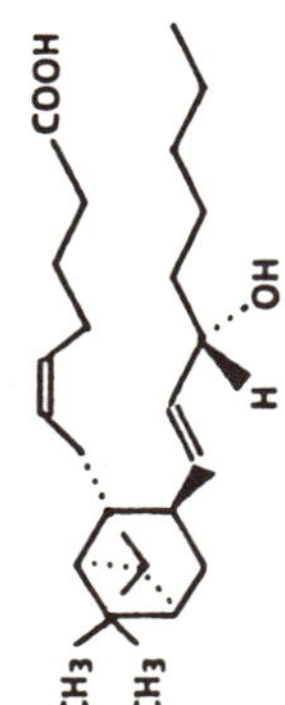

15S-Pinane-Thromboxane $A_2$
($PTA_2$)

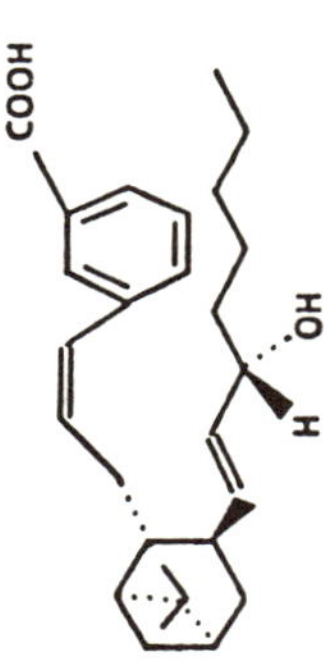

5C-15S $BPTA_2$

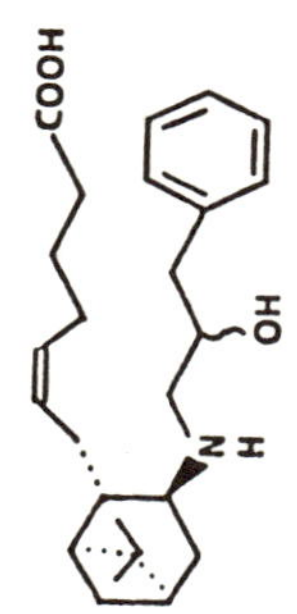

ONO-11120

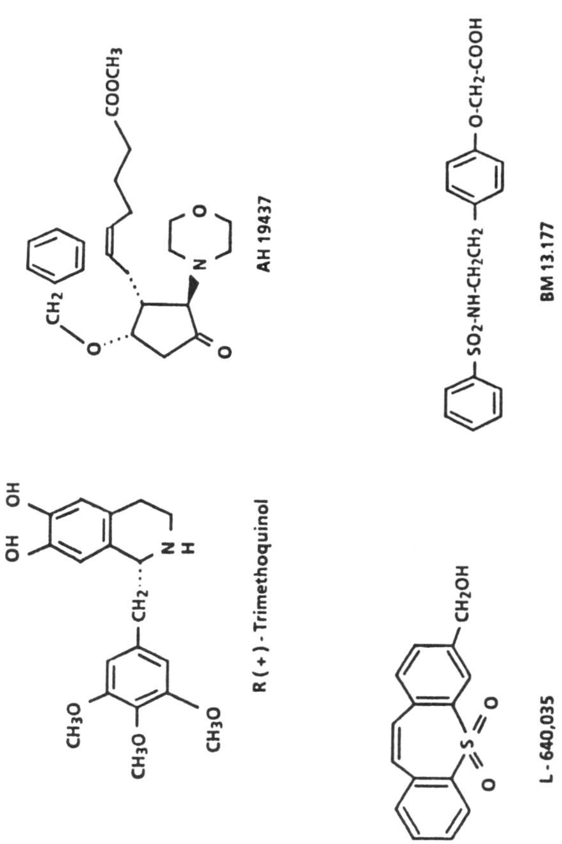


FIGURE 3. Thromboxane antagonists.

inhibits the second phase of ADP-induced aggregation, but not the first phase or aggregation induced by thrombin.

Trimethoquinol is a nonprostanoid that inhibits platelet aggregation induced by endoperoxides and $TXA_2$, and like several of the prostanoid analogues, it inhibits the secondary wave of aggregation induced by ADP without affecting the primary wave.[53] The inhibition of aggregation by trimethoquinol was found to be stereospecific,[54] but it has been reported not to bind to thromboxane receptors on human platelets.[126]

AH 19437 inhibits thromboxane $A_2$- and U-46619-induced platelet aggregation and vascular smooth-muscle stimulation with essentially the same potency, thus providing no evidence for different thromboxane receptors involved in these two types of thromboxane activities.[79]

L-640,035 is another nonprostanoid that shows thromboxane-inhibitory activity. It inhibits platelet aggregation induced by U-46619, arachidonic acid, and collagen, but not the primary wave of ADP-induced aggregation. Administration (i.v.) also inhibits aggregation of platelets induced by U-46619 in the thorax of guinea pigs and by electrical stimulation of the carotid artery in rabbits.[127] BM 13.177, a sulfonamidophenylcarboxylic acid, inhibits platelet shape change, aggregation, and the release of 5-HT induced by U-46619 and U-44069 in aspirin-treated platelet-rich plasma and untreated platelets. As typical of thromboxane antagonists, it inhibits the secondary wave of ADP- and epinephrine-induced aggregation, but not the primary wave.[42] *In vivo* activity of BM 13.177 was demonstrated in rabbits by inhibition of silver-nitrate-induced thrombus formation and arachidonate-induced sudden death, and in guinea pigs by inhibition of collagen-induced bronchoconstriction.[43]

**Airways Smooth Muscle**

FPL-55712 is a potent inhibitor of contractions produced by SRS or leukotrienes on isolated airways smooth muscle from humans or experimental animals. It was initially reported to selectively inhibit contractions produced by leukotrienes $A_4$, $C_4$, and $D_4$.[16,128] It produced 50% inhibition of SRS-induced contractions at concentrations of 0.087, 0.33, and 0.22 μg/ml on guinea-pig-lung strips, human-lung strips, and human-bronchial strips, respectively.[16] It did not inhibit $LTB_4$- or $LTC_1$-induced contractions on guinea-pig-lung strips,[129,130] but it has been reported to inhibit $LTC_1$ in guinea-pig ileum and tracheal chains.[84] It inhibited contractions produced by arachidonic acid in guinea-pig-lung strips in a noncompetitive way.[131] Drazen et al.[130] reported that FPL 55712 inhibits contractions produced in guinea-pig-lung strips by low concentrations of LTD, but it does not inhibit contractions produced by higher concentrations. They postulated that there are two types of LTD receptors in this tissue: low affinity and high affinity, and that FPL 55712 antagonizes only the high-affinity receptors, but not in a simple competitive manner since they obtained Schild plots with slopes less than one. Since they found no inhibition of $LTC_1$-induced contractions, they proposed that $LTC_1$ stimulates the low-affinity receptors.

FPL 55712 inhibits $LTC_4$-induced contractions in superfused guinea-pig-lung strips,[132,133] but not when the strips are suspended in a tissue bath.[130,134] Contractions produced in superfused lung strips by both C and D leukotrienes are inhibited by indomethacin,[132,135] but when the strips are mounted in a tissue bath, indomethacin appears to inhibit only those contractions that are produced by relatively high concentrations of leukotrienes.[35,136,137] It has been proposed[35] that in superfused tissues, the contractions are mediated by $TXA_2$ released by the high concentrations of leukotriene that are need to produce contractions, but in a tissue bath, lower concentrations of leukotrienes can cause direct stimulation of the tissue which is not antagonized by FPL 55712. The inhibition of $LTC_4$-induced contractions in superfused tissues may be due to its demonstrated ability to inhibit thromboxane synthetase.[138]

Tracheal strips as well as lung strips may contain multiple types of leukotriene receptors. Jones et al.[139] found that FPL 55712 concentrations up to $5.7 \times 10^{-6}$ *M* inhibit $LTC_4$,

$LTE_4$, and $LTF_4$-induced contractions in a competitive manner, but at higher concentrations the antagonism appeared to be noncompetitive, at least against $LTC_4$, and it appeared to be noncompetitive (but potent) at all concentrations against $LTD_4$. Further evidence of different types of tracheal receptors was presented by Krell et al.[140] who found a bimodal distribution of $K_B$ values for $LTD_4$ in guinea-pig tracheal strips. Furthermore, FPL 55712, is a more potent $LTD_4$ antagonist on guinea-pig ileum than on trachea or parenchyma, indicating that the ileal receptors are different than they are in the airways preparations.[141]

It now appears that in tracheal as well as parenchymal smooth muscle, FPL 55712 does not directly antagonize the activity of $LTC_4$. If the conversion of $LTC_4$ to $LTD_4$ is blocked by serine borate, FPL 55712 has no or weak inhibitory activity against $LTC_4$.[31,142] Experiments indicating $LTC_4$ antagonism should be carefully evaluated to determine if the inhibition is due to direct receptor antagonism of $LTC_4$ or if it might be due to inhibition of the release of thromboxane or the antagonism of $LTD_4$ after its conversion from $LTC_4$.

FPL 55712 will inhibit bronchoconstriction in guinea pigs if it is injected i.v. immediately before challenge by SRS or leukotrienes, but its rapid clearance by the liver seriously restricts its *in vivo* activity.[16] A related compound, FPL 59257, (Figure 2) has a longer duration of action *in vivo*, possibly because it is strongly bound to the leukotrience receptors.[16,18] FPL 55712 and FPL 59257, administered by aerosol, inhibited bronchoconstriction and coughing induced by inhalation of $LTC_4$ in two normal humans,[143] and FPL 55712 increased forced respiratory volume in two asthmatic patients, although its effect was not significant overall in the four patients in which it was tested.[144]

LY171883 was found to be competitive and selective against $LTD_4$ on guinea-pig ileum and lung strips with a $K_B$ five times higher on lung strips than on ileum.[27,36] It appeared to be noncompetitive on guinea-pig trachea, however, possibly because it inhibits only one of the two types of LTD receptors that are postulated to be present in this tissue.[140] LY171883, like FPL 55712, has low activity against $LTC_4$ *in vitro*, but it appears to be fully active against this leukotriene *in vivo*, suggesting that it inhibits the action of $LTC_4$ only after its conversion to $LTD_4$.[27,36] LY171883 is not effective against $LTB_4$, but it had a slight activity on guinea-pig trachea against the thromboxane mimic, U-46619.[27] Oral administration of LY171883 to guinea pigs inhibits increased pulmonary resistance induced by $LTD_4$ or antigen, and $LTD_4$-induced vascular permeability. LY171883 also inhibits phosphodiesterase, and at higher concentrations, it is a general smooth-muscle relaxant.[27]

Wy-44,329 competitively antagonizes $LTD_4$ in guinea-pig isolated ileum with somewhat greater potency than FPL 55712. It also has some weak activity against histamine. When it is administered i.v. to guinea pigs, it inhibits bronchoconstriction induced by $LTC_4$, $LTD_4$, PAF-acether, and antigen with a longer duration of action than FPL 55712, but unlike LY171883, it is inactive when administered orally.[35,145]

REV 5901 is a relatively potent 5-lipoxygenase inhibitor as well as an $LTC_4$ antagonist. *In vitro* $LTC_4$ antagonism was demonstrated in guinea-pig lung strips,[29] and *in vivo* activity was demonstrated against anaphylactic bronchoconstriction when the compound was administered intraduodenally or orally.[146]

SK&F 101132 [4(R), 5(S), 6(Z)-2-nor $LTD_1$] inhibits contractions induced by $LTC_4$, $LTD_4$, and $LTE_4$ in guinea-pig trachea and by $LTD_4$ in guinea-pig-lung strips.[28,32] Selectivity against the leukotrienes is indicated by its inactivity against histamine, carbachol, $PGF_{2\alpha}$, and KCl. The antagonism against $LTD_4$ appeared to be competitive in tracheal spirals, but not in lung strips. Unlike the FPL 55712-type compounds, SK&F 101132 is as potent against $LTC_4$ as it is against $LTD_4$, even in the presence of serine borate to block the conversion of $LTC_4$ to $LTD_4$.[31] *In vivo* activity has been demonstrated in anesthetized guinea pigs in which the compound blocked $LTD_4$-induced bronchoconstriction when it was injected i.v. 1 min before the leukotriene challenge. It was not effective, however, when it was injected 3 min before the challenge, indicating a short duration of action.[32] Certain desamino-2-nor leukotriene analogues have been found to be more potent antagonists than the original compound, but they have agonistic activities at higher doses.[19]

SK&F 88046 was first thought to be a receptor-oriented leukotriene antagonist in airways smooth muscle,[147] but it was later found to be an inhibitor of $TXA_2$, $PGD_2$, and $PGF_{2\alpha}$.[148] Its leukotriene inhibition is apparently due to inhibition of the action of the thromboxane that was released by high concentrations of leukotriene.

Polyphloretin phosphate selectively inhibits contractions produced by $PGF_{2\alpha}$ and some of its derivatives on guinea-pig tracheal chains[149] and human bronchial strips.[101,150] The inhibition appears to be competitive against $PGI_2$ as well as $PGF_{2\alpha}$ on guinea-pig-lung strips.[151] It is also reported to inhibit contractions produced by SRS without affecting acetylcholine-induced contractions,[152] but it does not inhibit $PGE_1$- or $PGE_2$-induced relaxation of human bronchial strips.[150] PPP also inhibits bronchoconstriction produced by $PGF_{2\alpha}$ and SRS in guinea pigs and cats.[101-103] This inhibition appears to be selective against the eicosanoids because PPP did not inhibit bronchoconstriction produced by carbachol[103] or histamine.[102] PPP is not highly potent in this regard, and doses of 20 to 80 mg/kg i.v.[102] or 200 mg/kg i.v. or i.p.[103] were employed. At a dose of 40 mg/kg i.v., PPP did not inhibit increases in respiratory rate induced by $PGE_2$ or $PGF_{2\alpha}$.[104]

SC-19220 has been observed to competitively inhibit contractions produced by prostaglandins and arachidonic acid on guinea-pig tracheal tubes or chains; it also reduced the tone of the preparations,[153,154] but it did not inhibit $PGE_2$- or angiotensin II-induced relaxation of cat tracheal rings.[155]

Flufenamic acid, mefanamic acid, and meclofenamate also inhibit $PGF_{2\alpha}$-induced contractions in guinea-pig tracheal chains[156] and human bronchial muscle.[157] Fluprofen and flurbiprofen inhibit contractions produced by SRS as well as those produced by $PGF_{2\alpha}$.[158] AH 19437 inhibits guinea-pig-lung strip contractions produced by $TXA_2$, U-46619, and $PGH_2$ in a competitive manner.[39] The leukotriene antagonists are fully reviewed by Musser et al. in this volume.

**Cyclic Nucleotides**

Prostaglandins of the E type generally stimulate the production of cyclic-AMP by activating adenylate cyclase, and the effect of 7-OPA on this prostaglandin activity has been studied in various tissues with several different results. The findings include competitive antagonism in mouse ovaries[159] and human astrocytoma cells,[160] undefined inhibition in bovine thyroid preparations,[161-164] and nonselective inhibition in human synovial fibroblasts,[165] mouse fibroblasts,[166] and in intestinal epithelium.[166] No inhibition of prostaglandin-induced cyclic-AMP production was seen in porcine granulosa cells,[167] rat brain slices,[168] or rabbit vagus nerve.[169] No inhibition was seen with low concentrations ( 5 to 10 μg/ml) of 7-OPA on rat anterior pituitaries,[170] but higher concentrations were agonistic.[170,171]

Polyphloretin phosphate selectively inhibits prostaglandin-stimulated cyclic-AMP production in human astrocytoma cells,[160] rat uterus,[172] rat adrenal cortex,[173] and canine gastric mucosa.[174] It also inhibits this activity in bovine thyroid cells,[163,175] although it was not tested for selectivity. It was judged to be nonspecific in mouse fibroblasts and intestinal epithelial tissue.[166] No inhibition was seen in mouse ovaries and myometrium[176] or in rabbit vagus nerves.[169] Diphloretin phosphate (4 $\mu M$) was reported to be competitive in human neuroblastoma cells but noncompetitive at a concentration of 18 $\mu M$ in human astrocytoma cells.[177]

One group found no inhibition by SC-19220 against prostaglandin-induced cyclic-AMP formation in cultured bone cells,[178] while another group observed inhibition of cyclic-AMP formation and release from bone cells with a greater effect on cyclic-AMP formation than on release.[179] SC-19220 did not inhibit prostaglandin-induced cyclic-AMP accumulation in guinea-pig stomach fundus mucosa,[180] rat brain slices,[168] or rat neuroblastoma cells.[181]

Flufenamic acid, indomethacin, meclofenamic acid, and mefanamic acid have all been found to inhibit prostaglandin-stimulated cyclic-AMP accumulation in rat ovaries[182] and human astrocytoma cells.[160] The antagonism was selective against $PGE_1$ and appeared to be competitive.

Desacetyl-1-nantradol inhibits cyclic-AMP production induced by $PGD_2$, but not $PGE_2$ in platelets, thus supporting specific-binding studies that indicate that this cannabinoid-related compound is a selective antagonist of D prostaglandins.[183] The leukotriene antagonist, FPL 55712, also inhibits cyclic-AMP and cyclic-GMP phosphodiesterases.[184]

## Eicosanoid Formation and Inactivation

There is considerable interrelationship between antagonism of the actions of eicosanoids and antagonism of the enzymes that form or inactivate them (see chapter by D. L. Smith et al. in Volume IA). 15-Hydroxy prostaglandin dehydrogenase is the enzyme that is responsible for the first step in the inactivation of the primary prostaglandins, and 7-OPA, PPP, and DPP have all been found to inhibit this enzyme.[74,185] This inhibition by PPP appeared to be competitive and was seen at lower concentrations of all these agents than are generally necessary for prostaglandin antagonism. Thus the inhibition of prostaglandin inactivation (as well as the partial agonistic activity of 7-OPA) might account for some of the prostaglandin-like activities of these compounds. No inhibition of 15-hydroxy prostaglandin dehydrogenase was seen with SC-19220.[74] 7-OPA has also been observed to inhibit the formation of prostaglandins *in vitro*.[186,187]

As indicated above, the fenamates and related compounds, and even indomethacin, all of which are generally recognized cyclooxygenase inhibitors, may also antagonize prostaglandin activities, as well as inhibiting their formation.[154,156,157] As a corollary, the prostaglandin antagonist, N-0164, also inhibits the biosynthesis of prostaglandins and thromboxanes.[188] It was found to be 15 to 20 times as potent as indomethacin as an inhibitor of $TXA_2$ formation, although it was only 1/20th as active as an inhibitor of prostaglandin-endoperoxide formation.

Several leukotriene antagonists are known to be 5-lipoxygenase inhibitors, and thus inhibit the formation as well as the actions of leukotrienes. FPL 55712 inhibits leukotriene production in cell-free homogenates of rat basophilic leukemia cells, but higher concentrations are required to inhibit the production of leukotrienes than to inhibit their actions.[189] Cyclooxygenase was not inhibited in these experiments, so prostaglandin production was not affected. FPL 55712 has also been reported to inhibit thromboxane synthetase.[137] 5-Lipoxygenase inhibition as well as leukotriene antagonism has also been reported for KC-404,[23] Wy-44,329,[145] and REV 5901.[29]

## Miscellaneous Enzymes

PPP and 7-OPA inhibit several enzymes that have no direct relationship to prostaglandins. PPP was initially found to be an inhibitor of hyaluronidase, alkaline phosphatase, and urease.[190] More recently it has been found to inhibit cyclic-AMP and cyclic-GMP phosphodiesterases from guinea-pig heart and lung[191] and phospholipase $A_2$ from isolated rat auricles.[192] It was more potent than papaverine against phosphodiesterase. PPP and a high molecular-weight fraction of PPP inhibited cholesterol esterification, an activity similar to that seen with $PGE_1$, $PGE_2$, $PGF_{2\alpha}$, and $PGA_1$.[193] DPP and PPP have been reported to inhibit the transport system responsible for removal of prostaglandins from the circulation while SC-19220 and 7-OPA were ineffective against this system.[194]

As well as inhibiting the enzymes responsible for the formation and inactivation of prostaglandins, 7-OPA also inhibits the actions of cyclic-AMP-dependent protein kinase[195] and adenylate kinase.[196,197] It also activates ATPase from human platelets, rat mitochondria, and human erythrocytes.[196]

### Receptor Binding

7-OPA has a positive but weak affinity for prostaglandin-binding sites in rat adipocytes,[198,199] bovine corpus luteum,[200-204] human platelet membranes,[205] smooth endoplasmic reticulum fraction of rat skin,[206] rat forestomach,[207] bovine thyroid membranes,[208] and hamster uterus,[209] and thus inhibits prostaglandin binding in a competitive manner. 7-OPA has also been reported to inhibit angiotensin-II binding in bovine adrenal glomerulosa cells and kidney cortex cells.[210]

D-L-11,15-Bisdeoxy $PGE_1$ and its congeners inhibit $^3HPGE_1$ binding to sites from rat adipocytes.[57] Dithiothreitol also inhibited $^3HPGE_1$ binding to uterine sites, thus implicating the involvement of disulfide linkages in this prostaglandin binding.[211] Indomethacin has been observed to have a weak affinity for $PGE_1$-binding sites in bovine corpus-luteal cell membranes.[200] On the other hand, neither polyphloretin phosphate nor SC-19220 appreciably inhibited binding of $PGE_1$ to rat forestomach[207] or adipocyte preparations at concentrations up to 125,000 times the $PGE_1$ concentrations.[198]

FPL 55712 has been found to compete with $LTC_4$ and $LTD_4$ binding in several tissues including guinea-pig ileum longitudinal muscle,[212] rat lung,[213] guinea-pig lung,[214,215] and human fetal lung.[216] It was generally weak against $LTC_4$, and in a direct comparison between $LTC_4$ and $LTD_4$ binding, it was found to be considerably more effective against $LTD_4$, supporting the conclusion that it is a selective antagonist only at the LTD-receptor sites.

Pinane thromboxane $A_2$ ($PTA_2$) and EP 045 both displace U-46619 from its binding sites on washed human platelets. Experiments with the 15(R) and 15(S) epimers of $PTA_2$ indicate two types of displaceable binding. A minor component of the binding of the 15(S) epimer of U-46619 was displaced by both 15(S) and 15(R) $PTA_2$, but the major component was displaced by only 15(S) $PTA_2$. This binding activity correlates with the more potent biological activity of 15(S) $PTA_2$ compared to the 15(R) epimer, and it was assumed that the major component represents the pharmacological receptor.[126] High- and low-affinity binding sites for 13-azaprostanoic acid (13-APA) have also been described. *Trans*-13-APA was used as the radioligand in these experiments. U-46619 and $PGF_{2\alpha}$ both competed at the high-affinity site, but the biologically inert compounds, *cis*-13-APA, thromboxane $B_2$, and 6-keto $PGF_{1\alpha}$ did not.[217]

### Temperature Regulation

Administration (i.p.) of SC-19220 was said to produce hypothermia in rats and to inhibit $PGE_2$-induced hyperthermia at a dose of 100 mg/kg but not 50 mg/kg, but it did not produce a significant inhibition of pyrogen-induced fever in rabbits.[9] Intracerebral ventricular injection of 15 μmol of SC-19220 or 440 nmol of HR 546 inhibits hyperthermia induced in rabbits by $PGE_1$ or $PGE_2$ but not by sodium arachidonate or leukocyte pyrogen.[218,219] Injection (i.p.) of 3 to 9 mg/kg of SC-19220 in cats caused hypothermia and inhibition of $PGE_1$- or leukocyte-pyrogen-induced hyperthermia accompanied by emesis, mydriasis, ataxia, head bobbing, defecation, and vocalization.[220]

When PPP (30 mg/kg) was injected i.p., it prolonged $PGE_2$- and endotoxin-induced fever in rats,[221] while intracerebral ventricular injection of 10 or 25 μg antagonized hyperthermia induced by intracerebral ventricular injection of $PGF_{2\alpha}$ but not $PGE_2$.[222]

### Inflammation and Pain

Early tests indicated that SC-19220 was not an effective inhibitor of inflammation,[11] but later tests at higher doses showed that 34 mg/kg administered i.p. inhibited mycoplasma-induced arthritis in mice, and intragastric administration of 100 mg/kg inhibited cotton-pellet-induced granuloma formation in adrenalectomized rats.[9] Doses (i.p.) of 17.5 and 30 mg/kg weakly inhibited carrageenin-induced abscess formation, accompanied by sedation, disorientation, lethargy, and ataxia in rats.[223] Injected (s.c.) SC-19220 in rats did not inhibit adjuvant-induced arthritis at a dose of 20 mg/kg or carrageenin-induced foot edema at a dose of 200 mg/kg,[9] but i.p. pretreatment with 50 to 66 mg/kg of SC-19220 suspended in 0.1% polysorbate 80 inhibited carrageenin-induced rat-paw edema and blocked the potentiating activity of $PGE_1$.[224] Injection (s.c.) of 50 mg/kg inhibited writhing induced in mice by acetylcholine, ATP, $PGE_1$, and acetic acid, but not $MgSO_4$.[225] Topical application of SC-19220 will also inhibit croton-oil-induced inflammation of rat ears and vascular permeability produced by pyridine and ether applied to rat skin.[10]

Polyphloretin phosphate (50 to 200 mg/kg i.v.) has been found to inhibit rat-paw edema induced by $PGE_1$.[226] Intradermal injections antagonized increased vascular permeability induced in rat skin by phospholipase A or $PGE_2$[227] and also reduced $PGE_1$-induced erythema in human skin, but it was not effective at a dose of 100 mg administered i.v. to humans.[228] PPP inhibited $PGE_1$-enhancement of pain responses produced by bradykinin, or to a lesser extent, by acetylcholine, in perfused rabbit ears.[229]

Diphloretin phosphate (60 mg/kg i.v.) was found to inhibit vascular permeability induced in rabbit skin by arachidonic acid.[230] Topically applied N-0164 delayed development of U.V.-induced erythema in guinea pigs and inhibited croton-oil-induced edema in rat ears.[61] FPL-55712 shows potent inhibition of leukotriene $E_4$-induced vascular permeability in rat skin with a 50% inhibitory dose of 1.2 mg/kg administered i.v. immediately before the leukotriene.[231]

**The Eye**

Polyphloretin phosphate has been studied for antagonism of the ocular effects of prostaglandins. Intra-arterial infusion or subconjunctival administration of PPP inhibits prostaglandin-induced intraocular pressure increases in rabbit eyes,[232-234] and 20 mg administered intra-arterially inhibited $PGE_1$-induced intraocular pressure increases in rabbit eyes.[235] Subconjunctival administration of PPP in rabbits inhibits vasodilatation, vascular permeability, and intraocular pressure increases induced by $PGE_1$, $PGE_2$, and formaldehyde,[233,236] but the effect on vasodilatation appeared to be quite nonspecific.[237]

**Conclusions**

FPL-55712 is one of the most potent of the commonly available eicosanoid antagonists. Recent evidence indicates that it is quite selective against D and E leukotrienes, with little or no inhibition of the activities or receptor binding of B or C leukotrienes, at least in airways smooth muscle. If the *in vitro* concentration is raised high enough, it may also inhibit the actions of the primary prostaglandins and other smooth-muscle stimulants. The primary drawback of FPL-55712, however, is its rapid metabolism and short duration of action *in vivo*.

Wy-44,329 and LY171883 have antagonistic properties similar to FPL 55712, with longer durations of action, but Wy-44,329, is active only when injected. LY171883, on the other hand, is orally active and may have therapeutic utility. SK&F 101132 has an interesting spectrum of activity in that it is equally active against $LTC_4$ and $LTD_4$. Several leukotriene antagonists also inhibit the formation of leukotrienes by 5-lipoxygenase. This is especially true of REV 5901, which is a relatively potent 5-lipoxygenase inhibitor as well as an $LTC_4$ antagonist.

7-Oxa-13-prostynoic acid is the only prostaglandin antagonist that has been found to compete with prostaglandins at their binding sites, but it suffers from unclear *in vitro* activity, lack of demonstrable *in vivo* activity, partial agonism (at least on vascular smooth muscle), and inhibitory action against several enzymes, especially cyclooxygenase and prostaglandin-15-dehydrogenase.

Several *in vivo* activities have been demonstrated for polyphloretin phosphate and diphloretin phosphate, but high doses, typically in the neighborhood of 100 mg/kg are required.

PPP inhibits both E and F prostaglandins, and possibly leukotrienes. It may be somewhat more active against F prostaglandins than against E prostaglandins. PPP suffers from its inhibitory activities against various enzymes, especially prostaglandin-15-dehydrogenase.

SC-19220 has moderate potency and selectivity *in vitro*, but it has failed to show prostaglandin antagonism on several human tissues. There have not been many clear-cut demonstrations of *in vivo* activity, perhaps because of its low water solubility which restricts i.v. dosing. It appears to be more active against E prostaglandins than against F prostaglandins. It has not been shown to be an enzyme inhibitor or a partial agonist.

Several nonsteroidal anti-inflammatory agents, especially the fenamates, inhibit some eicosanoid activities, but more attention has been devoted to their inhibition of cyclooxygenase than to antagonism of its products.

Thromboxane antagonism has been demonstrated primarily against the actions of thromboxane-like endoperoxide analogues in vascular smooth muscle and blood platelets. The eicosanoid compounds, 13-aza-prostanoic acid, EP 045, and pinane thromboxane $A_2$ have been shown to bind to thromboxane receptors, but receptor binding has not been demonstrated with the non-eicosanoids, trimethoquinol, AH 19437, L-640,035, or BN 13.177. *In vivo* activities have been reported with 13-APA, L-640,035, and BM 13.177.

It is obvious that no one agent can be considered to be a universal eicosanoid antagonist, and it is unlikely that there will ever be such an agent because there are so many eicosanoids, and there are probably many types of eicosanoid receptors. A compound that antagonizes all the actions of only one eicosanoid would be as unlikely as a compound that antagonizes all the activities of epinephrine, acetylcholine, or histamine.

Indeed, the apparent diversity of eicosanoid receptors makes it likely that compounds can be developed that are selective against only certain activities of eicosanoids. Absolute specificity will probably never be achieved either, but the presently available agents indicate that it is possible to find antagonists that are sufficiently selective to be used to define eicosanoid receptors, to determine the physiological roles of arachidonic acid products, and possibly to develop therapeutic agents based on their antagonistic activities.

## ABBREVIATIONS USED IN TABLES

| | |
|---|---|
| AA | Arachidonic acid |
| APCP | Adenosine α,β-methylene diphosphate |
| c-AMP | Cyclic adenosine 3′, 5′ monophosphate |
| ADP | Adenosine diphosphate |
| concn. | Concentration |
| $CTA_2$ | Carbocyclic thromboxane $A_2$ |
| CTAP | Connective-Tissue-Activating peptide |
| EP 092 | (±)5-Endo-(6′-carboxyhex-2′Z′enyl)-6-exo-{1″-[*N*-(phenylthiocarbamoyl)-hydrazono]-ethyl}-bicyclo[2,2,1] heptane |
| GABA | Gama aminobutyric acid |
| HR-546 | 8-Ethoxycarbonyl-10,11-dihydro-A-prostaglandin |
| KC-404 | 3-Isobutyryl-2-isopropylpyrazolo[1,5-α]pyridine |
| LATS | Long-Acting thyroid stimulator |
| LH | Leuteinizing hormone |
| LT | Leukotriene |
| LY163443 | 1-[2-Hydroxy-3-propyl-4-[[4-91H-tetrazol-5-yl methyl) phenoxy]methyl]phenyl]ethanone |
| ONO-11105 | 9,11-Dimethylmethano-11,12-methano-16-(4-ethyl-phenylthio)-13,14-dihydro-13-aza-15αβ-ω-tetranor-$TXA_2$ |
| ONO-11119 | 9,11-Dimethylmethano-11,12-methano-13,14-dihydro-13-aza-15αβ-trihomo-$TXA_2$ |
| PG | Prostaglandin |

| | |
|---|---|
| SK&F 88046 | {*N,N'-bis*[7-(3-chlorobenzeneaminosulfonyl)-1,2,3,4-tetrahydroisoquinolyl]disulfonylimide |
| SK&F 101132 | 4(R),15(S),6(Z)-2-nor-$LTD_1$ = 4(R)-hydroxy-5(S)-1-cysteinylglycine-6(Z)-nonadecenoic acid |
| SK&F 102922 | 4,6-Dithia-5(2-[8-phenyloctyl]phenyl)nonanedioic acid |
| SQ 26,655 | ([1S-1α,2β(5Z),3α(1E,3S),4α)]-7-[3-(3-hydroxy-1-octenyl)-7-oxabicyclo-[2.2.1]hept-2-yl]-5-heptenoic acid |
| SRS | Slow-reacting substance |
| $STA_2$ | 9,11-Epithio-11,12-methano-$TXA_2$ |
| TSH | Thyroid-stimulating hormone |
| TX | Thromboxane |
| U-44069 | 15(S)-hydroxy-9α,11α-(epoxymethano) prosta-5(Z),13(E)-dienoic acid |
| U-46619 | 15(S)-hydroxy-11α,9α-(epoxymethano)-prosta-5(Z),13(E)-dienoic acid |
| Wy17186 | 11-Deoxy-15-methyl-15(RS)-$PGE_2$ |

*Note:* Additional chemical structures are shown in Figures 1, 2, and 3.

# REFERENCES


1. **Ambache, N.,** The unsaturated nature of irin and its interaction with lactones, *J. Physiol. (London),* 140, 24P, 1957.
2. **Ambache, N.,** Further studies on the preparation, purification and nature of irin, *J. Physiol. (London),* 146, 255, 1959.
3. **Anggard, E. and Samuelsson, B.,** Smooth muscle stimulating lipids in sheep iris. The identification of prostaglandin $F_{2\alpha}$. Prostaglandins and related factors 21, *Biochem. Pharmacol.,* 13, 281, 1964.
4. **Ambache, N. and Brummer, H. C.,** A simple chemical procedure for distinguishing E from F prostaglandins with application to tissue extracts, *Br. J. Pharmacol.,* 33, 162, 1968.
5. **Eliasson, R.,** The spasmolytic effect of patulin, *Experientia,* 14, 460, 1958.
6. **Fried, J., Santhanakrishnan, T. S., Himizu, J., Lin, C. H., Ford, S. H., Rubin, B., and Grigas, E. O.,** Prostaglandin antagonists: synthesis and smooth muscle activity, *Nature (London),* 223, 208, 1969.
7. **Sanner, J. H.,** Antagonism of prostaglandin $E_2$ by 1-acetyl-2-(8-chloro-10,11-dihydrodibenz[b,f][1,4] oxazepine-10-carbonyl) hydrazine (SC-19220), *Arch. Int. Pharmacodyn. Ther.,* 180, 46, 1969.
8. **Eakins, K. E. and Karim, S. M. M.,** Polyphloretin phosphate—a selective antagonist for prostaglandins $F_{1\alpha}$ and $F_{2\alpha}$, *Life Sci.,* 9, 1, 1970.
9. **Sanner, J. H. and Eakins, K. E.,** Prostaglandin antagonists, in *Prostaglandins: Chemical and Biochemical Aspects,* Karim, S. M. M., Ed., MTP, Lancaster, England, 1976, 139.
10. **Sanner, J. H.,** Substances that inhibit the actions of prostaglandins, *Arch. Intern. Med.,* 133, 133, 1974.
11. **Eakins, K. E. and Sanner, J. H.,** Prostaglandin antagonists, in *The Prostaglandins Progress in Research,* Karim, S. M. M., Ed., MTP, Oxford, 1972, 263.
12. **Bennett, A.,** Prostaglandin antagonists, in *Advances in Drug Research 8,* Harper, N. J. and Simmonds, A. B., Eds., Academic Press, New York, 1974, 83.
13. **Augstein, J., Farmer, J. B., Lee, T. B., Sheard, P., and Tattersall, M. L.,** Selective inhibitor of slow reacting substance of anaphylaxis, *Nature (London) New Biol.,* 245, 215, 1973.
14. **Murphy, R. C., Hammarstrom, S., and Samuelsson, B.,** Leukotriene C: a slow-reacting substance from murine mastocytoma cells, *Proc. Natl. Acad. Sci. U.S.A.,* 76, 4275, 1979.
15. **Lewis, R. A., Austen, K. F., Drazen, J. M., Clark, D. A., Marfat, A., and Corey, E. J.,** Slow reacting substances of anaphylaxis: identification of leukotrienes C-1 and D from human and rat sources, *Proc. Natl. Acad. Sci. U.S.A.,* 77, 3710, 1980.
16. **Sheard, P., Holroyde, M. C., Ghelani, A. M., Bantick, J. R., and Lee, T. B.,** Antagonists of SRS-A and leukotrienes, in *Leukotrienes and Other Lipoxygenase Products,* Samuelsson, B. and Paoletti, R., Eds., Raven Press, New York, 1982, 229.
17. **Chand, N.,** FPL 55712-An antagonist of slow reacting substance of anaphylaxis (SRS-A): a review, *Agents Actions,* 9, 133, 1979.
18. **Sheard, P.,** Effects of anti-allergic compounds on SRS-A and leukotrienes, in *SRS-A and Leukotrienes,* Piper, P. J., Ed., Research Studies Press, Chichester, 1981, 209.

19. **Perchonock, C. D., Uzinskas, I., Ku, T. W., McCarthy, M. E., Bondinell, W. E., Volpe, B. W., Gleason, J. G., Weichman, B. M., Muccitelli, R. M., DeVan, J. F., Tucker, S. S., Vickery, L. M., and Wasserman, M. A.,** Synthesis and $LTD_4$-antagonist activity of desamino-2-nor-leukotriene analogs, *Prostaglandins,* 29, 75, 1985.
20. **Snyder, D. W., Bernstein, P. R., and Krell, R. D.,** Pharmacology of chemically stable analogs of peptide leukotrienes (LT), *Fed. Proc. Fed. Am. Soc. Exp. Biol.,* 44, 901, 1985.
21. **Ali, F. E., Dandridge, P. A., Gleason, J. G., Krell, R. D., Kruse, C. H., Lavanchy, P. G., and Snader, K. M.,** Imidodisulfamides. I. A novel class of antagonists of slow-reacting substance of anaphylaxis, *J. Med. Chem.,* 25, 947, 1982.
22. **Ali, F. E., Gleason, J. G., Hill, D. T., Krell, R. D., Kruse, C. H., Lavanchy, P. G., and Volpe, B. W.,** Imidodisulfamides. II. Substituted 1,2,3,4-tetrahydro isoquinolinylsulfonic imides as antagonists of slow-reacting substance of anaphylaxis, *J. Med. Chem.,* 25, 1235, 1982.
23. **Nishino, K., Ohkubo, H., Ohashi, M., Hara, S., Kito, J., and Irikura, T.,** KC-404: a potential anti-allergic agent with antagonistic action against slow reacting substance of anaphylaxis, *Jpn. J. Pharmacol.,* 33, 267, 1983.
24. **Goetzl, E. J. and Pickett, W. C.,** Novel structural determinants of the human neutrophil chemotactic activity of leukotriene B, *J. Exp. Med.,* 153, 482, 1981.
25. **Showell, H. J., Otterness, I. G., Marfat, A., and Corey, E. J.,** Inhibition of leukotriene $B_4$-induced neutrophil degranulation by leukotriene $B_4$ dimethylamide, *Biochem. Biophys. Res. Commun.,* 106, 741, 1982.
26. **Rinkema, L. E., Haisch, K. D., MCullough, D., Carr, F. P., Dillard, R. D., and Fleisch, J. H.,** LY-163,443, an aryloxy methylacetophenone, antagonizes pharmacological responses to leukotriene (LT) $D_4$ and $LTE_4$, *Fed. Proc. Fed. Am. Soc. Exp. Biol.,* 44, 492, 1985.
27. **Fleisch, J. H., Rinkema, L. E., Haisch, K. D., Swanson-Bean, D., Goodson, T., Ho, P. P. K., and Marshall, W. S.,** LY171883, 1-<2-hydroxy-3-propyl-4-<- (1H-tetrazol-5-yl)butoxy>phenyl>ethanone, an orally active leukotriene $D_4$ antagonist, *J. Pharmacol. Exp. Ther.,* 233, 148, 1985.
28. **Gleason, J. G., Ku, T. W., McCarthy, M. E., Weichman, B. M., Holden, D., Osborn, R. R., Zabko-Potapovich, B., Berkowitz, B., and Wasserman, M. A.,** 2-Nor-leukotriene analogs: anatagonists of the airway and vascular smooth muscle effects of leukotriene $C_4$, $D_4$, and $E_4$, *Biochem. Biophys. Res. Commun.,* 117, 732, 1983.
29. **Couts, S., Khandwala, A., Van Inwegen, R., Bruens, J., Jariwal, N., Dally-Meade, V., Ingram, R., Chakraborty, U., Musser, J., Jones, H., Pruss, T., Neiss, E., and Weinryb, I.,** Arylmethyl pheny ethers: a new class of specific inhibitors of 5-lipoxygenase, *Prostaglandins and Leukotrienes '84: Their Biochemistry, Mechanism of Action and Clinical Applications,* Abstr. 70.
30. **Wasserman, M. A., Muccitelli, R. M., Tucker, S. S., Vickery, L. M., DeVan, J. F., Weichman, B. M., Newton, J., Perchonock, C. D., and Gleason, J. G.,** SK&F 102922: an effective and selective antagonist of leukotriene-mediated bronchoconstriction, *Fed. Proc. Fed. Am. Soc. Exp. Biol.,* 44, 491, 1985.
31. **Weichman, B. M. and Tucker, S. S.,** Differentiation of the mechanisms by which leukotrienes $C_4$ and $D_4$ elicit contraction of the guinea pig trachea, *Prostaglandins,* 29, 547, 1985.
32. **Weichman, B. M., Wasserman, M. A., Holden, D. A., Osborn, R. R., Woodward, D. F., Ku, T. W., and Gleason, J. G.,** Antagonism of the pulmonary effects of the peptidoleukotrienes by a leukotriene $D_4$ analog, *J. Pharmacol. Exp. Ther.,* 227, 700, 1983.
33. **Lewis, A. J., Kreft, A., Blumenthal, A., Schwalm, S., Dervinis, A., Chang, J., Hand, J. M., and Klanbert, D. H.,** WY-44,329, a potent leukotriene antagonist in models of bronchoconstriction *in vitro* and *in vivo, Prostaglandins and Leukotrienes '84: Their Biochemistry, Mechanism of Action and Clinical Applications,* Abstr. 276.
34. **Bray, M. A.,** Leukotriene receptors, in *Leukotrienes in Cardiovascular and Pulmonary Function,* Alan R. Liss, New York, 17, 1985.
35. **Dahlen, S.-E.,** Pulmonary effects of leukotrienes, *Acta Physiol. Scand. (Suppl),* 512, 1, 1983.
36. **Fleisch, J. H., Rinkema, L. E., and Marshall, W. S.,** Pharmacologic receptors for the leukotrienes, *Biochem. Pharmacol.,* 33, 3919, 1984.
37. **Lewis, R. A. and Austen, K. F.,** The biologically active leukotrienes. Biosynthesis, metabolism, receptors, functions, and pharmacology, *J. Clin. Invest.,* 73, 889, 1984.
38. **McLean, J. R. and Gluckman, M. I.,** On the mechanism of the pharmacologic activity of meclofenamate sodium, *Arzneim. Forsch/Drug Res.,* 33, 627, 1983.
39. **Coleman, R. A., Humphrey, P. P. A., Kennedy, I., Levy, G. P., and Lumley, P.,** Further evidence that AH 19437 is a specific thromboxane receptor blocking drug, *Br. J. Pharmacol.,* 73, 258P, 1981.
40. **LeBreton, G. C., Venton, D. L., Enke, S. E., and Haluska, P. V.,** 13-Aza prostanoic acid: a specific antagonist of the human blood platelet thromboxane/endoperoxide receptor, *Proc. Natl. Acad. Sci. U.S.A.,* 76, 4097, 1979.

41. **Kam, S. T., Portoghese, P. S., Dunham, E. W., and Gerrard, J. M.,** 9,11-Azo-13-oxa-15-hydroxyprostanoic acid: a potent thromboxane synthetase inhibitor and a $PGH_2/TXA_2$ receptor antagonist., *Prostaglandins Med.*, 3, 279, 1979.
42. **Patscheke, H. and Stegmeier, K.,** Investigations on a selective non-prostanoic thromboxane antagonist, BM 13.177, in human platelets, *Thromb. Res.*, 33, 277, 1984.
43. **Stegmeier, K., Pill, J., Müller-Beckmann, B., Schmidt, F. H., Witte, E.-C., Wolff, H.-P., and Patscheke, H.,** The pharmacological profile of the thromboxane $A_2$ antagonist BM 13.177. A new antiplatelet and anti-thrombotic drug, *Thromb. Res.* 35, 379, 1984.
44. **Jones, R. L., Peesapati, V., and Wilson, N. H.,** Antagonism of the thromboxane-sensitive contractile systems of the rabbit aorta, dog saphenous vein and guinea-pig trachea, *Br. J. Pharmacol.*, 76, 423, 1982.
45. **Armstrong, R. A., Jones, R. L., Peesapati, V., Will, S. G., and Wilson, N. H.,** Effect of the thromboxane receptor antagonist EP 092 on the early phase of endotoxin shock in the sheep, *Br. J. Pharmacol.*, 81 (Suppl.), 72P.
46. **Fitzpatrick, F. A., Bundy, G. L., Gorman, R. R., and Honohan, T.,** 9,11-Epoxyiminoprosta-5,13-dienoic acid is a thromboxane $A_2$ antagonist in human platelets, *Nature (London)*, 275, 764, 1978.
47. **Katsura, M., Miyamoto, T., Hamanaka, N., Kondo, K., Terada, T., Ohgaki, Y., Kawasaki, A., and Tsuboshima, M.,** *In vitro* and *in vivo* effects of new powerful thromboxane antagonists (3 alkylamino pinane derivatives), *Adv. Prostaglandin Thromboxane Leukotriene Res.*, 11, 351, 1983.
48. **Nicolaou, K. C., Magolda, R. L., Smith, B. J., Aharony, D., Smith, E. F., and Lefer, A. M.,** Synthesis and biological properties of pinane-thromboxane $A_2$, a selective inhibitor of coronary artery constriction, platelet aggregation, and thromboxane formation, *Proc. Natl. Acad. Sci. U.S.A.*, 76, 2566, 1979.
49. **Roth, D. M., Lefer, A. M., Smith, J. B., and Nicolaou, K. C.,** Anti-thromboxane $A_2$ actions of pinane thromboxane derivatives, *Prostaglandins Leukotrienes Med.*, 9, 503, 1982.
50. **Shimizu, K., Kohli, J. D., Goldberg, L. I., Kittisopikul, S., and Fried, J.,** Stable carbocyclic analog of thromboxane $A_2$ as antagonist of prostaglandin receptors, *Adv. Prostaglandin Thromboxane Leukotriene Res.* 11, 333, 1983.
51. **Harris, D. N., Greenberg, R., Phillips, M. B., Michel, I. M., Goldenberg, H. J., Haslinger, M. F., and Steinbacher, T. E.,** Effects of SQ 27,427, a thromboxane $A_2$ receptor antagonist, in the human platelet and isolated smooth muscle, *Eur. J. Pharmacol.*, 103, 9, 1984.
52. **Ogletree, M. L., Harris, D. N., Greenberg, R., Haslanger, M. F., and Nakane, M.,** Pharmacological actions of SQ 29,548, a novel selective thromboxane antagonist, *J. Pharmacol. Exp. Ther.*, 234, 435, 1985.
53. **Macintyre, D. E. and Willis, A. L.,** Trimethoquinol is a potent prostaglandin endoperoxide antagonist, *Br. J. Pharmacol.*, 63, 361P, 1978.
54. **Mayo, J. R., Navran, S. S., Huzoor-Akbar, Miller, D. D., and Feller, D. R.,** Stereo-dependent inhibition of human platelet function by the optical isomers of trimethoquinol, *Biochem. Pharmacol.*, 30, 2237, 1981.
55. **Mukhopadhyay, A., Navran, S. S., Amin, H. M., Abdel-Aziz, S. A., Chang, J., Sober, D. J., Miller, D. D., and Feller, D. R.,** Effect of trimethoquinol analogs for antagonism of endoperoxide/thromboxane $A_2$-mediated responses in human platelets and rat aorta, *J. Pharmacol. Exp. Ther.*, 232, 1, 1985.
56. **Eakins, K. E., Karim, S. M. M., and Miller, J. D.,** Antagonism of some smooth muscle actions of prostaglandins by polyphloretin phosphate, *Br. J. Pharmacol.*, 39, 556, 1970.
57. **Eakins, K. E. and Miller, J. D.,** Personal communication, 1970.
58. **Sanner, J. H.,** Dibenzoxazepine hydrazides as prostaglandin antagonists, *Intra-Sci. Chem. Rep.*, 6, 1, 1972.
59. **Tolman, E. L., Partridge, R., and Barris, E. T.,** Prostaglandin E antagonist activity of 11,15-bisdeoxy prostaglandin E1 and congeners, *Prostaglandins*, 14, 11, 1977.
60. **Maddox, Y. T., Ramwell, P. W., Shiner, C. S., and Corey, E. J.,** Amide and 1-amino derivatives of F prostaglandins as prostaglandin antagonists, *Nature (London)* 273, 549, 1978.
61. **Eakins, K. E., Rajadhyaksha, and Schoroer, R.,** Prostaglandin antagonism by sodium p-benzyl-4-[1-oxo-2-(4-chlorobenzyl)-3-phenylpropyl]phenyl phosphonate (N-0164), *Br. J. Pharmacol.*, 58, 333, 1976.
62. **Fried, J., Lin, C., Mehra, M., Kao, W., and Dalven, P.,** Synthesis and biological activity of prostaglandins and prostaglandin antagonists, *Ann. N.Y. Acad. Sci.*, 180, 38, 1971.
63. **Flack, J. D.,** Discussion in *Recent Prog. Horm. Res.*, 26, 174, 1970.
64. **Harris, C. J., Whittaker, N., Higgs, G. A., Armstrong, J. M., and Reed, P. M.,** The synthesis and biological activities of some 12-aza prostaglandin analogs, *Prostaglandins*, 16, 773, 1978.
65. **Bennett, A., Jarosik, C., Sanger, G. J., and Wilson, D. E.,** Antagonism of prostanoid-induced contractions of rat gastric fundus muscle by SC-19220, sodium meclofenamate, indomethacin or trimethoquinol, *Br. J. Pharmacol.*, 71, 169, 1980.
66. **Bennett, A. and Posner, J.,** Studies on prostaglandin antagonists, *Br. J. Pharmacol.*, 42, 584, 1971.
67. **Posner, J.,** Prostaglandin $E_2$ and the bovine sphincter pupillae, *Br. J. Pharmacol.*, 49, 415, 1973.
68. **Eakins, K. E., Whitelocke, R. A. F., Perkins, E. S., Bennett, A., and Unger, W. G.,** Prostaglandin release in ocular inflammation in rabbits and man, *Adv. Biosci.*, 9, 427, 1973.

69. **Splawinski, J. A., Nies, A. S., Sweetman, B., and Oates, J. A.,** The effects of arachidonic acid, prostaglandin $E_2$ and prostaglandin $F_{2\alpha}$ on the longitudinal stomach strip of the rat, *J. Pharmacol. Exp. Ther.,* 187, 501, 1973.
70. **Sanger, G. J. and Bennett, A.,** Trimethoquinol selectively antagonizes contractions of rat gastric fundus to $TXB_2$ and epoxymethano analogs of $PGH_2$, *Adv. Prostaglandin Thromboxane Res.,* 8, 1559, 1980.
71. **Sanner, J. H., Mueller, R. A., and Schulze, R. H.,** Structure-activity relationships of some dibenzoxazepine derivatives as prostaglandin antagonists, *Adv. Biosci.,* 9, 139, 1973.
72. **Ozaki, N., Kohli, J. D., Goldberg, L. I., and Fried, J.,** Vascular smooth muscle activity of 7-oxa-13-prostynoic acid, *Blood Vessels,* 16, 52, 1979.
73. **Ganesan, P. A. and Karim, S. M. M.,** Polyphloretin phosphate temporarily potentiates prostaglandin $E_2$ on the rat fundus, probably by inhibiting PG 15-hydroxydehydrogenase, *J. Pharm. Pharmacol.,* 25, 229, 1973.
74. **Marrazzi, M. A. and Matschinsky, F. M.,** Properties of 15-hydroxy prostaglandin dehydrogenase: structural requirements for substrate binding, *Prostaglandins,* 1, 373, 1972.
75. **Bennett, A., Eley, K. G., and Stockley, H. C.,** The effects of prostaglandins on guinea-pig isolated intestine and their possible contribution to muscle activity and tone, *Br. J. Pharmacol.,* 54, 197, 1975.
76. **Bennett, A., Eley, K. G., and Stockley, H. L.,** Inhibition of peristalsis in guinea pig isolated ileum and colon by drugs that block prostaglandin synthesis, *Br. J. Pharmacol.,* 57, 335, 1976.
77. **Yagasaki, O., Funaki, H., and Yanagiya, I.,** Contribution of endogenous prostaglandins to excitation of the myenteric plexus of guinea pig ileum: are adrenergic factors involved? *Eur. J. Pharmacol.,* 103, 1, 1984.
78. **Ambache, N., Verney, J., and Aboo Zar, M.,** Evidence for the release of two atropine-resistant spasmogens from Auerbach's plexus, *J. Physiol. (London),* 207, 761, 1970.
79. **Kennedy, I., Coleman, R. A., Humphrey, P. P. A., Levy, G. P., Lumley, P.,** Studies on the characterisation of prostanoid receptors: a proposed classification, *Prostaglandins,* 24, 667, 1982.
80. **Eakins, K. E.,** Prostaglandin antagonism by polymeric phosphates of phloretin and related compounds, *Ann. N.Y. Acad. Sci.,* 180, 386, 1971.
81. **Karim, S. M. M.,** The effect of polyphloretin phosphate and other compounds on prostaglandin-induced diarrhea in man, *Ann. Acad. Med.,* 3, 201, 1974.
82. **Engel, J. J., Scruggs, W., and Wilson, D. E.,** Failure of SC-19220 to affect prostaglandin ($PGE_1$) gastric antisecretory actions, *Prostaglandins,* 4, 65, 1973.
83. **Engel, J. J. and Wilson, D. E.,** Failure of a prostaglandin inhibitor (SC-19220) to affect prostaglandin $E_1$ ($PGE_1$) gastric antisecretory actions, *Clin. Res.* 21, 511, 1973.
84. **Holme, G., Brunet, G., Piechuta, H., Masson, P., Girard, Y., and Rokach, J.,** The effects of synthetic leukotriene C (LTC-1) on isolated guinea pig trachea and ileum, *Prostaglandins,* 20, 717, 1980.
85. **Welton, A. F., Crowley, H. J., Miller, D. H., and Yaremko, B.,** Biological activities of a chemically synthesized form of leukotriene $E_4$, *Prostaglandins,* 21, 287, 1981.
86. **Sanger, G. J. and Bennett, A.,** Fenamates may antagonize the actions of prostaglandin endoperoxides in human myometrium, *Br. J. Clin. Pharmacol.,* 8, 479, 1979.
87. **Sorrentino, L., Capasso, F., and DiRosa, M.,** Indomethacin and prostaglandins, *Eur. J. Pharmacol.,* 17, 306, 1972.
88. **Marmo, E., Caputi, A. P., Rossi, F., and Lampa, E.,** Prostaglandin $F_{2\alpha}$ and uterine muscle: an experimental study in animals, in *Obstetric and Gynaecological Uses of Prostaglandins,* Karim, S. M. M., Ed., University Park Press, Baltimore, 1976, 261.
89. **Ganatra, V. M., Dhumal, V. R., Bhatt, J. D., and Sachdev, K. S.,** Antagonism of some contractile responses to prostaglandins by cyproheptadine, *Arch. Int. Pharmacodyn. Ther.,* 240, 203, 1979.
90. **Whalley, E. T.,** The action of bradykinin and oxytocin on the isolated whole uterus and myometrium of the rat in oestrus, *Br. J. Pharmacol.,* 64, 21, 1978.
91. **Ishizawa, M. and Pickles, V. R.,** A comparison of some smooth muscle effects of GABA and of prostaglandin E1, *Br. J. Pharmacol.,* 54, 279, 1975.
92. **Baudouin-Legros, M., Meyer, P., and Worcel, M.,** Action of 7-oxa-13-prostynoic acid on rat uterine contractility and sensitivity to $PGF_{2\alpha}$ and angiotensin II, *Prostaglandins,* 9, 203, 1975.
93. **Johnson, M., Jessup, R., Ramwell, P. W.,** The significance of protein disulfide and sulfhydryl groups in prostaglandin action, *Prostaglandins,* 5, 125, 1974.
94. **Strandberg, K. and Tuvemo, T.,** Reduction of the tone of the isolated human umbilical artery by indomethacin, eicosa-5,8,11,14-tetraynoic acid and polyphloretin phosphate, *Acta Physiol. Scand.,* 94, 319, 1975.
95. **Park, M. K. and Dyer, D. C.,** Effect of polyphloretin phosphate and 7-oxa-13-prostynoic acid on vasoactive actions of prostaglandin $E_2$ and 5-hydroxytryptamine on isolated human umbilical arteries, *Prostaglandins,* 3, 913, 1973.
96. **Toda, N. and Miyazaki, M.,** Responses of isolated dog cerebral and peripheral arteries to prostaglandins after application of aspirin and polyphloretin phosphate, *Stroke,* 9, 490, 1978.

97. **Ganesan, P. A. and Karim, S. M. M.,** Effect of prostaglandins $A_1$, $A_2$, $B_1$, $B_2$, $E_2$, and $F_{2\alpha}$ on human umbilical cord vessels, *Prostaglandins,* 8, 411, 1974.
98. **Toda, N.,** Different responsiveness of a variety of isolated dog arteries to prostaglandin $D_2$, *Prostaglandins,* 23, 99, 1982.
99. **Burka, J. F. and Eyre, P.,** Studies of prostaglandins and prostaglandin antagonists on bovine pulmonary vein *in vitro, Prostaglandins,* 6, 333, 1974.
100. **Allen, G. and Levy, R.,** The cardiac effects of prostaglandins and their modification by the prostaglandin antagonist N-0164, *J. Pharmacol. Exp. Ther.,* 214, 45, 1980.
101. **Mathe, A. A.,** Studies on actions of prostaglandins in the lung, *Acta Physiol. Scand. (Suppl.),* 441, 1, 1976.
102. **Mathe, A. A., Strandberg, K., and Fredholm, B.,** Antagonism of prostaglandin $F_{2\alpha}$-induced bronchoconstriction and blood pressure changes by polyphloretin phosphate in the guinea pig and cat, *J. Pharm. Pharmacol.,* 24, 378, 1972.
103. **Villanueva, R., Hinds, L., Katz, R. L., and Eakins, K. E.,** The effect of polyphloretin phosphate on some smooth muscle actions of prostaglandins in the cat, *J. Pharmacol. Exp. Ther.,* 180, 78, 1972.
104. **McQueen, D. S.,** The effects of prostaglandin $E_2$, prostaglandin $F_{2\alpha}$ and polyphloretin phosphate on respiration and blood pressure in anesthetized guinea pigs, *Life Sci.,* 12 (Part 1), 163, 1973.
105. **White, R. P. and Pennink, M.,** Reversal of the pressor response of prostaglandin $F_{2\alpha}$ by polyphloretin phosphate in dogs, *Arch. Int. Pharmacodyn. Ther.,* 197, 274, 1972.
106. **Chand, N. and Eyre, P.,** Effects of prostaglandins $E_1$, $E_2$ and $F_{2\alpha}$ and polyphloretin phosphate on carotid blood pressure of domestic fowl, *Arch. Int. Pharmacodyn. Ther.,* 221, 261, 1976.
107. **Levy, B. and Lindner, H. R.,** Selective blockade of the vasodepressor response to prostaglandin $F_{2\alpha}$ in the anesthetized rabbit, *Br. J. Pharmacol.,* 43, 236, 1971.
108. **Nakano, J., Prancan, A. V., and Moore, S.,** Effect of the prostaglandin antagonists on the vasoactivities of prostaglandins $E_1$ ($PGE_1$), $E_2$ ($PGE_2$), $A_1$ ($PGA_1$) and $F_{2\alpha}$ ($PGF_{2\alpha}$), *Clin. Res.,* 19, 712, 1971.
109. **Burka, J. F. and Eyre, P.,** A study of prostaglandins and prostaglandin antagonists in relation to anaphylaxis in calves, *Can. J. Physiol. Pharmacol.,* 52, 942, 1974.
110. **Park, M. K., Rishor, C., and Dyer, D. C.,** Vasoactive actions of prostaglandins and serotonin on isolated human umbilical arteries and veins, *Can. J. Physiol. Pharmacol.,* 50, 393, 1972.
111. **Marmo, E., Rossi, F., Lampa, E., Giordano, L., Caputi, A. P., Vacca, C., Ariello, B., and Rosatti, F.,** Cardiovascular research on prostaglandin $I_2$, 6-keto prostaglandin $F_{1\alpha}$ prostaglandin $F_{2\alpha}$ and 15-S-15 methyl prostaglandin $F_{2\alpha}$, *Adv. Prostaglandin Thromboxane Res,* 7, 701, 1980.
112. **Nakano, J.,** Relationship between the chemical structure of prostaglandins and their vasoactivities in dogs, *Br. J. Pharmacol.,* 44, 63, 1972.
113. **Fitzpatrick, T. M., Alter, I. Corey, E. J., Ramwell, P. W., Rose, J. C., and Kot, P. A.,** Antagonism of the pulmonary vasoconstrictor response to prostaglandin $F_{2\alpha}$ by N-dimethylamino substitution of prostaglandin $F_{2\alpha}$, *J. Pharmacol. Exp. Ther.,* 206, 139, 1978.
114. **Stinger, R. B., Fitzpatrick, T. M., Corey, E. J., Ramwell, P. W., Rose, J. C., and Kot, P. A.,** Selective antagonism of prostaglandin $F_{2\alpha}$-mediated vascular responses by N-dimethylamino substitution of prostaglandin $F_{2\alpha}$, *J. Pharmacol. Exp. Ther.,* 220, 521, 1982.
115. **Brody, M. J. and Kadowitz, P. J.,** Prostaglandins as modulators of the autonomic nervous system, *Fed. Proc. Fed. Am. Soc. Exp. Biol.,* 33, 48, 1974.
116. **Stinger, R. B., Fitzpatrick, T. M., Van Dam, J., Ramwell, P. W., and Kot, P. A.,** Selective antagonism of the systemic vasodepressor response to $PGE_1$ by d,l-11,15-bisdeoxy $PGE_1$, *Prostaglandins,* 19, 213, 1980.
117. **Jones, R. L. and Wilson, N. H.,** Thromboxane receptor antagonism shown by a prostanoid with a bicyclo[2,2,1]heptane ring, *Br. J. Pharmacol.,* 73, 220P, 1981.
118. **Horn, P. T., Kohli, J. D., LeBreton, G. C., and Venton, D. L.,** Antagonism of prostanoid-induced vascular contraction by 13-azaprostanoic acid (13-APA), *J. Cardiovasc. Pharmacol.,* 6, 609, 1984.
119. **Bennett, A. and Sanger, G. J.,** Pinane thromboxane $A_2$ analogues are non-selective prostanoid antagonists in rat and human stomach muscle, *Br. J. Pharmacol.,* 77, 591, 1982.
120. **Burke, S. E., Roth, D. M., and Lefer, A. M.,** Antagonism of platelet aggregation by 13-azaprostanoic acid in acute myocardial ischemia and sudden death, *Thromb. Res.,* 29, 473, 1983.
121. **LeBreton, G. C. and Venton, D. L.,** Thromboxane $A_2$ receptor antagonism selectively reverses platelet aggregation, *Adv. Prostaglandin Thromboxane Res.,* 6, 497, 1980.
122. **LeBreton, G. C., Lipowski, J. P., Feinberg, H., Venton, D. L., Ho, T., and Wu, K. K.,** Antagonism of thromboxane $A_2$/prostaglandin $H_2$ by 13-azaprostanoic acid prevents platelet deposition to the de-endothelialized rabbit aorta *in vivo, J. Pharmacol. Exp. Ther.,* 229, 80, 1984.
123. **Jones, R. L., Wilson, N. H., Armstrong, R. A., Peesapati, V., and Smith, G. M.,** Effects of thromboxane antagonist EPO45 on platelet aggregation, *Adv. Prostaglandin Thromboxane Leukotriene Res.,* 11, 345, 1983.

124. **Hassid, A.,** Stimulation of prostacyclin synthesis by thromboxane $A_2$-like prostaglandin endoperoxide analogues in cultured vascular smooth muscle cells, *Biochem. Biophys. Res. Commun.*, 123, 21, 1984.
125. **Harris, D. N., Phillips, M. B., Michel, I. M., Goldenberg, H. J., Heikes, J. E., Sprague, P. W., and Antonaccio, M. J.,** 9α-Homo-9,11-epoxy-5,13-prostadienoic acid analogues: specific stable agonist (SQ 26,538) and antagonist (SQ 26,536) of the human platelet thromboxane receptor, *Prostaglandisn*, 22, 295, 1981.
126. **Armstrong, R. A., Jones, R. L., and Wilson, N. H.,** Ligand binding to thromboxane receptors on human platelets: correlation with biological activity, *Br. J. Pharmacol.*, 79, 953, 1983.
127. **Chan, C. C., Nathaniel, D. J., Yusko, P. J., Hall, R. A., and Ford-Hutchinson, A. W.,** Inhibition of prostanoid-mediated platelet aggregation *in vivo* and *in vitro* by 3-hydroxymethyldibenzo (b,f) thiepin 5,5-dioxide (L640,035), *J. Pharmacol. Exp. Ther.*, 229, 276, 1984.
128. **Sirois, P., Roy, S., Tetrault, J. P., Borgeat, P., Picard, S., and Corey, E. J.,** Pharmacological activity of leukotrienes $A_4$, $B_4$, $C_4$ and $D_4$ on selected guinea-pig, rat, rabbit and human smooth muscles, *Prostaglandins Med.*, 7, 327, 1981.
129. **Sirois, P., Borgeat, P., Jeanson, A., Roy, S., and Girard, G.,** The action of leukotriene $B_4$ ($LTB_4$) on the lung, *Prostaglandins Med.*, 5, 429, 1980.
130. **Drazen, J. M., Austen, K. F., Lewis, R. A., Clark, D. A., Gotto, G., Marfat, A., and Corey, E. J.,** Comparative airway and vascular activities of leukotrienes C-1 and D *in vivo* and *in vitro, Proc. Natl. Acad. Sci. U.S.A.*, 77, 4354, 1980.
131. **Yen, S. S.,** Inhibition of arachidonic acid-induced contraction of guinea pig lung strips, *Prostaglandins*, 22, 183, 1981.
132. **Piper, P. J. and Samhoun, M. N.,** The mechanism of action of leukotrienes $C_4$ and $D_4$ on guinea pig isolated perfused lung and parenchymal strips of guinea pig, rabbit and rat, *Prostaglandins*, 21, 793, 1981.
133. **Sirois, P., Roy, S., and Borgeat, P.,** Specificity of receptors for leukotrienes $A_4$, $B_4$, $C_4$, $D_4$, $E_4$ and histamine on the guinea pig parenchyma. Effect of FPL-55712 and desensitization of the myotropic activity, *Prostaglandins*, 26, 91, 1983.
134. **Krell, R. D., Osborn, R., Vickery, L., Falcone, K., O'Donnell, M., Gleason, J., Kinzig, C., Bryan, D.,** Contraction of isolated airway smooth muscle by synthetic leukotrienes $C_4$ and $D_4$, *Prostaglandins*, 22, 387, 1981.
135. **Zijlstra, F. J., Vincent, J. E., and Bonta, I. L.,** Separation of the two components of the contractile activity of leukotriene $C_4$ on the guinea pig lung parenchymal strip, *Prostglandins Leukotrienes Med.*, 11, 385, 1983.
136. **Austen, K. F., Corey, E. J., Drazen, J. M., and Leitch, A. G.,** The effect of indomethacin on the contractile response of the guinea-pig lung parenchymal strip to leukotrienes $B_4$, $C_4$, $D_4$, and $E_4$, *Br. J. Pharmacol.*, 80, 47, 1983.
137. **Weichman, B. M., Muccitelli, R. M., Osborn, R. R., Holden, D. A., Gleason, J. G., and Wasserman, M. A.,** *In vitro* and *in vivo* mechanisms of leukotriene-mediated bronchoconstriction in the guinea pig, *J. Pharmacol. Exp. Ther.*, 222, 202, 1982.
138. **Welton, A. F., Hope, W. C., Tobias, L. D., and Hamilton, J. G.,** Inhibition of antigen-induced histamine release and thromboxane synthetase by FPL 55712, a specific SRS-A antagonist? *Biochem. Pharmacol.*, 30, 1378, 1981.
139. **Jones, T., Denis, D., Hall, R., and Ethier, D.,** Pharmacological study of the effects of leukotrienes $C_4$, $D_4$, $E_4$, and $F_4$ on guinea pig trachealis: interaction with FPL-55712, *Prostaglandins*, 26, 833, 1983.
140. **Krell, R. D., Tsai, B. S., Berdoulay, A., Barone, M., and Giles, R. E.,** Heterogeneity of leukotriene receptors in guinea pig trachea, *Prostaglandins*, 25, 171, 1983.
141. **Fleisch, J. H., Rinkema, L. E., and Baker, S. R.,** Evidence for multiple leukotriene $D_4$ receptors in smooth muscle, *Life Sci.*, 31, 577, 1982.
142. **Snyder, D. W. and Krell, R. D.,** Pharmacological evidence for a distinct leukotriene $C_4$ receptor in guinea pig trachea, *J. Pharmacol. Exp. Ther.*, 231, 616, 1984.
143. **Holroyde, M. C., Altounyan, R. E. C., Cole, M., Dixon, M., and Elliott, E. V.,** Selective inhibition of bronchoconstriction induced by leukotrienes C and D in man, in *Leukotrienes and Other Lipoxygenase Products*, Samuelsson, B. and Paoletti, R., Eds., Raven Press, New York, 1982, 237.
144. **Lee, T. H., Walport, M. J., Wilkinson, A. H., Turner-Warwick, M., and Kay, A. B.,** Slow-reacting substance of anaphylaxis antagonist FPL 55712 in chronic asthma, *Lancet*, 304, 1981.
145. **Lewis, A. J., Chang, J., Hand, J., Carlson, R. P., and Kreft, A.,** Wy 44,329: a leukotriene antagonist with lipoxygenase inhibitory and antiallergic properties, *Int. J. Immunopharmacol.*, 7, 384, 1985.
146. **Gordon, R. J., Travis, J., Godfrey, H. R., Sweeney, D., Wolf, P. S., Pruss, T. P., Neiss, E., Musser, J., Chakraberty, U., Jones, H., and Leibowitz, M.,** *In vivo* activity of a lipoxygenase inhibitor and leukotriene antagonist, REV 5901-A, in *Prostaglandins and Leukotrienes '84: Their Biochemistry, Mechanism of Action and Clinical Applications*, Abstr. 266.

147. **Gleason, J. G., Krell, R. D., Weichman, B. M., Ali, F. E., and Berkowitz, B.,** Comparative pharmacology and antagonism of synthetic leukotrienes on airway and vascular smooth muscle, in *Leukotrienes and other Lipoxygenase Products,* Samuelsson, B. and Paoletti, R., Eds., Raven Press, New York, 1982, 243.
148. **Weichman, B. M., Wasserman, M. A., and Gleason, J. G.,** SK&F 88046: a unique pharmacologic antagonist of bronchoconstriction induced by leukotriene $D_4$, thromboxane and prostaglandins $F_{2\alpha}$ and $D_2$ *in vitro, J. Pharmacol. Exp. Ther.,* 228, 128, 1984.
149. **Lo, P. Y.,** Effects of pulmonary metabolites of prostaglandins $E_2$ and $F_{2\alpha}$ on guinea pig respiratory tract, *J. Pharm. Pharmacol.,* 29, 752, 1977.
150. **Mathe, A. A., Strandberg, K., and Astrom, A.,** Blockade by polyphloretin phosphate of the prostaglandin $F_{2\alpha}$ action on isolated human bronchi, *Nature (London) New Biol.,* 230, 215, 1971.
151. **Vargaftig, B. B. and Lefort, J.,** Enhancement by prostacyclin of the contractility of the guinea-pig airways smooth muscle, *Eur. J. Pharmacol.,* 74, 141, 1981.
152. **Mathe, A. A. and Strandberg, K.,** Antagonism of slow reacting substance by polyphloretin phosphate in isolated human bronchi, *Acta Physiol. Scand.,* 82, 460, 1971.
153. **Lambley, J. E. and Smith, A. P.,** Effects of arachidonic acid, indomethacin, and SC-19220 on guinea pig tracheal muscle tone, *Eur. J. Pharmacol.,* 30, 148, 1975.
154. **Farmer, J. B., Farrar, D. G., and Wilson, J.,** Antagonism of tone and prostaglandin-mediated responses in a tracheal preparation by indomethacin and SC-19220, *Br. J. Pharmacol.,* 52, 559, 1974.
155. **Turker, R. K. and Ercan, Z. S.,** The effects of angiotensin I and angiotensin II on the isolated tracheal muscle of the cat, *J. Pharm. Pharmacol.,* 28, 298, 1976.
156. **Temple, D. M., McIntyre, H. J., and Smith, I. D.,** Interactions between prostaglandins and anti-inflammatory drugs on respiratory tissue, *Clin. Exp. Pharmacol. Physiol.* 2, 448, 1975.
157. **Collier, H. O. J. and Sweatman, W. J. F.,** Antagonism by fenamates of prostaglandin $F_{2\alpha}$ and of slow reacting substance on human bronchial muscle, *Nature (London),* 219, 864, 1968.
158. **Greig, M. E. and Griffin, R. L.,** Antagonism of slow reacting substance in anaphylaxis (SRS-A) and other spasmogens on the guinea pig tracheal chain by hydratropic acids and their effects on anaphylaxis, *J. Med. Chem.,* 18, 112, 1975.
159. **Kuehl, F. A., Jr., Humes, J. L., Tarnoff, J., Cirillo, V. J., and Ham, E. A.,** Prostaglandin receptor site: evidence for an essential role in the action of luteinizing hormone, *Science,* 169, 883, 1970.
160. **Ortman, R. and Perkins, J. P.,** Stimulation of cyclic AMP formation by prostaglandins in human astrocytoma cells. Inhibition by nonsteroidal anti-inflammatory agents, *J. Biol. Chem.,* 252, 6018, 1977.
161. **Sato, S., Szabo, M., Kowalski, K., and Burke, G.,** Role of prostaglandin in thyrotropin action on thyroid, *Endocrinology,* 90, 343, 1972.
162. **Burke, G., Kowalski, K., and Barbiarz, D.,** Effects of thyrotropin, prostaglandin $E_1$ and a prostaglandin antagonist on iodide trapping in isolated thyroid cells, *Life Sci.,* 10 (Part 2), 513, 1971.
163. **Burke, G. and Sato, S.,** Effects of long-acting thyroid stimulator and prostaglandin antagonists on adenyl cyclase activity in isolated bovine thyroid cells, *Life Sci.,* 10 (Part 2), 969, 1971.
164. **Kowalski, K., Sato, S., and Burke, G.,** Thyrotropin- and prostaglandin $E_2$-responsive adenyl cyclase in thyroid plasma membranes, *Prostaglandins,* 2, 441, 1972.
165. **Fahey, J. V., Ciosek, C. P., and Newcombe, D. S.,** Human synovial fibroblasts. The relationships between cyclic-AMP, bradykinin and prostaglandins, *Agents Actions,* 7, 255, 1977.
166. **Hynie, S., Cepelik, J., Cernohorsky, M., Klenorova, V., Shrivanova, J., and Wenke, M.,** 7-Oxa-13-prostynoic acid and polyphloretin phosphate as non-specific antagonists of the stimulatory effects of different agents in adenylate cyclase from various tissues, *Prostaglandins,* 10, 971, 1975.
167. **Kolena, J. and Channing, C. P.,** Stimulatory effects of LH, FSH and prostaglandins upon cyclic 3′5′-AMP levels in porcine granulosa cells, *Endocrinology (Baltimore),* 90, 1543, 1972.
168. **Dismukes, K. and Daly, J. W.,** Accumulation of adenosine 3′,5′-monophosphate in rat brain slices. Effects of prostaglandins, *Life Sci.,* 17, 199, 1975.
169. **Kalix, P.,** Prostaglandins cause cyclic AMP accumulation in peripheral nerve, *Brain Res.,* 162, 159, 1979.
170. **Tal, E., Szabo, M., and Burke, G.,** TRH and prostaglandin action on rat anterior pituitary: dissociation between cyclic AMP levels and TSH release, *Prostaglandins,* 5, 175, 1974.
171. **Lippman, W.,** Inhibition of prostaglandin $E_2$-induced cyclic AMP accumulation in the rat anterior pituitary by 11-deoxy-prostaglandin E analogs (9 ketoprostynoic acids), *Prostaglandins,* 10, 479, 1975.
172. **Vesin, M. F. and Harbon, S.,** The effects of epinephrine, prostaglandins and their antagonists on adenosine cyclic 3′,5′-monophosphate concentrations and motility of the rat uterus, *Mol. Pharmacol.,* 10, 457, 1974.
173. **Shima, S., Kawashima, Y., Hirai, M., Asakura, M., and Kouyama, H.,** Cyclic nucleotides in the adrenal gland 10. Effects of ACTH and prostaglandin on adenylate cyclase activity in the adrenal cortex, *Endocrinology,* 106, 948, 1980.
174. **Dozois, R. R., Kim, J. K., and Dousa, T. P.,** Interaction of prostaglandins with canine gastric mucosal adenylate cyclase-cyclic AMP system, *Am. J. Physiol.,* 235, E546, 1978.

175. **Sato, S., Kowalski, K., and Burke, G.,** Effects of a prostaglandin antagonist, polyphloretin phosphate, on basal and stimulated thyroid function, *Prostaglandins,* 1, 345, 1972.
176. **Kuehl, F. A., Humes, J. L., Mandel, L. R., Cirillo, V. J., Zanetti, M. E., and Ham, E. A.,** Prostaglandin antagonists: studies on the mode of action of polyphloretin phosphate, *Biochem. Biophys. Res. Commun.,* 44, 1464, 1971.
177. **Ortmann, R., Nutto, D., and Jackisch, R.,** Phosphorylated derivatives of phloretin inhibit cyclic AMP accumulation in neuronal and glial tumor cells in culture, *Naunyn-Schmiedebergs Arch. Pharmakol.,* 305, 233, 1978.
178. **Yu, J. H., Wells, H., Ryan, W. J., Jr., and Lloyd, W. S.,** Effects of prostaglandins and other drugs on the cyclic AMP content of cultured bone cells, *Prostaglandins,* 12, 501, 1976.
179. **Yu, J. H., Wells, H., Moghadam, B., and Ryan, W. J., Jr.,** Cyclic AMP formation and release by cultured bone cells stimulated wtih prostaglandin $E_2$, *Prostaglandins,* 17, 61, 1979.
180. **Perrier, C. V. and Griessen, M.,** Action of $H_1$ and $H_2$ inhibitors on the response of histamine sensitive adenylyl cyclase from guinea-pig mucosa, *Eur. J. Clin. Invest.,* 6, 113, 1976.
181. **Traber, J., Fischer, K., Latzin, S., and Hamprecht, B.,** Cultures of cells derived from the nervous system: synthesis and action of prostaglandin E, *Excerpta Med Int. Congr. Ser.,* 359, 956, 1974.
182. **Zor, U., Bauminger, S., Lamprecht, S. A., Koch, Y., Chobsieng, P., and Lindner, H. R.,** Stimulation of cyclic AMP production in the rat ovary by luteinizing hormone: independence of prostaglandin mediation, *Prostaglandins,* 4, 499, 1973.
183. **Horne, W. C.,** Desacetyl-1-nantradol: a selective prostaglandin antagonist, *Prostaglandins Leukotrienes Med.,* 15, 129, 1984.
184. **Chasin, M. and Scott, C.,** Inhibition of cyclic nucleotide phosphodiesterase by FPL 55712, an SRS-A antagonist., *Biochem. Pharmacol.,* 27, 2065, 1978.
185. **Crutchley, D. J. and Piper, P. J.,** Inhibition of the pulmonary inactivation of prostaglandins *in vivo* by di-4-phloretin phosphate, *Br. J. Pharmacol.,* 54, 301, 1975.
186. **Fried, J., Lin, C. H., Mehra, M. M., Kao, W. L., and Dalven, P.,** Synthesis and biological activity of prostaglandins and prostaglandin antagonists, *Ann. N.Y. Acad. Sci.,* 180, 38, 1971.
187. **McDonald-Gibson, R. G., Flack, J. D., and Ramwell, P. W.,** Inhibition of prostaglandin biosynthesis by 7-oxa- and 5-oxa-prostaglandin analogues, *Biochem. J.,* 132, 117, 1973.
188. **Eakins, K. E. and Kulkarni, P. S.,** Selective inhibitory actions of sodium-*p*-benzyl-4-[1-oxo-2-(4-chlorobenzyl)-3-phenyl propyl] phenyl phosphonate (N-0164) and indomethacin on the biosynthesis of prostaglandins and thromboxanes from arachidonic acid, *Br. J. Pharmacol.,* 60, 135, 1977.
189. **Casey, F. B., Appleby, B. J., and Buck, D. C.,** Selective inhibition of the lipoxygenase metabolic pathway of arachidonic acid by the SRS-A antagonist, FPL 55712, *Prostaglandins,* 25, 1, 1983.
190. **Diczfalusy, E., Ferno, O., Fex, H., Hogberg, B., Linderot, T., and Rosenberg, T.,** Synthetic high molecular weight enzyme inhibitors. I. Polymeric phosphates of phloretin and related compounds, *Acta Chem. Scand.,* 7, 913, 1953.
191. **Curtis-Prior, P. B. and Chan, Y. H.,** Effects of polyphloretin phosphate (PPP) and quinterenol on cyclic nucleotid phosphodiesterase activities, *Pharmacol. Res. Commun.,* 13, 331, 1981.
192. **Giessler, C., Mentz, P., and Forster, W.,** The action of phospholipase $A_2$ on parameters of cardiac contraction, excitation and biosynthesis of prostaglandins, *Pharmacol. Res. Commun.,* 9, 117, 1977.
193. **Morin, R. J. and Richards, D.,** *In vitro* pharmacologic inhibition of rabbit adrenal microsomal cholesterol esterification, *Pharmacol. Res. Commun.,* 7, 281, 1975.
194. **Eling, T. E., Hawkins, H. J., and Anderson, M. W.,** Structural requirements for, and the effects of chemicals on, the rat pulmonary inactivation of prostaglandins, *Prostaglandins,* 14, 51, 1977.
195. **Law, E. and Lewis, A. J.,** The effect of systemically and topically applied drugs on ultraviolet induced erythema in the rat, *Br. J. Pharmacol.,* 59, 591, 1977.
196. **Johnson, M. and Ramwell, P. W.,** Prostaglandin modification of membrane-bound enzyme activity, *Adv. Biosci.,* 9, 205, 1973.
197. **Johnson, M. and Ramwell, P. W.,** Prostaglandin modification of membrane-bound enzyme activity: a possible mechanism of action? *Prostaglandins,* 3, 703, 1973.
198. **Kuehl, F. A., Jr. and Humes, J. L.,** Direct evidence for a prostaglandin receptor and its application to prostaglandin measurements, *Proc. Natl. Acad. Sci. U.S.A.,* 69, 480, 1972.
199. **Gorman, R. R. and Miller, O. V.,** Specific prostaglandin $E_1$ and $A_1$ binding sites in rat adipocyte plasma membranes, *Biochim. Biophys. Acta,* 323, 560, 1973.
200. **Rao, C. V.,** Differential properties of prostaglandin and gonadotropin receptors in the bovine corpus luteum cell membranes, *Prostaglandins,* 6, 313, 1974.
201. **Kuehl, F. A., Jr., Cirillo, V. J., Ham, E. A., and Humes, J. L.,** The regulatory role of the prostaglandins on the cyclic 3′,5′-AMP system, *Adv. Biosci.* 9, 155, 1973.
202. **Rao, C. V.,** Receptors for prostaglandins and gonadotropins in the cell membranes of bovine corpus luteum, *Prostaglandins,* 4, 567, 1973.

203. **Powell, W. S., Hammarstrom, S., and Samuelsson, B.,** Interactions between prostaglandin analogues and a receptor in bovine corpora lutea. Correlation of dissociation constants with luteolytic potencies in hamsters, *Eur. J. Biochem.* 59, 271, 1975.
204. **Rao, C. V.,** Properties of prostaglandin $F_{2\alpha}$ receptors in bovine corpus luteum cell membranes, *Mol. Cell. Endocrinol.,* 6, 1, 1976.
205. **Gorman, R. R.,** Specific $PGE_1$ and $PGE_2$ binding sites in platelet membranes, *Prostaglandins,* 6, 542, 1974.
206. **Lord, J. T., Ziboh, V. A., and Warren, S. K.,** Specific binding of prostaglandin $E_2$ and $F_2$ by membrane preparations from rat skin, *Endocrinology (Baltimore),* 102, 1300, 1978.
207. **Miller, O. V. and Magee, W. E.,** Specificity of prostaglandin binding sites in rat forestomach tissue and their possible use as a quantitative assay, *Adv. Biosci.* 9, 83, 1973.
208. **Moore, W. V. and Wolff, J.,** Binding of prostaglandin $E_1$ to beef thyroid membranes, *J. Biol. Chem.,* 248, 5705, 1973.
209. **Kimball, F. A. and Wyngarden, L. J.,** Prostaglandin specific binding in hamster myometrial low speed supernatant, *Prostaglandins,* 9, 413, 1975.
210. **Simpson, R. U., Campanile, C. P., and Goodfriend, T. L.,** Specific inhibition of receptors for angiotensin II and angiotensin III in adrenal glomerulosa, *Biochem. Pharmacol.,* 29, 927, 1980.
211. **Johnson, M., Jessup, R., Jessup, S., and Ramwell, P. W.,** Reversible physical and chemical manipulation of the prostaglandin receptor, *Prostaglandins,* 6, 543, 1974.
212. **Nicosia, S., Crowley, H. J., Oliva, D., and Welton, A. F.,** Binding sites for $^3H$-$LTC_4$ in membranes from guinea pig ileal longitudinal muscle, *Prostaglandins,* 27, 483, 1984.
213. **Pong, S. S., DeHaven, R. N., Kuehl, F. A., and Egan, R. W.,** Leukotriene $C_4$ binding to rat lung membranes, *J. Biol. Chem.,* 258, 9616, 1983.
214. **Cheng, J. G., Lang, D., Bewtra, A., and Townley, R. G.,** Tissue distribution and functional correlation of [$^3H$] leukotriene $D_4$ binding sites in guinea pig uterus and lung preparations, *J. Pharmacol. Exp. Ther.,* 232, 80, 1985.
215. **Pong, S. S. and De Haven, R. N.,** Ionic regulation of leukotriene $C_4$ and $D_4$ receptors in guinea pig and rat lung membranes, *Prostaglandins (Suppl.),* 27, 21, 1984.
216. **Lewis, M. A., Mong, S., Vessella, R. L., Hogaboom, G. K., Wu, H.-L., and Crooke, S. T.,** Identification of specific binding sites for leukotriene $C_4$ in human fetal lung, *Prostaglandins,* 27, 961, 1984.
217. **Hung, S. C., Ghali, N. I., Venton, D. L., and LeBreton, G. C.,** Specific binding of the thromboxane $A_2$ antagonist 13-azaprostanoic acid to human platelet membranes, *Biochim. Biophys. Acta,* 728, 171, 1983.
218. **Cranston, W. I., Duff, G. W., Hellon, R. F., Mitchell, D., and Townsend, Y.,** Evidence that brain prostaglandin synthesis is not essential in fever, *J. Physiol. (London),* 259, 239, 1976.
219. **Laburn, H., Mitchell, D., and Rosendorff, C.,** Effects of prostaglandin antagonism on sodium arachidonate fever in rabbits, *J. Physiol. (London),* 267, 559, 1977.
220. **Clark, W. G. and Cumby, H. R.,** Effects of prostaglandin antagonist SC-19220 on body temperature and on hyperthermic responses to prostaglandin $E_1$ and leukocytic pyrogen in the cat, *Prostaglandins,* 9, 361, 1975.
221. **Splawinski, J. A., Wojtaszek, B., and Swies, J.,** Endotoxin fever in rats: is it triggered by a decrease in breakdown of prostaglandin $E_2$? *Neuropharmacology,* 18, 111, 1979.
222. **Bras, R., Herman, Z. S., Szkilnik, R., Slominska, J., Jamrozik, Z., and Kryk, A.,** Influence of polyphloretin phosphate on the central effects of prostaglandin $E_2$ and $F_{2\alpha}$ in rats, *Psychopharmacology,* 59, 273, 1978.
223. **Barbieri, E. J., Orzechowski, R. F., and Rossi, G. V.,** Measurement of prostaglandin $E_2$ in an inflammatory exudate: effects of nonsteroidal anti-inflammatory agents, *J. Pharmacol. Exp. Ther.,* 201, 769, 1977.
224. **Smith, M. J. H., Ford-Hutchinson, A. W., Elliott, P. N. C., and Bolam, J. P.,** Prostaglandins and the anti-inflammatory activity of a human plasma fraction in carageenan-induced paw oedema in the rat, *J. Pharm. Pharmacol.,* 26, 692, 1974.
225. **Gyires, K. and Torma, Z.,** The use of the writhing test in mice for screening different types of analgesics, *Arch. Intern. Pharmacodyn. Ther.,* 131, 1984.
226. **Blaszo, G. and Gabor, M.,** Influence of polyphloretin phosphate (PPP) on rat-paw edema induced by prostaglandin $E_1$ ($PGE_1$), *Prostaglandins,* 16, 513, 1978.
227. **Arrigoni-Martelli, E., Selva, D., and Schiatti, P.,** Different efficacy of anti-inflammatory drugs in inhibiting the reactions to intradermal phospholipase A and $PGE_2$, *J. Int. Med. Res.,* 1, 120, 1973.
228. **Sondergaard, J. and Jorgensen, H. P.,** Blockade by polyphloretin phosphate of the prostaglandin $E_1$-induced human cutaneous reaction, *Br. J. Dermatol.,* 88, 51, 1973.
229. **Juan, H. and Lembeck, F.,** Polyphloretin phosphate reduces the algesic action of bradykinin by interfering with E-type prostaglandins, *Agents Actions,* 6, 646, 1976.
230. **Ikeda, K., Tanaka, K., and Katori, M.,** Potentiation of bradykinin-induced vascular permeability increase by prostaglandin $E_2$ and arachidonic acid in rabbit skin, *Prostaglandins,* 10, 747, 1975.

231. **Rinkema, L. E., Bemis, K. G., and Fleisch, J. H.,** Production and antagonism of cutaneous vascular permeability in the guinea pig in response to histamine, leukotrienes and A23187, *J. Pharmacol. Exp. Ther.*, 230, 550, 1984.
232. **Beitch, B. R. and Eakins, K. E.,** The effects of prostaglandins on the intraocular pressure of the rabbit, *Br. J. Pharmacol.*, 37, 158, 1969.
233. **Bethel, R. A. and Eakins, K. E.,** The mechanism of the antagonism of experimentally induced ocular hypertension by polyphloretin phosphate, *Exp. Eye Res.*, 13, 83, 1971.
234. **Starr, M. S.,** Further studies on the effect of prostaglandin on intraocular pressure in the rabbit, *Exp. Eye Res.*, 11, 170, 1971.
235. **Kelly, R. G. M. and Starr, M. S.,** Effects of prostaglandins and a prostaglandin antagonist on intraocular pressure and protein in the monkey eye, *Can. J. Ophthalmol.*, 6, 205, 1971.
236. **Whitelocke, R. A. F. and Eakins, K. E.,** Vascular changes in the anterior uvea of the rabbit produced by prostaglandins, *Arch. Ophthalmol.*, 89, 495, 1973.
237. **Starr, M. S.,** Effects of prostaglandin on blood flow in the rabbit eye, *Exp. Eye Res.*, 11, 161, 1971.
238. **Coleman, R. A. and Kennedy, I.,** Characterisation of the prostanoid receptors mediating contraction of guinea-pig isolated trachea, *Prostaglandins*, 29, 363, 1985.
239. **Geisow, J. P., Hornbym, E. J., McCabe, P. J., and Brittain, R. T.,** Inhibition of platelet aggregation by AH 19437, a thromboxane receptor blocking drug, *Br. J. Pharmacol.*, 73, 219P, 1981.
240. **Hart, S. L.,** The actions of prostaglandins $E_2$ and $F_{2\alpha}$ on human fetal intestine, *Br. J. Pharmacol.*, 50, 159, 1974.
241. **Tolman, E. L. and Partridge, R.,** Multiple site of interaction between prostaglandins and non-steroidal anti-inflammatory agents, *Prostaglandins*, 9, 349, 1975.
242. **Birnbaum, J. E. and Tolman, E. L.,** Prostaglandin E antagonist activity of 11-deoxy-16,16-trimethyl-eneprostaglandin $E_1$, *Prostaglandins*, 18, 349, 1979.
243. **Witiak, D. T., Kakodkar, S. V., Johnson, T. P., Baldwin, J. R., and Rahwan, R. G.,** 2-Indanpropionic acids: structural leads for prostaglandin $F_{2\alpha}$ antagonist development, *J. Med. Chem.*, 22, 77, 1979.
244. **Dong, Y. J. and Jones, R. L.,** Effects of prostaglandins and thromboxane analogues on bullock and dog iris sphincter preparations, *Br. J. Pharmacol.*, 76, 149, 1982.
245. **Bennett, A., Pratt, D., and Sanger, G. J.,** Antagonism by fenamates of prostaglandin action in guinea-pig and human alimentary muscle, *Br. J. Pharmacol.*, 68, 357, 1980.
246. **Smith, E. F., Schmunk, G. A., and Lefer, A. M.,** Antagonism of thromboxane analog-induced vaso-constriction by non-steroidal anti-inflammatory agents, *J. Cardiovasc. Pharmacol.*, 3, 791, 1981.
247. **Ghelani, A. M., Holroyde, M. C., and Sheard, P.,** Response of human isolated bronchial and lung parenchymal strips to SRS-A and other mediators of asthmatic bronchospasm, *Br. J. Pharmacol.*, 71, 107, 1980.
248. **Burke, J. A., Levi, R., Guo, Z.-G., and Corey, E. J.,** Leukotrienes $C_4$, $D_4$, and $E_4$: effects on human and guinea pig cardiac preparations *in vitro*, *J. Pharmacol. Exp. Ther.*, 221, 235, 1982.
249. **Murphy, R. C., Hammarstrom, S., and Samuelsson, B.,** Leukotriene C: a slow-reacting substance from murine mastocytoma cells, *Proc. Natl. Acad. Sci. U.S.A.*, 76, 4275, 1979.
250. **Holroyde, M. C. and Ghelani, A. M.,** Kinetics of action of two leukotriene antagonists on guinea pig ileum, *Eur. J. Pharmacol.*, 90, 251, 1983.
251. **Appleton, R. A., Bantick, J. R., Chamberlain, T. R., Hardern, D. N., Lee, T. B., and Pratt, A. D.,** Antagonists of slow reacting substance of anaphylaxis. Synthesis of a series of chromone-2-carboxylic acids, *J. Med. Chem.*, 20, 371, 1977.
252. **Jakschik, B. A., Kulczycki, A., Jr., McDonald, H. H., and Parker, C. W.,** Release of slow reacting substance (SRS) from rat basophilic leukemia (RBL-1) cells, *J. Immunol.*, 119, 618, 1977.
253. **Jones, D. G. and Kay, A. B.,** Inhibition of eosinophil chemotaxis by the antagonist of slow reacting substance of anaphylaxis—compound FPL 55712. *J. Pharm. Pharmacol.*, 26, 917, 1974.
254. **Krell, R. D. and Chakrin, L. W.,** Pharmacologic regulation of antigen-induced mediator release from canine lung, *Int. Arch. Allerg. Appl. Immun.*, 56, 39, 1978.
255. **Liebig, R., Bernauer, W., and Peskar, B. A.,** Prostaglandin, slow-reacting substance, and histamine release from anaphylactic guinea-pig hearts, and its pharmacological modification, *Naunyn-Schmiedebergs Arch. Pharmakol.*, 289, 65, 1975.
256. **Sirois, P., Engineer, D. M., Piper, P. J., and Moore, E. G.,** Comparison of rat, mouse, guinea-pig and human slow reacting substance of anaphylaxis (SRS-A), *Experientia*, 35, 361, 1979.
257. **Mong, S., Wu, H.-L., Scott, M. O., Lewis, M. A., Clark, M. A., Weichman, B. M., Kinzig, C. M., Gleason, J. G., and Crooke, S. T.,** Molecular heterogeneity of leukotriene receptors: correlation of smooth muscle contraction and radioligand binding in guinea-pig lung, *J. Pharmacol. Exp. Ther.*, 234, 316, 1985.
258. **Ballermann, B. J., Lewis, R. A., Corey, E. J., Austen, K. F., and Brenner, B. M.,** Identification and characterization of leukotriene $C_4$ receptors in isolated rat renal glomeruli, *Circ. Res.*, 56, 324, 1985.
259. **Levinson, S. L.,** Peptidoleukotriene binding in guinea pig uterine membrane preparations, *Prostaglandins*, 28, 229, 1984.

260. **Arndt, H. C., Biddlecom, W. G., Kleunder, H. C., Peruzzotti, G. P., and Woessner, W. D.,** The synthesis of prostaglandin analogs containing hydroxy-cyclohexenyl rings, *Prostaglandins,* 9, 521, 1975.
261. **Buckle, D. R., Outred, D. J., Ross, J. W., Smith, H., Smith, R. J., Spicer, B. A., and Gasson, B. C.,** Aryloxyakyloxy- and aralkoxy-4-hydroxy-3-nitrocoumarins which inhibit histamine release in the rat and also antagonize the effects of a slow reacting substance of anaphylaxis, *J. Med. Chem.,* 22, 158, 1979.
262. **Carrier, R., Cragoe, E. J., Ethier, D., Ford-Hutchinson, A. W., Girard, Y., Hall, R. A., Hamel, P., Rokach, J., Share, N. N., Stone, C. A., and Yusko, P.,** Studies on L-640,035: a novel antagonist of contractile prostanoids in the lung, *Br. J. Pharmacol.,* 82, 389, 1984.
263. **Feinmark, S. J., Lindgren, J. A., Claesson, H. E., Malmsten, B., and Samuelsson, B.,** Stimulation of human leukocyte degradation by leukotriene $B_4$ and its ω-oxidized metabolics, *FEBS Lett.,* 136, 141, 1981.
264. **Panczenko, B., Grodzinska, L., and Gryglewski, R.,** The dual action of meclofenamate on the contractile response to $PGF_{2\alpha}$ in the guinea-pig trachea, *Pol. J. Pharmacol. Pharm.,* 27, 273, 1975.
265. **MacIntyre, D. E. and Gordon, J. L.,** Discrimination between platelet prostaglandin receptors with a specific antagonist for bisenoic prostaglandins, *Thromb. Res.,* 11, 705, 1977.
266. **Miller, O. V. and Gorman, R. R.,** Evidence for distinct prostaglandin $I_2$ and $D_2$ receptors in human platelets, *J. Pharmacol. Exp. Ther.,* 210, 134, 1979.
267. **Tynan, S. S., Andersen, N. H., Wills, M. T., Harker, L. A., and Hanson, S. R.,** On the multiplicity of platelet prostaglandin receptors II. The use of N-0164 for distinguishing the loci of action for $PGI_2$, $PGD_2$, $PGE_2$ and hydantoin analogs, *Prostaglandins* 27, 683, 1984.
268. **Vulliemoz, Y., Verosky, M., and Triner, L.,** Effect of a prostaglandin antagonist, N-0164, on c-AMP generation and hydrolysis in the rat uterus, *Biochem. Pharmacol.,* 30, 1941, 1981.
269. **Enyedi, P., Spat, A., and Antoni, F. A.,** Role of prostaglandins in the control of the function of adrenal glomerulosa cells, *J. Endocrinol.,* 427, 1981.
270. **Sharpe, G. L. and Larsson, K. S.,** Studies on closure of the ductus arteriosus. X. *In vivo* effect of prostaglandin, *Prostaglandins,* 9, 703, 1975.
271. **Illiano, G. and Cuatrecasas, P.,** Endogenous prostaglandins modulate lipolytic processes in adipose tissue, *Nature (London) New Biol.,* 234, 72, 1971.
272. **Channing, C. P.,** Effects of prostaglandin inhibitors, 7-oxa-13-prostynoic acid and eicosa-5,8,11,14-tetraynoic acid upon luteinization of rhesus monkey granulosa cells in culture, *Prostaglandins,* 2, 351, 1972.
273. **Park, M. K., Dyer, D. C., and Vincenzi, F. F.,** Prostaglandin $E_2$ and its antagonists: effects on autonomic transmission in the isolated sino-atrial node, *Prostaglandins,* 4, 717, 1973.
274. **Frew, R. and Baer, H. P.,** Adenosine-α,β-methylene diphosphate effects in intestinal smooth muscle: sites of action and possible prostaglandin involvement, *J. Pharmacol. Exp. Ther.,* 211, 525, 1979.
275. **Ahren, K. and Perklev, T.,** Effects of $PGE_1$ and 7-oxa-13-prostynoic acid on the isolated prepubertal rat ovary, *Adv. Biosci.,* 9, 717, 1973.
276. **Magnusson, C., Selstam, G., and Ahren, K.,** Lack of specific prostaglandin antagonistic effects of 7-oxa-13-prostynoic acid on ovarian metabolism *in vitro, Acta Physiol. Scand.,* 105, 239, 1979.
277. **Lamprecht, S. A., Zor, U., Tsafriri, A., and Lindner, H. R.,** Action of prostaglandin $E_2$ and of luteinizing hormone on ovarian adenylate cyclase, protein kinase and ornithine decarboxylase activity during postnatal development and maturity in the rat, *J. Endocrinol.* 57, 217, 1973.
278. **Ellsworth, L. R. and Armstrong, D. T.,** Effect of indomethacin and 7-oxa-13-prostynoic acid on luteinization of transplanted rat ovarian follicles induced by luteinizing hormone and prostaglandin $E_2$, *Prostaglandins,* 7, 165, 1974.
279. **Ratner, A., Wilson, M. C., and Peake, G. T.,** Antagonism of prostaglandin-promoted pituitary cyclic AMP accumulation and growth hormone secretion *in vitro* by 7-oxa-13-prostynoic acid, *Prostaglandins,* 3, 413, 1973.
280. **Grouin, J. and Labrie, F.,** Specificity of the stimulatory effect of prostaglandins on hormone release in rat anterior pituitary cells in culture, *Prostaglandins,* 11, 355, 1976.
281. **Dajani, E. Z. and Driskill, D. R.,** Effects of 7-oxa-13-prostynoic acid (7-OPyA) and prostaglandin $E_1$ methyl ester on canine gastric secretion, *Prostaglandins,* 14, 659, 1977.
282. **Castor, C. W.,** Connective tissue activation: evidence supporting a role for prostaglandins, *Clin. Res.,* 21, 875, 1973.
283. **Castor, C. W., Harnsberger, S. C., Scott, M. E., and Ritchie, J. C.,** Connective tissue activation. Part 7. Evidence supporting a role for prostaglandins and cyclic nucleotides, *J. Lab. Clin. Med.,* 85, 392, 1975.
284. **Kimball, F. A., Kirton, K. T., Spilman, C. H., and Wyngarden, L. J.,** Prostaglandin $E_1$ specific binding in human myometrium, *Biol. Reprod.,* 13, 482, 1975.
285. **Foucard, T. and Strandberg, K.,** Inhibition by derivatives of phloretin of anaphylactic histamine release from human lung tissue and of prostaglandin $F_{2\alpha}$-induced bronchoconstriction, *Int. Arch. Allerg. Appl. Immun.,* 48, 132, 1975.

286. **Eakins, K. E., Fex, H., Fredholm, B., Hogberg, B., and Veige, S.,** On the prostaglandin inhibitory action of polyphloretin phosphate, *Adv. Biosci.*, 9, 135, 1973.
287. **Gross, K. B. and Gills, C. N.,** Metabolism of prostaglandins $A_1$ and $E_1$ in the perfused rabbit lung and the effects of selected inhibitors, *J. Pharmacol. Exp. Ther.*, 198, 716, 1976.
288. **Westwick, J. and Webb, H.,** Selective antagonism of prostaglandin (PG) $E_1$, $PGD_2$ and prostacyclin ($PGI_2$) on human and rabbit platelets by di-4-phloretin phosphate (DPP), *Thromb. Res.*, 12, 973, 1978.
289. **Ishizawa, M. and Miyazaki, E.,** Inhibitory actions of polyphloretin phosphate and related compounds on the response to prostaglandin in the smooth muscle of guinea-pig stomach, *Prostaglandins*, 11, 829, 1976.
290. **Jackson, R. T., Waitzman, M. B., Pickford, L., and Nathanson, S. E.,** Prostaglandins in human middle ear effusions, *Prostaglandins*, 10, 365, 1975.
291. **Eakins, K. E., Miller, J. D., and Karim, S. M. M.,** The nature of the prostaglandin-blocking activity of polyphloretin phosphate, *J. Pharmacol. Exp. Ther.*, 176, 441, 1971.
292. **Gagnon, D. J. and Sirois, P.,** The rat isolated colon as a specific assay organ for angiotensin, *Br. J. Pharmacol.*, 45, 89, 1972.
293. **Green, K.,** Permeability properties of the ciliary epithelium in response to prostaglandins, *Invest. Ophthalmol.*, 12, 752, 1973.
294. **Chand, N. and Eyre, P.,** The pharmacology of anaphylaxis in the chicken intestine, *Br. J. Pharmacol.*, 57, 399, 1976.
295. **Gagnon, D. J., Cousineau, D., and Boucher, P. J.,** Release of vasopressin by angiotensin II and prostaglandin $E_2$ from the rat neuro-hypophysis *in vitro*, *Life Sci.*, 12 (Part 1), 487, 1973.
296. **Perklev, T. and Ahren, K.,** Effects of prostaglandins, LH and polyphloretin phosphate on the lactic acid production of the prepubertal rat ovary, *Life Sci.*, 10 (Part 1), 1387, 1971.
297. **Elsworth, L. R. and Armstrong, D. T.,** Inhibition of luteinization of transplanted rat ovarian follicles by polyphloretin phosphate, *Endocrinology (Baltimore)*, 94, 892, 1974.
298. **Mentz, P., Foerster, W., and Giessler, C.,** Direkte Hemmwirkungen von Prostaglandinen und Phenylisopropyl-Adenosin auf die Aktivitaet einer Pankreas-Triglyzeridlipase und Antagonistische effekte durch Polyphloretin-Phosphat, *Arch. Int. Pharmacodyn. Ther.*, 211, 141, 1974.
299. **Gimeno, M. F., Gimeno, A. L., Lima, F., and Borda, E.,** Effect of polyphloretin phosphate, an inhibitor of prostaglandins on the spontaneous and induced motility of isolated rat uterus, *Acta Physiol. Lat. Am.*, 23, 105, 1973.
300. **Limas, C. J. and Cohn, J. N.,** Stimulation of vascular smooth muscle sodium potassium-adenosinetriphosphatase by vasodilators, *Circ. Res.*, 35, 601, 1974.
301. **Hedqvist, P. and von Euler, U. S.,** Prostaglandin-induced neurotransmission failure in field-stimulated, isolated vas deferens, *Neuropharmacology*, 11, 177, 1972.
302. **Anderson, N. H., Eggerman, T. L., and Harker, L. A.,** On the multiplicity of platelet prostaglandin receptors. I. Evaluation of competitive antagonism by aggregometry, *Prostaglandins*, 19, 711, 1980.
303. **Aharony, D., Smith, J. B., Smith, E. F., Lefer, A. M., Magolda, R. L., and Nicolaou, K. D.,** Pinane thromboxane $A_2$: a $TXA_2$ antagonist with antithrombotic properties, *Adv. Prostaglandin Thromboxane Res.*, 6, 489, 1980.
304. **Kurland, J. I. Hadden, J .W., and Moore, M. A. S.,** Role of cyclic nucleotides in the proliferation of committed granulocyte-macrophage progenitor cells, *Cancer Res.*, 37, 4534, 1977.
305. **Hillier, K. and Templeton, W. W.,** Regulation of noradrenaline overflow in rat cerebral cortex by prostaglandin $E_2$, *Br. J. Pharmacol.*, 70, 469, 1980.
306. **Sanger, G. J. and Bennett, A.,** Regional differences in the responses to prostanoids of circular muscle for guinea-pig isolated intestine, *J. Pharm. Pharmacol.*, 32, 705, 1980.
307. **Dong, Y. J., Jones, R. L., and Wilson, N. H.,** Prostaglandin E receptor subtypes in smooth muscle: agonist activities of stable prostacyclin analogues, *Br. J. Pharmacol.*, 87, 97, 1986.
308. **Radzialowski, F. M. and Novak, L.,** Reversal of the antilipolytic effect of prostaglandin $E_2$ by an oxazepine derivative (SC-19220), *Life Sci.*, 10 (Part 1), 1261, 1971.
309. **Radzialowski, F. M. and Rosenberg, L. N.,** Effect of SC-19220, a prostaglandin inhibitor on the antilipolytic action of prostaglandin $E_2$, propanalol and insulin in the isolated rat adipocyte, *Life Sci.*, 12 (Part 2), 337, 1973.
310. **Pillai, N. P., Ramaswamy, S., Gopalakrishnan, V., and Ghosh, M. N.,** Contractile effect of prolactin on guinea-pig isolated ileum, *Eur. J. Pharmacol.*, 72, 11, 1981.
311. **Sanner, J.,** Prostaglandin inhibition with a dibenzoxazepine hydrazide derivative and morphine, *Ann. N.Y. Acad. Sci.*, 180, 396, 1971.
312. **Gustafsson, L., Hedqvist, P., and Lagercrantz, H.,** Potentiation by prostaglandins $E_1$, $E_2$, and $F_{2\alpha}$ of the contraction response to transmural stimulation in the bovine iris sphincter muscle, *Acta Physiol. Scand.*, 95, 26, 1975.
313. **Gustafsson, L. E.,** Studies on modulation of transmitter release and effector responsiveness in autonomic cholinergic neurotransmission, *Acta Physiol. Scand. (Suppl.)*, 489, 1, 1980.

314. **Rakovska, A. and Milenov, K.,** Antagonistic effect of SC-19220 on the responses of guinea-pig gastric muscles to prostaglandins $E_1$, $E_2$ and $F_{2\alpha}$, *Arch. Int. Pharmacodyn. Ther.,* 268, 59, 1984.
315. **Suria, A. and Costa, E.,** Diazepam inhibition of post-tetanic potentiation in bullfrog sympathetic ganglia: possible role of prostaglandins, *J. Pharmacol. Exp. Ther.,* 189, 690, 1974.
316. **Ambache, N. and Aboo Zar, M.,** An inhibitory effect of prostaglandin $E_2$ on neuromuscular transmission in the guinea-pig vas deferens, *J. Physiol. (London),* 208, 30P, 1970.
317. **Harris, D. N., Phillips, M. B., Michel, I. M., Goldenberg, H. J., Heikes, J. E., Sprague, P. W., and Antonaccio, M. J.,** 9-Homo-9,11-epoxy-5,13-prostadienoic acid analogues: specific stable agonist (SQ 26,538) and antagonist (SQ 26,536) of the human platelet thromboxane receptor, *Prostaglandins,* 22, 295, 1981.
318. **Stahl, G. L., Darius, H., and Lefer, A. M.,** Antagonism of thromboxane actions in the isolated perfused rat heart, *Life Sci.,* 38, 2037, 1986.
319. **Filep, J., Rigter, B., and Frölich, J. C.,** Vascular and renal effects of leukotriene $C_4$ in conscious rats, *Am. J. Physiol.,* 249, F739, 1985.
320. **Boyd, L. M., Ezra, C., Feuerstein, G., and Goldstein, R. E.,** Effects of FPL-55712 or indomethacin on leukotriene-induced coronary constriction in the intact pig heart, *Eur. J. Pharmacol.,* 89, 307, 1983.
321. **Young, J. M., Maloney, P. J., Jubb, S. N., and Clark, J. S.,** Pharmacological investigation of the mechanisms of platelet-activating factor induced mortality in the mouse, *Prostaglandins,* 30, 545, 1985.
322. **Chand, N. and Eyre, P.,** Acute systemic anaphylaxis in adult domestic fowl—possible role of vasoactive lipids and peptides, *Arch. Int. Pharmacodyn. Ther.,* 236, 164, 1978.
323. **Hedge, G. A.,** The effects of prostaglandins on ACTH secretion, *Endocrinology (Baltimore),* 91, 925, 1972.
324. **Warberg, J.,** Potentiation of prostaglandin $E_2$-induced release of LH by the prostaglandin analog, 7-oxa-13-prostynoic acid, *Acta Endocrinol. (Copenhagen),* 97, 297, 1981.
325. **Fujimoto, S., Endo, Y., and Hisada, S.,** Poly- and di-phloretin phosphate-induced alterations on diuresis and antidiuresis in response to intracerebroventricular prostaglandin $A_2$, *Jpn. J. Pharmacol.,* 27, 583, 1977.
326. **Grennan, D. M., Zeitlin, I. J., Mitchell, W. S., Buchanan, W. W., and Dick, W. C.,** The effects of prostaglandins $PGE_1$, $PGE_2$, $PGF_{,1\alpha}$ and $PGF_{2\alpha}$ on canine synovial perfusion, *Prostaglandins,* 9, 799, 1975.
327. **Forster, W., Mentz, P., Blass, K. E., and Mest, H. J.,** Anti-arrhythmic effects of arachidonic, linoleic, linolenic, and oleic acid, and the influence of indomethacin and polyphloretinphosphate, *Adv. Prostaglandin Thromboxane Res.,* 1, 433, 1976.
328. **Juan, H. and Lembeck, F.,** Prostaglandin $F_{2\alpha}$ reduces the algesic effect of bradykinin by antagonizing the pain enhancing action of endogenously released prostaglandin E, *Br. J. Pharmacol.,* 59, 385, 1977.
329. **Greenberg, R., Antonaccio, M. J., and Steinbacher, T.,** Thromboxane $A_2$ mediated bronchoconstriction in the anesthetized guinea pig, *Eur. J. Pharmacol.,* 80, 19, 1982.
330. **Darius, H. and Lefer, A. M.,** Blockade of thromboxane and the prevention of eicosanoid-induced sudden death in mice, *Proc. Soc. Exp. Biol. Med.,* 180, 364, 1985.

# LEUKOTRIENE ANTAGONISTS

**John H. Musser, Anthony F. Kreft, and Alan J. Lewis**

## INTRODUCTION

The current interest in leukotriene-receptor antagonists can be traced back to 1938 when Feldberg and Kellaway[1] first demonstrated that stimulated lung tissue produces a material which slowly induces sustained contractions of guinea-pig smooth muscle. The contractions were different from those induced by histamine and the material was referred to as slow-reacting substance (SRS). Two years later Kellaway and Trethewie[2] showed that a similar material was released from the guinea-pig pulmonary system upon immunological challenge. Brocklehurst,[3] in 1960 first used the term "slow-reacting substance of anaphylaxis (SRS-A)" to describe material produced by guinea-pig or human lungs following immunological challenge by antigens. Although the structure of SRS-A was not known, the crude material was intensively studied during the next 20 years in a number of laboratories, including those of Austen, Orange, Bach, Ishizaka, Parker, Piper, and Lichtenstein.[4-12] This work led to the appreciation of the circumstances leading to SRS-A release and emphasized the potential importance of SRS-A in the pathogenesis of bronchial asthma. However, the significance of SRS-A in allergy and inflammation awaited two events: the determination of its chemical structure and the discovery of an effective receptor antagonist.

As irony would have it, a receptor antagonist was discovered (FPL-55,712; Table 1, Compound 1) before the structure of SRS-A was known, and in fact played an important role in the isolation and characterization of SRS-A. Samuelsson made the key structural breakthrough when in 1979 his research group[13-15] discovered new metabolites derived from arachidonic acid via the 5-lipoxygenase pathway with chemical and biological properties of SRS and SRS-A. These metabolites were named leukotrienes (LT) because they were first isolated from leukocytes and their structures contained a conjugated triene system. The synthetic work of Corey et al.[16,17] was critical to the understanding of the structure and stereochemistry of the LTs. Thus, SRS and SRS-A were determined to be composed of $LTC_4$, $LTD_4$, and $LTE_4$ which are together referred to as sulfidopeptide leukotrienes since they all contain cysteine (Figure 1).

FPL-55,712 was the first compound described as an antagonist of sulfidopeptide LTs.[18] As a pharmacological tool, it has been extensively used to define the role sulfidopeptide LTs play in immediate hypersensitivity reactions in man and animals. Unfortunately, FPL-55,712 has a short biological half-life,[19] and has not been developed as a drug. However, further clinical studies show that it does have activity when administered by aerosol.[20] The carboxylic acid homologue of FPL-55,712, FPL-59,257 (2), is a longer acting $LTD_4$ antagonist; however, it is still inactive orally.[21] While FPL-55,712 competitively antagonizes $LTD_4$ using guinea-pig ileum, FPL-59,257 is a noncompetitive antagonist.[22]

Armed with the structure of sulfidopeptide LTs and an effective receptor antagonist, researchers have made great strides in defining the role sulfidopeptide LTs may play in the pathophysiology of such diseases as asthma, psoriasis, ulcerative colitis, and rheumatoid arthritis.[23,24] The sulfidopeptide LTs, $LTC_4$, $LTD_4$, and $LTE_4$ are known to contract isolated airways and evoke bronchoconstriction in the guinea pig and man.[25] In humans, $LTC_4$ and $LTD_4$ may produce airway mucosal edema by enhancing post capillary permeability and may also stimulate the secretion of mucus from airways.[26]

Administration of $LTC_4$, $LTD_4$, and $LTB_4$ intradermally to normal volunteers produces a wheal and flare response.[27] In asthmatic children, plasma levels of $LTC_4$ correlate with severity of the disease.[28] The nonpeptidic leukotriene $LTB_4$, is a potent chemokinetic,

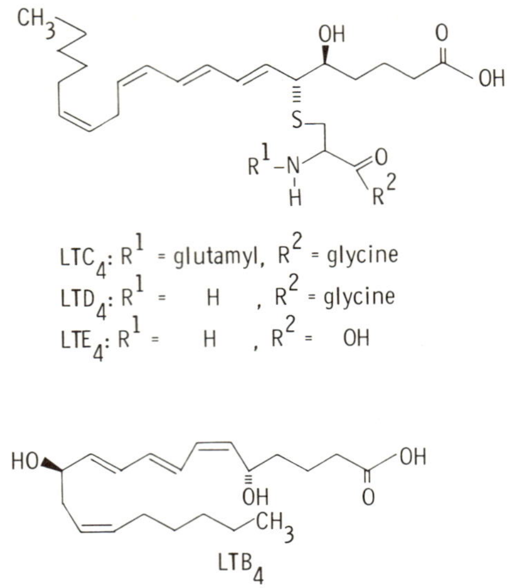


FIGURE 1. Structures of the leukotrienes.

chemotactic, and aggregating agent for a variety of leukocytes *in vitro; in vivo*, it stimulates cell accumulation and effects vascular smooth muscle.[29]

The multiple actions of LTs at low doses and the potential association of LTs in the pathophysiology of a number of diseases have prompted the development of agents that can inhibit their formation or actions.[30,31] In this chapter we intend to review those agents that primarily antagonize the action of LTs at their receptor sites.

## SULFIDOPEPTIDE-LT RECEPTORS

Functional studies, examining relative potencies of agonists or blockade by antagonists, provide evidence that several subtypes of receptors for sulfidopeptide LTs exist in peripheral tissue.[32-34] Radioligand-binding studies support this contention. Binding of [$^3$H]$LTC_4$ and [$^3$H]$LTD_4$ to guinea-pig and rat lung homogenates demonstrate the presence of specific, stereoselective, reversible, high-affinity, and saturable binding sites for both agonists.[35-38] [$^3$H]$LTC_4$-binding sites seem ubiquitous[39,40] and have been identified in numerous tissues including guinea-pig heart,[47] ileum,[42] and uterus,[43] human fetal lung,[44] human lung parenchyma, and bronchi,[45] rat glomeruli[46] and brain,[47] human glomerular epithelial cells,[48] and clonally derived smooth-muscle cells.[49] The equilibrium dissociation constant ($K_d$) and maximum number of binding sites ($B_{max}$) for [$^3$H]$LTC_4$ specific binding are 5 to 40 n*M* and 8.5 to 80 to pmol/mg protein, respectively. It is noteworthy that specific binding sites for $LTC_4$ occur in tissues that do not appear functionally sensitive to sulfidopeptide LTs, suggesting that these sites are not true receptors.[40] For example, the liver is an organ with no sulfidopeptide-LT-mediated biologic activity, yet it is one of the richest sources of $LTC_4$-binding activity.[40] Sun et al.[50] recently reported that $LTC_4$ binding in rat liver is due to the high-affinity binding of this sulfidopeptide LT to the subunit 1, or $Y_a$, of the cytosolic enzyme glutathione S-transferase. This introduces a further complication in the search for $LTC_4$ receptors since the presence of nonreceptor ligand-binding protein indicates a need to reevaluate the assignment of putative $LTC_4$ receptors to membrane preparations based only on radioligand-binding studies. However, it explains the discrepancy between the capacity for inhibition of [$^3$H]$LTC_4$ binding and the biological activities of certain $LTC_4$ analogues.[40]

This might also explain why specific binding of [$^3$H]$LTC_4$ in guinea-pig lung membrane is not to a contractile receptor but is more likely to be a $LTC_4$ uptake site.

Autoradiography has also been used to identify sulfidopeptide-LT-binding sites. A very high density of specific labeling of airway epithelium and smooth muscle, from trachea and terminal bronchioles, by [$^3$H]$LTD_4$ binding was observed using guinea-pig airways.[51] Specific [$^3$H]$LTD_4$ binding was localized to the alveolar walls with surprisingly little labeling of airways or vessels in this study. The subcellular distribution of $LTC_4$ binding was demonstrated in cultured bovine aortic endothelial cells.[52] It is possible that these subcellular binding sites represent a recirculating pool of receptors which may reenter the plasma membrane.

In contrast to $LTC_4$, high affinity but low capacity $LTD_4$-specific-binding sites have been described in a minority of tissues, including guinea-pig lung and trachea ($K_d$ = 0.2—1.8 n*M*, $B_{max}$ = 1.1—2.1 pmol/mg protein).[38,39] This suggests that [$^3$H]$LTD_4$-specific binding sites in guinea-pig lung represent the pharmacologically relevant receptors. Similarly, $LTD_4$-specific binding sites have been identified in adult and fetal human lung with similar apparent $K_m$ (0.15 and 0.12 n*M*, respectively) and $B_{max}$ (68 and 62 fmol/mg protein, respectively.[53] Human alveolar macrophages also possess $LTD_4$-binding sites.[54]

$LTD_4$ receptors in guinea-pig lung are coupled to $G_i$ protein which, when activated, induces arachidonic acid mobilization via phospholipase activation and subsequent prostanoid biosynthesis.[55] Indeed, $LTD_4$-induced smooth-muscle contraction and guinea-pig-lung contraction are mediated largely through prostanoid metabolites.[56] Whether sulfidopeptide LTs induce prostanoid synthesis in human tissue is debatable. Indomethacin, a prostaglandin-synthetase inhibitor, does not alter contractions to LTs ($C_4$, $D_4$, $E_4$) in human airways[57,58] nor does $LTC_4$ cause formation of cycloxygenase products in human lung.[59]

FPL-55,712 inhibits smooth-muscle contraction induced by $LTD_4$ and $LTE_4$ but not that induced by $LTC_4$.[60-63] This was confirmed by binding studies suggesting FPL-55,712 more effectively competes with [$^3$H]$LTD_4$ for $LTD_4$-receptor sites than with [$^3$H]$LTC_4$ for $LTC_4$-receptor sites.[39] However, not all $LTD_4$-induced smooth-muscle contractile responses are blocked by FPL-55,712, suggesting the existence of receptor subtypes.[65]

[$^3$H]$LTE_4$ also binds to $LTD_4$-binding sites in guinea-pig lung membranes suggesting that both $LTD_4$ and $LTE_4$ contractile responses are mediated by similar receptors in guinea-pig lung.[66,67] However, other studies indicate that the action of $LTE_4$ may be expressed at its own receptor since its action is blocked by cholinergic antagonists[68] and $LTE_4$ can induce guinea-pig tracheal hyperresponsiveness, unlike $LTC_4$ or $LTD_4$.[69]

Bioconversion of $LTC_4$ to $LTD_4$ (via $\gamma$-glutamyltranspeptidase) and $LTD_4$ to $LTE_4$ (via dipeptidase) by tissues responding to these sulfidopeptide LTs can affect the magnitude and time course of response.[70] The metabolism of the sulfidopeptide LTs varies with species; for example, rapid conversion of $LTC_4$ to $LTD_4$ occurs in human and guinea-pig lung, whereas in the rat lung, $LTD_4$ to $LTE_4$ conversion occurs rapidly.[71]

## CLASSIFICATION OF LEUKOTRIENE ANTAGONISTS

LT antagonists can be classified both by receptor type and by chemical structure. There are two main classes of LT receptors: the sulfidopeptide-LT receptors and the $LTB_4$ receptors. The sulfidopeptide-LT antagonists can be subdivided into the four structural categories shown in Tables 1 to 4: compounds based on FPL-55,712; compounds based on the structures of $LTC_4$, $LTD_4$, and $LTE_4$; compounds of novel structure that putatively act at the receptor level; and miscellaneous compounds that indirectly antagonize the effects of the sulfidopeptide LTs. However, it should be stressed that overlaps are inevitable and this adopted format provides only a basis for a discussion of LT antagonists.

**Sulfidopeptide-Leukotriene Antagonists Containing a Hydroxyacetophenone Moiety (Table 1)**

Numerous research groups have synthesized sulfidopeptide-LT antagonists by substantial modification of the right-hand portion of FPL-55,712 while retaining the left-hand hydroxyacetophenone moiety.[18-22, 72-103] Table 1 summarizes these compounds (3 to 23) along with their biological profiles. Several of the compounds in Table 1 are undergoing clinical trials. In comparison to FPL-55,712, Ro 23-3544 (Compound 14) is 300-fold, 80-fold, and 16-fold more potent as an antagonist of $LTC_4$, $LTD_4$, and $LTE_4$, respectively, via aerosol in the guinea pig. Ro 23-3544 is also a potent antagonist of antigen-induced bronchoconstriction and surprisingly, it is active against $LTB_4$-induced bronchoconstriction in the guinea pig.[83]

We have extensively studied Wy-44,329 (Table 1, Compound 8) and found that it not only competitively antagonizes $LTD_4$ on guinea-pig ilea but also inhibits the bronchoconstriction in guinea pig induced by $LTD_4$, $LTC_4$, and ovalbumin (OA).[77,94] While the *in vivo* potency of Wy-44,329 is comparable to FPL-55,712 upon $LTC_4$ or $LTD_4$ challenge, it is an order of magnitude more potent against OA. This may in part be due to its additional activity as a mediator-release inhibitor. Wy-44,329 also possesses a much longer duration of action (>40 min when administered i.v.) than FPL-55,712. Like FPL-55,712 which is reported to be a 5-lipoxygenase (LO) inhibitor in a cell-free system,[95] Wy-44,329 inhibits 5-LO in rat neutrophils.[94] Unfortunately, like the FPL compounds it is orally inactive.

In contrast to FPL-55,712 and Wy-44,329, LY-171,883 (Compound 10) is orally active against both $LTD_4$- and OA-induced increases in total pulmonary resistance in the guinea pig.[96] LY-171,883 is a competitive antagonist of $LTD_4$ on guinea-pig ilea and parenchyma; however, it is a noncompetitive $LTD_4$ antagonist on guinea-pig trachea and is not effective against $LTC_4$ on guinea-pig ilea. LY-171,883 is also found to antagonize the thromboxane agonist U-46,619 with a $pK_B$ value of 5.97 which is approximately tenfold less than the $pK_B$ reported for $LTD_4$ antagonism which may explain why it protects against shock in the cat model.[97] In addition, LY-171,883 appears to be a bronchodilator which may be partially explained by its potent phosphodiesterase-inhibitory activity. LY-171,883 is currently under clinical development as an anti-asthma drug.

Another orally active sulfidopeptide-LT antagonist in the guinea pig is LY-163,443 (Compound 15) which antagonizes OA- or $LTD_4$-induced increases in total pulmonary impedence and also inhibits $LTD_4$-mediated dermal vascular leakage. *In vitro*, it antagonizes $LTD_4$ contractions of guinea-pig ileum, trachea, and lung parenchyma. However, $LTC_4$-induced contractions of the guinea-pig ileum are only minimally reduced by LY-163,443.[98,99]

The structure-activity relationship of Wy-46,235 (Compound 16) series was studied in detail.[85] Contrary to the results obtained for the FPL-55,712 series and presumably others in Table 1, Wy-46,235 was the most potent $LTD_4$ antagonist despite lacking the propyl chain on the hydroxacetophenone. We speculated that at least for our series the propyl chain may confer greater affinity for the receptor *in vitro* but its presence lowers potency *in vivo*.

L-649,923 (Compound 9) is a potent orally active $LTD_4$ antagonist (>50% inhibition at 5.0 mg/kg i.d.) in the guinea pig, which is presently undergoing clinical trials; however, there have been reports of unwanted side effects (diarrhea).[100]

Besides a potential role in asthma therapy, sulfidopeptide-LT antagonists may have a role as cytoprotective agents.[101] Thus, L-649,923 blocks the increase in pepsin secretion caused by $LTD_4$ in anesthetized cats; however, it did not reduce the transgastric electrical potential differential suggesting the presence of functionally different sulfidopeptide-LT-receptor subtypes in the gastric mucosa.[102]

Among the more recent sulfidopeptide-LT antagonists based on FPL-55,712 (Table 1) are CGP-35,949 (Compound 19), YM-16,638 (Compound 21), and L-648,051 (Compound 23). CGP-35,949 (Compound 19) is not only an orally active sulfidopeptide-LT antagonist, but also a phospholipase-$A_2$ and -C inhibitor.[87,88,103] YM-16,638 (Compound 21) is an orally active $LTD_4$ antagonist (at 10 mg/kg), which is also effective against antigen-induced bronchoconstriction.[90,91] L-648,051 (Compound 23) is efficacious in the conscious squirrel monkey against both $LTD_4$- or antigen-induced bronchoconstriction.[93]

**Analogues of Sulfidopeptide Leukotrienes as Antagonists (Table 2)**

The synthesis of sulfidopeptide-LT antagonists based on $LTC_4$, $LTD_4$, and $LTE_4$ has been pioneered by several groups. One problem with this approach is the frequent occurrence of agonist and mixed agonist/antagonist properties. SKF-101,132 (Compound 24) antagonizes contractions induced by $LTD_4$, $LTD_4$, and $LTE_4$ in guinea-pig trachea at 10 $\mu M$ and also blocks $LTD_4$-induced bronchconstriction in the guinea pig (5 mg/kg i.v.).[104] It appears that the *cis* double-bond geometry is critical for activity in the SKF-101,132 series.[105] SKF-101,392 (Compound 25) competitively antagonizes both $LTD_4$ and $LTE_4$-induced contractions of guinea-pig trachea ($K_B$ = 0.29 $\mu M$ vs. $LTD_4$, $pA_2$ = 5.9 vs. $LTE_4$);[106] however, SKF-101,392 and other compounds of this series have mixed agonist/antagonist activities.

SKF-102,081 (Compound 26) not only blocks $LTD_4$-induced contractions on isolated guinea-pig trachea ($pK_B$ = 6.0) but also inhibits $LTD_4$-induced changes in airway resistance and dynamic compliance when administered either i.v. or by aerosol to guinea pigs.[107] SKF-102,922 (Compound 27) blocks $LTD_4$- and $LTC_4$-induced guinea-pig tracheal contractile responses but does not alter the contractile response to $PGF_{2\alpha}$, histamine, carbachol, $TxA_2$, $PGD_2$, and KCl.[108] In addition, it reverses an on-going $LTD_4$-induced contraction ($IC_{50}$ = 1.6 $\mu M$) and inhibits OA-induced contractions of trachea isolated from sensitized guinea pigs. Aerosolized SKF-102,922 (0.4%) inhibits $LTD_4$ and $LTC_4$ changes in dynamic lung compliance and airway resistance in anesthetized guinea pig.[108] However, no oral efficacy was reported for this compound.

In the SKF-102,081/SKF-102,972 series there is an optimal chain length of 10 to 12 atoms (or its equivalent) in the lipid tail and two methylenes in the polar region. In the aromatic series, the ortho- and meta-substituted analogues have comparable activity, whereas the para derivatives are inactive. Conformational restriction of either the polar region or lipid tail produced compounds devoid of activity.[109]

In guinea pigs SKF-104,353 (Compound 28) antagonized $LTD_4$-induced changes in pulmonary airway resistance and dynamic lung compliance when administered by either aerosol (0.003 to 0.4%) or oral (25 mg/kg) route. In isolated guinea-pig trachea, SKF-104,353 antagonized the response to $LTD_4$ ($pA_2$ = 8.6) and $LTE_4$ ($pK_B > 8.9$) but was essentially without effect vs. $LTC_4$.[110] SKF has also described the sulfidopeptide-LT-based antagonist (Compound 29) which had good *in vitro* activity ($pK_B$ = 6.9 vs. $LTD_4$, guinea-pig trachea).[111]

ICI-19,350 (Compound 30) antagonized the action of $LTE_4$ at 10 $\mu M$ (guinea-pig trachea), although other related analogues were agonists.[112] The diacid (Compound 31) exhibited potent antagonist activity versus $LTC_4$ in the isolated guinea-pig parenchyma ($IC_{50}$ = 2.8 $\mu M$); however, other compounds in the series were agonists.[113] Substitution of a methyl group for a carboxyl in the sulfidopeptide-LT structure lead, after several additional modifications, to CGP-34064A (Compound 32), a compound that is not only a sulfidopeptide-LT antagonist but also a phospholipase-$A_2$ inhibitor.[114]

The mixed agonist/antagonist profile of the above compounds may be due to the presence of a long lipophilic chain. We feel that the 5-hydroxyl group, a portion of the cysteine and the 1-carboxyl group of $LTD_4$ are receptor recognition points for binding and that, once bound, the long lipophilic $C_{15}H_{21}$ tail of $LTD_4$ then changes conformation, distorts, and activates the receptor. Of course, the presence of a long lipophilic chain does not necessarily imply that a molecule will possess agonist activities. Only those chains capable of adopting a certain critical conformation will result in an agent possessing agonist properties.

**Structurally Novel Sulfidopeptide-Leukotriene-Receptor Antagonists (Table 3)**

Structurally unrelated to the above compounds, which all contain a hydroxyacetophenone

TABLE 1
SULFIDOPEPTIDE LT ANTAGONISTS BASED ON FPL-55, 712

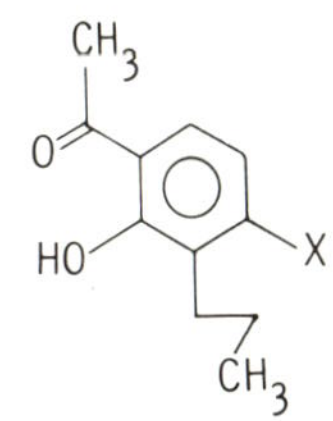

| Compound # (Code #) | X | Biological data | Ref |
|---|---|---|---|
| 1 (FPL-55, 712) | 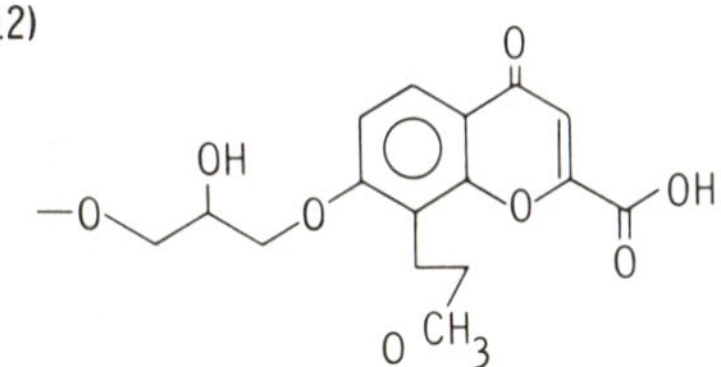 | $pA_2$ = 7.35 vs $LTD_4$ (GP ileum)<br>$IC_{50}$ = 0.032 µg/ml vs $LTD_4$ (GP ileum)<br>$ED_{50}$ = 12.8 mg/kg iv vs SRS-A (GP) | 18-22 |
| 2 (FPL-59, 257) | 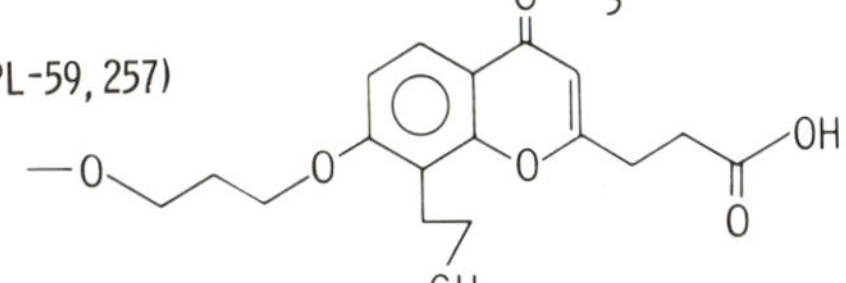 | $pA_2$ = 7.75 vs $LTD_4$ (GP ileum)<br>$IC_{50}$ = 0.26 µg/ml vs $LTD_4$ (GP ileum) | 21, 22 |
| 3 (BRL-19, 880) | 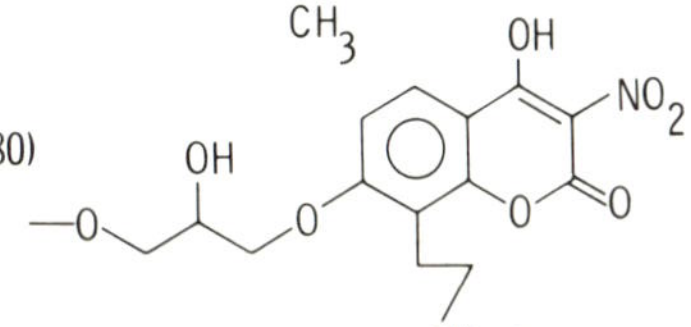 | $IC_{50}$ = 0.2 µM vs SRS-A (GP ileum) | 72 |
| 4 | 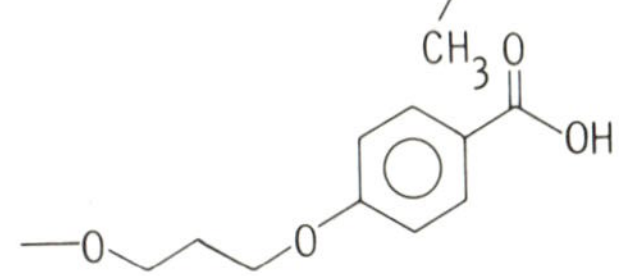 | $ED_{50}$ = 10mg/kg id vs $LTD_4$ (GP) | 73,82 |

| | | | | |
|---|---|---|---|---|
| 5 | | 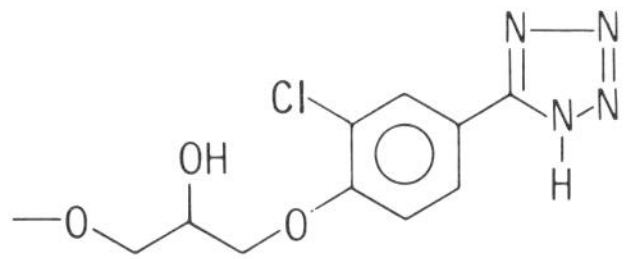 | 93% inhibition of $LTD_4$-induced bronchoconstriction at 5 mg/kg iv (GP) | 74 |
| 6 | | 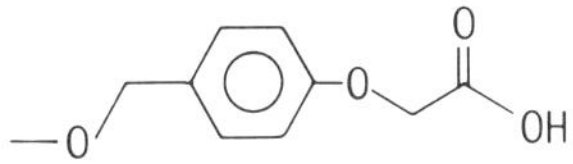 | $IC_{50} \approx 100$ μM vs $LTD_4$ (GP trachea) | 75 |
| 7 | | 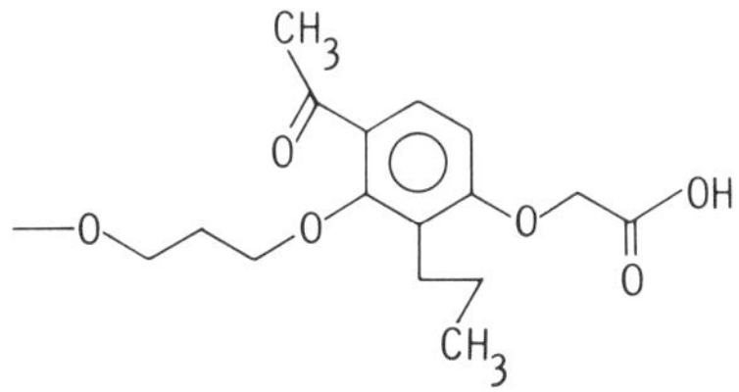 | 95% inhibition of $LTE_4$-induced bronchoconstriction at 10 mg/kg iv (GP) | 76 |
| 8 | (WY-44, 329) | 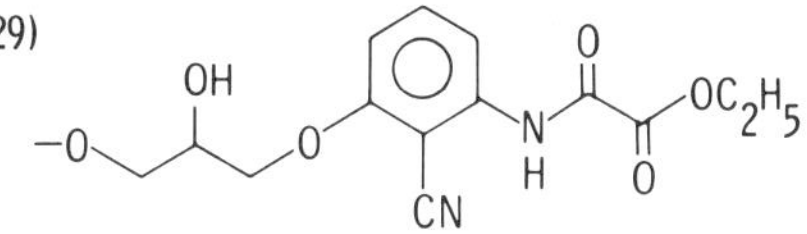 | $ED_{50}$ = 0.11 mg/kg iv vs $LTD_4$ (GP)<br>= 0.17 mg/kg iv vs $LTC_4$ (GP)<br>$pA_2$ = 9.4 vs $LTD_4$ (GP ileum) | 77, 94 |

TABLE 1 (continued)

| Compound # | (Code #) | X | Biological data | Ref |
|---|---|---|---|---|
| 9 | (L-649, 923) | 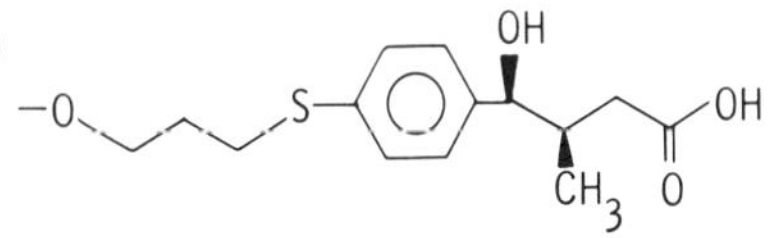 | $ED_{50}$ = 5mg/kg id vs $LTD_4$ (GP)<br>$pA_2$ = 8.1 vs $LTD_4$ (GP ileum) | 78 |
| 10 | (LY-171, 883) | 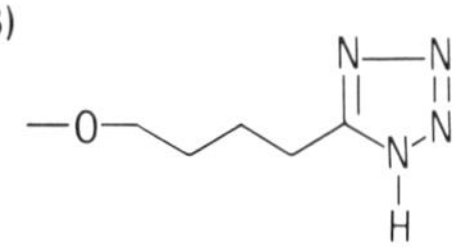 | $pA_2$= 7.19 vs $LTD_4$ (GP ileum)<br>Effective against both<br>$LTC_4$ and $LTD_4$ induced<br>bronchospasm in GP (30mg/kg po) | 79, 96 |
| 11 | | 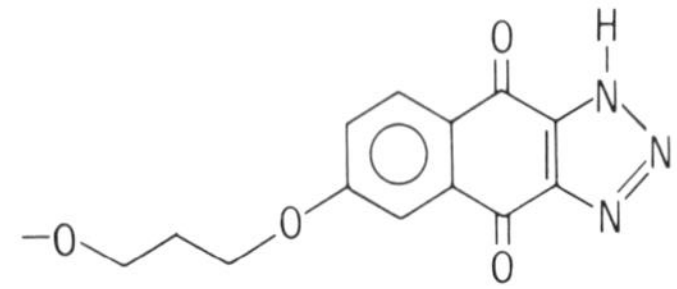 | $IC_{50}$ = 0.4 μM vs SRS-A (GP ileum) | 80 |
| 12 | | 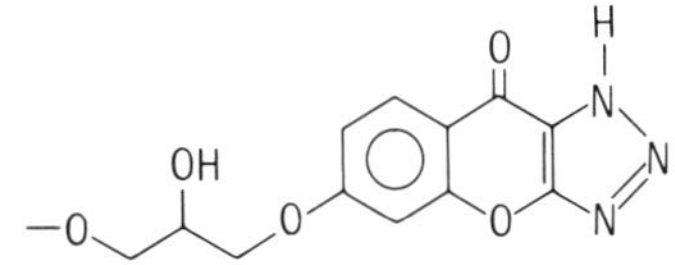 | $IC_{50}$ = 0.063 μM vs SRS-A (GP ileum) | 81 |
| 13 | | 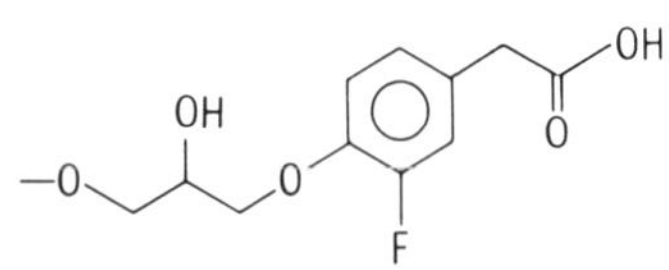 | $ED_{50}$ = 2.5 mg/kg id vs $LTD_4$ (GP) | 82 |

| | | | | |
|---|---|---|---|---|
| 14 | (Ro 23-3544) | 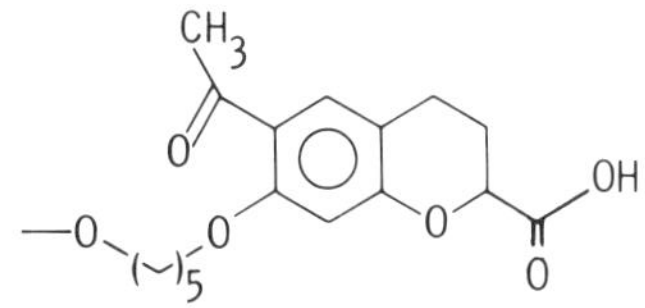 | $IC_{50}$ = 0.006% aero vs $LTD_4$ (GP) | 83 |
| 15 | (LY-163, 443) | 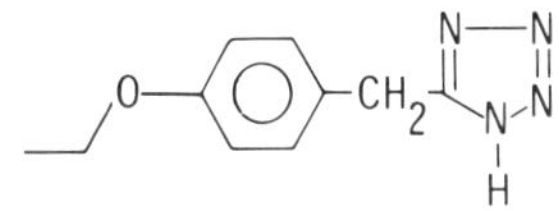 | $pK_B$ = 8.1 vs $LTD_4$ (GP ileum) | 84, 98, 99 |
| 16 | (WY-46, 235) | 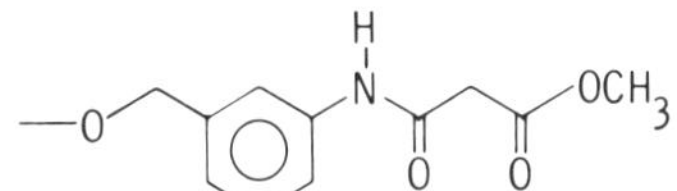 (despropyl hydroxyacetophenone) | 56% inhibition of $LTD_4$-induced bronchoconstriction 50 mg/kg po in GP | 85 |
| 17 | | 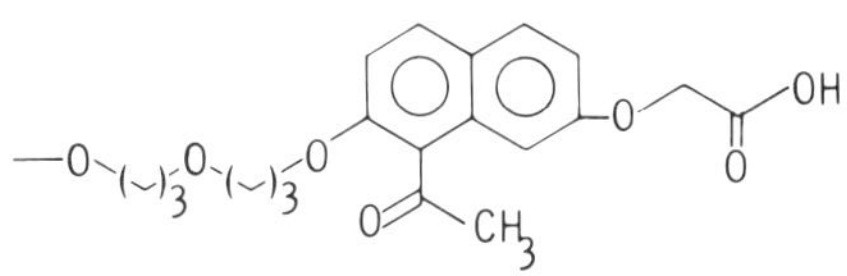 | $IC_{50}$ = 0.15 μM vs SRS-A (GP ileum) | 86 |
| 18 | | 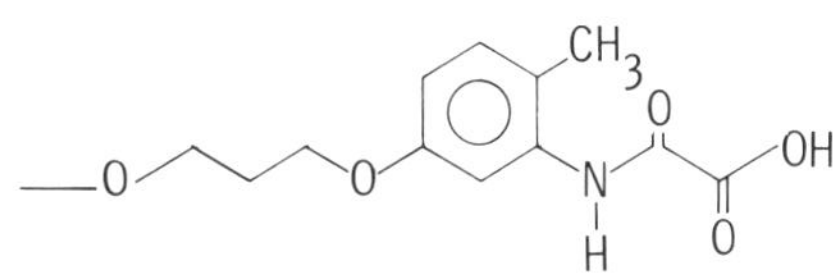 | $IC_{50}$ = 0.06 μM vs $LTD_4$ (GP ileum) $IC_{50}$ = 0.024% aero vs $LTD_4$ (GP) | 87 |

TABLE 1 (continued)

| Compound # | (Code #) | X | Biological data | Ref |
|---|---|---|---|---|
| 19 | (CGP-35,949) | 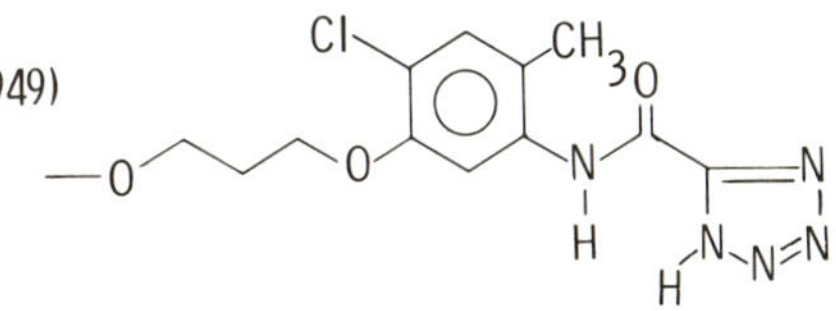 | $pA_2$ = 8.2 vs $LTD_4$ (GP ileum) | 87,88,103 |
| 20 | | 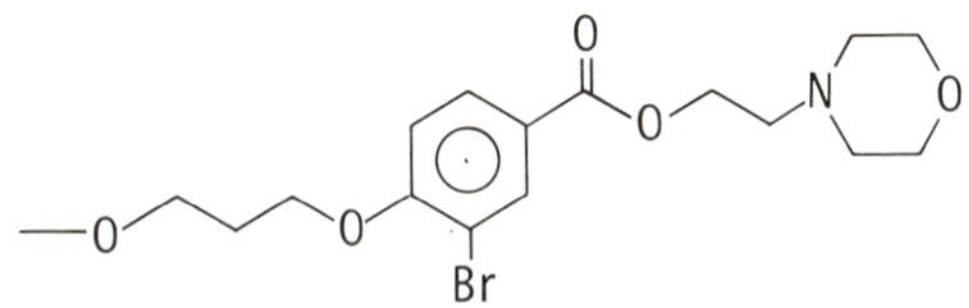 | $ID_{50}$ = 41 μmol/kg po in GP | 89 |
| 21 | (YM-16,638) | 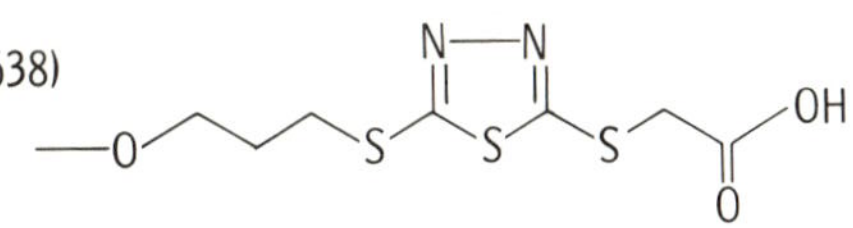 | $IC_{50}$ = 0.11 μM vs $LTD_4$ (GP ileum) | 90,91 |
| 22 | | 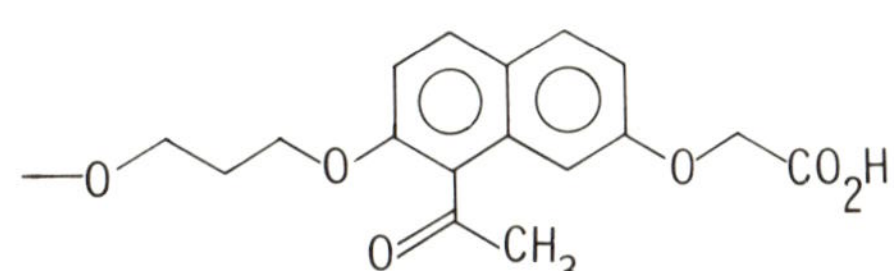 | 90% inhibition of $LTD_4$-induced bronchoconstriction in GP at 10 mg/kg iv | 92 |
| 23 | (L-648,051) | 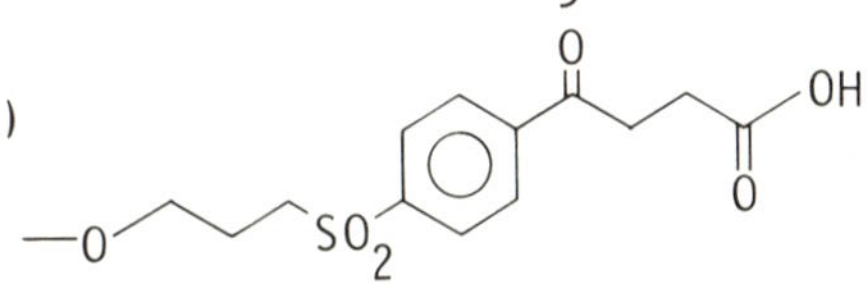 | $pA_2$ = 7.7 vs $LTD_4$ (GP ileum) | 93 |

*Note:* GP, guinea pig; iv, intravenous; id, intraduodenal; po, oral; and aero, aerosol.

moiety or are analogues of the sulfidopeptide LTs, is Wy-45,911 (Compound 33). When tested as an inhibitor of $LTD_4$- and antigen-induced bronchospasm in the guinea pig, it has $ED_{50}$s of 3.3 mg/kg and 27.4 mg/kg (intraduodenally), respectively.[115] When tested *in vitro* as an antagonist of $LTD_4$-induced contraction of isolated guinea-pig trachea spiral strips, it is a competitive inhibitor with a $pK_B$ value of 6.6.[116] Wy-45,911 exhibits mutagenic activity in the Ames assay and is not being developed further.[117]

Additional analogues of Wy-45,911 have been described. Wy-46,496 (Compound 34), Wy-46,543 (Compound 35), Wy-46,255 (Compound 36), and Wy-46,928 (Compound 37) are all reported to inhibit $LTD_4$-induced bronchospasm in the guinea pig when given intraduodenally.[117-121] Since Wy-46,496 and Wy-46,255 have chemical stability problems, they are of no further interest; however, Wy-46,928 shows promise and it or a related compound will be developed as a $LTD_4$ antagonist for the treatment of asthma.

Other structurally novel sulfidopeptide-LT antagonists have been reported and those of note include REV-5901 (Compound 38), ONO-RS411 (Compound 39), and ICI-198,615 (Compound 40). REV-5901, initially designed as a specific 5-LO inhibitor ($IC_{50}$ = 0.12 $\mu M$, rat neutrophils) was also determined to be an orally active $LTC_4$ antagonist.[123] The reported $LTC_4$-antagonism activity will probably turn out to be $LTD_4$-antagonism activity because the reported experimental section notes that no agent such as glutathione was added *in vitro* to inhibit the conversion of $LTC_4$ to $LTD_4$. Considerable affinity for the $LTD_4$ receptor is demonstrated with ONO-RS411 (Compound 39) which is also orally effective against $LTD_4$-induced bronchoconstriction in the guinea pig ($ID_{50}$ = 1.0 mg/kg).[124,125] In contrast to the above, ICI-198,615 (Compound 40) appears to competitively antagonize both $LTC_4$- and $LTD_4$-induced contractions of human bronchi and pulmonary vein ($pK_B$ = 9.8 and 9.2, respectively).[126,127] In isolated guinea-pig trachea ICI-198,615 (Compound 40) had potent activity vs. $LTE_4$ ($pA_2$ = 10.1) and $LTD_4$ ($pA_2$ = 9.7); however, it was weakly active vs. $LTC_4$ ($pK_B$ = 5.4). In an intact guinea-pig model, ICI-198,615 (Compound 40) demonstrated a dose-related antagonism of $LTC_4$ and $LTD_4$ when administered orally (5.7 mg/kg) with a fairly long half-life (>960 min). Although LY-137,617 (41) is a potent sulfidopeptide-LT antagonist *in vitro*, it is strongly protein bound, which appears to limit its *in vivo* activity.[128]

**Agents that Antagonize the Effects of Sulfidopeptide Leukotrienes (Table 4)**

Several compounds have been described which antagonize the effects of sulfidopeptide LTs although their site of action may not be at the sulfidopeptide-LT receptor. For example, SKF-88,046 (Compound 46) was initially reported to be a selective $LTD_4$ antagonist; however, it is now known to be an end-organ antagonist of $TxA_2$, $PGF_{2\alpha}$, and $PGD_2$, and thus acts indirectly.[134,135] KC-404 (Compound 42) inhibits SRS-A-induced bronchoconstriction in guinea pigs ($ED_{50}$ = $1.4 \times 10^{-3}$ and $6.5 \times 10^{-3}$ mg/kg, i.v. and intraduodenally, respectively).[129,130] This compound appears to not only interfere with the interaction of sulfidopeptide LTs and their receptors, but also appears to interfere with cyclooxygenase products involved in contractile responses.

The pyridoquinazoline (Compound 43) inhibits both SRS-A-induced contractions of guinea-pig ileum ($IC_{50}$ = 1 $\mu M$) and $LTE_4$-induced bronchoconstriction in the intact guinea pig (10 mg/kg i.v.).[131] A series of compounds (represented by Compound 44) are reported in the patent literature to antagonize the actions of SRS-A on guinea-pig ileum at 100 $\mu M$ but no details were presented.[132] Amoxanox (Compound 45) caused a dose-dependent reduction of 58% of the $LTD_4$-induced bronchoconstriction in the guinea pig (20 mg/kg i.v.).[133] Amoxanox inhibited $LTD_4$-induced contractions in guinea-pig ileum in a noncompetitive manner, suggesting that the effect of amoxanox is due to a mechanism other than direct blockage of the sulfidopeptide-LT receptors.[136]

TABLE 2
ANALOGUES OF SULFIDOPEPTIDE LEUKOTRIENES AS ANTAGONISTS

| Compound # | (Code #) | Structure | Biological data | Ref |
|---|---|---|---|---|
| 24 | (SKF-101, 132) | 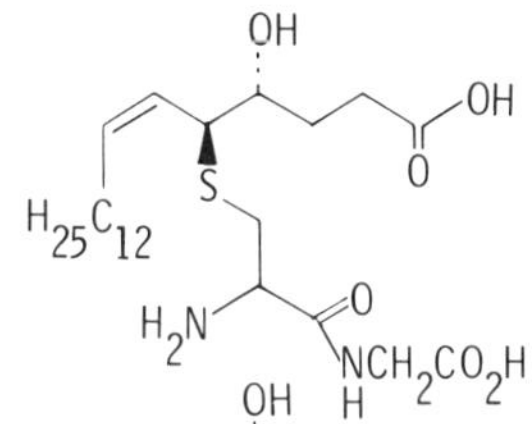  | $K_B$ = 6.3 µM vs $LTD_4$ (GP trachea) | 104, 105 |
| 25 | (SKF-101, 392) | 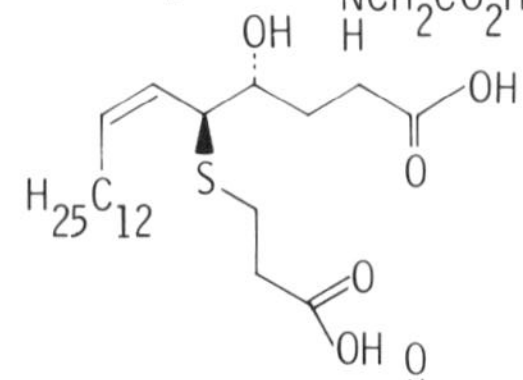  | $K_B$ = 0.29 µM vs $LTD_4$ (GP trachea)<br>$pA_2$ = 5.9 vs $LTE_4$ (GP trachea) | 106 |
| 26 | (SKF-102, 081) | 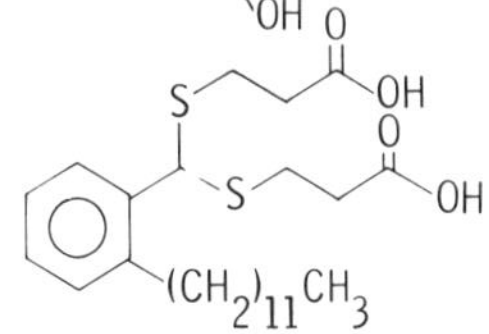  | $pK_B$ = 6.0 vs $LTD_4$ (GP trachea) | 107, 109 |
| 27 | (SKF-102, 922) | 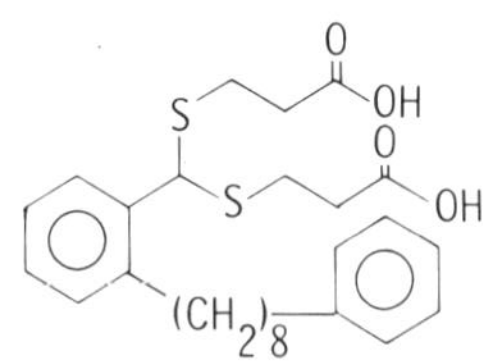  | $pK_B$ = 6.7 vs $LTD_4$ (GP trachea)<br>$IC_{50}$ = 1.6 µM vs $LTD_4$ (GP trachea) | 107-109 |

| | | | | |
|---|---|---|---|---|
| 28 | (SKF - 104, 353) | 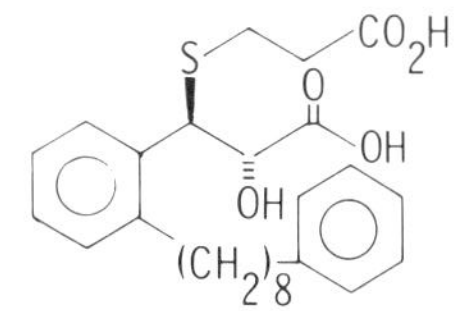 | $pA_2$ = 8.6 vs $LTD_4$ (Human bronchi) $pK_B$ = 8.0 vs $LTD_4$ (Human bronchi) | 110 |
| 29 | | 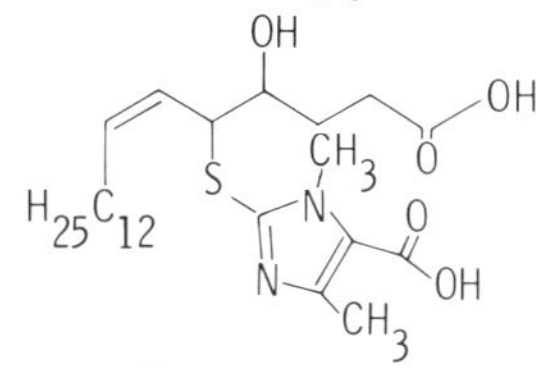 | $pK_B$ = 6.9 vs $LTD_4$ (GP trachea) | 111 |
| 30 | (ICI-19, 350) | 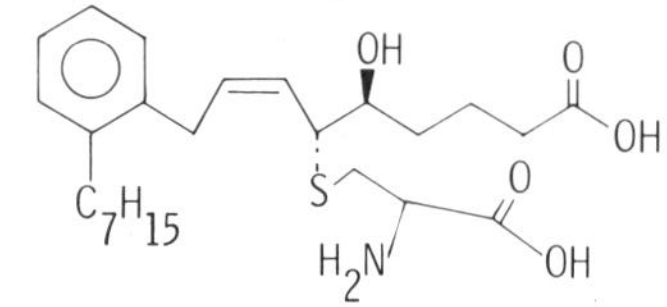 | Active at 10 μM vs $LTE_4$ (GP trachea) | 112 |
| 31 | | 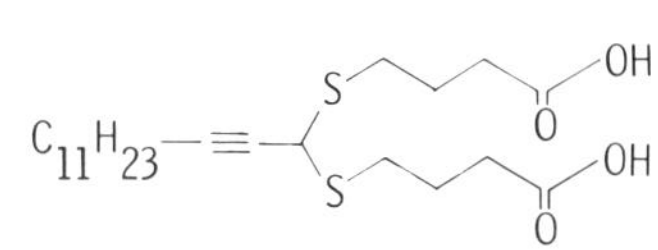 | $IC_{50}$ = 2.8 μM vs $LTC_4$ (GP lung strip) | 113 |
| 32 | (CGP-34, 064A) | 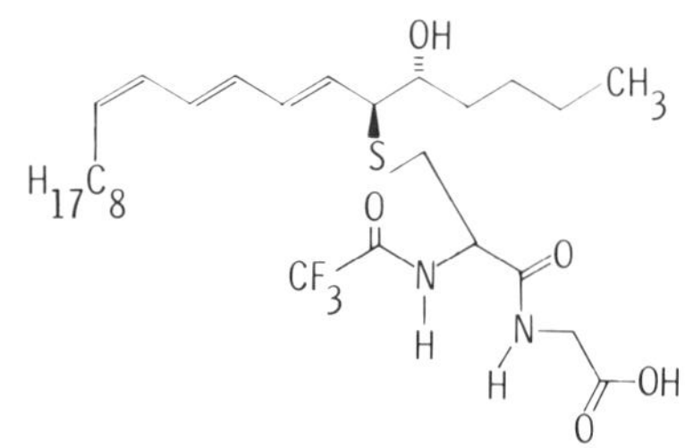 | | 114 |

*Note:* GP, guinea pig.

TABLE 3

NOVEL SULFIDOPEPTIDE LEUKOTRIENE ANTAGONISTS ACTING AT THE RECEPTOR LEVEL

| Compound # | (Code #) | Structure | Biological data | Ref |
|---|---|---|---|---|
| 33 | (Wy-45, 911) | 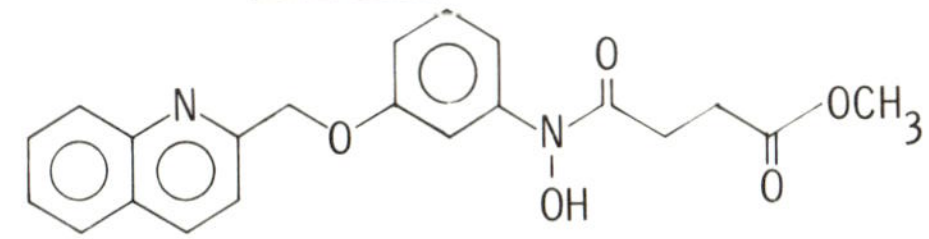 | pKB = 6.60 vs $LTD_4$ (GP trachea) $ED_{50}$ = 3.3 mg/kg id vs $LTD_4$ (GP) | 115-117 |
| 34 | (WY-46, 496) | 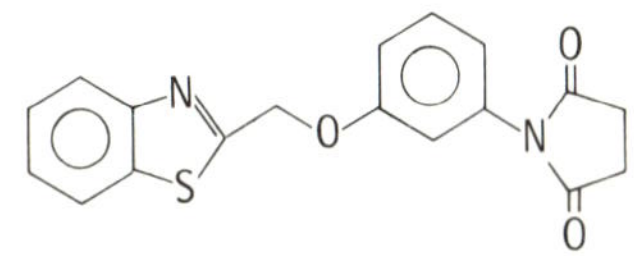 | 68% inhibition of $LTD_4$-induced broncho-constriction at 50 mg/kg id (GP) | 117, 118 |
| 35 | (WY-46, 543) | 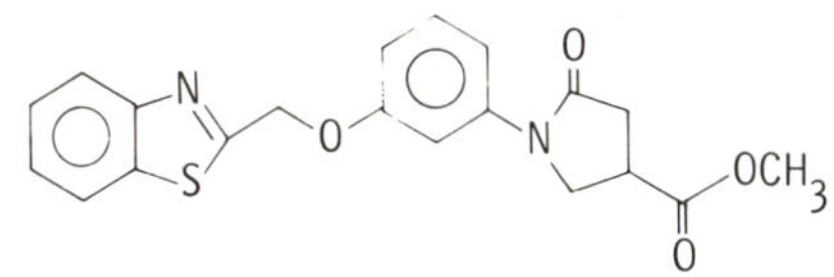 | 68% inhibition of $LTD_4$-induced broncho-constriction at 50 mg/kg id (GP) | 117, 119 |
| 36 | (WY-46, 255) | 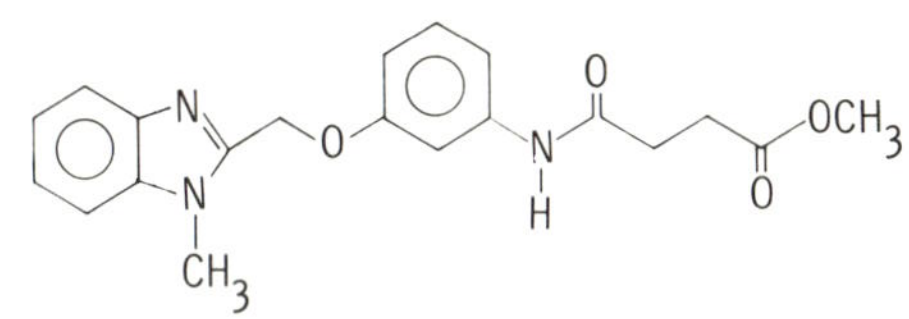 | 82% inhibition of $LTD_4$-induced broncho-constriction at 50 mg/kg id (GP) | 117, 120 |
| 37 | (WY-46, 928) | 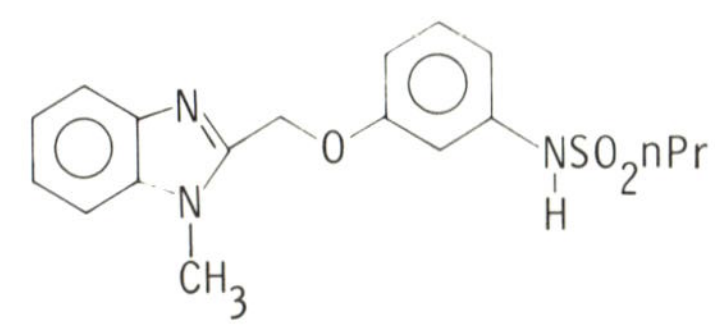 | 86% inhibition of $LTD_4$-induced broncho-constriction at 50 mg/kg id (GP) | 121 |

| | | | | |
|---|---|---|---|---|
| 38 | (REV 5,901) | 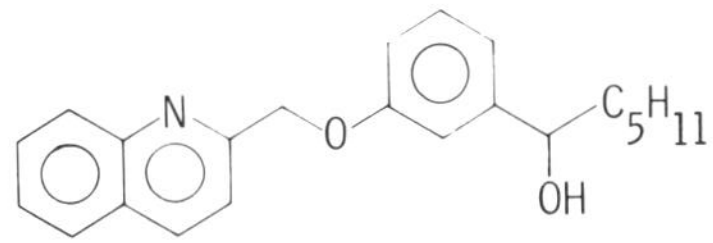 | $pK_B$ = 5.44 vs $LTD_4$ (GP trachea) | 122,123 |
| 39 | (RS 411) (ONO 1078) | 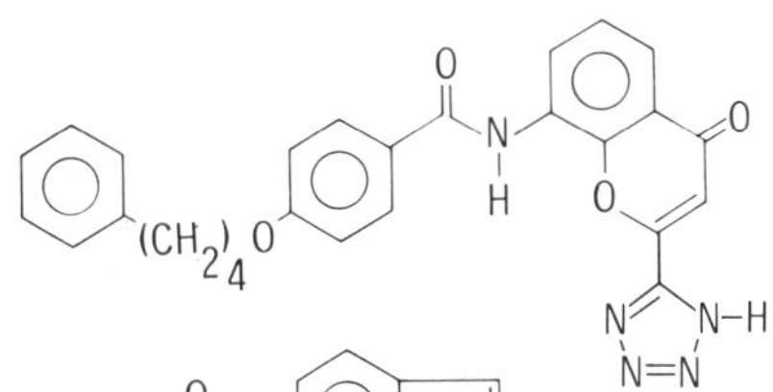 | $pK_B$ = 10.4 vs $LTD_4$ (GP ileum)<br>$ID_{50}$ = 1.0 mg/kg po vs $LTD_4$ (GP) | 124,125 |
| 40 | (ICI-198,615) | 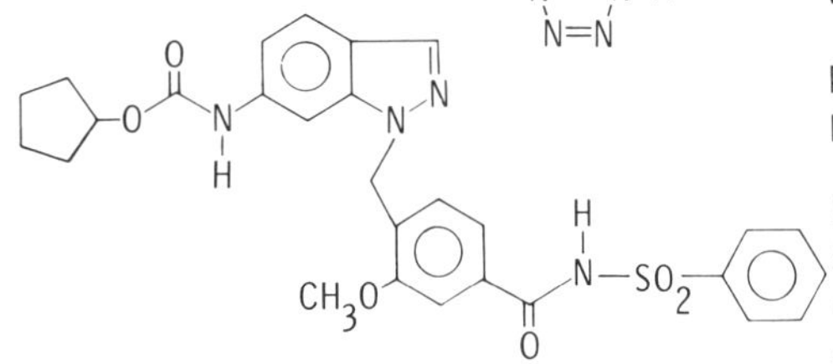 | $pK_B$ = 9.7 vs $LTD_4$ (GP trachea)<br>$pA_2$ = 9.6 vs $LTD_4$ (GP parenchyma)<br>$pK_B$ = 9.8 vs $LTC_4$ or $LTD_4$ (Human bronchi) | 126,127 |
| 41 | (LY-137,617) | 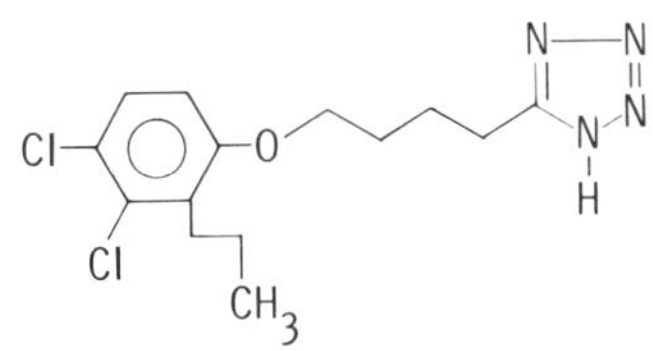 | $pK_B$ = 6.7 vs $LTD_4$ (GP trachea) | 128 |

*Note:* Gp, guinea pig; id, intraduodenal; and po, oral.

TABLE 4

MISCELLANEOUS COMPOUNDS THAT ANTAGONIZE THE EFFECTS OF SULFIDOPEPTIDE LEUKOTRIENES

| Compound # | (Code#) | Structure | Biological data | Ref |
|---|---|---|---|---|
| 42 | (KC-404) | 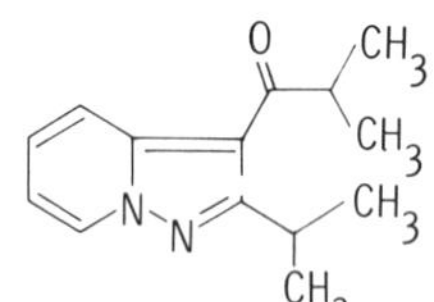 | $ED_{50}$ = 0.0065 mg/kg id vs SRS-A (GP) | 129, 130 |
| 43 | | 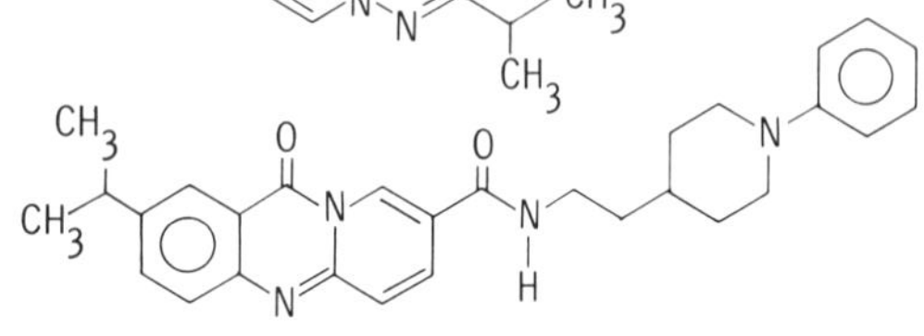 | $IC_{50}$ = 1μM vs SRS-A (GP ileum) | 131 |
| 44 | | 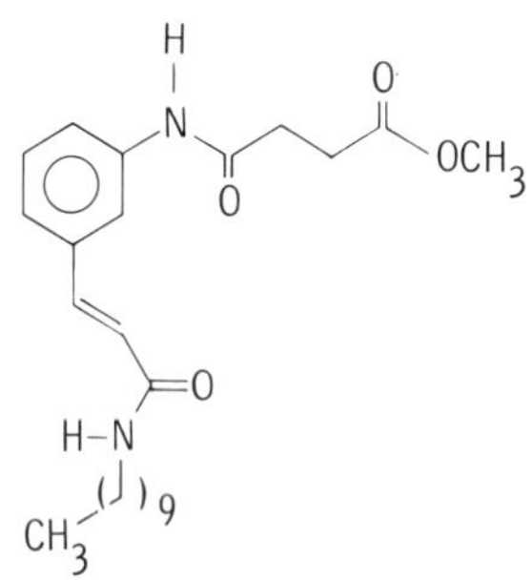 | Antagonizes action of SRS-A at 100 μM (GP ileum) | 132 |

| | | | | |
|---|---|---|---|---|
| 45 | (AMOXANOX) | 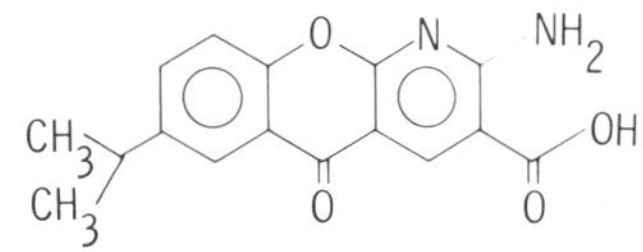 | 58% reduction of $LTD_4$-induced broncho-constriction at 20 mg/kg iv (GP) | 133, 136 |
| 46 | (SKF-88, 046) | 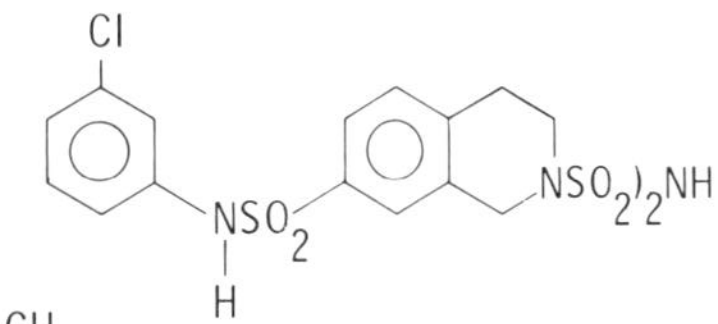 | Inhibited $LTD_4$-induced pulmonary changes at 5 mg/kg iv (GP) | 134, 135 |
| 47 | | 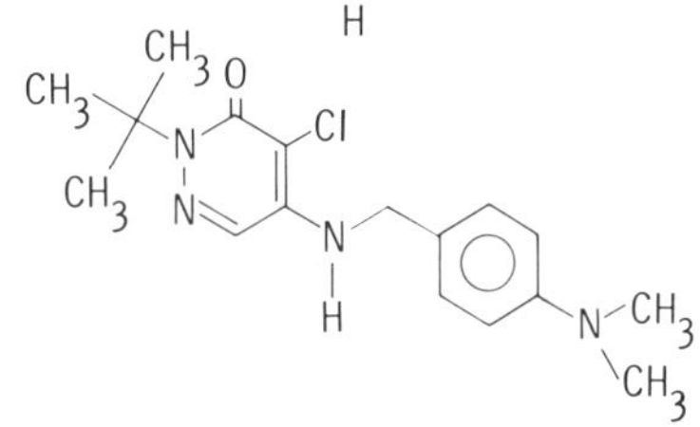 | 73% inhibition of $LTD_4$-induced bronchoconstriction at 2 mg/kg iv (GP) | 137 |

*Note:* GP, guinea pig; id, intraduodenal; and iv, intravenous.

**Leukotriene-$B_4$ Receptors and Antagonists (Table 5)**

Considering the significant amount of activity in the area of sulfidopeptide-LT antagonists, the limited progress in the development of $LTB_4$ antagonists is striking, especially considering the putative role for $LTB_4$ as an inflammatory mediator. Four analogues of $LTB_4$ have been reported to antagonize the effects of $LTB_4$. The diacetate (Compound 48) competitively inhibits the chemotactic response of $LTB_4$ (equimolar concentrations).[138] The dimethylamide of $LTB_4$ (Compound 49) ($K_D = 0.2\ \mu M$)[139] and an $LTB_4$ isomer (Compound 50) antagonize $LTB_4$-induced degranulation.[140] Finally, SM-9064 (Compound 51) inhibited the chemotaxis of rat PMNs induced by $LTB_4$ ($IC_{50} = 0.13\ \mu M$).[141] It suppressed the Arthus-reaction-induced inflammation in mice (10 mg/kg p.o.); however it was inactive in the carrageenin-induced rat-paw-edema model (50 mg/kg p.o.).

The potent effects of $LTB_4$ on monocytes and PMNs has resulted in an examination of specific $LTB_4$-receptor sites on these cells. A fluorescence-activated flow-cytometry study demonstrated that the interaction of fluorescein-conjugated $LTB_4$ with human T-lymphocytes was stereoselective and not mimicked by $LTC_4$.[142] The use of [$^3$H]-labeled $LTB_4$ has provided more direct evidence for specific receptors on PMNs.[143-145] Goldman and Goetzl described two classes of receptors on human PMNs that are specific for $LTB_4$.[145] The high-affinity receptor ($K_d = 0.39$ n$M$; mean of 4,400 per PMN) modulates chemotaxis while the low-affinity receptors ($K_d = 62$ n$M$; mean of 270,000 per PMN) modulates degranulation. Other investigators have confirmed the presence of high- and low-affinity binding sites for $LTB_4$ on human-PMN plasma membrane.[146] This binding may have a functional correlate since the exposure of PMNs to nanmolar concentrations of $LTB_4$ stimulates maximal chemokinetic and chemotactic migration,[147,148] while 100-fold higher concentrations are required to evoke generation of superoxide[149] and lysosomal degranulation.[150]

The high-affinity receptors are down-regulated selectively by prior exposure of PMNs to $LTB_4$ and require guanine-nucleotide-binding proteins for optimal expression and signal transduction.[151] Affinity radiolabeling and solubilization of $LTB_4$ receptors have permitted isolation and fragmentation of the receptor protein in sufficient quantities for structural studies.[152] A monoclonal $IgG_{2b}$ anti-$LTB_4$ that binds [$^3$H] $LTB_4$ with a specificity identical to that of PMN chemotactic receptors has been produced using immunized rabbits.[153] Anti-idiotypes produced to this monoclonal anti-$LTB_4$ resemble $LTB_4$ and bind preferentially to the high-affinity receptors and elicit PMN chemotaxis.

Recently, a high-affinity binding site ($K_d = 1.8$ n$M$, $B_{max} = 274$ fmol/mg protein) in guinea-pig spleen membranes was described.[154] Felodipine, a calcium channel blocker, inhibits $LTB_4$ binding to this spleen homogenate at $\mu M$ concentrations. The low-affinity binding of [$^3$H] $LTB_4$ to the guinea-pig PMN argues against the concept that high-affinity binding is attributed to this cell in the spleen. It is possible that these binding sites in the spleen play a role in the immunoregulation of T and B lymphocytes.[155,156]

## SUMMARY

Research on LT-receptor antagonists is at a stage of considerable ferment. Several sulfidopeptide-LT antagonists based on FPL-55,712 are currently undergoing clinical evaluation for the treatment of asthma while newer agents structurally related to sulfidopeptide LTs are rapidly being developed. Further back in development are sulfidopeptide-LT antagonists of novel structure that are eagerly awaited because they are reported to possess high receptor affinity and/or potent oral activity in animal models. Clearly the pharmaceutical industry is committing significant resources to this area, although the therapeutic value of sulfidopeptide-LT antagonist has yet to be conclusively demonstrated. By contrast, the area of $LTB_4$-receptor antagonists has received little attention but represents a novel approach to the treatment of inflammation.

The numbers and subtypes of LT receptors have only recently been investigated and more work is needed to evaluate the distribution of receptors on tissues and cells in both normal and pathological states. Classification of the heterogeneity of LT receptors may assist in the discovery of new anti-allergy and anti-inflammatory drugs much in the same way as the study of different adrenergic receptors has benefited cardiovascular drug discovery. The clinical evaluation of the currently available sulfidopeptide-LT antagonists is awaited with interest; however, their therapeutic role in the treatment of asthma, a primary goal for the majority of these agents, will require painstaking clinical appraisal. The currently used β-agonist bronchodilators are problematic because they relieve symptoms without treating the underlying disease. The sharp rise in the number of deaths from asthma during the past decade could reflect the limitations of this type of therapy.[157] If the LT antagonists modify the hyperactive state that prevails in asthma, they could represent a therapeutic advance over the currently used bronchodilators.

## ACKNOWLEDGMENT

We would like to thank M. E. Fiala for preparing the manuscript.

## ADDENDUM

In contrast to animal experiments where $LTC_4$ and $LTD_4/LTE_4$ occupy two distinct receptors in guinea-pig airways, recent studies indicate that all the sulfidopeptide LTs occupy the same receptor in human airways.[158] Therefore, it may be possible that a $LTD_4$ antagonist can fully inhibit sulfidopeptide LT-mediated pharmacological responses in man.

The recent demonstration of efficacy in clinical trials with $LTD_4$ antagonists from different structural classes has indicated that the $LTD_4$ antagonist approach to asthma therapy, indeed, may be valid. In addition, the lack of side effects of $LTD_4$ antagonists suggests that their importance in homeostasis is minimal. The first $LTD_4$ antagonist to show efficacy in asthma was LY-171,883 (Compound 10).[159] Although LY-171,883 was suspended because of long term toxicity (tumor formation in female mice), studies on this compound have shown clinical efficacy in cold-air-induced bronchospasm and exercise-induced asthma.[160,161] A related compound, YM-16638 (Compound 21), was reported to have clinical efficacy against not only antigen challenge, but also aspirin-induced asthma.[162] In contrast to the above orally active $LTD_4$ antagonists, SKF-104,353 (Compound 28) has been shown to be clinically efficacious only in an aerosol formulation.[163] This compound was shown to block both antigen and $LTD_4$ challenge in man.

We at Wyeth-Ayerst have recently announced Wy-48,252 as our clinical candidate in the $LTD_4$ antagonist area.[164-165] Against an i.v. $LTD_4$ challenge, a 2 h intragastric pretreatment with Wy-48,252 gave an $ID_{50}$ of 0.1 mg/kg equivalent to that (0.07 mg/kg) obtained with i.v. (10 min pretreatment) Wy-48,252. Its potency was further emphasized in a comparative study where intragastric Wy-48,252 was shown to be 300-fold more potent that similarly administered LY-171,883.

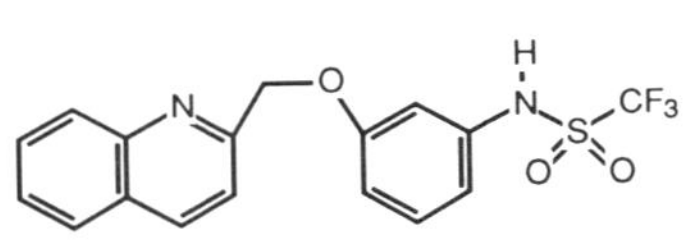


Wy-48,252

TABLE 5
ANTAGONISTS OF $LTB_4$

| Compound # | (Code #) | Structure | Biological data | Ref |
|---|---|---|---|---|
| 48 | | 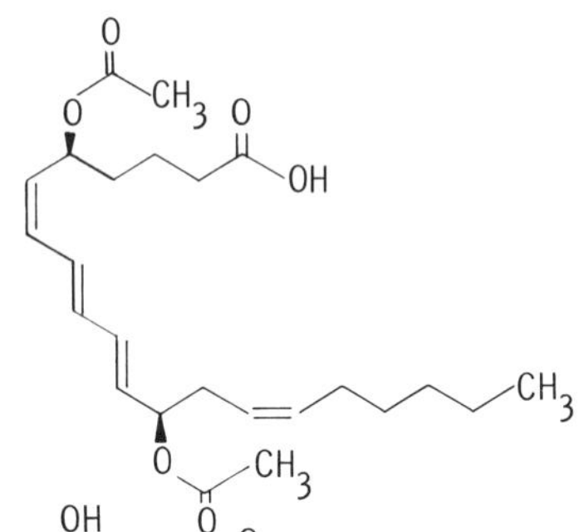 | $IC_{50} \approx 1$ ng/ml vs $LTB_4$-induced chemotaxis (human neutrophils) | 138 |
| 49 | | 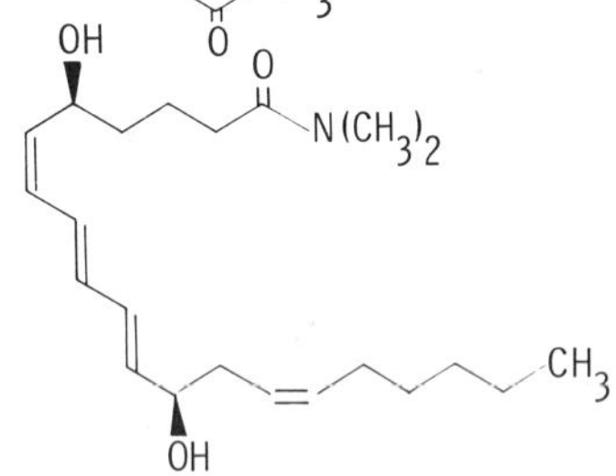 | $K_D = 0.2\ \mu M$ vs $LTB_4$-induced neutrophil degranulation (rabbit) | 139 |

| | | | | |
|---|---|---|---|---|
| 50 | | 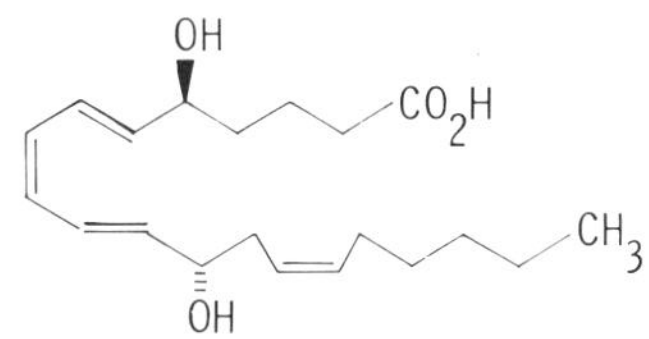 | 42% inhibition of $LTB_4$-stimulated lysozyme release at 1 μM (human PMNS) | 140 |
| 51 | (SM-9064) | 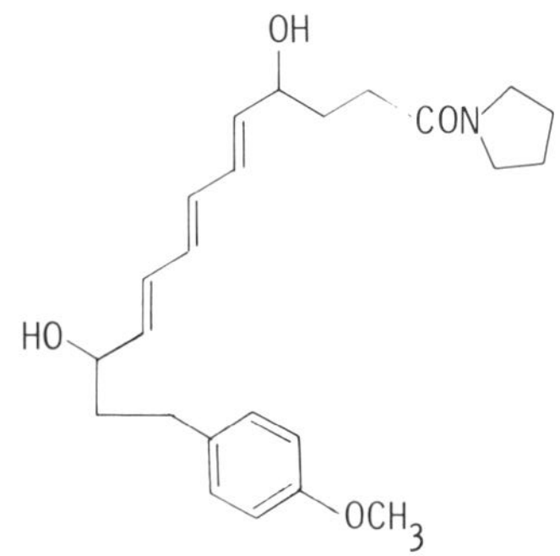 | $IC_{50}$ = 0.13 μM vs $LTB_4$-induced chemotaxis of rat PMN | 141 |

## REFERENCES

1. **Feldberg, W. and Kellaway, C. H.,** Liberation of histamine and formation of lysocithin-like substances by cobra venom, *J. Physiol.*, 94, 187, 1938.
2. **Kellaway, C. H. and Trethewie, E. R.,** The liberation of a slow reacting smooth muscle-stimulating substance in anaphylaxis, *Q. J. Exp. Physiol.*, 38, 121, 1940.
3. **Brocklehurst, W. E.,** The release of histamine and formation of a slow reacting substance (SRS-A) during anaphylactic shock, *J. Physiol.*, 151, 416, 1960.
4. **Orange, R. P. and Austen, K. F.,** Slow reacting substance of anaphylaxis, in *Advances in Immunology*, Vol. 10, Dixon, F. J., Jr. and Kunkel, H. G., Eds., Academic Press, New York, 1969, 105.
5. **Ishizaka, T., Ishizaka, K., Orange, R. P., and Austen, K. F.,** Pharmacologic inhibition of the antigen-induced release of histamine and slow-reacting substance of anaphylaxis (SRS-A) from monkey lung tissue mediated by human IgE, *J. Immunol.*, 106, 1267, 1971.
6. **Orange, R. P., Murphy, R. C., Karnovsky, M. L., and Austen, K. F.,** The physiochemical characteristics and purification of slow-reacting substance of anaphylaxis, *J. Immunol.*, 110, 760, 1973.
7. **Lewis, R. A., Wasserman, S. T., Goetzl, E. J., and Austen, K. F.,** Formation of slow-reacting substance of anaphylaxis in human lung tissue and cells before release, *J. Exp. Med.*, 140, 1133, 1974.
8. **Bach, M. K. and Brashler, J. R.,** *In vivo* and *in vitro* production of a slow-reacting substance in the rat upon treatment with calcium ionophore, *J. Immunol.*, 113, 2040, 1974.
9. **Grant, J. A. and Lichtenstein, L. M.,** Release of slow-reacting substance of anaphylaxis from human leukocytes, *J. Immunol.*, 112, 897, 1974.
10. **Engineer, D. M., Piper, P. J., and Sirois, P.,** Interaction between the release of SRS-A and of prostaglandins, *Br. J. Pharmacol.*, 57, 460P, 1976.
11. **Jakschik, B. A., Kulezycki, A., Jr., Macdonald, H. H., and Parker, C. W.,** Release of slow-reacting substance (SRS) from rat basophilic leukemia (RBL-1) cells, *J. Immunol.*, 119, 618, 1977.
12. **Jakschik, B. A., Falkenheim, S., and Parker, C. W.,** Precursor role of arachidonic acid in release of slow-reacting substance from rat basophilic leukemia cells, *Proc. Natl. Acad. Sci. U.S.A.*, 74, 4577, 1977.
13. **Sammuelsson, B.,** Leukotrienes: mediators of allergic reactions and inflammation, *Int. Arch. Allerg. Appl. Immunol.*, 66 (Suppl. 1), 98, 1981.
14. **Sammuelsson, B.,** Leukotrienes: mediators of immediate hypersensitivity reactions and inflammation, *Science*, 220, 568, 1983.
15. **Sammuelsson, B., Borgent, P., Hammarstrom, S., and Murphy, R. C.,** Leukotrienes: a new group of biologically active compounds, *Adv. Prostaglandin Thromboxane Res.*, 6, 1, 1980.
16. **Corey, E. J., Niwa, H., Falck, J. R., Mioskowski, C., Arai, Y., and Marfat, A.,** Recent studies on the chemical synthesis of eicosanoids, *Adv. Prostanglandin Thromboxane Res.*, 6, 19, 1980.
17. **Corey, E. J., Clark, D. A., Goto, G., Marfat, A., Mioskowski, C, Samuelsson, B., and Hammarstrom, S.,** Stereospecific total synthesis of a "slow-reacting" of anaphylaxis, leukotriene C-1, *J. Am. Chem. Soc.*, 102, 1436, 1980.
18. **Augstein, J., Farmer, J. B., Lee, T. B., Sheard, P., and Tattersall, M. L.,** Selective inhibitor of slow reacting substance of anaphylaxis, *Nature (London) New Biol.*, 245, 215, 1973.
19. **Chand, N.,** FPL-55,712—an antagonist of slow reacting substance of anaphylaxis (SRS-A): a review, *Agents Actions*, 9, 133, 1979.
20. **Holroyde, M. C., Altounyan, R. E. C., Cole, M., Dixon, M., and Elliott, E. V.,** Selective inhibition of bronchoconstriction induced by leukotrienes C and D in man, in *Advances in Prostaglandin, Thromboxane and Leukotriene Research*, Samuelsson, B. and Paolettim, R. Eds., Raven Press, New York, 1982, 237.
21. **Sheard, P., Holroyde, M. C., Ghelani, A. M., Bantick, J. R., and Lee, T. B.,** Antagonists of SRS-A and leukotrienes, in *Advances in Prostaglandin, Thromboxane and Leukotriene Research*, Samuelsson, B. and Paoletti, R., Eds., Raven Press, New York, 1982, 237.
22. **Holroyde, M. C. and Ghelani, A. M.,** Kinetics of action of two leukotriene antagonists on guinea pig ileum, *Eur. J. Pharmacol.*, 90, 251, 1983.
23. **Ford-Hutchinson, A. and Letts, G.,** Biological actions of leukotrienes, *Hypertension*, 8(Suppl. II), 44, 1986.
24. **Ford-Hutchinson, A. W.,** Leukotrienes: their formation and role as inflammatory mediators, *Fed. Proc. Fed. Am. Soc. Exp. Biol.*, 44, 25, 1985.
25. **Piper, P. J.,** Leukotrienes: potent mediators of airway constriction, *Int. Arch. Allergy Appl. Immunol.*, 76(Suppl. 1), 43, 1985.
26. **Maron, Z., Shelhamer, J. H., Bach, M. K., Morton, D. R., and Kaliner, M.,** Slow reacting substances, leukotriene $C_4$ and $D_4$ increase the release of mucus from human airways *in vitro*, *Am. Rev. Resp. Dis.*, 126, 449, 1982.
27. **Camp, R. D. R., Coutts, A. A., Greaves, M. W., Kay, A. B., and Walport, M. J.,** Responses of human skin to intradermal injections of leukotrienes $C_4$, $D_4$ and $B_4$, *Br. J. Pharmacol.*, 80, 497, 1983.

28. **Isono, T., Koshihara, Y., Murota, S., Fukuda, Y., and Furukawa, S.,** Measurement of immunoreactive leukotriene $C_4$ in blood of asthmatic children, *Biochem. Biophys. Res. Commun.*, 130, 486, 1985.
29. **Bray, M. A.,** The pharmacology and pathophysiology of leukotriene $B_4$, *Br. Med. Bull.*, 39, 249, 1983.
30. **Bach, M. K.,** Prospects for the inhibition of leukotriene synthesis, *Biochem. Pharmacol.*, 33, 515, 1984.
31. **Chakrin, L. W. and Bailey, D. M., Eds.,** *The Leukotrienes: Chemistry and Biology*, Academic Press, Orlando, FL, 1984.
32. **Fleisch, J. H., Rinkema, L. E., and Baker, S. R.,** Evidence for multiple leukotriene $D_4$ receptors in smooth muscle, *Life Sci.*, 31, 577, 1982.
33. **Weichman, B. M. and Tucker, S. S.,** Contraction of guinea pig uterus by synthetic leukotrienes, *Prostaglandins*, 24, 245, 1982.
34. **Buckner, C. K., Krell, R. D., Laravuso, R. B., Coursin, D. B., Bernstein, P. R., and Will, J. A.,** Pharmacological evidence that human intralobar airways do not contain different receptors that mediate contractions to leukotriene $C_4$ and luekotriene $D_4$, *J. Pharmacol. Exp. Ther.*, 237, 558, 1986.
35. **Pong, S. S., DeHaven, R. N., Kuehl, F. A., Jr., and Egan, R. W.,** Leukotriene $C_4$ binding to rat lung membranes, *J. Biol. Chem.*, 258, 9616, 1983.
36. **Pong, S. S. and DeHaven, R. N.,** Characterization of leukotriene $D_4$ receptor in guinea pig lung, *Proc. Natl. Acad. Sci. U.S.A.*, 80, 7415, 1983.
37. **Bruns, R., Thomsen, W. J., and Pugsley, T. A.,** Binding of leukotriene $C_4$ and $D_4$ to membranes from guinea pig lung. Regulation by ions and nucleotides, *Life Sci.*, 33, 645, 1983.
38. **Mong, S., Wu, H. L., Hogaboom, G. K., Clark, M. A., and Crooke, S. T.,** Characterization of the leukotriene $D_4$ receptor in guinea pig lung, *Eur. J. Pharmacol.*, 102, 1, 1984.
39. **Cheng, J. B., Lang, D., Bewtra, A., and Townley, R. G.,** Tissue distribution and functional correlation of [$^3$H]leukotriene $C_4$ and [$^3$H]leukotriene $D_4$ binding sites in guinea pig uterus and lung preparations, *J. Pharmacol. Exp. Ther.*, 232, 80, 1985.
40. **Mong, S., Wu, H. L., Scott, M. O., Lewis, M. A., Clark, M. A., Weichman, B. M., Kinzig, C. M., Gleason, J. G., and Crooke, S. T.,** Molecular heterogenecity of leukotriene receptors: correlation of smooth muscle contraction and radiology and binding in guinea pig lung, *J. Pharmacol. Exp. Ther.*, 234, 316, 1985.
41. **Hogaboom, G. K., Mong, S., Stadel, J. M., and Crooke, S. T.,** Characterization of guinea pig myocardial leukotriene $C_4$ binding sites regulation by cations and sulhydryl-directed reagents, *Mol. Pharmacol.*, 27, 236, 1985.
42. **Krilis, S., Lewis, R. A., Corey, E. J., and Austin, K. F.,** Specific binding of leukotriene $C_4$ to ileal segments and subcellular fractions of ileal smooth muscle cell, *Proc. Natl. Acad. Sci. U.S.A.*, 81, 4529, 1984.
43. **Levinson, S. L.,** Binding of $^3$H-leukotriene $C_4$ to specific receptor sites in guinea pig uterine membrane preparations, *Pharmacologist*, 25, 201, 1983.
44. **Lewis, M. A., Mong, S., Vesella, R. L., Hogaboom, G. K., Wu, H. L., and Crooke, S. T.,** Identification of specific binding sites for leukotriene $C_4$ in human fetal lung, *Prostaglandins*, 27, 961, 1984.
45. **Civelli, M., Folco, G. C., Mezzetti, M., Nicosia, S., Oliva, D., Rovati, G. E., and Sautebin, L.,** Specific binding of $LTC_4$ to membrane from human lung parenchyma and bronchi, *Br. J. Pharmacol.*, 86, 647P, 1985.
46. **Ballermann, B. J., Lewis, R. A., Corey, E. J., Austen, K. F., and Brenner, B. M.,** Identification and characterization of leukotriene $C_4$ receptors in isolated rat renal glomeruli, *Circ. Res.*, 56, 324, 1985.
47. **Schalling, M., Neil, A., Terenius, L., Lindgren, J. A., Miamoto, T., Hokfelt, T., and Samuelsson, B.,** Leukotriene $C_4$ binding sites in the rat central nervous system, *Eur. J. Pharmacol.*, 122, 251, 1986.
48. **Band, L., Sraer, J., Perez, J., Nivey, M. P., and Ardaillou, R.,** Leukotriene $C_4$ binds to human glomerular epithelial cells and promotes their proliferation *in vitro*, *J. Clin. Invest.*, 76, 374, 1985.
49. **Krilis, S., Lewis, R. A., Corey, E. J., and Austen, K. F.,** Specific receptors for leukotriene $C_4$ on a smooth muscle cell line, *J. Clin. Invest.*, 72, 1516, 1983.
50. **Sun, F. F., Chau, L.-Y., Spur, B., Corey, E. J., Lewis, R. A., and Austen, K. F.,** Identification of a high affinity leukotriene $C_4$-binding protein in rat liver cytosol as glutathione S-transferase, *J. Biol. Chem.*, 261, 8540, 1986.
51. **Norman, P., Carstairs, J. A., Abram, T. S., and Barnes, P. J.,** Differential autoradiographic localization of leukotriene binding sites in guinea-pig airways, *Adv. Prostaglandin Thromboxane Res.*, 17A, 505, 1987.
52. **Chau, L.-Y., Hoover, R. L., Austen, K. F., and Lewis, R. A.,** Subcellular distribution of leukotriene $C_4$ binding units in cultured bovine aortic endothelium cells, *J. Immunol.*, 137, 1985, 1986.
53. **Lewis, M. A., Mong, S., Vessella, R. L., and Crooke, S. T.,** Identification and characterization of leukotriene $D_4$ receptors in adult and fetal human lung, *Biochem. Pharmacol.*, 34, 4311, 1985.
54. **Opmeer, F. A. and Hoogsteden, H. C.,** Characterization of specific receptors for leukotriene $D_4$ on human alveolar macrophages, *Prostaglandins*, 28, 183, 1984.
55. **Mong, S., Wu, H.-L., Clark, M. A., and Crooke, S. T.,** Leukotriene $D_4$ receptor-mediated synthesis of arachidonic acid metabolites in minced guinea pig lung, *Fed. Proc. Fed. Am. Soc. Exp. Biol.*, 45, 1814, 1986.

56. **Piper, P. J. and Samhoun, M. N.,** The mechanism of action of leukotrienes $C_4$ and $D_4$ in guinea pig isolated perfused lung and parenchymal strips of guinea pig, rabbit and rat, *Prostaglandins,* 21, 793, 1981.
57. **Dahlen, S.-E., Hansson, G., Hedqvist, P., Bjorck, T., Granstrom, E., and Dahlen, B.,** Allergen challenge of lung tissue from asthmatics elicits bronchial contraction that correlates with the release of leukotrienes $C_4$, $D_4$ and $E_4$, *Proc. Natl. Acad. Sci. U.S.A.,* 77, 4354, 1980.
58. **Jones, T. R., Davis, C., and Daniel, E. E.,** Pharmacological study of the contractile activity of leukotriene $C_4$ and $D_4$ on isolated human airway smooth muscle, *Can. J. Physiol. Pharmacol.,* 60, 638, 1982.
59. **Sautebin, L., Vigano, T., Grassi, E., Crivellari, M. T., Galli, G., Berti, F., Mezzetti, M., and Folco, G.,** Release of leukotrienes, induced by the $Ca^{++}$ ionophone A23187, from human lung parenchyma *in vitro, J. Pharmacol. Exp. Ther.,* 234, 217, 1985.
60. **Drazen, J. M., Austen, K. F., Lewis, R. A., Clark, D. A., Gotto, G., Marfat, A., and Corey, E. J.,** Comparative airway and vascular activities of leukotriene C-1 and D *in vivo* and *in-vitro, Proc. Natl. Acad. Sci. U.S.A.,* 77, 4354, 1980.
61. **Krell, R. D., Osborn, R., Vickery, L., Falcone, K., O'Donnell, M., Gleason, J., Kiwzig, C., and Bryan, D.,** Contraction of isolated airway smooth muscle by synthetic leukotriene $C_4$ and $D_4$, *Prostaglandins,* 22, 387, 1981.
62. **Snyder, D. W. and Krell, R. D.,** Pharmacological evidence for a distinct leukotriene $C_4$ receptor in guinea pig trachea, *J. Pharmacol. Exp. Ther.,* 231, 616, 1984.
63. **Tucker, S. and Weichman, B. M.,** Effect of serine borate (SB) on antagonism of leukotriene (LT) $C_4$ induced contraction of guinea pig trachea, *Fed. Proc. Fed. Am. Soc. Exp. Biol.,* 43, 956, 1984.
64. **Jones, T., Denis, D., Hall, R., and Ethier, D.,** Pharmacological study of the effects of leukotrienes C-4, D-4, E-4 and F-4 in guinea pig trachealis: interaction with FPL-55,712, *Prostaglandins,* 26, 833, 1983.
65. **Feniuk, L., Kennedy, I., Whelan, C. J., and Wright, G.,** Evidence for the existence of multiple leukotriene (LT) receptors from studies on a range of isolated tissues, *Prostaglandins,* 28, 675, 1984.
66. **Cheng, J. F. and Townley, R. G.,** Evidence for a similar receptor site for binding of [$^3$H] leukotriene $E_4$ and [$^3$H] leukotriene $D_4$ to the guinea pig crude lung membrane, *Biochem. Biophys. Res. Commun.,* 122, 949, 1984.
67. **Mong, S., Scott, M. O., Lewis, M. A., Wu, H.-L., Hogaboom, G. K., Clark, M. A., and Crooke, S. T.,** Leukotriene $E_4$ binds specifically to leukotriene receptors in guinea pig lung membranes, *Eur. J. Pharmacol.,* 109, 183, 1985.
68. **Jones, T. R. and Masson, P.,** Comparative study of the pulmonary effects in intravenous leukotrienes and other bronchoconstriction in anaesthetized guinea pigs, *Prostaglandins,* 29, 799, 1985.
69. **Lee, T. H., Austen, K. F., Corey, E. J., and Drazen, J. M.,** Leukotriene $E_4$ induced airway hyperresponsiveness of guinea pig tracheal smooth muscle to histamine and evidence for three separate sulfidopeptide leukotriene receptors, *Proc. Natl. Acad. Sci. U.S.A.,* 81, 4922, 1984.
70. **Krilis, S., Lewis, R. A., Corey, E. J., and Austen, K. F.,** Bioconversion of C-6 sulfidopeptide leukotrienes by the responding guinea pig ileum determines the time course of its contraction, *J. Clin. Invest.,* 71, 909, 1983.
71. **Kuehl, F. A., DeHaven, R. N., and Pong, S. S.,** Lung tissue receptors for sulfidopeptide leukotrienes, *J. Allerg. Clin. Immunol.,* 73, 378, 1984.
72. **Buckle, D. R., Outred, D. J., Ross, J. W., Smith, H., Smith, R. J., Spicer, B. A., and Gasson, B. C.,** Aryloxyalkoxy- and aralkyloxy-4-hydroxy-3-nitrocoumarins which inhibit histamine release in the rat and also antagonize the effects of a slow reacting substance of anaphylaxis, *J. Med. Chem.,* 22, 158, 1979.
73. **Oxford, A. W. and Ellis, F.,** Phenol Derivatives, U.K. Patent Application GB 2,058,785, 1981.
74. **Nohara, A. and Maki, Y.,** Diphenoxypropane derivatives, their production and use, European Patent EP 80,371, 1985.
75. **Bernstein, P. R. and Willard, A. K.,** Pharmaceutically active phenyl carboxylic acid derivatives, European Patent EP 83,228, 1985.
76. **Carson, M., Lemahieu, R. A. and Nason, W. C.,** Phenoxyalkyl carboxylic acid derivatives, German Patent Application DE 3,312,675, 1983.
77. **Kreft, A. F., Klaubert, D. H., Bell, S. C., Pattison, T. W., Yardley, J. P., Carlson, R. P., Hand, J. M., Chang, J. Y., and Lewis, A. J.,** Novel 1,3 bis(aryloxy)propanes as leukotriene $D_4$ antagonists, *J. Med. Chem.,* 29, 1134, 1986.
78. **Young, R. N. et al.,** Design and synthesis of sodium ($\beta$R*, $\gamma$S*)-4-[[3-(4-acetyl-3-hydroxy-2-propylphenoxy) propyl]thio]-$\gamma$-hydroxy-$\beta$-methyl-benzenebutanoate: a novel, selective, and orally active receptor antagonist of leukotriene $D_4$, *J. Med. Chem.,* 29, 1573, 1986.
79. **Marshall, W. S. and Verge, J. P.,** Leukotriene antagonists, European Patent Application EP 108,592, 1984.
80. **Smith, H. and Buckle, D. R.,** Pharmacologically active naphthotriazole derivatives, European Patent EP 112,419, 1986.

81. **Buckle, D. R. and Smith, H.,** Pharmacologically active compounds, European Patent EP 54,398, 1985.
82. **Belanger, P., Guindon, Y., Fortin, R., Yaokim, C., and Rokach, J.,** Leukotriene antagonists, European Patent Application EP 123,541, 1984.
83. **O'Donnell, M., Brown, D., Cohen, N., Weber, G. F., and Welton, A. F.,** Pharmacological profiles of a new aerosol leukotriene receptor antagonist, *Ann. Allerg.*, 55, 278, 1985.
84. **Dillard, R. D.,** Leukotriene antagonists, European Patent Application EP 132,366, 1985.
85. **Musser, J. H. and Kees, K. L.,** Aromatic compounds as antiallergic agents, U.S. Patent 4,528,392, 1985.
86. **LeMahieu, R. A.,** Naphthyloxyalkylcarboxylic acid derivatives, U.K. Patent Application GB 2,139,226A, 1984.
87. **Wenk, P., Sallmann, A. and Beck, A.,** New resorcinol ethers, European Patent Application EP 165,897, 1985.
88. **Beck, A., Sallman, A., Wenk, P., Marki, F., and Bray, M. A.,** CGP35949, a $LTD_4$-antagonist with phospholipase inhibitory activity: a new approach to the treatment of asthma, Abstr. 6th Int. Conf. Prostaglandins Related Compounds, Florence, Italy, June 3 to 6, 1986, 329.
89. **Nohar, A. and Maki, Y.,** Benzoic acid analogues and their production, European Patent Application EP 180,416, 1986.
90. **Murase, K., Mase, T., Hwa, H., and Tomioka, K.,** Heterocyclic compounds, their production, and medicants containing them, European Patent Application EP 181,779, 1986.
91. **Tomioka, K., Yamada, T., Takeda, M., Hosono, T., Mase, T., Hara, H. and Murase, K.,** Pharmacological properties of YM-16638, an orally active leukotriene antagonist. Abstr. 6th Int. Conf. Prostaglandins Related Compounds, Florence, Italy, June 3 to 6, 1986, 356.
92. **LeMahieu, R. A.,** (Naphthalenyloxy)alkanoic acids, U.S. Patent 4,550,190, 1985.
93. **Jones, T. R., Guindon, Y., Young, R., Champion, E., Charette, L., DeHaven, R. N., Denis, D., Ethier, D., McFarlane, C., Piechuta, H., Ford-Hutchinson, A. W., Masson, P., Fortin, R., Yoakim, C., Mayrock, A., Pong, S. S. and Rokach, J.,** L-648,051 sodium 4-[3-(4-acetyl-3-hydroxy-2-propylphenoxy)propylsulfonyl]-γ-oxo-benzene-butanoate: a leukotriene $D_4$ receptor antagonist, Abstr. 6th Int. Conf. Prostaglandins Related Compounds, Florence, Italy, June 3 to 6, 1986, 418.
94. **Lewis, A. J., Chang, J., Hand, J., Carlson, R. P., and Kreft, A.,** Wy-44,329: a leukotriene antagonist with lipoxygenase inhibitory and antiallergic properties, *Int. J. Immunopharmacol.*, 7, 384, 1985.
95. **Casey, F. B., Appleby, B. J., and Buck, D. C.,** Selective inhibition of the lipoxygenase metabolic pathway of arachidonic acid by the SRS-A antagonist, FPL-55,712, *Prostaglandins*, 25, 1, 1983.
96. **Fleisch, J. H., Rinkema, L. E., Haisch, K. P., Swanson-Bean, D., Goodson, T., Ho, P. P. K., and Marshall, W. S.,** Ly-171,883, 1-[2-hydroxy-3-propyl-4-[4-(1H-tetrazol-5-yl)butoxy]phenyl]ethanone, an orally active leukotriene $D_4$ antagonist, *J. Pharmacol. Exp. Ther.*, 233, 148, 1985.
97. **Hock, C. E. and Lefer, A. M.,** Protective effects of a new $LTD_4$ antagonist (Ly-171,883) in traumatic shock, *Circ. Shock*, 17, 263, 1985.
98. **Rinkema, L. E., Haisch, K. D., McCullough, D., Carr, F. P., Dillard, R. D., and Fleisch, J. H.,** Ly-163,443, an aryloxymethylacetophenone antagonizes pharmacologic responses to leukotriene (LT) $D_4$ and $LTE_4$, *Fed. Fed. Am. Soc. Exp. Biol.*, 44, 492, 1985.
99. **Dillard, R. D., Carr, E. P., McCullough, D., Haisch, K. D., Rinkema, L. E., and Fleisch, J. H.,** New aryloxymethylacetophenones: antagonists of $LTD_4$-induced contractions of guinea pig ileum, *Fed. Proc. Fed. Am. Soc. Exp. Biol.*, 44, 491, 1985.
100. **Britton, J. R., Hanley, S. P., and Tattersfield, A. E.,** The effects of an oral leukotriene $D_4$ antagonist L-649,923 on the response to inhaled antigen in asthma, in Abstr. 6th Int. Conf. Prostaglandins Related Compounds, Florence, Italy, June 3 to 6, 1986, 417.
101. **Goldenberg, M.,** Use of leukotriene antagonists for producing cytoprotective pharmaceutical compositions and process for producing cytoprotective pharmaceutical compositions, European Patent Application 156,223, 1985.
102. **Pendleton, R. G. and Stavorski, J. R.,** Evidence for differing leukotriene receptors in gastric mucosa, *Eur. J. Pharmacol.*, 125, 297, 1986.
103. **Bray, M. A., Beck, A., Wenk, P., Marki, F., Niederhauser, U., Kuhn, M., and Sallman, A.,** CGP 35,949: a potent orally active, leukotriene antagonist and inhibitor of phospholipase. Biological profile. Abstr. 6th Int. Conf. Prostaglandins Related Compounds, Florence, Italy, June 3 to 6, 1986, 252.
104. **Weichman, B. M., Wasserman, M. A., Holden, D. A., Osborn, R. R., Woodward, D. F., Ku, T. W., and Gleason, J. G.,** Antagonism of the pulmonary effects of the peptidoleukotrienes by a leukotriene $D_4$ analog, *J. Pharmacol. Exp. Ther.*, 227, 700, 1983.
105. **Ku, T. W., McCarthy, M. E., Weichman, B. M., and Gleason, J. G.,** Synthesis and $LTD_4$ antagonist activity of 2-norleukotriene analogues, *J. Med. Chem.*, 28, 1847, 1985.
106. **Perchonock, C. D., Uzinskas, I., Ku, T. W., McCarthy, M. E., Bondinell, W. E., Volpe, B. W., Gleason, J. G., Weichman, B. M., Muccitelli, R. M., DeVan, J. F., Tucker, S. S., Vickery, L. M., and Wasserman, M. A.,** Synthesis and $LTD_4$-antagonist activity of desamino-2-nor-leukotriene analogs, *Prostaglandins*, 29, 75, 1985.

107. **Perchonock, C. D., McCarthy, M. E., Erhard, K. F., Gleason, J. G., Wasserman, M. A., Muccitelli, R. M., DeVan, J. F., Tucker, S. S., Kitchman, T., Vickery, L. M., Weichman, B. M., Mong, S., Cooke, S. T., and Newton, J. F.,** Synthesis and pharmacological characterization of 5-(2-Dodecylphenyl)-4,6-dithianonanedioic acid and 5-[2-(8-phenyloctyl)phenyl]-4,6-dithianonanedioic acid: prototypes of a novel class of leukotriene antagonists, *J. Med. Chem.*, 28, 1145, 1985.
108. **Wasserman, M. A., Muccitelli, R. M., Tucker, S. S., Vickery, L. M., DeVan, J. F., Weichman, B. M., Newton, J., Perchonock, C. D., and Gleason, J. G.,** SKF 102,922: An effective and selective antagonist of leukotriene mediated bronchoconstriction, *Fed. Proc. Fed. Am. Soc. Exp. Biol.*, 44, 491, 1985.
109. **Perchonock, C. D., Uzinskas, I., McCarthy, M. E., Erhard, K. F., Gleason, J. G., Wasserman, M. A., Muccitelli, R. M., DeVan, J. F., Tucker, S. S., Vickery, L. M., Kirchner, T. M., Weichman, B. M., Mong, S., Scott, M. O., Chi-Russo, G., Wu, H., Crooke, S. T., Newton, J. F.,** Synthesis and structure-activity, relationship studies of a series of 5-aryl-4,6-dithianonanedioic acids and related compounds: a novel class of leukotriene antagonists, *J. Med. Chem.*, 29, 1442, 1986.
110. **Wasserman, M. A., Torphy, T. J., Hay, D. W. P., Muccitelli, R. M., Tucker, S. S., Wilson, K., Osborn, R. R., Vickery-Clark, L., Hall, F. R., Erhard, K. F., and Gleason, J. G.,** Pharmacologic profile of SKF 104353, a novel highly potent and selective peptidoleukotriene antagonist, Abstr. 6th Int. Conf. Prostaglandins Related Compounds, Florence, Italy, June 3 to 6, 1986, 253.
111. **Bondinell, W. E., Hill, D. T., and Weichman, B. M.,** Leukotriene antagonists, European Patent Application 168,950, 1986.
112. **Synder, D. W., Berstein, P. R., Krell, R. D.,** Pharmacology of chemically stable analogs of peptide leukotrienes (LT), *Fed. Proc. Fed. Am. Soc. Exp. Biol.*, 44, 901, 1985.
113. **Saksena, A. K., Green, M. J., Mangiaracina, P., Wong, J. K., Kreutner, W., and Gulbenkian, A. R.,** Synthesis of butanoic acid 4,4′-[(4E, 6Z, 9Z-pentadecatrien-2-ynylidene)]-bis with leukotriene-like activity: novel acetylenic acetals and dithioacetals as antagonists of leukotriene-$C_4$, *Tetrahedron Lett.*, 26, 6427, 1985.
114. **Von Sprecher, A., Ernest, I., Main, A., Beck, A., Breitenstein, W., Marki, F., and Bray, M. A.,** Novel leukotriene (LT) antagonists: structure/activity of analogs of $LTD_4$. Replacement of the 1-carboxylic group by a methyl group (''methyl principle'') results in LT antagonists and phospholipase inhibitors, in Abstr. 6th Int. Conf. Prostaglandins Related Compounds, Florence, Italy, June 3 to 6, 1986, 252.
115. **Musser, J. H., Kubrak, D. M., Hand, J. M., Chang, J., and Lewis, A. J.,** Synthesis of naphthalenylmethoxy and quinolinylmethoxy phenylaminoalkanoic acid esters. A novel series of leukotriene $D_4$ antagonists and 5-lipoxygenase inhibitors, *J. Med. Chem.*, 29, 1429, 1986.
116. **Schwalm, S. F., Skowronek, M., Marinari, L., Chang, J., Musser, J. H., and Hand, J. M.,** *In vitro* and *in vivo* pharmacology of Wy-45,911: a leukotriene (LT) antagonist, *Pharmacologist*, 28, 146, 1986.
117. **Musser, J. H., Kubrak, D. M., Chang, J., DiZio, S. M., Hite, M., Hand, J. M., and Lewis, A. J.,** Leukotriene $D_4$ antagonists and 5-lipoxy-genase inhibitors. Synthesis of benzoheterocyclic methoxyphenylaminooxoalkanoic acid esters, *J. Med. Chem.*, 30, 400, 1987.
118. **Musser, J. H. and Tio, C. O.,** Novel heterocyclic compounds as antiallergic agents, U.S. Patent 4,550,172, 1985.
119. **Musser, J. H.,** Heterocyclic compounds as antiallergic agents, U.S. Patent 4,554,355, 1985.
120. **Musser, J. H. and Kubrak, D. M.,** Heterocyclic compounds as antiallergic agents, U.S. Patent 4,594,425, 1986.
121. **Musser, J. H. and Kubrak, D. M.,** Heterocyclic sulfonamides, U.S. Patent 4,581,457, 1986.
122. **Hand, J. M., Schwalm, S. F., Kreft, A. F., Chang, J., and Lewis, A. J.,** Comparison of leukotriene (LT) antagonist properties of Wy-44,329, FPL-55712, Ly-171,883 and Rev 5901 on isolated guinea pig trachea, *Am. Rev. Resp. Dis.*, 133 (No. 4), p. 2, A94, 1986.
123. **Musser, J. H., Chakraborty, U. R., Sciotino, S., Gordon, R. J., Khandwala, A., Neiss, E. S., Pruss, T. P., Van Inwegen, R., Weinryb, I., and Coutts, S. M.,** Substituted arylmethyl phenyl ethers. Part 1, a novel series of 5-lipoxygenase inhibitors and leukotriene antagonists, *J. Med. Chem.*, 30, 96, 1987.
124. **Toda, M., Nakai, H., Kosuge, S., Konno, M., Arai, Y., Miyamoto, T., Obata, T., Katsube, N., and Kawasaki, A.,** A potent antagonist of the slow-reacting substance of anaphylaxis, in *Advances in Prostaglandin Thromboxane and Leukotriene Research,* Vol. 15, Hayaishi, O. and Yamamoto, S., Eds., Raven Press, New York, 1985, 307.
125. **Obata, T., Katsube, N., Miyamoto, T., Toda, M., Okegawa, T., Nakai, H., Kosuge, S., Konno, M., Arai, Y., and Kawasaki, A.,** New antagonists of leukotrienes: ONO-RS-411 and ONO-RS-347, in *Advances in Prostaglandin, Thromboxane and Leukotriene Research,* Vol. 15, Hayaski, O. and Yamamoto, S., Eds., Raven Press, New York, 1985, 229.
126. **Synder, D. W., Krell, R. D., Keith, R. A., Buckner, C. K., Giles, R. E., Yee, Y. K., Bernstein, P. R., Brown, F. J., and Hesp, B.,** ICI 198,615, a novel peptidoleukotriene (LT) receptor antagonist: *in vitro* pharmacology, *Pharmacologist,* 28, 185, 1986.

127. **Krell, R. D., Synder, D. W., Giles, R. E., Yee, Y. K., Bernstein, P. R., Brown, F. J., and Hesp, B.**, ICI 198,615, a novel peptidoleukotriene (LT) receptor antagonist: *in vivo* pharmacology, *Pharmacologist*, 28, 185, 1986.
128. **Herron, D. K., Whitesitt, C. A., Mallett, B. L., Rinkema, L. E., Haisch, K. D., Eacho, P. I., Foxworthy, P. S., and Fleisch, J. H.**, SAR and pharmacology of Ly-137,617: an $LTD_4$ antagonist, *Pharmacologist*, 27, 256, 1985.
129. **Nishino, K., Ohkubo, H., Ohashi, M., Hara, S., Kito, J., and Irikura, T.**, KC-404: a potential anti-allergic agent with antagonistic action against slow reacting substance of anaphylaxis, *Jpn. J. Pharmacol.*, 33, 267, 1983.
130. **Sato, T., Takayanagi, I., Ohashi, M., Koike, K., Hisayama, T., Iwasaki, S., and Nagai, H.**, Anti-leukotriene $D_4$ action of a new anti-asthmatic drug (KC-404) on the guinea pig isolated trachea, *Gen. Pharmacol.*, 17, 287, 1986.
131. **Tilley, J. W., Levitan, P., Welton, A. F., and Crowley, H. J.**, Antagonists of slow-reacting substance of anaphylaxis 1. Pyrido[2,1-b]quinazolinecarboxylic acid derivatives, *J. Med. Chem.*, 26, 1638, 1983.
132. **Kadin, S. B.**, (Carboxyacylamino)phenylalkenamides and esters thereof as SRS-A antagonists, U.S. Patent 4,296,129, 1981.
133. **Saijo, T., Kuriki, H., Ashida, Y., Makino, H., and Maki, Y.**, Inhibition by amoxanox (AA-673) of immunologically, leukotriene $D_4$ or platelet activating factor stimulated bronchoconstriction in guinea pigs and rats, *Int. Arch. Allerg. Appl. Immunol.*, 77, 315, 1985.
134. **Gleason, J. G., Krell, R. D., Weichman, B. M., Ali, F. E., and Berkowitz, B.**, Comparative pharmacology and antagonism of synthetic leukotrienes on airway and vascular smooth muscle, in *Advances in Prostaglandin, Thromboxane and Leukotriene Research*, Sammuelsson, B. and Paoletti, R., Eds., Raven Press, New York, 1982, 243.
135. **Wasserman, M. A., Weichman, B. M., and Gleason, J. G.**, SKF-88,046: a functional antagonism of *in vitro* bronchoconstriction induced by contractile arachidonate products, *Pharmacologist*, 25, 122, 1983.
136. **Saijo, T., Kuriki, H., Ashida, Y., Makino, H., and Maki, Y.**, Mechanism of the action of amoxanox (AA-673), an orally active antiallergic agent, *Int. Arch. Allerg. Appl. Immunol.*, 78, 43, 1985.
137. **Mutsukado, M., Tanikawa, K., Shikada, K., and Sakoda, R.**, 3(2H)pyridazinone, process for its preparation and antiallergic agent containing it, European Patent Application EP 186,817, 1986.
138. **Goetzl, E. J. and Pickett, W. C.**, Novel structural determinants of the human neutrophil chemotactic activity of leukotriene B, *J. Exp. Med.*, 153, 482, 1981.
139. **Showell, H. J., Otterness, I. G., Marfat, A., and Corey, E. J.**, Inhibition of leukotriene $B_4$-induced neutrophil degranulation by leukotriene $B_4$-dimethylamide, *Biochem. Biophys. Res. Commun.*, 106, 741, 1982.
140. **Feinmark, S. J., Lindgren, J. A., Claesson, H. E., Malmsten, C., and Samuelsson, B.**, Stimulation of human leukocyte degranulation by leukotriene $B_4$ and its -oxidized metabolites, *FEBS Lett.*, 136, 141, 1981.
141. **Namiki, M., Igarashi, Y., Sakamoto, K., Nakamura, T., and Koga, Y.**, Pharmacological profiles of a potential $LTB_4$-antagonist, SM-9064, *Biochem. Biophys. Res. Commun.*, 138, 540, 1986.
142. **Payan, D. G., Missirian-Bastian, A., and Goetzl, E. J.**, Human T-lymphocyte subset specificity of the regulatory effects of $LTB_4$, *Proc. Natl. Acad. Sci. U.S.A.*, 81, 3501, 1981.
143. **Kreisle, R. A. and Parker, C. W.**, Specific binding of leukotriene $B_4$ to a receptor on human polymorphonuclear leukocytes, *J. Exp. Med.* 157, 628, 1983.
144. **Goldman, D. W. and Goetzl, E. J.**, Selective transduction of human polymorphonuclear leukocyte functions by subsets of receptors for leukotriene $B_4$, *J. Allerg. Clin. Immunol.*, 76, 373, 1984.
145. **Goldman, D. W. and Goetzl, E. J.**, Heterogenicity of human polymorphonuclear leukocyte receptors for leukotriene $B_4$, *J. Exp. Med.*, 159, 1027, 1984.
146. **Bomalaski, J. S. and Mong, S.**, Binding of leukotriene $B_4$ ($LTB_4$) and its analogs to human polymorphonuclear leukocyte membrane receptors, *Arth. Rheum.*, 29, S36, 1986.
147. **Goetzl, E. J. and Pickett, W. C.**, The human PMN leukocyte chemotactic activity of complex hydroxy-eicosatetaenoic acids (HETEs), *J. Immunol.*, 125, 1789, 1980.
148. **Ford-Hutchinson, A. W., Bray, M. A., Doig, M. V., Shipley, M. E., and Smith, M. J. H.**, Leukotriene $B_4$, a potent chemokinetic and aggregating substance released from polymorphonuclear leukocytes, *Nature (London)*, 286, 264, 1980.
149. **Palmblad, J., Gyllenhammar, H., Lindgren, J. A., and Malmsten, C. L.**, Effects of leukotriene and f-met-leu-phe on oxidative metabolism of neutrophils and eosinophils, *J. Immunol.*, 132, 3041, 1984.
150. **Rae, S. A. and Smith, M. J. H.**, The stimulation of lysosomal enzyme secretion from human polymorphonuclear leukocytes by leukotriene $B_4$, *J. Pharm. Pharmacol.*, 33, 616, 1981.
151. **Goldman, D. W., Gifford, L. A., Marotti, T.**, Chernov-Rogan, T., and Goetzl, E. J., Molecular and cellular properties of human neutrophil receptors for leukotriene $B_4$, *Fed. Proc. Fed. Am. Soc. Exp. Biol.*, 65, 625, 1986.

152. **Marotti, T., Young, R. N., Gifford, L. A., Goldman, D. W., and Goetzl, E. J.,** Solubilization and cleavage of human neutrophil affinity-labeled receptors for $LTB_4$, *Fed. Proc. Fed. Am. Soc. Exp. Biol.*, 45, 853, 1986.
153. **Gifford, L. A., Chernov-Rogan, T., Lorry, K. H., Goldman, D. W., and Goetzl, E. J.,** Recognition of the ligand-binding site of human neutrophil receptors for $LTB_4$ by antibodies to idiotypes (Anti-Ids) of mouse monoclonal anti-$LTB_4$, *Fed. Proc. Fed. Am. Soc. Exp. Biol.*, 45, 213, 1986.
154. **Cheng, J. B., Cheng, E. I. P., Kohi, F., and Townley, R. G.,** [$^3$H]Leukotriene $B_4$ binding to the guinea-pig spleen membrane preparation: a rich tissue source for a high-affinity leukotriene $B_4$ receptor site, *J. Pharmacol. Exp. Ther.*, 236, 126, 1986.
155. **Rola-Pleszczynski, M., Gagnon, L., and Sirois, P.,** Leukotriene $B_4$ augments human natural cytotoxic cell activity, *Biochem. Biophys. Res. Commun.*, 113, 531, 1983.
156. **Atluru, D. and Goodwin, J.,** Leukotriene $B_4$ induces an OKT8$^+$ radio-sensitive suppressor cell from resting, human OKT8$^-$T cells, *J. Clin. Invest.*, 74, 1444, 1984.
157. **Sears, M. R.,** Fatal asthma in New Zealand, *N. Eng. J. Med.*, 315, 1029, 1986.

## ADDITIONAL REFERENCES

158. **Buckner, C. K., Krell, R. D., Laravuso, R. B., Coursin, D. B., Bernstein, P. R., and Will, J. A.,** Pharmacological evidence that human intralobar airways do not contain different receptors that mediate contractions of leukotriene $C_4$ and leukotriene $D_4$, *J. Pharmacol. Exp. Ther.*, 237, 558, 1986.
159. **Could, M., Enas, G., Kemp, J., Platt-Mills, T., Altman, L., Townley, R., Tinkelman, D., King, T., Middleton, E., Scheffer, A., and McFadden, E.,** Efficacy and safety of LY-171883 in patients with mild chronic asthma, *J. Allergy Clin. Immunol.*, 79, 256, 1987.
160. **Israel, E., Juniper, G. F., Morris, M. M., Dowell, A. R., Hargreave, F. G., and Drazen, J. M.,** A leukotriene $D_4$ ($LTD_4$) receptor antagonist, LY-171883, reduces the bronchoconstriction induced by cold air challenge in asthmatics: a randomized double-blind, placebo-controlled trial, *Am. Rev. Resp. Dis.*, 137, 27, 1988.
161. **Shaker, G., Glovsky, M. M., Kebo, D., Glovsky, S., and Dowell, A.,** Reversal of exercise induced asthma by the $LTD_4$, $LTE_4$ antagonist (LY-171883), *J. Allergy Clin. Immunol.*, 81, 315, 1988.
162. **Tomioka, K., Yamada, T., Mase, T., Tsuzuke, R., Hara, H., Murase, K., and Abraham, W. M.,** Pharmacological properties of YM-16638 and YM-1755, orally active leukotriene (LT) antagonists, Abstr. Book 2nd Int. Conf. Leukotrienes and Prostanoids in Health and Disease, Jerusalem, Israel, October 9—14, 1988, p. 50.
163. **Gelason, J. G., Hall, R. F., Frazee, J. S., Smallheer, J., Ku, T. W., Eaggleston, D. Newton, J., Wasserman, M., and Hay, D. P.,** Studies on the design of high affinity leukotriene receptor antagonists, Abstr. Book 2nd Int. Conf. Leukotrienes and Prostanoids in Health and Disease, Jerusalem, Israel, October 9—14, 1988, p. 49.
164. **Hand, J. M., Musser, J. H., Kreft. A. F., Schwalm, S., Englebach, I., Auen, M., Skowronek, M., and Chang, J. Y.,** Wy-48,252 (1,1,1-trifluoro-N-[3-(2-quinolinyl methoxy)phenyl]-methane sulfonamide): a selective orally active leukotriene antagonist, *Pharmacologist,* 29, 174, 1987.
165. **Musser, J. H., Kreft, A. F., Bender, R. H. W., Kurbrak, D. M., Chank, J., Lewis, A. J., and Hand, J. M.,** N-[(Quinoloinylmethoxy)phenyl] and N-[(quinolinylmethoxy)naphthyl] sulfonamides. A novel series of potent orally active $LTD_4$ antagonists, *J. Med. Chem.*, Vol. 32, 1989.

# REGULATION OF CYCLIC NUCLEOTIDE METABOLISM IN HUMAN PLATELETS BY PROSTANOIDS

**Robert Alvarez**

## INTRODUCTION

Circulating platelets aggregate during the process of normal hemostasis or thrombosis and release constituents which promote further aggregation. Numerous studies have demonstrated that prostanoids have an important role in the regulation of these platelet functions.

Several aspects of the mechanism of action of prostanoids have been clarified during the past decade, including effects on cyclic AMP metabolism, evidence for the presence of multiple prostaglandin receptors, and the phenomenon of agonist-specific desensitization. In addition, agents which increase intracellular cyclic AMP regulate prostanoid metabolism and the metabolism of inositol phospholipids. These findings have implications for the search and development of novel inhibitors of platelet aggregation with therapeutic potential as antithrombotic agents.

## CYCLIC AMP METABOLISM

It is widely accepted that the mechanism of action of numberous mammalian hormones involves a receptor-mediated stimulation of membrane-bound adenylate cyclase activity and the subsequent increase in intracellular cyclic AMP. Similarly, prostaglandins mediate their effects via receptors coupled to adenylate cyclase. However, they are rapidly degraded and do not appear to function as circulating hormones nor are they stored in cells.[1]

Several key observations support the concept that cyclic AMP mediates the effect of prostaglandins on platelet function. Those prostaglandins which inhibit platelet aggregation also stimulate adenylate cyclase activity in broken-cell preparations[2-5] and elevate the intracellular concentrations of cyclic AMP.[3-6] An increase in cyclic AMP coincides with the inhibition of platelet aggregation by $PGI_2$[6] and the order of potency of various prostaglandins as inhibitors of aggregation corresponds to their order of potency in elevating cyclic AMP[3,7,8] or stimulating adenylate cyclase.[8] Inhibitors of cyclic AMP phosphodiesterase and either cyclic AMP or dibutyryl cyclic AMP block platelet aggregation.[4,9,10] Finally, the combination of a submaximal concentration of a prostaglandin and a phosphodiesterase inhibitor results in a synergistic effect on cyclic-AMP formation and inhibition of platelet aggregation.[11]

Active prostaglandins do not elevate cyclic AMP in intact cells to the same maximum level. For example, $PGE_1$ exhibits lower efficacy than $PGI_2$ and appears to be a partial agonist of the $PGI_2$ receptor.[6] In broken-cell preparations, however, both prostaglandins exhibit the same efficacy but different potency in stimulating adenylate cyclase activity.[8]

## ADENYLATE CYCLASE

Prostaglandin-sensitive adenylate cyclase in human platelets is associated with the plasma membrane and dense tubular system (smooth endoplasmic reticulum) and requires and $Mg^{2+}$ ion.[12-16] Under appropriate conditions, adenosine and epinephrine stimulate enzyme activity via different receptors.[16-18] It is not yet clear whether the receptor-mediated increase in adenylate-cyclase activity produced by these agonists involves a stimulation of a transducing protein ($G_s$).[19] Nonhormonal activators include forskolin, fluoride ion, and guanine nucleotides.[12,20-23]

Several studies have demonstrated the presence of distinct receptors for $PGI_2$ and $PGD_2$

on human platelets.[24-30] Although early experiments were performed with $PGE_1$, it is unlikely that this prostaglandin is important in the regulation of platelet function under physiological conditions.[27]

Low concentrations of $PGE_2$ which are insufficient to stimulate adenylate-cyclase activity potentiate aggregation induced by ADP[7,31] and desensitize platelets for subsequent stimulation by $PGI_2$.[27] These observations suggest that receptor occupation but not necessarily an alteration in cyclic AMP content is required for desensitization in this system.

Suggestions have been made for the use of prostaglandins as antithrombotic agents.[32-34] A desirable profile for such a drug would include oral activity, prolonged duration of action, and platelet selectivity. Although considerable progress has been made in this area during the past few years, to date such a compound has not been identified.

It is clear that the capacity of $PGI_2$ and $PGD_2$ to raise the intracellular level of cyclic AMP greatly exceeds the amount required to completely inhibit the aggregation of platelets *in vitro*.[39-40] It seems unnecessary, therefore, to eliminate synthetic prostaglandins which lack the efficacy of $PGI_2$ and $PGD_2$ analogues from consideration as antiplatelet drugs. Because agonist-specific desensitization has been demonstrated for both $PGI_2$ and $PGD_2$,[27,35-38] the potential problem of tachyphyllaxis may limit the use of prostaglandin analogues to acute administration.

The use of $PGD_2$ or a suitable analogue as a potential antithrombotic agent has been considered because platelets have a distinct receptor for this prostaglandin while several other tissues either do not respond or respond only weakly to this compound.[33,41] $PGD_2$ is produced by platelets and released into plasma during aggregation. Thus, $PGD_2$ has the potential to influence the reactivity of other platelets. Agonist-specific desensitization has been demonstrated with $PGD_2$ and this may provide an explanation for the observation that patients with myeloproliferative disorders or acute thrombosis have platelets which exhibit a diminished response to $PGD_2$ but respond normally to $PGI_2$ or $PGE_1$.[36,42]

Platelets obtained from patients with familial hypercholesterolemia exhibit an increased sensitivity to epinephrine and ADP.[43,44] A similar effect has been produced *in vitro* by elevating the cholesterol content of human platelets by incubation with cholesterol-rich lecithin dispersions.[43-46] Using this method, Sinha et al.[45] observed an increased sensitivity to aggregating agents and the stimulation of adenylate cyclase activity by $PGE_1$ was abolished. This effect appears to be the consequence of decreased fluidity of the platelet membrane.

Ticlopidine, a substituted tetrahydrothienopyridine, inhibits the aggregation of human platelets to a variety of inducers.[47] This effect develops after repeated oral dosing with maximum inhibition after 5 to 8 d. The mechanism of action of this compound is not known. Studies with rat platelets[48-50] have revealed an enhanced stimulation of adenylate cyclase by $PGE_1$ after ticlopidine treatment. These observations have been confirmed with human platelets[51] but the enhancement was relatively small (20 %). Although it seems unlikely that such potentiation is essential to the mechanism of action of ticlopidine, it may contribute to the pharmacological profile of the drug *in vivo*.

## CYCLIC AMP PHOSPHODIESTERASE

Prostacyclin and other prostaglandins indirectly stimulate the activity of a high-affinity form of cyclic AMP phosphodiesterase when preincubated with washed human[8] or rat platelets.[52] The transient increase in intracellular cyclic AMP produced by prostacyclin appears to involve a sequential activation of adenylate cyclase and cyclic AMP phosphodiesterase.[8] In this system phosphodiesterase activation may represent a homeostatic mechanism in the regulation of cyclic AMP metabolism.

Human platelets contain at least three different forms of cyclic AMP phosphodiesterase, which can be separated by DEAE cellulose column chromatography.[53,54] These forms differ with respect to their substrate affinities and kinetic characteristics. Types I and II (mol wt ≅ 240,000 Da) have a low affinity (Km = 500 and 100 $\mu M$, respectively) for cyclic AMP while Type IV (mol wt ≅ 180,000 Da) exhibits a high affinity for the substrate ($K_m$ = 0.4 $\mu M$). Low concentrations of cyclic GMP activate Type I but this nucleotide competitively inhibits Types II and IV.[54] Both soluble and membrane-bound platelet phosphodiesterases require divalent metal cations ($Mg^{2+}$ or $Mn^{2+}$).[55] Grant and Colman[56] have partially purified the high-affinity, soluble form of platelet phosphodiesterase. This enzyme is not stimulated by calmodulin and cyclic GMP is a competitive inhibitor of cyclic AMP hydrolysis.

Evidence that platelets contain interconvertible forms of phosphodiesterase has been presented by Pichard and Cheung[60] using sucrose density-gradient centrifugation. They propose that these forms are different aggregated states of the enzyme and have presented evidence that the ratio of these forms can be altered by changes in enzyme concentration, dibutyryl cyclic AMP, or temperature.[58-60]

Consideration of the proposed role of $PGI_2$ in thrombosis and the strong synergistic effect obtained *in vitro* in the presence of a phosphodiesterase inhibitor suggests that phosphodiesterase inhibitors may have useful antithrombotic properties. Several platelet-selective inhibitors have been synthesized during the past 10 years. They include anagrelide,[61] cilostamide,[62] trequinsin,[63] and lixazinone (RS-82856).[64] These compounds are potent inhibitors of the high-affinity form (Type IV) of phosphodiesterase found in human platelets.

Selective inhibitors of the other enzyme forms also may be of pharmacological interest. Dipyridamole, for example, is a coronary vasodilator and antiplatelet agent and selectively inhibits the activity of Type I platelet phospodiesterase.[65] Dipyridamole, however, has several other biochemical effects[66] and its mechanism of action has not been clearly established. Some clinical studies suggest that this compound may have useful antithrombotic properties when administered alone or concurrently with aspirin.[66]

Type I phosphodiesterase forms a complex with calmodulin and is stimulated by calcium ion.[54] In addition to hydrolysis of cyclic AMP at high substrate concentrations, this enzyme has a high affinity for cyclic GMP with a $K_m$ of 0.5 $\mu M$.[53] MY-5445[67] and M&B 22948[68] selectively inhibit the hydrolysis of cyclic GMP by Type I phosphodiesterase.

Inhibitors of basal Type-II-phosphodiesterase activity include vinpocetine and HA-558.[67] Chlorpromazine and *N*-(6-aminohexyl)-5-chloro-1-napthalene-sulfonamide (W-7) selectively inhibit the activation of this enzyme by calmodulin.[67]

Thrombin diminishes the ability of prostaglandins to elevate the intracellular concentration of cyclic AMP in platelets and this effect has been attributed to the inhibition of adenylate cyclase activity. Related studies have demonstrated that the activity of a membrane-associated cyclic AMP phosphodiesterase increases following exposure of rabbit platelets to thrombin.[68] This observation opens the possibility that two mechanisms may contribute to the lowering of cyclic AMP. Recent studies with human platelets, however, indicate that although stimulation of phosphodiesterase activity can be demonstrated following the addition thrombin, adenylate cyclase inhibition represents the primary biochemical event responsible for the lowering of total intracellular cyclic AMP.[69] The possibility that activation of a membrane-associated phosphodiesterase contributes to the lowering of a distinct pool or compartment of cyclic AMP was not excluded.

## CYCLIC GMP

Arachidonic acid, collagen, thrombin, and ADP increase the formation of prostaglandin endoperoxides and this is accompanied by an elevation in intracellular cyclic GMP.[71-73] Although these observations are compatible with a role for cyclic GMP in the release reaction and secondary phase of aggregation, other studies do not support this possibility.[71,72,74-75] Also, although low concentrations of cyclic GMP stimulate the activity of Type II phosphodiesterase, it is not yet clear whether this phenomenon is of importance in the regulation of intracellular cyclic AMP. Studies with the selective inhibitor of cyclic GMP phosphodiestase in platelets (MY-5445) indicate that low concentrations of this compound elevate cyclic GMP but not cyclic AMP and this appears to be sufficient to inhibit platelet aggregation in response to a variety of inducers.[67] Thus, although additional studies are required to clarify the involvement of cyclic GMP in platelet function, these studies suggest that both cyclic AMP and cyclic GMP can function in a unidirectional manner to inhibit aggregation.

Similarly, both cyclic AMP and cyclic GMP act in a unidirectional manner to relax vascular smooth muscle.[76] Recent evidence suggests that endothelium-derived relaxing factor may be nitric oxide or some closely related radical species.[77,78] Nitric oxide activates soluble guanylate cyclase in vascular smooth muscle.[78]

## REGULATION OF PROSTANOID SYNTHESIS AND INOSITOL PHOSPHOLIPID METABOLISM BY CYCLIC AMP

Increases in intracellular cyclic AMP produced by prostaglandins, adenosine, and phosphodiesterase inhibitors clearly inhibit platelet aggregation and a wide variety of inducers such as ADP, collagen, thromboxane $A_2$, and arachidonic acid lower cyclic-AMP levels.[79] The latter biochemical effect does not appear to be essential to the aggregation process.[80,81] However, lowering the intracellular level of cyclic AMP with an inhibitor of adenylate cyclase (SQ 22536) does enhance aggregation obtained in the presence of $PGG_2$ and $PGH_2$.[82] In addition, inhibition of adenylate-cyclase activity by SQ 22536 diminishes the ability of $PGE_1$ to inhibit platelet aggregation.[83] This observation suggests that the lowering of intracellular cyclic AMP by thrombin, epinephrine, and ADP may promote platelet aggregation *in vivo* by interfering with the antithrombotic properties of $PGI_2$.[69]

Thrombin, collagen, and ADP initiate the arachidonic-acid pathway by stimulating the activity of a membrane-bound phospholipase $A_2$.[84,85] This enzyme catalyzes the hydrolysis of phospholipids (particularly phosphatidylcholine and phosphatidylethanolamine) to release arachidonic acid. The latter serves as a substrate for a cyclooxygenase in the formation of the chemically unstable endoperoxides ($PGG_2$ and $PGH_2$). In platelets, the endoperoxides are metabolized or nonenzymatically degraded to three stable prostaglandins ($PGE_2$, $PGD_2$, and $PGF_{2\alpha}$) and to thromboxane $A_2$. The *net* effect of these metabolites is proaggregatory. In contrast, endothelial cells of the vascular wall have the capacity to synthesize prostacyclin from $PGH_2$ and release it into the circulation where it may inhibit platelet aggregation.[86-93]

$PGI_2$[94] and other agents which increase the formation or accumulation of intracellular cyclic AMP inhibit phospholipase $A_2$ activity. Thus, not only do prostanoids regulate cyclic-AMP metabolism but cyclic AMP modulates prostanoid metabolism.

Other inhibitors of phospholipase $A_2$ activity have been identified including endogenous factors,[95,96] steroids,[97,98] nonsteroidal anti-inflammatory agents,[99] and serine proteinase inhibitors.[100]

In addition to phospholipase $A_2$, the activity of a soluble phospholipase C increases in response to either thrombin or collagen.[101-104] This enzyme catalyzes the hydrolysis of inositol phospholipids. One of the products of phosphoinositide turnover, 1,2-diacylglycerol, stimulates protein kinase C activity.[105-107] The subsequent phosphorylation of target proteins by this calcium-dependent protein kinase has been proposed to mediate, in part, the release of various constituents of platelet granules and lysosomes.[107] Once again, agents which elevate intracellular cyclic AMP inhibit phospholipase-C activity.[107]

Aspirin, an inhibitor of cyclooxygenase activity irreversibly blocks the conversion of arachidonic acid to the cyclic endoperoxide $PGG_2$.[108,109] Other nonsteroidal anti-inflammatory drugs such as indomethacin, phenylbutazone, naproxen, and ibuprofen[66] do not exhibit the prolonged inhibition of platelet function which follows acetylation of the cyclooxygenase by aspirin. Endothelial cells (but not platelets) are able to synthesize new enzyme within hours after aspirin treatment. Also, the platelet enzyme may be more sensitive to aspirin. These observations have led to the suggestion that an optimal, low-level dose of aspirin might selectively inhibit thromboxane $A_2$ synthesis in platelets and permit prostacyclin formation in endothelial cells.[110,111]

Difficulty in obtaining platelet-selective inhibition of cyclo-oxygenase could be circumvented through the use of thromboxane synthetase inhibitors (such as imidazole or dazoxiben). Conceivably, this strategy provides platelet-derived endoperoxides which may be converted to prostacyclin by endothelial cells. Recent studies have demonstrated a synergism between thromboxane synthetase inhibitors and cyclic AMP phosphodiesterase inhibitors.[112] Also, bifunctional molecules which exhibit both activities have been synthesized and may be of pharmacological interest.[113]

## SUMMARY

The biochemical observations summarized here indicate that prostanoids have multiple effects on cyclic nucleotide metabolism. Some prostanoids increase, while others decrease, intracellular cyclic AMP. In addition, cyclic AMP inhibits both prostanoid synthesis and the metabolism of inositol phospholipids. From a pharmacological perspective, these findings suggest several research strategies which may lead to the development of compounds with useful antithrombotic properties. For example, such agents may include a variety of agonists that stimulate adenylate cyclase or selectively inhibit cyclic nucleotide phosphodiesterase in human platelets. Inhibitors of phospholipases, cyclooxygenase, or thromboxane synthetase may also be of interest.

## REFERENCES

1. **MacIntyre, D. E.,** Platelet prostaglandin receptors, in *Platelets in Biology and Pathology,* Vol. 2. Gordon, J. L., Ed., Elsevier, New York, 1981, 211.
2. **Wolfe, S. M. and Shulman, N. R.,** Adenyl cyclase activity in human platelets, *Biochem. Biophys. Res. Commun.,* 35, 265, 1969.
3. **Marquis, N. R., Vigdahl, R. L., and Tavormina, P. A.,** Platelet aggregation. I. Regulation by cyclic AMP and prostaglandin $E_1$, *Biochem. Biophys. Res. Commun.,* 36, 965, 1969.
4. **Mills, D. C. B. and MacFarlane, D. E.,** Stimulation of human platelet adenylate cyclase by prostaglandin $D_2$, *Thromb. Res.,* 5, 401, 1974.
5. **Gormon, R. R., Bunting, S., and Miller, O. V.,** Modulation of human platelet adenylate cyclase by prostacyclin, *Prostaglandins,* 13, 377, 1977.
6. **Tateson, J. E., Moncada, S., and Vane, J. R.,** Effects of prostacyclin (PGX) on cyclic AMP concentrations in human platelets, *Prostaglandins,* 13, 389, 1977.
7. **Kloeze, J.,** Influence of prostaglandins on platelet adhesiveness and platelet aggregation, in *Prostaglandin: Proceedings of the 2nd Nobel Symposium,* Bergstrom, S. B. and Samuelsson, B., Eds. Almquist and Wiksell, Stockholm, 1967, 241.
8. **Alvarez, R., Taylor, A., Fazzari, J. J., and Jacobs, J. R.,** Regulation of cyclic AMP metabolism in human platelets: sequential activation of adenylate cyclase and cyclic AMP phosphodiesterase by prostaglandins, *Mol. Pharmacol.,* 20, 302, 1981.
9. **Marcus, A. J. and Zucker, M. B.,** *The Physiology of Blood Platelets,* Grune & Stratton, New York, 1965.
10. **Salzman, E. W. and Neri, L. L.,** Cyclic 3′,5′-adenosine monophosphate in human blood platelets, *Nature (London),* 224, 609, 1969.
11. **Mills, D. C. B. and Smith, J. B.,** The influence on platelet aggregation of drugs that affect the accumulation of adenosine 3′,5′-cyclic monophosphate in platelets, *Biochem. J.,* 121, 185, 1971.
12. **Krishna, G., Harwood, J. P., Barber, A. J., and Jamieson, G. A.,** Requirement for guanosine triphosphate in the prostaglandins activation of adenylate cyclase of platelet membranes, *J. Biol. Chem.,* 247, 2253, 1972.

13. **Rodan, G. A. and Feinstein, M. B.,** Interrelationships between $Ca^{2+}$ and adenylate and guanylate cyclases in the control of platelet secretion and aggregation, *Proc. Natl. Acad. Sci. U.S.A.*, 73, 1829, 1976.
14. **Cutler, L., Rodan, G. A., and Feinstein, M. B.,** Cytochemical localization of adenylate cyclase and of calcium ion, magnesium ion-activated ATPases in the dense tubular system of human blood platelets, *Biochim. Biophys. Acta*, 542, 357, 1978.
15. **Stein, J. M. and Martin, B. R.,** The role of GTP in prostaglandin $E_1$ stimulation of adenylate cyclase in platelet membranes, *Biochem. J.*, 214, 231, 1983.
16. **Johnson, R. A., Saur, W., and Jacobs, K. H.,** Effects of prostaglandin $E_1$ and adenosine on metal and metal-ATP kinetics of platelet adenylate cyclase, *J. Biol. Chem.*, 254, 1094, 1979.
17. **Haslam, R. J. and Lynham, J. A.,** Activation and inhibition of blood platelet adenylate cyclase by adenosine or by 2-chloroadenosine, *Life Sci.*, 11 (Part II), 1143, 1972.
18. **Jakobs, K. H., Saur, W., and Johnson, R. A.,** Regulation of platelet adenylate cyclase by adenosine, *Biochim. Biophys. Acta*, 583, 409, 1979.
19. **Levitski, A.,** β-Adrenergic receptors and their mode of coupling to adenylate cyclase, *Physiol. Rev.*, 66, 819, 1986.
20. **Zieve, P. D., and Greenough, W. B., III,** Adenyl cyclase in human platelets: activity and responsiveness, *Biochem. Biophys. Res. Commun.*, 35, 462, 1969.
21. **Insel, P. A., Stengel, D., Ferry, N., and Hannoune, J.,** Regulation of human platelet adenylate cyclase by forskolin, *Fed. Proc.*, 41, 1411, 1982.
22. **Siegl, A. M., Daly, J. W., and Smith, J. B.,** Inhibition of aggregation and stimulation of cyclic AMP generation in intact human platelets by the diterpene forskolin, *Mol. Pharmacol.*, 21, 680, 1982.
23. **Insel, P. A., Stengel, D., Ferry, N., and Hanoune, J.,** Regulation of adenylate cyclase of human platelet membranes by forskolin, *J. Biol. Chem.*, 257, 7485, 1982.
24. **Mills, D. C. B. and MacFarlane, D. E.,** Stimulation of human platelet adenylate cyclase by prostaglandin $D_2$, *Thromb. Res.*, 5, 401, 1974.
25. **Schafer, A. I., Cooper, B., O'Hara, D., and Handin, R. I.,** Identification of platelet receptors for prostaglandin $I_2$ and $D_2$, *J. Biol. Chem.*, 254, 2914, 1979.
26. **Siegl, A. M., Smith, J. B., and Silver, M. J.,** Selective binding site for [$^3$H] prostacyclin on platelets, *J. Clin. Invest.*, 63, 215, 1979.
27. **Miller, O. V. and Gorman, R.,** Evidence for distinct prostaglandin $I_2$ and $D_2$ receptors in human platelets, *J. Pharmacol. Exp. Ther.*, 210, 134, 1979.
28. **Westwick, J. and Webb, H.,** Selective antagonism of prostaglandin ($PGE_1$), $PGD_2$ and prostacyclin ($PGI_2$) on human and rabbit platelets by di-4-phoretin phosphate (DPP), *Thromb. Res.*, 12, 973, 1978.
29. **Whittle, B. J. R., Moncada, S., and Vane, J. R.,** Comparison of the effects of prostacyclin ($PGI_2$), prostaglandin $E_1$, and $D_2$ on platelet, *Prostaglandins*, 16, 373, 1978.
30. **Andersen, N. H., Eggerman, T. L., Harker, L. A., Wilson, C. W., and De, B.,** On the multiplicity of platelet prostaglandin receptors. I. Evaluation of competitive antagonism by aggregometry, *Prostaglandins*, 19, 711, 1980.
31. **Shio, H. and Ramwell, P. W.,** Effect of prostaglandin $E_2$ and aspirin on the secondary aggregation of human platelets, *Nature (London)*, 236 (61), 45, 1972.
32. **Smith, J. B., Silver, M. J., Ingerman, C. M., and Kocsis, J. J.,** Prostaglandin $D_2$ inhibits the aggregation of human platelets, *Thromb. Res.*, 5, 291, 1974.
33. **Nishizawa, E. E., Miller, W. L., Gorman, R. R., and Bundy, G. L.,** Prostaglandin $D_2$ as a potential antithrombotic agent, *Prostaglandins*, 9, 109, 1975.
34. **Bundy, G. L., Morton, D. R., Peterson, D. C., Nishizawa, E. D., and Miller, W. L.,** Synthesis and platelet aggregation inhibiting activity of prostaglandin $D_2$ analogues, *J. Med. Chem.*, 26, 790, 1983.
35. **Cooper, B., Schafer, A. I., Puchalsky, D., and Handin, R. I.,** Desensitization of prostaglandin-activated platelet adenylate cyclase, *Prostaglandins*, 17, 561, 1979.
36. **Cooper, B.,** Diminished platelet adenylate cyclase activation by prostaglandin $D_2$ in acute thrombosis, *Blood*, 54, 684, 1979.
37. **Cooper, B. and Ahern, D.,** Characterization of the prostaglandin $D_2$ receptor, *J. Clin. Invest.*, 64, 586, 1979.
38. **Cooper, B.,** Agonist regulation of the human platelet prostaglandin $D_2$ receptor, *Life Sci.*, 25, 1361, 1979.
39. **Tateson, J. E., Moncada, S., and Vane, J. R.,** Effects of prostacyclin (PGX) on cyclic AMP concentrations in human platelets, *Prostaglandins*, 13, 389, 1977.
40. **Dembinska-Kiec, A., Rucker, W., Schönhöfer, P. S., and C. Gandolfi, C.,** *Thromb. Haemostasis*, 42, 1340, 1979.
41. **Nugteren, D. H. and Hazelhof, E.,** Isolation and properties of intermediates in prostaglandin biosynthesis, *Biochim. Biophys. Acta*, 326, 448, 1973.
42. **Cooper, B., Schafer, A. I., Puchalsky, D., and Handin, R. I.,** Platelet resistance to prostaglandin $D_2$ in patients with myeloproliferative disorders, *Blood*, 52, 618, 1978.

43. **Shattil, S. S. and Cooper, R. A.,** Membrane microviscosity and human platelet function, *Biochemistry,* 15, 4832, 1976.
44. **Shattil, S. S., Anaya-Galindo, R., Bennett, J., Colman, R. W., and Cooper, R. A.,** Platelet hypersensitivity induced by cholesterol incorporation, *J. Clin. Invest.,* 55, 636, 1975.
45. **Sinha, A. K., Shattil, S. J., and Colman, R. W.,** Cyclic AMP metabolism in cholesterol-rich platelets, *J. Biol. Chem.,* 252, 3310, 1977.
46. **Insel, P. A., Nirenberg, P. A., Turnbull, J., and Shattil, S. J.,** Relationships between membrane cholesterol, α-adrenergic receptors, and platelet function, *Biochemistry,* 17, 5269, 1978.
47. **Johnson, M., Walton, P. L., Cotton, R. C., and Strachan, C. J. L.,** Pharmacological evaluation of ticlopidine, a novel inhibitor of platelet function, *Thromb. Haemostasis,* 38, 64, 1977.
48. **Ashida, S. and Abiko, Y.,** Mode of action of ticlopidine in inhibition of platelet aggregation in the rat. *Thromb. Haemostasis,* 42, 436, 1979.
49. **Bonne, C., Martin, B., and Regnault, F.,** Potentiation of antiaggregating prostaglandins by ticlopidine, *Thromb. Haemostasis,* 46, 67, 1981.
50. **Bonne, C., Martin, B., and Regnault, F.,** Hypothetic mechanism of ticlopidine-induced hypersensitivity to $PGE_1$ in rat platelets, *Thromb. Res.,* 21, 157, 1981.
51. **Alvarez, R., Lundell, G. R., and Bruno, J. J.,** Cyclic AMP accumulation in human platelets in response to prostaglandin $E_1$: effect of oral administration of ticlopidine, in *Ticlopidine Quo Vadis,* Sanofi Research, Montpellier, 1983, 76.
52. **Hamet, P., Franks, D. J., Tremblay, J., and Coquil, J. F.,** Rapid activation of cyclic AMP phosphodiesterase in rat platelets, *Can. J. Biochem.,* 61, 1158, 1983.
53. **Hidaka, H. and Asano, T.,** Human blood platelet 3′,5′-cyclic nucleotide phosphodiesterase: isolation of low-$K_m$ and high-$K_m$ phosphodiesterase, *Biochim. Biophys. Acta,* 429, 485, 1976.
54. **Hidaka, H., Yamaki, T., Ochiai, Y., Asano, T., and Yamabe, H.,** Cyclic 3′,5′-nucleotide phosphodiesterase determined in various human tissues by DEAE-cellulose chromatography, *Biochim. Biophys. Acta,* 484, 398, 1977.
55. **Song, S.-Y. and Cheung, W. Y.,** Cyclic 3′,5′ nucleotide phosphodiesterase: properties of the enzyme of human blood platelets, *Biochim. Biophys. Acta,* 242, 593, 1971.
56. **Grant, P. G. and Colman, R. W.,** Purification and characterization of a human platelet cyclic nucleotide phosphodiesterase, *Biochemistry,* 23, 1801, 1984.
57. **Pichard, A.-L., Hanoune, J., and Kaplan, J.-C.,** Multiple forms of cyclic adenosine 3′,5′-monophosphate phosphodiesterase from human blood platelets. I. Kinetic and electrophoretic characterization of two molecular species, *Biochim. Biophys. Acta,* 315, 370, 1973.
58. **Pichard, A.-L. and Kaplan, J.-C.,** Effect of $N^6$,2′-0-dibutyryl cyclic AMP upon the interconvertible forms of cyclic AMP phosphodiesterase from human platelets, *Biochem. Biophys. Res. Commun.,* 64, 342, 1975.
59. **Pichard, A.-L., Choury, D., and Kaplan, J.-C.,** 3′,5′-Cyclic nucleotide phosphodiesterase from human platelets: effect of heat upon the multiple forms and their interconversion, *Biochimie,* 63, 603, 1981.
60. **Pichard, A.-L. and Cheung, W. Y.,** Cyclic 3′,5′-nucleotide phosphodiesterase: interconvertible multiple forms and their effects on enzyme activity and kinetics, *J. Biol. Chem.,* 251, 5726, 1976.
61. **Tang, S. S. and Frojmovic, M. M.,** Inhibition of platelet function by antithrombotic agents 3′,5′-adenosine monophosphate phosphodiesterase, *J. Lab. Clin. Med.,* 95, 241, 1980.
62. **Hidaka, H., Hayashi, H., Kohri, H., Kimura, Y., Hosokawa, T., Igawa, T., and Saitoh, Y.,** Selective inhibitor of platelet cyclic adenosine monophosphate phosphodiesterase, cilostamide, inhibits platelet aggregation, *J. Pharmacol. Exp. Ther.,* 211, 26, 1979.
63. **Ruppert, D. and Weithmann, K. U.,** HL 725, an extremely potent inhibitor of platelet phosphodiesterase and induced platelet aggregation *in vitro, Life Sci.,* 31, 2037, 1982.
64. **Alvarez, R., Bruno, J. J., Jones, C. H., Strosberg, A. M., and Venuti, M. C.,** The chemistry and biology of RS-82856 as a positive inotropic agent, Abstr. 12, *American Chemical Society,* 188th Meet. Div. Med. Chem., Aug. 26 to 31, Philadelphia, 1984.
65. **McElroy, F. A. and Philp, R. B.,** Relative potencies of dipyridamole and related agents as inhibitors of cyclic nucleotide phosphodiesterases: possible explanation of mechanism of inhibition of platelet function. *Life Sci.,* 17, 1479, 1976.
66. **Weiss, H. J.,** *Platelets: Pathophysiology and Antiplatelet Drug Therapy,* Alan R. Liss, New York, 1982, 57.
67. **Hidaka, H., Tanaka, T., and Itoh, H.,** Selective inhibitors of three forms of cyclic nucleotide phosphodiesterases, *Trends Pharm. Sci.,* 5, 237, 1984.
68. **Hashimoto, S.,** Thrombin-sensitive membrane-bound cyclic adenosine 3′,5′-monophosphate phosphodiesterase in rabbit platelets, *Biomed. Res.,* 2, 472, 1981.
69. **Alvarez, R., Liittschwager, K., and Osburn, L.,** Stimulation of cyclic AMP phosphodiesterase activity in human platelets by thrombin, *Mol. Pharmacol.,* submitted.

70. **Stoclet, J. C.,** Inhibitors of cyclic nucleotide phosphodiesterase, *Trends Pharm. Sci.*, 1, 98, 1979.
71. **Haslam, R. J. and McClenaghan, M. D.,** Effects of collagen and of aspirin on the concentration of guanosine 3′,5′-cyclic monophosphate in human blood platelets: measurement by a prelabeling technique, *Biochem. J.*, 138, 317, 1974.
72. **Davies, T., Davidson, M. M. L., McClenaghan, M. D., Say, A., and Haslam, R. J.,** Factors affecting platelet cyclic GMP levels during aggregation induced by collagen and by arachidonic acid, *Thromb. Res.*, 9, 387, 1976.
73. **Glass, D. B., Gerrard, J. M., Townsend, D., Carr, D. W., White, J. G., and Goldberg, N. D.,** The involvement of prostaglandin endoperoxide formation in the elevation of cyclic GMP levels during platelet aggregation, *J. Cyclic Nucl. Res.*, 3, 37, 1977.
74. **Weiss, A., Baenziger, N. L., and Atkinson, J. P.,** Platelet release reaction and intracellular cGMP, *Blood*, 52, 524, 1978.
75. **Schoepflin, G. S., Pickett, W., Austen, K. F., and Goetzl, E. J.,** Elevation of the cyclic GMP concentration of human platelets by sodium ascorbate and 5-hydroxytryptamine, *J. Cyclic Nucl. Res.*, 3, 355, 1977.
76. **Ignarro, L. J. and Kadowitz, P. J.,** The pharmacological and physiological role of cyclic GMP in vascular smooth muscle relaxation, *Annu. Rev. Pharmacol. Toxicol.*, 25, 171, 1985.
77. **Radomski, M. W., Palmer, R. M. J., and Moncada, S.,** Comparative pharmacology of endothelium-derived relaxing factor, nitric oxide and prostacyclin in platelets, *Br. J. Pharmacol.*, 92, 181, 1987.
78. **Ignarro, L. J., Byrns, R. E., Buga, G. M., Wood, K. W., and Chaudhuri, G.,** Pharmacological evidence that endothelium-derived relaxing factor is nitric oxide: use of pyrogallol and superoxide dismutase to study endothelium-dependent and nitric oxide-elicited vascular smooth muscle relaxation, *J. Pharmacol. Exp. Ther.*, 244, 181, 1988.
79. **Steer, M. L. and Salzman, E. W.,** Cyclic nucleotides in hemostasis and thrombosis, *Adv. Cyclic Nucl. Res.*, 12, 71, 1980.
80. **Haslam, R. J., Davidson, M. M. L., Davies, T., Lynham, J. A., and McClenaghan, M. D.,** Regulation of blood platelet function by cyclic nucleotides, *Adv. Cyclic Nucl. Res.*, 9, 533, 1978.
81. **Haslam, R. J., Davidson, M. M. L., and Desjardins, J. V.,** Role of cyclic AMP in platelet function: evidence from inhibition of adenylate cyclase in intact platelets by adenosine analogues. *Thromb. Haemostasis*, 38, 6, 1977.
82. **Salzman, E. W., MacIntyre, D. E., Steer, M. L., and Gordon, J. L.,** Effect on platelet activity of inhibition of adenylate cyclase, *Thromb. Res.*, 13, 1089, 1978.
83. **Haslam, R. J., Davidson, M. M. L., and Desjardins, J. V.,** Inhibition of adenylate cyclase by adenosine analogues in preparations of broken and intact human platelets, *Biochem. J.*, 176, 83, 1978.
84. **Bills, T. K., Smith, J. B., and Silver, M. J.,** Metabolism of [$^{14}$C] arachidonic acid by human platelets, *Biochim. Biophys. Acta*, 424, 303, 1976.
85. **Blackwell, G. L., Duncombe, W. G., Flower, R. J., Parsons, M. F., and Vane, J. R.,** The distribution and metabolism of arachidonic acid in rabbit platelets during aggregation and its modification by drugs, *Br. J. Pharmacol.*, 59, 353, 1977.
86. **Moncada, S., Gryglewski, R., Bunting, S., and Vane, J. R.,** An enzyme isolated from arteries transforms prostaglandin endoperoxides to an unstable substance that inhibits platelet aggregation, *Nature (London)*, 263, 663, 1976.
87. **Gryglewski, R. J., Bunting, S., Moncada, S., Flower, R. J., and Vane, J. R.,** Arterial walls are protected against deposition of platelet thrombi by a substance (prostaglandin X) which they make from prostaglandin endoperoxides, *Prostaglandins*, 12, 685, 1976.
88. **Weksler, B. B., Marcus, A. J., and Jaffe, E. A.,** Synthesis of prostaglandin $I_2$ (prostacyclin) by cultured human and bovine endothelial cells, *Proc. Natl. Acad. Sci. U.S.A.*, 74, 3922, 1977.
89. **Moncada, S., Korbut, R., Bunting, S., and Vane, J. R.,** Prostacyclin is a circulating hormone, *Nature (London)*, 237, 767, 1978.
90. **Gryglewski, R. J., Korbut, R., and Ocetkiewicz, A.,** Generation of prostacyclin by lungs *in vivo* and its release into the arterial circulation, *Nature (London)*, 273, 765, 1978.
91. **MacIntyre, D. E., Pearson, J. D., and Gordon, J. L.,** Localization and stimulation of prostacyclin production in vascular cells, *Nature (London)*, 271, 549, 1978.
92. **Higgs, G. A., Moncada, S., and Vane, J. R.,** Prostacyclin ($PGI_2$) inhibits the formation of platelet thrombi induced by adenosine diphosphate (ADP) *in vivo*. *Br. J. Pharmacol.*, 61, 137, 1977.
93. **Samuelsson, G., Goldyne, M., Granström, E., Hamberg, M., Hammarström, S., and C. Malmsten,** Prostaglandins and thromboxanes, *Annu. Rev. Biochem.*, 47, 997, 1978.
94. **Lapetina, E. G., Schmitges, C. J., Chandrabose, K., and Cuatrecasas, P.,** Cyclic adenosine 3′,5′-monophosphate and prostacyclin inhibit membrane phospholipase activity in platelets, *Biochem. Biophys. Res. Commun.*, 76, 828, 1977.
95. **Ballou, L. R. and Cheung, W. Y.,** Marked increase of human platelet phospholipase $A_2$ activity *in vitro* and demonstration of an endogenous inhibitor, *Proc. Natl. Acad. Sci. U.S.A.*, 80, 5203, 1983.

96. **Miwa, M., Kubota, I., Ichihashi, T., Motajima, H., and Matsumoto, M.,** Studies on phospholipase A inhibitor in blood plasma. I. Purification and characterization of phospholipase inhibitor in bovine plasma, *J. Biochem.*, 96, 761, 1984.
97. **Flower, R.,** Steroidal anti-inflammatory drugs as inhibitors of phospholipase $A_2$, *Adv. Prostaglandin Thromboxane Res.*, 3, 105, 1978.
98. **Flower, R. J. and Blackwell, G. J.,** Anti-inflammatory steroids induce biosynthesis of a phospholipase inhibitor which prevents prostaglandin generation, *Nature (London)*, 278, 456, 1979.
99. **Franson, R. C. Eisen, D., Jesse, R., and Lanni, C.,** Inhibition of highly purified mammalian phospholipases by non-steroidal anti-inflammatory agents, *Biochem. J.*, 186, 633, 1980.
100. **Feinstein, M. B., Becker, E. L., and Fraser, C.,** Thrombin, collagen, and A23187 stimulated endogenous platelet arachidonate metabolism: differential inhibition by $PGE_1$, local anesthetics and a serine-protease inhibitor, *Prostaglandins*, 14, 1075, 1977.
101. **Lapetina, E. G. and Cuatrecasas, P.,** Stimulation of phosphatidic acid production in platelets precedes the formation of arachidonate and parallels the release of serotonin, *Biochim. Biophys. Acta*, 573, 394, 1979.
102. **Rittenhouse-Simmons, S.,** Production of diglyceride from phosphatidylinositol in activated human platelets, *J. Clin. Invest.*, 63, 580, 1979.
103. **Bell, R. L., Kennerly, D. A., Stanford, N., and Majerus, P. W.,** Diglyceride lipase: a pathway for arachidonate release from human platelets, *Proc. Natl. Acad. Sci. U.S.A.*, 76, 3238, 1979.
104. **Broekman, M. J., Ward, J. W., and Marcus, A. J.,** Phospholipid metabolism in stimulated human platelets: changes in phosphatidylinositol, phosphatidic acid, and lysophospholipids, *J. Clin. Invest.*, 66, 275, 1980.
105. **Takai, Y., Kishimoto, A., Kikkawa, U., Mori, T., and Nishizuka, Y.,** Unsaturated diacylglycerol as a possible messenger for the activation of calcium-activated, phospholipid dependent protein kinase system, *Biochem. Biophys. Res. Commun.*, 91, 1218, 1979.
106. **Kishimoto, A., Takai, Y., Mori, T., Kikkawa, U., and Nishizuka, Y.,** Activation of calcium and phospholipid-dependent protein kinase by phosphatidylinositol diacylglycerol, its possible relation to phosphatidylinositol turnover, *J. Biol. Chem.*, 255, 2273, 1980.
107. **Nishizuka, Y.,** The role of protein kinase C in cell surface signal transduction and tumor promotion, *Nature (London)*, 308, 693, 1984.
108. **Willis, A. L. and Kuhn, D. C.,** A new potential mediator of arterial thrombosis whose biosynthesis is inhibited by aspirin, *Prostaglandins*, 4, 127, 1973.
109. **Hamberg, M., Svenson, J., Wakabayski, T., and Samuelsson, B.,** Isolation and structures of two prostaglandin endoperoxides that cause platelet aggregation, *Proc. Natl. Acad. Sci. U.S.A.*, 71, 345, 1974.
110. **Weksler, B. B., Pett, S. B., Alonso, D., Richter, R. C., Stelzer, P., Subramanian, V., Tack-Goldman, K., and Gay, W. A., Jr.,** Differential inhibition by aspirin of vascular and platelet prostaglandin synthesis in atherosclerotic patients, *N. Eng. J. Med.*, 308, 800, 1983.
111. **Weksler, B. B., Tack-Goldman, K., Subramanian, V. A., and Gay, W. A., Jr.,** Cumulative inhibitory effect of low-dose aspirin on vascular prostacyclin and platelet thromboxane production in patients with atherosclerosis, *Circulation*, 71, 332, 1985.
112. **Smith, J. B.,** Effect of thromboxane synthetase inhibitors on platelet function: enhancement by inhibition of phosphodiesterase, *Thromb. Res.*, 28, 477, 1982.
113. **Bruno, J. J., Walker, K. A., and Alvarez, R.,** Unpublished results.

# OPPOSITE EFFECTS OF PROSTAGLANDINS ON HUMAN PLATELETS MEDIATED BY DISTINCT PROTEIN KINASES

**Berta Strulovici**

## INTRODUCTION

A wide variety of hormones initiate their effects on target cells by binding to specific cell-surface receptors. There appear to be two major cell-surface-receptor mechanisms operative in mediating the effects of hormones on intracellular processes. Many hormones interact with plasma membrane-bound receptors to activate the adenylate cyclase to increase the production of cAMP and thus activate a cAMP-dependent protein kinase.[1] Numerous other extracellular messengers stimulate the inositol-phospholipid breakdown by a phospholipase C mechanism.[2] One of the primary products of phosphatidylinositol turnover is diacylglycerol, which serves as a messenger of this hormonal stimulation to activate a Ca/phospholipid-dependent enzyme, protein kinase C.[3,4] Diacylglycerol greatly increases the affinity of protein kinase C for $Ca^{2+}$, and thereby renders this enzyme fully active without a net increase in the $Ca^{2+}$ concentration.[5] Thus, the receptor-mediated activation of this protein kinase is biologically independent of $Ca^{2+}$ because its $Ca^{2+}$ sensitivity is modulated. In many cell types, including the human platelet, activation of protein kinase C appears to be a prerequisite requirement, and acts synergistically with $Ca^{2+}$ for eliciting full activation of cellular functions.[5,6] The proposed pathway of such a signal transduction is outlined in Figure 1. Recently, it was found that active tumor-promoting phorbol esters such as 12-O-tetradecanoylphorbol-13-acetate (TPA) intercalate into the membrane, substitute for diacylglycerol, and activate protein kinase C directly.[7]

This chapter will briefly outline current knowledge of protein kinase C regulation in human platelets and its relationship to changes in platelet shape and functions such as aggregation and serotonin release.

## PROTEIN KINASE C IN PLATELETS: LINK TO SIGNAL-INDUCED PROTEIN PHOSPHORYLATION

The best evidence for *in vivo* activation of protein kinase C and its relationship to inositol phospholipid turnover comes from studies on human blood platelets by Nishizuka.[8]

When human platelets are stimulated by thrombin, collagen, or platelet activating factor (PAF), various constituents of platelet granules are released such as serotonin, adenine nucleotides, PDGF, and acid hydrolases. These release reactions are associated with phosphorylation of predominantly two endogenous platelet proteins with approximate molecular weights of 40,000 and 20,000 (40 kDa and 20 kDa[9,10]). The 20 kDa protein appears to be identical to the myosin light chain, and the enzyme responsible for this reaction, myosin-light-chain kinase, is calmodulin dependent and absolutely requires mobilization of $Ca^{2+}$.[11] On the other hand, protein kinase C is identified as the enzyme that is responsible for the phosphorylation of the 40 kDa protein.[9]

When stimulated, platelets rapidly produce a diacylglycerol, which comprises mostly the 1-stearoyl-2-arachidonyl backbone[12] and this reaction is accompanied by the concomitant disappearance of inositol phospholipids.[9,13] This diacylglycerol is present in membranes only transiently; within a minute of formation it disappears, either returning to inositol phospholipids or becoming further degraded to arachidonic acid for thromboxane and prostaglandin synthesis (Figure 2). This transient appearance of diacylglycerol in membranes is always associated with protein kinase C activation as judged by 40 kDa protein phosphorylation.[9]

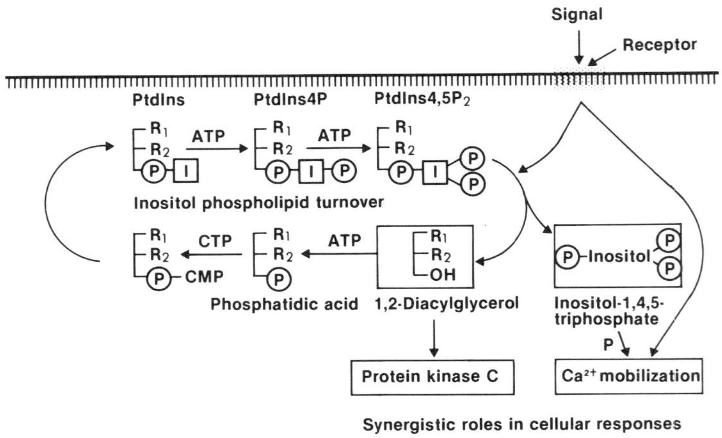


FIGURE 1. A proposed pathway of signal transduction. PtdIns phosphatidylinositol: PtdIns4P, phosphatidylinositol-4-phosphate: PtdIns4.5P, phosphatidylinositol-4,5-bisphosphate: $R_1$ and $R_2$ fatty acyl groups: I. inositol and P. phosphoryl group. (From Kikkawa et al., in *Phospholipids and Cellular Regulation*, Vol. II, CRC Press, Boca Raton, FL, 1985. With permission.)

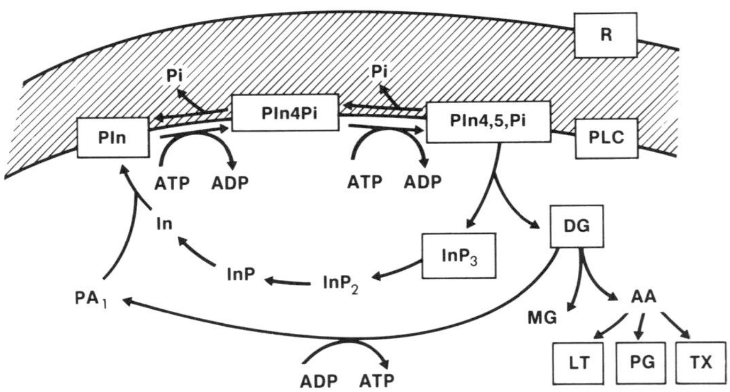


FIGURE 2. Schematic illustration of turnover of membrane phosphoinositides and cell activation. Reaction of occupied hormone receptor (R) with a specific phospholipase C (PLC), by a mechanism not yet known, leads to hydrolysis of phosphatidylinositol 4,5-bisphosphate ($PIn,4,5P_1$), leads to production of diacylglycerol (DG) rich in arachidonic acid or other polyunsaturated acids and to inositol triphosphate ($InP_3$). The latter compound may serve as mediator of release from intracellular source, but it is also rapidly dephosphorylated to inositol bisphosphate ($P_2$), inositol monophosphate (InP), and eventually free inositol (In), which may combine with phosphatidic acid ($PA_1$) to reform phosphatidylinositol (PIn). Generated DG was as activator of C kinase (not shown) and as substrate for a DG lipase, which causes the rise of monoglyceride (MG) and of arachidonic acid (AA), which in turn serves as substrate synthesis of leukotrienes (LT), prostaglandins (PG), and thromboxanes (TX), many of which serve either an autocrine or paracrine function in controlling cellular response. (From Rasmussen, Y. and Barrett, P. Q., *Physiol. Rev.*, 3, 64, 1984. With permission.)

# PROSTAGLANDINS, PROSTAGLANDIN ENDOPEROXIDE ANALOGUES REGULATE PLATELET FUNCTION VIA DISTINCT PROTEIN KINASES

An early biochemical response to platelet stimulation is the degradation of phospholipids by phospholipases C and $A_2$.[13,14] Thrombin, PAF, collagen, and arachidonic acid induce the activation of phospholipase C during shape change of human platelets;[15,16] the degree of phospholipase C activation correlates with protein phosphorylation, serotonin release, and aggregation. All these reactions have been shown to be inhibited by incubation of platelets with agents that stimulate cAMP production such as $PGE_1$, $PGD_2$, dibutyryl cAMP, or forskolin (see References 17, 18; for a review, see Reference 19). Work by Takai et al.[20] demonstrated that the inhibition of these reactions by cAMP is inversely related to phosphorylation of another group of proteins. These proteins, having molecular weights of 50,000 (50 kDa), 24,000 (24 kDa), and 22,000 (22 kDa) were also phosphorylated when human platelets were incubated with prostacyclin or 8-bromo-cAMP.[21]

Prostaglandin endoperoxides have been shown to induce the whole cascade of platelet responses such as platelet shape change, release reaction, and aggregation.[22] Those substances and thromboxane $A_2$ bind to a common receptor on the platelet surface and induce the mobilization of intracellular $Ca^{++}$.[23] Using stable prostaglandins endoperoxide analogues which mimic the unstable prostaglandin endoperoxides, Siess et al.[24] have demonstrated that these agents induce the rapid formation of 1,2-diacylglycerol and phosphatidic acid, indicating the activation of phospholipase C. This effect preceded platelet change in shape, aggregation, and secretion and was accompanied by the rapid phosphorylation of the 40 and 20 kDa proteins, respectively. This effect was independent of formation of cyclooxygenase products or release of ADP. Prostacyclin and $PGE_1$ prevented platelet shape change, phospholipase C activation, and the phosphorylation reaction induced by prostaglandin-endoperoxide analogues.

Human platelets are aggregated by arachidonic acid. This fatty acid is metabolized via a cyclooxygenase enzyme to prostaglandin endoperoxides which in turn are transformed via thromboxane $A_2$-synthetase to thromboxane $A_2$.[25] Relatively small amounts of $PGE_2$, $PGD_2$, and $PGF_{2\alpha}$ are also formed. $PGE_2$, at low doses (100 to 500 n*M*) has been shown to exert a marked concentration-dependent pro-aggregatory effect.[24] This effect was prevented by $PGD_2$ or 13-aza-prostanoic acid, a selective antagonist of $TxA_2$ receptors. Early work by Willis et al.[26,26a] demonstrated that small concentrations of $PGH_2$ did not induce a significant release of serotonin, while preincubation with $PGE_2$ induced a dramatic increase in the amounts of serotonin released and also platelet aggregation. This effect of $PGE_2$ was not inhibited by aspirin, suggesting a direct effect. In relatively high concentrations ($10^{-5}$ to $10^{-4}$ *M*), $PGE_2$ inhibited the aggregation of human platelets stimulated by collagen.[27] This effect correlated with an increase in adenylate cyclase activity.

We sought to assess the mechanism by which $PGE_2$ and its potent long-acting synthetic analogue enprostil potentiate the second phase of aggregation. Figure 3 shows that enprostil acid is able to induce phosphorylation patterns similar to those induced by phorbol esters and diacylglycerols, suggesting that it stimulates protein kinase C in the platelets presumably via phospholipase-C mediated production of 1,2-diacylglycerol. This effect was not inhibited by pretreatment of platelets with aspirin. The protein kinase C inhibitor H-7(1-(5-isoquinolinylsulfonyl)-2-methylpiperazine) prevented the effect induced by enprostil acid. Moreover, RS-49323, an inactive derivative of enprostil acid (for structure, see Figure 4) did not stimulate phosphorylation of the 40 kDa protein (Figure 3). By quantitating the extent of phosphorylation of the 40 kDa protein vs. the 50, 24, 22 kDa proteins relative to the dose of $PGE_2$ present in the incubation mixture, we established an inverse relationship between the stimulation of the 40 kDa protein phosphorylation (via protein-kinase-C activation) and the 50, 24, 22 kDa protein phosphorylation (mediated via cAMP-dependent protein kinase) (Figure 5). This presumably correlates with the dual activity of $PGE_2$: at low doses — potentiation of platelet aggregation, while at high doses — inhibition of aggregation of stimulated platelets.

Understanding the role of protein kinase C in signal transduction requires, as an initial step, identification of its substrates for phosphorylation. Work by Touqui et al.[28] suggests that the 40 kDa protein which is the substrate for protein kinase C phosphorylation in the platelet is lipomodulin or lipocortin, on the basis of its cross-reactivity with a monoclonal

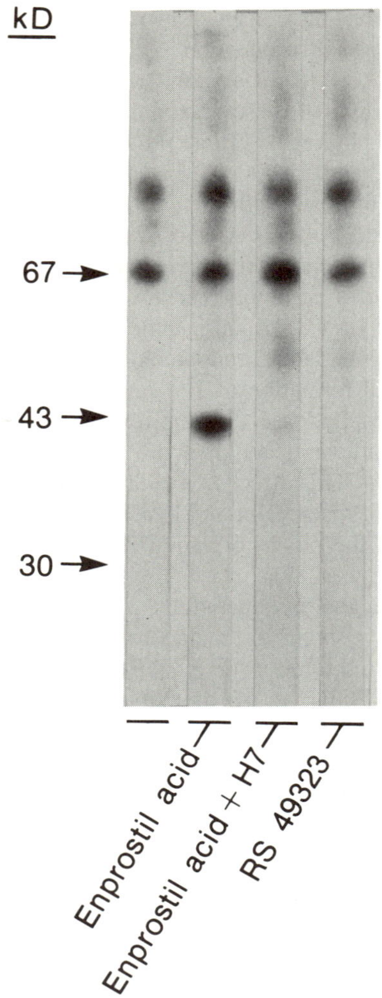


FIGURE 3. Autoradiograph of sodium dodecyl sulfate-polyacrylamide gel of $^{32}P$-labeled proteins from human platelets showing effect of enprostil acid and the inhibition of this effect on 40 kDa protein phosphorylation by H-7 (see text). Washed human platelets were labeled with radioactive phosphorus and then enprostil acid ($10^{-6}$ *M*), H-7 ($5 \times 10^{-5}$ *M*), or RS-49323 ($10^{-6}$ *M*) was added. (From Allison, A. C., Kowalski, W. J., and Strulovici, B., *Am. J. Med.*, 81, 270, 1986. With permission.)

antibody which recognizes this molecule. A role for protein kinase C in suppressing anti-phospholipase $A_2$ activity is suggested. The nature of the interaction between lipocortin (40 kDa protein) and phospholipase $A_2$ has not yet been elucidated. The authors suggest that lipocortin, in its unphosphorylated state, binds to and inactivates phospholipase $A_2$. Protein kinase C-mediated phosphorylation of lipocortin dissociates this complex, allowing, in the presence of an elevation in cytosolic calcium, optimal activity of phospholipase $A_2$. More recent work by Connolly et al.[29] demonstrates that protein kinase C phosphorylates and thereby increases the activity of inositol 1,4,5-triphosphate 5′-phosphomonoesterase, a phosphatase that hydrolyses inositol 1,4,5-triphosphate and inositol 1,2-cyclic 4,5-triphosphate to inert compounds. The 5′-phosphomonoesterase comigrates on SDS-polyacrylamide gels with the 40 kDa protein phosphorylated by thrombin or agents which stimulate protein kinase C directly (diacylglycerol or TPA). The authors propose that platelet $Ca^{2+}$ mobilization is

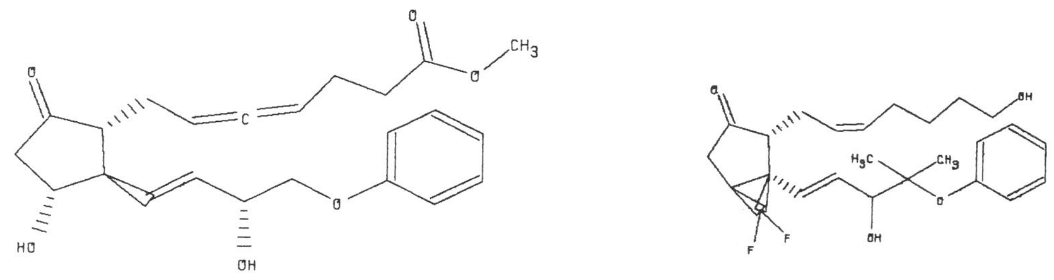


RS-049373-005

7509 (RS-084135-004) ENPROSTIL

FIGURE 4. Structure of enprostil acid and its inactive derivative RS-49373.

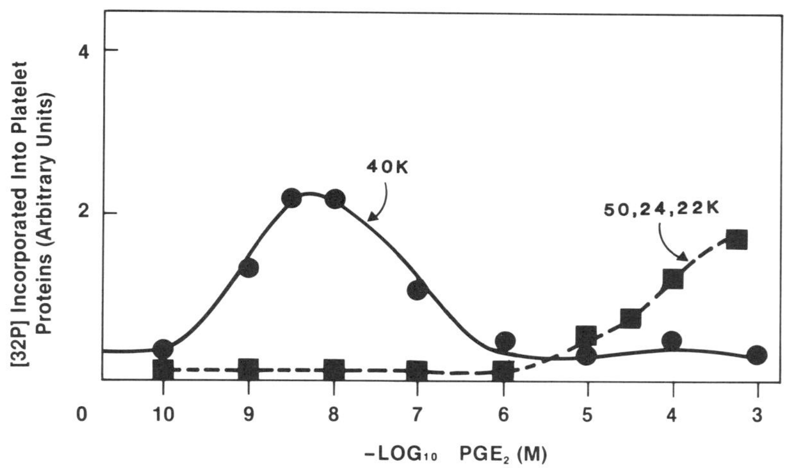


FIGURE 5. Dose response of $PGE_2$ on the phosphorylation of the 40 kDa protein (protein kinase C mediated) and the 50, 24, and 22 kDa proteins (cAMP-kinase) in washed human platelets. Quantitation of $^{32}P$-incorporation into substrate proteins was performed by densitometric scanning of autoradiographs of sodium dodecyl sulfate-polyacrylamide gels.

regulated by protein kinase C phosphorylation of the inositol 1,4,5-triphosphate 5′-phosphomonoesterase. These results could explain the observation that phorbol ester treatment of intact human platelets results in decreased levels of inositol triphosphate and decreased $Ca^{2+}$ mobilization upon subsequent thrombin addition.

However, the precise mechanism by which either one of the putative substrates for protein kinase C and cAMP-dependent protein kinase is regulated in the intact cell and its function in activation and inhibition of platelet functions remain to be determined.

In conclusion, in human platelets, the second messenger involved in the transduction of the signal induced by prostaglandin endoperoxides, thromboxane $A_2$, enprostil, and prostaglandin $E_2$ includes 1,2-diacylglycerol—one of the products of hydrolysis of inositol phospholipid. In contrast, prostaglandins that stimulate cAMP production following binding to their receptors in the platelet membrane, inhibit platelet aggregation. This suggests that the antagonistic actions of different types of prostaglandins, and the two intracellular signal transduction systems that they activate, are mediated by selective protein phosphorylation through protein kinase C and cAMP-dependent protein kinase, respectively.

## REFERENCES


1. **Rubin, C. S. and Rosen, O. M.,** Protein phosphorylation, *Annu. Rev. Biochem.*, 44, 831, 1975.
2. **Fain, J. N.,** Activation of plasma membrane phosphatidylinositol turnover by hormones, in *Vitamins and Hormones*, Harris, R. and Thiman, K. G., Eds., Academic Press, New York, 1984, 117.
3. **Nishizuka, Y., Takai, Y., Kishimoto, A., Kikkawa, U., and Kaibuchi, K.,** Phospholipid turnover in hormone action, *Recent Prog. Hormone Res.*, 40, 301, 1984.
4. **Nishizuka, Y.,** Studies and perspectives of protein kinase C, *Science*, 233, 305, 1986.
5. **Kaibuchi, K., Takai, Y., and Nishizuka, Y.,** Cooperative roles of various membrane phospholipids in the activation of calcium activated, phospholipid-dependent protein kinase, *J. Biol. Chem.*, 256, 7146, 1981.
6. **Kaibuchi, K., Takai, Y., Sawamura, M., Koshijima, M., Fujikura, T., and Nishizuka, Y.,** Synergistic functions of protein phosphorylation and calcium mobilization in platelet activation, *J. Biol. Chem.*, 258, 6701, 1983.
7. **Castagna, M., Takai, Y., Kaibuchi, K., Sano, K., Kikkawa, U., and Nishizuka, Y.,** Direct activation of calcium activated, phospholipid dependent protein kinase by tumor-promoting phorbol esters, *J. Biol. Chem.*, 257, 7847, 1982.
8. **Nishizuka, Y.,** The role of protein kinase C in cell-surface signal transduction and tumor promotion, *Nature (London)*, 308, 693, 1984.
9. **Kawahara, Y., Takai, Y., Minakuchi, R., Sano, K., and Nishizuka, Y.,** Phospholipid turnover as a possible transmembrane signal for protein phosphorylation during human platelet activation by thrombin, *Biochem. Biophys. Res. Commun.*, 97, 309, 1980.
10. **Sano, K., Takai, Y., Yamanishi, J., and Nishizuka, Y.,** A role of calcium-activated phospholipid-dependent protein kinase in human platelet activation. Comparison of thrombin and collagen actions, *J. Biol. Chem.*, 258, 2010, 1983.
11. **Hathaway, D. R. and Adelstein, R. S.,** Human platelet myosin light chain kinase requires the calcium-binding protein calmodulin for activity, *Proc. Natl. Acad. Sci. U.S.A.*, 76, 1653, 1979.
12. **Holub, B. J., Kuksis, A., and Thompson, W.,** Molecular species of mono-, di-, and tri-phosphoinositides of bovine brain, *J. Lipid Res.*, 11, 558, 1970.
13. **Rittenhouse-Simmons, S.,** Production of diglyceride from phosphatidyl-inositol in activated human platelets, *J. Clin. Invest.*, 63, 580, 1979.
14. **Bills, T. K., Smith, J. B., and Silver, M. J.,** Selective release of arachidonic acid from the phospholipids of human platelets in response to thrombin, *J. Clin. Invest.*, 60, 1, 1977.
15. **Siess, W., Siegel, F. L., and Lapetina, E. G.,** Arachidonic acid stimulates the formation of 1,2-diacylglycerol and phosphatidic acid in human platelets, *J. Biol. Chem.*, 258, 11236, 1983.
16. **Lapetina, E. G. and Siegel, F. L.,** Shape change induced in human platelets by platelet-activating factor. Correlation with the formation of phosphatidic acid and phosphorylation of a 40,000 dalton protein, *J. Biol. Chem.*, 258, 7241, 1983.
17. **Feinstein, M. B., Egan, J. J., Sha'afi, R., and White, J.,** The cytoplasmic concentration of free calcium in platelets is controlled by stimulators of cAMP production, *Biochem. Biophys. Res. Commun.*, 113, 598, 1983.
18. **Watson, S. P., McConnell, R. T., and Lapetina, E. G.,** The rapid formation of inositol phosphates in human platelets by thrombin is inhibited by prostacyclin, *J. Biol. Chem.*, 259, 13199, 1984.
19. **Haslam, R. J., Davidson, M. M. J., Davies, T., Lynham, J. A., and McCleneghan, M. D.,** Regulation of blood platelet function by cyclic nucleotides, *Adv. Cyclic Nucleotide Res.*, 9, 533, 1978.
20. **Takai, Y., Kaibuchi, K., Sano, K., and Nishizuka, Y.,** Counteraction of calcium-activated, phospholipid dependent protein kinase activation by adenosine 3′,5′-monophosphate and guanosine 3′,5′-monophosphate in platelets, *J. Biochem.*, 91, 403, 1982.
21. **Allison, A. C., Kowalski, W. J., and Strulovici, B.,** Effects of enprostil on platelets, endothelial cells and other cell types, and second messenger systems by which these effects are mediated, *Am. J. Med.*, 81, 270, 1986.
22. **Hamberg, M. and Samuelsson, B.,** Prostaglandin endoperoxides, novel transformations of arachidonic acid in human platelets, *Proc. Natl. Acad. Sci. U.S.A.*, 71, 3400, 1974.
23. **Kawahara, Y., Yamanishi, J., Furata, Y., Kaibuchi, K., Takai, Y., and Fukuzaki, H.,** Elevation of cytoplasmic free calcium concentration by stable thromboxane $A_2$ analogue in human platelets, *Biochem. Biophys. Res. Commun.*, 117, 663, 1983.
24. **Siess, W., Boehlig, B., Weber, P. C., and Lapetina, E. G.,** Prostaglandin endoperoxide analogues stimulate phospholipase C and protein phosphorylation during platelet shape change, *Blood*, 65, 1141, 1985.
25. **Kajtar, G., Cerletti, C., Castagnoli, M. N., Bertelé, V., and Gaetano, G.,** Prostaglandins and human platelet aggregation, *Biochem. Pharmacol.*, 34, 307, 1985.

26. **Willis, A. L., Vane, F. M., Kuhn, D. C., Scott, C. G., and Petrin, M.,** An endoperoxide aggregator (LASS), formed in platelets in response to thrombotic stimuli: purification, identification and unique biological significance, *Prostaglandins,* 8, 453, 1974.

26a. **Willis, A. L. and Smith, J. B.,** Some perspectives on platelets and prostaglandins, *Prog. Lipid Res.,* 20, 387, 1982.

27. **Bruno, J. J., Taylor, L. A., and Droller, M. J.,** Effects of prostaglandin $E_2$ on human platelet adenyl cyclase and aggregation, *Nature (London),* 251, 721, 1974.

28. **Touqui, L., Rothhut, B., Shaw, A. M., Fradin, A., Vargaftig, B. B., and Russo-Marie, F.,** Platelet activation—a role for a 40K anti-phospholipase $A_2$ protein indistinguishable from lipocortin, *Nature (London),* 321, 177, 1986.

29. **Connolly, T. M., Lawing, W. J., Jr., and Majerus, P. W.,** Protein kinase C phosphorylates human platelet inositol triphosphate 5′-phosphomono-esterase, increasing the phosphatase activity, *Cell,* 46, 951, 1986.

# *Index*

# INDEX

## A

## B



## C

## M

## Q



## R



## S

## T

## U



## V



## W



## Y



## Z